DIREC
FOR THE CITY OF
CHARLESTON,
SOUTH CAROLINA

FOR THE YEARS
1849, 1852, AND 1855

James W. Hagy

CLEARFIELD

Printed for
Clearfield Company, Inc. by
Genealogical Publishing Co., Inc.
Baltimore, Maryland
1998

Reprinted for
Clearfield Company, Inc. by
Genealogical Publishing Co., Inc.
Baltimore, Maryland
2002

International Standard Book Number: 0-8063-4822-4

Made in the United States of America

CONTENTS

INTRODUCTION

This is the fifth volume of city directories for Charleston, South Carolina. It represents a continuing effort to republish the directories of the city prior to the Civil War. The first volume contained the city directories for the years 1782, 1785, 1790, and 1802 as well as the census reports for 1790 and 1800. This appeared under the title of *People and Professions of Charleston, South Carolina, 1782-1802* (Baltimore: Clearfied, 1992). The second volume was *City Directories for Charleston, South Carolina for the Years, 1803, 1806, 1809 and 1813* (Baltimore: Clearfield, 1995). The third volume was *Charleston, South Carolina City Directories for the Years 1816, 1819, 1822, 1825, and 1829* (Baltimore: Clearfield: 1996). Volume four was *Directories for the City of Charleston, South Carolina for the Years, 1830-31, 1835-36, 1836, 1837-38, and 1840-41* (Baltimore: Clearfield: 1997).

These volumes often contain valuable information in addition to the usual listings such as streets, public buildings, churches, societies, city government, banks, insurance companies, military offices, fire companies, hospitals, commissioners of institutions, faculty of the College of Charleston and the Citadel, the high school of Charleston, the free schools, the Medical College, magistrates, and members of the legislature.

Street numbers in these directories create a problem as many houses were not numbered and the people compiling the directories often assigned numbers to them. The numbers on houses can give only a vague idea of where they were located on a street.

Copies of this book and those listed above may be ordered from: Clearfield Company, 220 East Eager St., Baltimore, Maryland 21202. Tel. 410-625-9004

The 1849 Directory

John H. Honour, a physician and head of the Penny Post in Charleston, published *A Directory of the City of Charleston and Neck for 1849; Containing the names, Residences and Occupations of the Inhabitants Generally: To Which Is Appended a List of the Banks, Insurance Companies, Societies, Fire Departments, Military, and Various Other Matters of General Interest* (Charleston: A. J. Burke, 1849). The business firms that were separately listed in the back of the book are included here because they often have names of individuals who did not appear in the directory. On occasion, however, the names are somewhat different. The directory as presented here has 4,948 entries. Photographers had appeared by this time and a number of them are noted as being "daguereotypists." This directory does not have a separate listing for free persons of color and includes only a few of them. Streets names with "N." before them are north of Boundary St.

Abbott, Anna, Mrs, 12 Middle St.
Abbott, Clark, Carpenter, 60 Meeting St.
Abbott, Eliza, Mrs., Milliner, 43 Wentworth St.
Abbott, George, Painter, 97 East Bay St., res. 91 East Bay St.
Abrahams, Alexander, 6 Elliott St., Neck
Abrahams, Elias, 4 Coming St.
Abrahamson, J. J., Dyer & Scourer, 15 St. Philip St.
Adams, E. L., Merchant, East Bay St., res. 25 Montague St.
Adams, Ezekiel, Mason, 18 Burns Lane
Adams, Mary A., Mrs., 47 Coming St.
Adams, William, Mason, 5 Burns Lane
Addison, E., N. St. Philip St.
Addison, G., Watchmaker, 7 Gadsden St.
Addison, J. B., Clerk, 81 Church St.
Addison, J. R., 15 South Bay St.
Addison, J. S., Shipwright, Gadsden's Wharf, res. 26 Marsh St.
Addisson & McIntosh, Shipwrights, Gadsden's Wharf, Joseph Addison, David N. McIntosh
Adger, J. B., Rev., cr. Charlotte & Alexander Sts.
Adger, James & Co., Commission Merchants, Adger's North Wharf, James Adger, Robert Adger, James R. Pringle
Adger, James, Merchant, Adger's Wharf, res. N. King St.
Adger, Robert, Merchant, Adger's Wharf, res. N. King St.
Adger, William & J. E., Hardware, 54 East Bay St.
Adger, William, Merchant, East Bay St., res. Charlotte St.
Adkins, Simpson, Pilot, 57 East Bay St.
Agrell, Charles, Clerk, 198 King St., res. 210 King St.
Ahrens, C. D., Grocer, 105 Queen St.
Ahrens, C., Grocer, America St.
Ahrens, John, Blacksmith, 81 Queen St.
Aiken, Louisa, Miss, Seamstress, 39 Beaufain St.
Aiken, William, Hon., Planter, Judith & Elizabeth Sts.
Aimar, C. P., Clerk, Market & King Sts., res. 36 Archdale St.

Aimar, Thomas, Clerk, 42 Meeting St., res. 36 Archdale St.
Ainger, Joseph, Cooper, 16 Cumberland St.
Albente, John, Tailor, 20 Tradd St.
Albergottie, T. E., Boarders, 347 King St.
Albers, H., Boundary St.
Alderman, Lewis, Baker, 19 Boundary St.
Alderson, J. F., Carpenter, 14 Tradd St.
Aldert, Sikke, Pilot, 7 Stoll's Alley
Aldrich, James T., Attorney, 15 Tradd St.
Aldrich, N., Rev., 15 Tradd St.
Aldrich, Robert, Wharfinger, Commercial Wharf, res. 15 Tradd St.
Aldrich, Thomas, Physician, 15 Tradd St.
Alexander, A. P., 290 King St.
Alexander, E., Clerk, 27 Hayne St.
Alexander, E., Miss, 7 Logan St.
Alexander, H. D., Officer, Union Bank, res. 7 Logan St.
Alexander, J., N. St. Philip St.
Alexander, John J., Student of Divinity, 7 Logan St.
Alexander, Joseph, 290 King St.
Alexander, Judah, Druggist, N., King St.
Alexander, Samuel, Harbor Master, East Bay St., res. 27 Cumberland St.
Alfs, C., Druggist, N. King St.
Alick, Morris, 104 Meeting St.
Allan, Cecelia S., Mrs., 41 Meeting St.
Allan, R., Janitor, Medical College
Allason, T., Jr., Saddler, 302 King St.
Allen, A., Pinckney St., Cannonborough
Allen, James, Pinckney St., Cannonborough
Allen, -----, Mrs., Seamstress, 5 Tradd St.
Allen, Thomas P., Bookseller, 116 Meeting St., res. 5 Society St.
Allender, B. R., 34 Bull St.
Alliers, C., Boundary St.
Allison, George, Bootmaker, 87 Church St.
Ally, John, Cabinet Maker, 92 Queen St., res. 39 Queen St.
Almers, R. F., Grocer, 87 Tradd St.
Alston, Charles, Planter, 15 East Bay St.
Alston, Robert, Clerk, 253 King St., res. 217 King St.
Alston, W., Thomas St.
Alston, William, Mariner, 47 State St.
Alvado, A., Clerk, 4 Beaufain St.
Ambler, D. A., Hatter, 161 Meeting St.
Amholtie, William, Carpenter, 16 Beaufain St.
Amme, D. H., Grocer, 22 St. Philip St.
Ancrum, Jane, Mrs., 66 Church St.
Anderson, A., Clerk, East Bay St.
Anderson, A. J., 68 Queen St.
Anderson, A. L., 23 St. Philip St.
Anderson, C., Mrs., 5 Coming St.
Anderson, E. K., Merchant, Adger's Wharf, res. 30 Society St.
Anderson, -----, Miss, 1 Atlantic St.
Anderson, R., Merchant, 23 St. Philip St.
Anderson, Robert, Engineer, 110 Meeting St.
Andrews, A. O., Merchant, Southern Wharf, res. 27 Hasell St.

1

Angel, Justus, Mrs., Planter, 118 Tradd St.
Angel, Robert, Mariner, 7 Water St.
Angus, J., Nassau St.
Angus, Thomas, Nassau St.
Annely, -----, Misses, 8 Rutledge St.
Ansel, John, Cabinet Maker, 304 King St.
Anton, P. W., Clerk, 147 Meeting St.
Archer, Benjamin, Coach Trimmer, Meeting &
 Wentworth Sts., res. 47 St. Philip St.
Arms, S., Miss, Teacher, 18 George St.
Armstrong, D. F., Clerk, 12 Wentworth St.
Armstrong, James, Packer, 46 Market St.
Armstrong, W. G., Clerk, Bennett's Mill, res. 12
 Wentworth St.
Arnau, F. M., Boundary St.
Arnau, Michael, Boundary St.
Arnold, C. M., Merchant, Hayne St., res. 323 King St.
Arnold, F., Bootmaker, 38 Queen St.
Arnold, George, Carpenter, 20 Boundary St.
Arnold, John, Stone Cutter, 11 Tradd St.
Arnold, Richard, Blacksmith, Church St., res. 7 College
 St.
Artman, John, Coachmaker, 5 Archdale St., res. 116
 King St.
Artman, -----, Misses, 7 Archdale St.
Artope, George, Superintendent, Bennett's Mills, East
 Bay St., res. 190 East Bay St.
Ash, Henry, Cap Maker, 328 King St.
Ashby, H., Mrs., 43 East Bay St.
Ashton, Mary E., Mrs., 96 Meeting St.
Ashton, William, Jeweller, 210 King St.
Astle, George, Jobber, 84 King St.
Atkinson, C., Merchant, Central Wharf, res. 77 Meeting
 St.
Auld, E., Miss, 8 George St.
Austin, Earle, Columbus St.
Aveilhe, P. A. (see Cay & Aveilhe)
Axson, Ann, Mrs., 33 King St.
Axson, Charles H., City Officer, Guard House, res. 6
 King St.
Axson, Eliza M., Mrs., 17 Meeting St.
Axson, S., Edward, Ship Carpenter, 33 King St.
Axson, W. J., Clerk, 17 Meeting St.
Axworthy, W. J., Mariner, 93 Wentworth St.
Babcock, W. R., Bookseller, King & Wentworth Sts.,
 res. Planters Hotel
Babson, Ann R., 55 State St.
Bachman, J., Rev., D. D., Pastor, Lutheran Church,
 Pinckney St., Cannonborough
Bachman, William, Pinckney St., Cannonborough
Backes, F., Watchmaker, 102 Church St.
Backus, F., Dry Goods, 140 King St.
Bacot, R. D., Clerk, 61 Coming St.
Bacot, R. Wainwright, Clerk, Southern Wharf, res. 62
 King St.
Bacot, Thomas W., Assistant Post Master, 62 King St.
Badger, Mary D., Mrs., 51 Queen St.
Badger, R., Miss, Teacher, 22 Pitt St.
Bahntge, F. W., Grocer, 98 Church St.
Bahntge, Henry, Storekeeper, 76 Church St.

Bailey, Alexander, Finisher, Railroad, res. 41 Middle St.
Bailey, H. I., Mrs., King St.
Bailey, Henry, Attorney, 65 Meeting St., res. 189
 Meeting St.
Bailey, J., Clerk, Adger's Wharf
Bairds, F., Musician, 103 Meeting St.
Baker, Ann, Mrs., Planter, 94 Tradd St.
Baker, B. E., Jr., Clerk, 8 Lamboll St.
Baker, B. E., Planter, 8 Lamboll St.
Baker, E. N., N. King St.
Baker, F. A., Plasterer, 80 Queen St.
Baker, H. F., Merchant, Fitzsimons' Wharf, res. 122 East
 Bay St.
Baker, H. H., Bookkeeper, 259 King St.
Baker, R. B., Planter, 8 Lamboll St.
Baker, R. L., 44 Boundary St.
Baker, R. S., Rev., D. D., 62 Wentworth St.
Baker, T., 122 East Bay St.
Balding, W. H., 19 Society St.
Baldwin, P., Clerk, 357 King St., res. 361 King St.
Ball, Amelia, Mrs., 25 Lynch St.
Ball, Elizabeth, 91 Queen St.
Ball, Isaac, Mrs., Planter, Vernon St.
Ball, John, Planter, Vernon St.
Ball, M. A., Mrs., 47 Boundary St.
Ballard, Joseph, Accountant, 75 King St.
Ballentine, Alexander, John St.
Bancroft, E. W., Dry Goods, 253 King St., res. 146
 Meeting St.
Bancroft, James & Co., Wholesale Grocers, 92 East Bay
 St., James Bancroft, J. M. Jeannerett
Bancroft, James K., Clerk, 253 King St., res. 297 King
 St.
Bancroft, James, Merchant, 92 East Bay St., res. 15
 Coming St.
Bange, William, 97 Church St.
Banks, Harriet L., Mrs., 9 Short St.
Banks, Hugh R., Merchant, 3 Hayne St., res. 75
 Wentworth St.
Barber, F. C., Accountant, 86 Church St.
Barber, John D., Clerk, 32 King St.
Barbot, A., 41 East Bay St.
Barbot, P. T., Merchant, Commercial Wharf, res. 41 East
 Bay St.
Barden, F., Mariner, 158 East Bay St.
Barfield, B. H., Clerk, Lucas Mills, res. 42 Beaufain St.
Barker, Henrietta C., Mrs., 30 Pitt St.
Barker, S. G., 70 Wentworth St.
Barksdale, M., Miss, 38 Wentworth St.
Barksdale, R. B., Mrs., 12 Church St.
Barksdale, Thomas, Planter, 12 New St.
Barnwell & Ravenel, Factors, 22 East Bay St., Nathaniel
 Barnwell, James Ravenel
Barnwell, E., Jr., Factor, Southern Wharf, res. 35
 Meeting St.
Barnwell, N., Factor, 22 East Bay St., res. 43 East Bay
 St.
Barnwell, W. H., Rev., Pastor, St. Peter's Church, 10
 Legare St.
Barnwell, William, Ship Carpenter, 3 Longitude Lane

Barr, John, Grocer, 23 State St.
Barrett, Isaac, Mrs., 93 Broad St.
Barrett, Jacob, Planter, 99 Broad St.
Barrett, S. J., 93 Broad St.
Barrow, David, Clerk, 50 East Bay St.
Barrow, John, Carpenter, 26 Mazyck St.
Bartels, A. F., Grocer, 63 Market St.
Bartless, W. H., Secretary, Railroad Co., State St., res.
　　Hudson St.
Bartlett, F. M., Shoe Dealer, 290 King St.
Bartlett, John, Capt.
Barton, A., Carpenter, Boundary St.
Basset, O., Printer, 3 Magazine St.
Bates, Edward, Engineer, 59 East Bay St.
Bates, Edwin, Clerk, 5 Liberty St.
Bates, J. R., Clerk, 288 King St.
Bates, -----, Misses, Teachers, 14 Church St.
Battersby, J., Merchant, East Bay St., res. Rutledge St.
Battley, John L., 37 Market St.
Baum, Henry, Cap Maker, 328 King St.
Baum, Herman, Cap Maker, 328 King St.
Baussang, Francis, Fruiterer, 78 King St.
Bay, John, Mrs., 62 King St.
Bay, -----, Mrs., 2 Rutledge St.
Bayle, Mary C., Mrs., 172 Meeting St.
Baylor, Mary, Mrs., 191 East Bay St.
Beach, E. M., Merchant, 23 Meeting St.
Beach, W. H., Clerk, 27 Hayne St.
Beam, John, Drayman, 63 Anson St.
Bear, Charles, Agriculturist, 51 Church St.
Beasly, W., Dry Goods, 349 King St.
Beatty, James, Butcher, Cannon St.
Beaufort, Andrew, Shoe Maker, 94 Meeting St.
Bebersen, G., Clerk, 40 Archdale St.
Becaise, Ann, Mrs., 8 Middle St.
Becaise, B. P., Gunsmith, 50 State St.
Becaise, P. P., Gunsmith, 50 State St.
Becand, Thomas, Sires St.
Becher, F. A., Druggist, cr. King & Vanderhorst Sts.
Becher, William, N. King St.
Becker, Rudolph, Clerk, 4 Beaufain St.
Beckley, J., Wood Factor, Warren St.
Beckmann, -----, 14 Elliott St., Tavern Keeper
Beckmann, Adolph, Painter, N. Coming St.
Beckmann, C. H., Carpenter, N. St. Philip St.
Beckmann, C. J., Miller, Market, N. St. Philip St.
Beckmann, E. R., Mrs., 19 St. Philip St., Neck
Beckmann, J. C., Miller, N. St. Philip St.
Beckmann, John F., Attorney, Court House Square, res.
　　19 St. Philip St.
Bee, Charlotte A., Mrs., 108 Tradd St.
Bee, Eliza, Mrs., Dress Maker, 39 Montague St.
Bee, G. W., Accountant, Southern Wharf, res. 8 Beaufain
　　St.
Bee, J. B., Officer, State Bank, res. 8 Beaufain St.
Bee, J. R., Clerk, 56 East Bay St.
Bee, J., St. Philip St.
Bee, James M., Officer, State Bank, res. 8 Beaufain St.
Bee, John P., Wharfinger, Southern Wharf, res. 71 Tradd
　　St.

Bee, Richard, Pinckney St., Cannonborough
Bee, Robert R., Cooper, Adger's Wharf, res. 38 South
　　Bay St.
Bee, Samuel, Clerk, Railroad Depot, res. John St.
Bee, Smith, Mrs., 58 Tradd St.
Bee, W., Pinckney St., Cannonborough
Bee, William C., Factor, Southern Wharf, res. 108 Tradd
　　St.
Bee, William H., Mariner, 33 King St.
Beesly, John, Tailor, 74 Tradd St.
Behleng, E., Clerk, 2 Laurens St.
Behleng, J. D., 152 East Bay St.
Behling, H. F., Grocer, 53 Market St.
Behr, H., N. Meeting St.
Behrens, F. U., Tailor, 93 King St.
Beile, A. M., Mrs., 17 George St.
Bekotter, -----, Bootmaker, 73 Meeting St.
Belin, A. H., Planter, 12 Lynch St.
Belin, E., Mrs., 15 Archdale St.
Bell, David, Accountant, 290 King St.
Bell, John, Cooper, 73 Meeting St.
Bell, Samuel, Pilot, 76 Church St.
Bell, William, Pilot, 3 Longitude St.
Bell, William, Planter, 38 Society St.
Bellinger, Israel, Bee St.
Bellinger, John, Physician, 11 College St.
Belser, F. S., Planter, 20 Friend St.
Benjamin, F., Mariner, 140 Queen St.
Benjamin, Philip, 9 Princess St.
Benjamin, Solomon, Clothing, 101 King St.
Bennet, Isaac, Charlotte St.
Bennet, Thomas, Lucas St.
Bennett, C., Printer, 109 Church St.
Bennett, Elias, Physician, 23 Rutledge St.
Bennett, S. P., Lumber Merchant, 98 Beaufain St.
Bennett, W. Jefferson, Miller, Smith St.
Bennette, F., Merchant, 236 King St.
Bensadon, Judah, Clerk, 42 Coming St.
Bensch, Charles, Cabinet Maker, 143 King St.
Benson, W. G., Morris St.
Benson, William, Merchant, 151 East Bay St.
Berger, A., Dancing Master, 56 Queen St.
Berghauser, John, Fruiterer, 73 Market St.
Berlin & Nathans, Country Store, N. E. corner King &
　　Boundary Sts., Ralph Berlin, Nathan Nathans
Bernard, S. B., Merchant, 168 Meeting St.
Berney, Mary, 9 Bull St.
Berney, William, Broker, Broad St., res. 71 Beaufain St.
Berrie, Clarie E., Mrs., 65 King St.
Berry, Ann, Mrs., 18 Pinckney St.
Bethge, L., Musician, 115 Church St.
Bethune, J. C., 244 King St.
Betsill, J. M., Coachmaker, 190 King St.
Bettison, E., Mrs., Mantuamaker, 15 Mayzck St.
Betts, E. C., 21 Cumberland St.
Betts, J. B., Merchant, Hayne St., res. 21 Cumberland St.
Betts, T. J., Hardware, 80 East Bay St., res. 51 Tradd St.
Betzerman, John, St. Philip St., Neck
Bieman, Dedrick, Grocer, 5 King St.
Bihr, Nicholas, Shoemaker, 143 King St.

3

Billings, Daniel, Blacksmith, 9 Magazine St.
Bingley, C. W., 253 East Bay St.
Bingley, David P., 253 East Bay St.
Birch, C. A., Mrs., 43 George St.
Bird, C. H., Clerk, 225 King St.
Bird, J. S., Jeweller, 225 King St.
Bird, John S. & Co., Military & Fancy Shop, 225 King St., John S. Bird, James M. Taylor, C. H. Bird
Bird, S. F., Mrs., 52 Church St.
Bird, William, Ship Carpenter, South Bay St., res. 10 Lynch St.
Birnie & Ogilvie, Hardware, 21 Broad St., William Birnie, M. Ogilvie
Birnie, William, President, Bank of S. C., res. 7 Smith St.
Bischoff, Henry, Storekeeper, 55 East Bay St.
Bischoff, -----, Merchant, 163 East Bay St.
Bischold, Grace, 7 Princess St.
Bize, A. F., Bricklayer, John St.
Bize, J. S., Mrs., John St.
Bize, R. B., Engineer, Woolf St.
Black, A. F., Wood Merchant, Southern Wharf, res. 11 Savage St.
Black, A. W., Notary, 75 East Bay St., res. 11 Savage St.
Black, Alexander, 32 Wentworth St.
Black, E. J., Clerk, 15 State St.
Black, F. C., Merchant, 11 Exchange St., res. 41 Wentworth St.
Black, G., Mason, 2 Society St.
Black, W. P., Baker, 189 King St.
Blacklock, John F., Factor, 2 Bull St.
Blackman, James, Clerk, Railroad Depot, res. 8 Liberty St.
Blackman, Joseph (see Dawson & Blackman)
Blackman, -----, Mrs., Milliner, 104 Queen St.
Blackwood, B. J., Clerk, 43 Society St.
Blackwood, G. G., Mason, 2 Society St.
Blackwood, T., Mrs., 28 Pitt St.
Blair, H. L., 101 East Bay St.
Blake, Edward, Officer, Bank of S. C., res. 10 Water St.
Blake, J., Boundary St.
Blamyer, William, Planter, 273 East Bay St.
Blanchard, Stanislaus, Carpenter, 51 Coming St.
Blanchard, W., 220 King St.
Blanck, Jacob, Laborer, 44 King St.
Blanding, H. W., 2 Logan St.
Blanding, Mary C., Mrs., 2 Logan St.
Blanding, Ormsby, 2 Logan St.
Blanding, William, Attorney, 34 Broad St., res. 2 Logan St.
Blane, L. T., Mrs., Teacher, 118 Queen St.
Blaze, C., Grocer, 7 Cumberland St.
Blin, Robert, Laborer, 50 Church St.
Block, H. A., Clerk, 23 Hayne St.
Blohme, J. C., Grocer, 87 King St.
Blondeau, E. & A. Marion, Confectioners, 247 King St.
Blondeau, E., Confectioner, 247 King St.
Bluett, John, Policeman, 17 Anson St.
Blum & Cobia, Auctioneers, Vendue Range, J. Charles Blum, Henry Cobia
Blum, F. C., Lumber Merchant, N. St. Philip St.

Blum, Henry, Grocer, 40 George St.
Blum, J. Charles, Auctioneer, 26 Vendue Range, res. 6 Beaufain St.
Blum, John A., Teacher, Mary St.
Blum, Mary S., Mrs., 18 Society St.
Boag, E. M., Mrs., Teacher, 185 Meeting St.
Bocken, C., Grocer, 135 King St.
Boesch, J. U., Coppersmith, 18 Market St.
Boesch, John, Dyer, 80 King St.
Boesch, Nicholas, Dyer, 80 King St.
Bogder, Jonathan, Pinckney St., Cannonborough
Bohl, John, N. King St.
Bohlman, H., Elizabeth St.
Bohls, H., Clerk, 24 Archdale St.
Bohls, L. E., Grocer, 24 Archdale St.
Boinest, Margaret, Mrs., 46 Queen St.
Bolger, M., Saddler, 92 Queen St.
Bolger, T W., Saddler, 70 Meeting St.
Bolles, A., Teacher, 9 College St.
Bolles, C. P., 9 College St.
Bolles, E. A., Rev., 9 College St.
Bolles, J. H., 9 College St.
Bomar, C., N. Meeting St.
Bomar, G. W., Boarders, Church & Queen Sts.
Boneaud, A., Dancing Master, 145 Meeting St.
Bones, William, 77 Meeting St.
Boning, D., Grocer, 4 Market St.
Bonneau, F., Clerk, 8 Liberty St.
Bonneau, Francis N., Clerk, 61 King St.
Bonneau, John E., Factor, Adger's Wharf, res. 265 East Bay St.
Bonneau, W. H., Physician, 23 Pinckney St.
Bonnell, F., 6 Atlantic St.
Bonnell, John, 6 Atlantic St.
Bonnell, John, Jr., Merchant, Boyce's Wharf, res. 6 Atlantic St.
Bonnell, Thomas, Merchant, Boyce's Wharf, 6 Atlantic St.
Bonner, John, Carpenter, 12 Pinckney St.
Bonniott, J. F., 370 King St.
Boone, William, Bricklayer, Bee St.
Booth, William, Mariner, 10 Magazine St.
Borance, Samuel, N. St. Philip St.
Borance, W., N. St. Philip St.
Bordeaux, M., Mrs., 2 Friend St.
Bordenave, John, Tobacconist, 113 East Bay St., res. 37 Anson St.
Borgard, John J. A., Bar Keeper, Meeting & Market Sts., res. 50 Market St.
Borner, F., Grocer, Meeting & John Sts.
Bouchineau, Charles, Customs Officer, 4 South Bay St.
Bounetheau, David, N. King St.
Bounetheau, E. W., Magistrate, N. King St.
Bounetheau, H. B., Artist, 196 East Bay St.
Bourke, O., Dry Goods, 30 Beaufain St.
Bours, J. B., Clerk, 39 Church St.
Boutan, Peter B., 118 King St.
Boutol, A., Baker, 113 Meeting St.
Bowen, Margaret, Mrs., 24 South Bay St.
Bowen, O. A., Clerk, 17 Hayne St.

4

Bowersmith, -----, Policeman, 119 King St.
Bowery, William, 41 Middle St.
Bowie, J. S. & L., Dry Goods, 17 Hayne St.
Bowie, J. S., Merchant, 17 Hayne St., res., 20 Hasell St.
Bowie, L., Merchant, Hayne St., res. 22 Hasell St.
Bowie, W. L., Merchant, 17 Hayne St.
Bowman, D., Miller, N. Meeting St.
Bowman, G. A., Clerk, 121 Queen St.
Bowman, -----, Misses, 3 Smith St.
Boyce, J., Drayman, 63 Anson St.
Boyce, J. P., Rev., 16 George St.
Boyce, Ker, 16 George St.
Boyden, Mary E., Mrs., 176 Meeting St.
Boyle, Adam, Mason, 184 Meeting St.
Boylston, Henry, Physician, 376 King St.
Braceman, John, 244 King St.
Bradford, W. J., Ship Carpenter, 19 Concord St.
Bradley, Charles, Cannon St.
Bradley, Elisha, Ship Carpenter, 130 King St.
Bradley, John, Cannon St.
Bradley, Margaret, Mrs., 193 East Bay St.
Bradley, Thaddeus, Cannon St.
Brady, Catharine, Mrs., 16 Anson St.
Brady, Edward, Clothing, 149 East Bay St.
Brady, Ellen, Mrs., Dress Maker, 11 Inspection St.
Brady, John, Wharfinger, Brown's Wharf, res. 122 Church St.
Brady, Mary, Dry Goods, 76 King St.
Brady, Patrick, 122 Church St.
Brady, Patrick, Policeman, 76 King St.
Brahm, Conrad, Cabinet Maker, 112 King St., res. 11 Wall St.
Brailsford, J. M., Physician, 15 East Bay St.
Brailsford, -----, Misses, 29 Church St.
Brailsford, Robert, Physician, Hasell & Meeting Sts., res. 50 Boundary St.
Brailsford, W. R., Clerk, 1 Orange St.
Brandes, Henry, Fruiterer, 345 King St.
Brandt, H. F., Confectioner, 299 King St.
Brandt, P. V., Clerk, 98 East Bay St.
Brandt, Thomas, 179 Meeting St.
Braner, -----, Grocer, 12 King St.
Branford, C. G., Carriage Maker, Mary St.
Brase, Peter, Constable, 102 King St.
Brawley, J. H., Merchant, East Bay St., res. 116 Meeting St.
Brayer, W., N. Coming St.
Breckelhuff, P. C., Fruiterer, 59 Market St.
Breckwedel, H., Clerk, 168 East Bay St.
Bredenburg, C. F., Boundary St.
Bredenburg, D., Boundary St.
Bredenburg, J. H., Grocer, 87 King St.
Breese, W. C., Officer, Bank of South Carolina, res. 3 Maiden Lane
Bremer, H., Grocer, 11 Cumberland St.
Bremer, John, Shoe Maker, 87 King St.
Brenan, Charles, Merchant, 54 Broad St.
Brenan, Peter, Musician, 155 King St.
Brenern, L., Laborer, 56 State St.
Brewer, Sarah E., Mrs., 82 Tradd St.

Brewster, C. R., Attorney, Meeting St., res. Vanderhorst St.
Bridges, John, Mariner, 50 Church St.
Bridgman, E. C., Shoe Dealer, 228 King St.
Brigelve, -----, Printer, 12 Atlantic St.
Briggman, William (see Oldendorff & Briggman)
Briggs, David, Painter, 41 Queen St.
Brightman, Sarah, Mrs., 10 Orange St.
Brillanceau, G., Confectioner, 19 Mazyck St.
Brisbane, A. H., Professor, Citadel.
Brissenden, H. I., Musician, 178 Meeting St.
Bristol & Bridgman, Boot & Shoe Store, 232 King St., T. M. Bristol, E. C. Bridgman
Bristol, A., Tailor, Horlbeck's Alley
Bristol, T. M., Shoe Dealer, 232 King St.
Bristol, W. B., Shoe Dealer, 228 King St.
Britton, T. J., Bootmaker, 18 Savage St.
Broadfoot, -----, Mrs., 5 Tradd St.
Brockelbank, W., Plasterer, 8 Inspection St.
Brodie, J. W., Lumber Merchant, 115 Queen St.
Brodie, R. H., Planter, 45 Coming St.
Brodie, Robert, Lumber Merchant, 79 Tradd St.
Brody, J., 43 State St.
Brom, John K., Cooper, 49 George St.
Broncard, William, 7 Longitude Lane
Bronger, E., Seaman, 8 Tradd St.
Brooks, Benjamin, Drake St.
Brooks, Sarah, Mrs., Milliner, 200 King St.
Broughton, Mary M., Mrs., 51 Wentworth St.
Broughton, Mary, Mrs., 37 Society St.
Broughton, T. A., Clerk, Post Office, res. 8 New St.
Brower, Henry, Tailor, 133 King St.
Brown & Porter, Attorneys, 38 Broad St., A. H. Brown, W. D. Porter
Brown & Stone, Crockery Dealers, 147 Meeting St., B. H. Brown, R. G. Stone
Brown & Strobel, Grocers, 147 East Bay St., George Grown, B. M. Strobel
Brown, A. H., Attorney, Broad St., res. 105 Tradd St.
Brown, A. Mc., Bookkeeper, 9 Hasell St.
Brown, Alfred, Watchmaker, 236 King St.
Brown, B., Cap Manufacturer, 101 King St.
Brown, C. P., Teacher, 49 Anson St.
Brown, -----, Crockery Merchant, 147 Meeting St., res. 150 Meeting St.
Brown, E. G., Clerk, 10 Hayne St., res. 146 Meeting St.
Brown, E. W., Builder, 6 Coming St.
Brown, Edmund, Pump Maker, 22 Smith St.
Brown, Eliza, Mrs., 15 West St.
Brown, Eliza, Mrs., 86 Broad St.
Brown, G., Grocer, 47 Broad St.
Brown, G. H., Clerk, 147 Meeting St.
Brown, G. W., Merchant, Brown's Wharf, res. 8 Montague St.
Brown, Henry, 24 Marsh St.
Brown, J. K., Planter, 49 Anson St.
Brown, J. S., Clerk, Adger's Wharf, 49 Anson St.
Brown, J. T., Dry Goods, 100 Meeting St.
Brown, J. W., Wood Factor, South Bay St., res. 68 Queen St.

Brown, James, Agent, 4 Beaufain St.
Brown, James, Cap Manufacturer, 101 King St.
Brown, James H., Gauger, 14 Liberty St.
Brown, John, Clerk, Railroad Depot, res. Burns Lane
Brown, John, Stone Mason, Meeting St., res. 2
  Philadelphia St.
Brown, Joseph, Cap Maker, 315 King St.
Brown, Joshua, Mrs., 105 Tradd St.
Brown, Judith, Mrs., Boarders, 4 Beaufain St.
Brown, Magdalen, Mrs., 23 Coming St.
Brown, -----, Mrs., Seamstress, 87 King St.
Brown, P., Reid & Hanover Sts.
Brown, P., St. Philip St.
Brown, Rachel, Mrs., 10 Savage St.
Brown, Robert & Son, Factors, Southern Wharf, Robert
  Brown, Robert E. Brown
Brown, Robert E., Factor, Southern Wharf, res. 43
  Church St.
Brown, Robert, Factor, Southern Wharf, res. 43 Church
  St.
Brown, S. B., Clerk, 66 Market St.
Brown, S. K., Carpenter, 24 Coming St.
Brown, Sarah, Mrs., 26 Bull St.
Brown, T. K., Butcher, 91 Market St.
Brown, W. H., 105 Church St.
Browne, Anna E., Mrs., 41 Tradd St.
Browne, G. B., Clerk, King & Hasell Sts., res. 2 Society
  St.
Browne, John D., Superintendent, Burial Ground, 3 Bull
  St.
Browne, R. C., Clerk, 41 Tradd St.
Browne, S. S., Printer, 5 Stoll's Alley
Browne, William, 41 Tradd St.
Brownell, E., Tailor, 33 Broad St.
Browning, A. F., Clerk, King & Market Sts., res. 3 Pitt
  St.
Bruning, Henry, Clerk, 19 South Bay St.
Brunyes, William, Grocer, 30 Coming St.
Brutton, John Von, 29 Meeting St.
Bryan, Elizabeth, Mrs., Seamstress, 124 Queen St.
Bryan, G. S., Attorney, Broad St., res. 27 Church St.
Bryan, J. B., N. King St.
Bryan, J. M., Grocer, 365 King St.
Bryan, Jonathan, Dry Goods, King St., res. 14 Hasell St.
Bryan, Jonathan, Jr., Officer, Planters & Mechanics Bank
Bryant, Jane, 97 Broad St.
Buckelew, F., Druggist, 107 East Bay St.
Buckheith, Philip, Columbus St.
Budd, T. G., Merchant, 21 Anson St.
Budd, T. S., Mariner, 21 Anson St.
Buhre, Daniel, Grocer, 83 Beaufain St.
Buhre, J. F., Grocer, 103 Meeting St.
Buhrman, Henry, Bar Keeper, 55 Market St.
Buist, C. B., Clerk, Boyce's Wharf, res. Pavilion Hotel
Buist, George, Attorney, St. Michael's Alley, res. 82
  Wentworth St.
Bunch, Sarah, 279 King St.
Bunger, C. R., Clerk, 47 Market St.
Burch, G., Mrs., 22 Cumberland St.
Burch, W. C., Carpenter, 22 Cumberland St.

Burchester, F., Mrs., Seamstress, 3 Clifford St.
Burckmyer & Moffett, Commission Merchants, 78 East
  Bay St., J. C. Burchmyer, J. R. Moffett
Burckmyer, C. L., & J. A., Commission Merchants, 96
  East Bay St.
Burckmyer, C. L., Merchant, East Bay St., res. Geroge
  St.
Burckmyer, J. A., Merchant, East Bay St., res. George St.
Burckmyer, J. C., Merchant, East Bay St., res. 15 Society
  St.
Burger, S. J., Clerk, 290 King St.
Burgerin, William, Clerk, 183 East Bay St.
Burie, George, Blacksmith, 20 Pinckney St.
Burie, J., Printer, Mercury Office, res. 23 Tradd St.
Burke, A. J., Printer, 40 Broad St., res. 74 Anson St.
Burke, G. R., Clerk, 149 Meeting St.
Burke, J. D., Painter, 112 Church St.
Burke, J. H., Pilot, 21 Tradd St.
Burke, John, Clerk, 75 Church St.
Burke, John, N. Meeting St.
Burke, Lawrence, 55 Boundary St.
Burke, M., Laborer, 47 State St.
Burke, S., Mrs., 14 Vernon St.
Burke, Samuel, Boat Builder, 33 Wall St.
Burn, Edward, Blacksmith, Cannon St.
Burn, Henry, Cannon St.
Burn, Henry, Jr., Cannon St.
Burn, William, Cannon St.
Burnett, A., Planter, 6 Legare St.
Burnham, Henry, Seaman, 2 Laurens St.
Burnham, R. W., Druggist, 343 King St.
Burnham, William, Locksmith, 2 Laurens St.
Busby, G. W., Mason, 31 Beaufain St.
Busch, Stephen, Grocer, 168 East Bay St.
Busha, James, Carpenter, 41 Queen St.
Bushell, -----, Bookseller, 101 Meeting St.
Bussell, J. F., Carpenter, 110 Meeting St.
Butler, A., 22 Market St.
Butler, P., 22 Market St.
Butler, Richard, Merchant, Commercial Wharf, res. 17
  Wentworth St.
Butler, William, Upholsterer, 166 King St.
Butterworth, A. H., Professor of Music, 309 King St.
Byrne, Thomas, Shoe Maker, 24 State St.
Cadow, William (see Mckenzie, Cadow & Co.)
Cagla, Leonard, Blacksmith, 52 King St.
Cahill, James, Carpenter, 110 King St.
Cahill, Martin, 22 Market St.
Cain, D. J. C., Physician, 20 Wentworth St.
Cain, D., Judith St.
Cain, John, N. St. Philip St.
Cain, John, Seaman, 34 Tradd St.
Calder, Alexander, Accountant, Vendue Range, res. 15
  Friend St.
Calder, James, Jr., Clerk, 78 Church St.
Calder, James, Sr., Cabinet Maker, 78 Church St.
Calder, William, Dry Goods, 248 King St.
Caldwell, A. P., Auctioneer, Vendue Range, res. 19 State
  St.
Caldwell, J. W., Ship Broker, 89 East Bay St., res. 19

State St.
Caldwell, James M., Factor, Magwood's Wharf, res. Judith St.
Caldwell, John, Miller, Beaufain St.
Caldwell, R. & A. P., Auctioneers, Vendue Range
Caldwell, R. & J., Factors, Central Wharf
Caldwell, Richard, Auctioneer, Vendue Range, res. 27 Cumberland St.
Caldwell, Robert, Laborer, 47 State St.
Caldwell, William S., Attorney, 19 State St.
Calhoun, P. C. (see Harral, Hare & Co.)
Callahan, William, Storekeeper, 73 Church St.
Callan, Thomas, Rigger, 38 King St.
Calvert, M., Mason, 20 Bull St.
Calvert, -----, Mrs., 32 Coming St.
Calvo, C. A., Printer, 14 Clifford St.
Cambridge, Ann, Miss, 71 King St.
Cambridge, St. John, Mrs., 5 Minority St.
Cameron, Archibald, Blacksmith, Hasell St., res. 14 Larens St.
Cameron, Duncan, Blacksmith, Hasell St., res. 20 Washington St.
Cameron, G. & H. & Co., Crockery Dealers, 145 Meeting St., G. S. Cameron, H. P. Cameron, D. Moore
Cameron, G. S., Crockery Dealer, 145 Meeting St.
Cameron, H. P., Crockery Dealer, 145 Meeting St.
Cameron, McDermid & Mustard, Hasell St. Continued
Camfield, A. W. (see Johnson & Camfield)
Caminade, Henry, Orderly, City Guard House, res. 182 East Bay St.
Cammer, John, Carpenter, 46 Bull St.
Campbell, C., Mariner, 24 Burns Lane
Campbell, H., N. Meeting St.
Campbell, I. M., Physician, 89 Broad St.
Campbell, J. B., Attorney, 40 Broad St., res. 84 Beaufain St.
Campbell, J. B., Rev., 1 Short St., Rector, St. Philip's Church.
Campbell, John, Storekeeper, 66 Market St.
Campbell, Maxwell, Meeting St.
Canaday, J., Boundary St.
Canady, James, Gas Pipe Fitter, 72 Meeting St.
Canale, Angelo, Fruiterer, 11 Market St.
Candler, Edward, Nautical Store, 69 East Bay St., res. 14 Savage St.
Canlier, George, Physician, 12 Queen St.
Canning, Charles, Printer, 24 Church St.
Cannon, George, Dry Goods, 312 King St.
Canter, Rebecca, Mrs., 101 King St.
Cantley, Sarah, Mrs., Seamstress, 35 Montague St.
Cantwell, Patrick, Customs Officer, 11 Marsh St.
Capers & Huger, Brokers & Auctioneers, 22 Broad St., T. F. Capers, D. E. Huger, Jr.
Capers, Samuel, Rev., cr. Duncan & St. Philip Sts.
Capers, Thomas, F., Broker, 22 Broad St. res. 12 Logan St.
Capers, William, Rev., D. D., Bishop, M. E. Church South, N. St. Philip St.
Capp, George, Carpenter, 93 Queen St.
Capp, Henry, Clerk, 102 Tradd St.

Capplemann, Eimer, Grocer, 22 New St.
Caradine, Peter, Seaman, 85 Church St.
Carberry, James, Charlotte St.
Carberry, John, Charlotte St.
Carberry, John, Jr., Charlotte St.
Cardozo, Isaac N., Customs Officer, 4 Society St.
Cardozo, J. N., Editor, Evening News, res. 4 Society St.
Carew, Edward, Planter, N. Meeting St.
Carew, John, E., Editor, Charleston Mercury, John St.
Carey, E. M., Druggist, 35 Broad St.
Carlisle, Margaret, Mrs., 10 Wall St.
Carmand, H., Mrs., 86 Queen St.
Carnighan, John, Pilot, 30 Tradd St.
Carpenter, William S., Mason, 32 King St.
Carr, C. D., Tailor, 30 Broad St., res. 21 Meeting St.
Carr, F. J., Rev., 80 Broad St.
Carr, John, Printer, 70 Meeting St.
Carr, Patrick, Laborer, 62 State St.
Carrere, M. E., Physician, 103 Tradd St.
Carrere, William, G., Wharfinger, Adger's Wharf, res. 1 Orange St.
Carrington, William, Watch Maker, 266 King St., res. 14 Rutledge St.
Carroll, B., Shoe Dealer, 126 Meeting St.
Carroll, Charles R., Planter, 31 Pitt St.
Carroll, James, Shoe Maker, 65 Anson St.
Carroll, Lawrence, Shoe Maker, 56 King St.
Carroll, P., Boundary St.
Carroll, William, Stone Cutter, Meeting St., res. 41 Archdale St.
Carson, E. & Co., Factors, Boyce & Co's. Wharf, Elisha Carson, David A. Carson
Carson, Elizabeth, Mrs., 90 Tradd St.
Carstang, E. C., Miss, Dress Maker, 196 King St.
Carsten, E. H., Lamplighter, 24 Montague St.
Carsten, John, Farmer, Ann St.
Carsten, Philip, Sires St.
Cart, Francis, Boundary St.
Cart, -----, Misses, 24 Bull St.
Carter, A., Book Seller, 163 Meeting St.
Carter, J. B., Clerk, 306 King St.
Carter, John, Miller, 48 Queen St.
Caruthers, James, 114 Church St.
Casey, Henry, City Inspector, City Hall, res. 184 King St.
Casey, John, Coming St.
Casey, S. C., Mrs., Dry Goods, 184 King St.
Caskins, T., Amherst St.
Caskins, Thomas, Nassau St.
Cassen, James D., Wood Factor, 18 Vernon St.
Cassen, W., Tinner, Queen St., res. 18 Vernon St.
Cassiday, Alice, Mrs., Boarders, 11 Elliott St.
Cassiday, Edward, Carpenter, 16 Horlbeck's Alley
Cassiday, John, N. St. Philip St.
Castillo, R., Cigar Maker, 144 East Bay St.
Cater, T., Clerk, 15 Laurens St.
Cauton, R., N. King St.
Caw, Peter, Mrs., 14 Friend St.
Cawson, Richard, Laborer, 14 Beaufain St.
Cay & Aveilhe, Commission Merchants, 171 East Bay St., John E. Cay, P. A. Aveilhe

Cay, John E., Jr., Clerk, 171 East Bay St.
Cay, John E., Merchant, 171 East Bay St.
Chadwick, H. G., 11 Meeting St.
Chadwick, S., 11 Meeting St.
Chafee & St. Amand, Wines & Cordials, 94 East Bay St.,
   O. J. Chaffee, J. P. St. Amand
Chafee, N. U., Merchant, 108 East Bay St.
Chafee, O. J., Merchant, 94 East Bay St., res. 15 George
   St.
Chalk, John, N. King St.
Chalmers, A., Millwright, 5 Wharf St.
Chalmers, James, Blacksmith, Hasell St., res. 5 Wharf St.
Chamberlain, C. V., Merchant, 288 King St., res. 181
   King St.
Chamberlin & Bancroft, Wholesale Dry Goods, corner
   King & Society Sts., C.V. Chamberlain, E. W. Bancroft
Chambers & White, Factors, Boyce & Co's. Wharf,
   James S. Chambers, Joseph H. White
Chambers, J. S., Factor, Boyce's Wharf, res. 46 Boundary
   St.
Champlin, A. J., Mason, 63 Beaufain St.
Champlin, O. P., 28 Magazine St.
Champlin, Samuel, Customs Officer, 28 Magazine St.
Chapeau, J. B., 94 Church St.
Chaplin, -----, 260 King St.
Chaplin, Leonard, Salesman, 40 Wentworth St., res. 30
   Pinckney St.
Chapman, J., Atlantic St.
Chapman, James, Merchant, Exchange St., res. 4 Water
   St.
Chapman, Samuel, Pilot, 33 Tradd St.
Chapman, William, Jeweller, 337 King St.
Chase, J. P., 82 Tradd St.
Chase, P. S., Clerk, 96 Queen St., res. 130 King St.
Chasteau, -----, Mrs., Dry Goods, 7 State St.
Chazal, Augustus, Clerk, 67 Meeting St.
Chazal, J. P., Physician, 48 Anson St.
Chazal, P. A., Clerk, Boyce's Wharf, 48 Anson St.
Chedel, George, Grocer, 32 Pitt St.
Cheesborough, E. R., Broker, State St., res. 18 Church
   St.
Cheesborough, John, Officer, Charleston Bank, res. 83
   Broad St.
Cheesborough, -----, Misses, Teachers, 18 Church St.
Cheney, E., Hotel Keeper, 101 East Bay St.
Cheves, J. R., Physician, 44 South Bay St.
Chew, T. R., Blacksmith, 3 Marsh St.
Chisolm, A. H., Miller, foot of Tradd St., res. 123 Broad
   St.
Chisolm, George, Mrs., 77 Beaufain St.
Chisolm, Jane, Mrs., Planter, 45 Anson St.
Chisolm, Octavius, City Officer, 106 Tradd St.
Chisolm, Robert T., Planter, Pinckney St.,
   Cannonborough
Chitty, J. W., Clerk, 33 Market St.
Chitty, M., Carpenter, 33 Market St.
Choate, Susan M. J., Mrs., 120 Tradd St.
Chreitzburg, C., Mrs., 17 Beaufain St.
Chreitzburg, R. S. R., Carpenter, 60 Wentworth St.
Chreitzburg, T. W., Carpenter, 26 Beaufain St.

Christean, Peter, Clerk, 23 State St.
Christean, -----, Woolf St.
Christiansen, J., Grocer, 180 King St.
Christophel, E., Boundary St.
Chupein, Lewis Y., Restaurateur, 105 East Bay St.
Clancey, John, Warren St.
Clancey, M. A., Mrs., Warren St.
Clancey, William, Warren St.
Clapp, J. M., Editor, 101 East Bay St.
Clark, Henry, Lumber Merchant, 87 Beaufain St.
Clark, Joseph, Fireman, Railroad, res. 28 Mazyck St.
Clark, Richard, Pilot, 11 Church St.
Clark, Robert A. (see Roosevelt, Hyde & Clark)
Clarke, Charles, 2 Motte's Lane
Clarke, G. E., Merchant, 151 Meeting St.
Clarke, H. B., Dry Goods, 213 King St.
Clarke, J. P., 160 Meeting St.
Clarke, J. S., Merchant, Hayne St., res. 146 Meeting St.
Clarke, James, N. King St.
Clarke, John, N. King St.
Clarke, R. A., Merchant, 146 Meeting St.
Clarke, S. S. & G., Fancy Dry Goods, 151 Meeting St.
Clarke, Solomon, Drake St.
Clarkson, John, 4 Smith St.
Clarkson, T. B., Factor, Central Wharf, res. 4 Smith St.
Classen, H. W., 184 East Bay St.
Claussen, H. W., Collector, 5 Market St.
Claussen, J. C., Grocer, 16 Archdale St.
Claussen, J. C. H., Baker, 115 Church St.
Clayton, William, Printer, 22 Queen St.
Cleapor, J. W., Dentist, 28 Wall St.
Cleapor, J. W., Sail Maker, cr. Boundary & Coming Sts.
Cleland, M., Clerk, Vendue Range, res. 6 Queen St.
Clement, J. P., Clerk, Commissioner, Cross Roads,
   Amherst St.
Cleveland, J. A., Dentist, 215 King St.
Cleveland, W. L., Druggist, 215 King St.
Clifford, Owen, Morris St.
Clissey, A., Miss, 82 King St.
Close, L. P. H., Clerk, 101 Meeting St.
Cluster, Charles, Boiler Maker, 4 Vernon St.
Clyne, J. C., Clerk, 22 South Bay St.
Coates, C., Teacher, 68 Wentworth St.
Coates, Mary A., Mrs., 59 Meeting St.
Coates, W. S., Superintendent, Cotton Press, Union
   Wharf, res. Pinckney St.
Cobb, E. W. (see Dunham, C.T. & Co.)
Cobia, Elizabeth, Miss, 16 Montague St.
Cobia, Francis, Butcher, Reid St.
Cobia, Henry, Auctioneer, Vendue Range, res. 88
   Beaufain St.
Cobia, M., Miss, 20 Anson St.
Cobia, Martha, Mrs., 26 Mazyck St.
Coburn, Peter K., Carpenter, John St.
Cochran, C. B., Teacher, N. King St.
Cochran, Clarence, Railroad Bank, Cannon St.
Cochran, John, N. St. Philip St.
Cochran, Patrick, President St.
Cochran, William, Washington St.
Coffee, Thomas, Laborer, 15 Queen St.

Coffey, J., Laborer, 9 Tradd St.
Coffin, G. M., Factor, Adger's Wharf, res. 86 Broad St.
Coffin, T. A., Planter, 7 Rutledge St.
Cogdell, Charles, Bank of State of S. C.
Cogdell, G. B., Organist, 169 Meeting St.
Cogdell, J. W., Attorney, 54 Broad St.
Cogdell, R. W., 65 Broad St.
Cogswell, -----, 4 St. Philip St.
Cohen, A. D., Rev., 57 Boundary St.
Cohen, D. D., Chapel St.
Cohen, H., John St.
Cohen, I. S., Merchant, Vendue Range, res. 15 Society St.
Cohen, Jacob, Broker, 20 Broad St., res. 12 Friend St.
Cohen, L. M., Mrs., 8 Wentworth St.
Cohen, Leopold, Fruiterer, 71 Market St.
Cohen, M. E., Planter, 3 Rutledge St.
Cohen, N. A., Tobacconist, 157 East Bay St., res. 46 Meeting St.
Cohen, Philip, 8 Wentworth St.
Cohen, S. I., N. Coming St.
Colburn, B. P., Charlotte St.
Colburn, Charles, 114 Church St.
Colburn, J. S., Dry Goods, 100 King St.
Colburn, James H., Clerk, 200 King St.
Colcock, John, Factor, Commercial Wharf, res. 2 Orange St.
Colcock, R. H., Factor, Commercial Wharf, res. 2 Orange St.
Colcock, R. W., Professor, Citadel
Coldes, D. C., Clerk, 12 King St.
Cole, George, F., Music Merchant, 127 King St.
Coleman, D., Storekeeper, 34 Tradd St.
Coleman, H. W., Merchant, 217 King St., res. 4 Clifford St.
Coleman, John, Grocer, 61 Tradd St.
Coley, B. J., Carpenter, 19 Anson St.
Collingwood, John, Cannon St.
Collins, E., Laborer, 212 King St.
Collins, Edward, 8 Linguard St.
Collins, James N., Teacher, 88 Queen St.
Collins, P., Plasterer, 212 King St.
Collins, Sarah, Mrs., 4 New St.
Collum, P., Laborer, 13 St. Philip St.
Colson, Charles, Dry Goods, 27 Middle St.
Commault, Ann, Mrs., 17 Berresford St.
Commins & McCaddon, Wholesale Boots & Shoes, 151 Meeting St. upstairs, John Commins, J. S. McCaddon
Commins, Edward, Clerk, 274 King St.
Commins, John, Storekeeper, 274 King St.
Commins, Michael, Clerk, 274 King St.
Compson, F., Thomas St.
Comstock, D. B., Clerk, 13 Hayne St.
Comyer, A., Boiler Maker, Railroad, res. 22 Washington St.
Comyer, Francis, Ship Carpenter, 22 Washington St.
Conclin, Owen, Coming St.
Condict, Jennings & Co., Saddlery, 157 Meeting St., S. H. Condict, D. Jennings, R. Tomlinson, P. Jacobus
Condray, William, Tailor, 144 East Bay St.

Condy & Dawes, Auctioneers & Brokers, 7 State St., T. D. Condy, H. P. Dawes
Condy, Ancrum, Bee St.
Condy, Poinsett, Bee St.
Condy, Thomas D., Broker, State St., res. Bee St.
Conly, Owen, Morris St.
Conner, Ann, Mrs., 103 King St.
Conner, H. W., President, Bank of Charleston, res. 9 Meeting St.
Conolly, Thomas, Clerk, 2 Hayne St.
Conway, James, Laborer, 20 Tradd St.
Cook, J., Grocer, 311 King St.
Cook, John A., Grocer, N. King St.
Cook, William, N. King St.
Cooper & Rivers, Attorneys, Court House Square, G. W. Cooper, E. Rivers
Cooper, G. W., Magistrate, cr. East Bay & Inspection Sts.
Cooper, Mary, Mrs., 64 Anson St.
Copalia, Marion, 4 Hard Alley
Copes, James, Mariner, 41 Church St.
Corbett, J. H., Planter, 23 Lynch St.
Corbett, James, Dry Goods, 322 King St.
Corbett, Mary, Mrs., 26 South Bay St.
Corbett, Thomas, Planter, 23 Lynch St.
Corbett, W. B., Physician, 322 King St.
Corby, Edward, Cannon St.
Corby, J. W., Ship Joiner, 15 Laurens St.
Corby, John, Blacksmith, Union Wharf, res. 15 Laurens St.
Corcker, G., Fisherman, 12 Vernon St.
Corcoran, J. A., Rev., D. D., 80 Broad St.
Corcoran, Thomas, Mason, 38 Market St.
Corcoran, Thomas, N. King St.
Corder, V., Mrs., Seamstress, 14 Chalmers St.
Corders, Albert, Baker, 45 Boundary St.
Cordes, D., Judith St.
Cordes, George, Grocer, 56 Anson St.
Cordes, Theodore, Tavern Keeper, 55 Market St.
Cordray, Thomas, Ship Joiner, 2 Hard Alley
Corkle, Thomas, Printer, 137 East Bay St.
Corley, Thomas, Guardman, 6 Linguard St.
Cornelius, Henry, Clerk, 183 East Bay St.
Cornly, Edward, Gas Fitter, 82 Queen St.
Corrie, S. B., Clerk, Coming St.
Corrie, W. C., Clerk, Coming St.
Corrigan, P., Dry Goods, 358 King St.
Corry, Joseph, Fruiterer, 55 Market St.
Costar, V., Storekeeper, 10 King St.
Coste, -----, Clerk, 216 King St.
Coswick, Bartole, Storekeeper, 3 Vendue Range
Cotchett, George, 18 Hasell St.
Cotter, John, Bogard St.
Courtney, E. S., Customs Officer, 16 Wentworth St.
Courtney, S. G., Clerk, 259 King St., res. 16 Wentworth St.
Courtney, Thomas, Merchant, 58 Wentworth St.
Courtney, W. C., Merchant, 8 Hayne St., res. 38 Broad St.
Cousins, Thomas, 18 Berresford St.

Coutt, William, Clerk, 101 Meeting St.
Covert, Thomas, Bookkeeper, 169 Meeting St.
Cowan, George, Mariner, 7 Montague St.
Cowan, John, Cabinet Maker, 5 Philadelphia St.
Cowell, Leopold, 159 East Bay St.
Cowen, E. R., Mrs., Whim's Court.
Cowgan, Meredith, Clerk, Hayne St., res. 99 Queen St.
Cowley, B. (see Force, L. M. & B. W. & Co.)
Cowperthwaite, E. R., Furniture Dealer, 251 King St., res. 29 Wentworth St.
Cox, Rodolph, Sail Maker, 14 Coming St.
Cox, S. B., Miss, 178 King St.
Cox, S. K., Rev., Pastor, Methodist Protestant Church, 297 King St.
Cox, W. H., 184 East Bay St.
Crafts, G. J., Attorney, 27 Legare St.
Crafts, Mary, Miss, 57 Tradd St.
Crafts, W. J., Clerk, 155 East Bay St.
Cramer, G. W., 19 Pinckney St.
Cramer, P., N. King St.
Crane, C. D., Coach Maker, Gadsden's Wharf
Crane, J. G., 45 Hayne St.
Crane, L., Clerk, 309 King St.
Cranston, Edward, Clerk, 29 Mazyck St.
Cranston, Harold, Mechanic, 29 Mazyck St.
Crawford, Grace, Mrs., 2 Magazine St.
Crawford, J. D., Laborer, 100 Meeting St.
Crawford, John, Mrs., 2 Rutledge St.
Crawford, William L., Tavern Keeper, 63 East Bay St.
Crews, A. J., Merchant, 28 East Bay St., res. 20 Mazyck St.
Crews, E. B., Auctioneer, Vendue Range, res. 90 Beaufain St.
Cripps, Mary, Miss, 23 Friend St.
Cripps, -----, Misses, 41 Meeting St.
Croft, A. E., Mrs., 156 East Bay St.
Croft, S. E., Mrs., 10 Orange St.
Croft, Thomas H., Merchant, 13 Logan St.
Crogan, James, Laborer, 62 State St.
Croggan, Peter, Laborer, 118 Church St.
Crogham, C. J., Rev., 80 Broad St.
Cromley, Daniel, Bootmaker, 30 Queen St.
Cromley, J., 13 Queen St.
Cromwell, -----, Miss, 44 Church St.
Cropper, Ann M., Miss, 99 King St.
Cross, M. A., Mrs., Confectioner, 69 King St.
Crouch, C. W., Teacher, 10 Burns Lane
Crouper, James, Baker, 78 King St.
Crovat, Gibbes, Judith St.
Crowell, Stephen, 24 State St.
Crowley, C. P., Capt., United States Navy, 64 Broad St.
Crozier, Charles, 114 Church St.
Cruikshank, -----, Mrs., 63 Coming St.
Cruikshank, R., Tailor, 19 Market St.
Cruikshank, S., Tanner, 22 Queen St., res. Hanover St.
Cudworth, John, Printer, 20 Hasell St.
Culbert, John, Amherst St.
Culbert, John, Nassau St.
Cullen, Joseph, Upholsterer, 160 King St.
Cullenane, P., Dry Goods, 360 King St.

Cumming, Thomas J., Rigger, Pritchard St., res. Longitude Lane
Cummings, John B., Bookkeeper, 35 East Bay St.
Cunningham & Robertson, Attorneys, Broad & Church Sts., J. Cunningham, L. F. Robertson
Cunningham, Andrew, Mason, 6 St. Philip St.
Cunningham, John, Attorney, 54 Broad St.
Curley, James, 23 Queen St.
Currant, Emanuel, Gilder, 44 Queen St.
Curtis, Ephraim, Carpenter, 3 Back Alley
Curtis, James M., Builder, 1 Lynch St.
Curtis, Joseph, Carpenter, 13 Inspection St.
Curtis, Robert, Portrait Painter, 1 Lynch St.
Curtis, William, 77 East Bay St.
Cuthbert, Ann, Mrs., Planter, 200 East Bay St.
Cuthbert, James H., Rev., Pastor, Wentworth St. Baptist Church, res. 82 Beaufain St.
D'Alvigny, N., Dentist, 274 King St.
Dadin, L. H., Jeweller, 155 King St.
Daggett, L., Machinist, Marsh St.
Daggett, Mary A. Amesbery, Mrs., 76½ Church St.
Daggett, S., Carpenter, Marsh St.
Daggett, William L., Printer, 76½ Church St.
Dahlees, Henry, Storekeeper, 23 Church St.
Dalcho, Mary, Mrs., 85 Broad St.
Dale, Elias, Carpenter, 102 Church St.
Dale, W., President St.
Dalgeish, William, Mason, 59 Broad St.
Dallwich, Edward, Upholsterer, 160 King St., res. 4 King St.
Dalmas, John, Baker, 113 Meeting St.
Daly, E. L., Shoe Dealer, 326 King St.
Daly, Henry, Shoe Dealer, 354 King St.
Daly, J. & E., Boots & Shoes, 326 King St.
Daly, John, Shoe Dealer, 326 King St.
Daly, Peter, Grocer, 37 Market St.
Daly, William, 95 Queen St.
Dana, W. C., Rev., Pastor, 3rd Presbyterian Church, 5 Laurens St.
Danaher, C., Coppersmith, 176 East Bay St.
Danem, George, Bar Keeper, 27 Market St.
Dangerfield, R., Carpenter, 179 Meeting St.
Daniels, S., Tailor, 2 Linguard St.
Dapray, J. A., Dentist, 218 King St.
Darby, John T., Clerk, N. St. Philip St.
Darby, R. H., Tailor, 37 Queen St.
Darby, William, Carpenter, 19 Magazine St.
Darrell, Ann H., 11 Lamboll St.
Darrell, James, Coming St.
Darrell, Nicholas, Engineer, 36 St. Philip St.
Darrow, A. H., Carriage Dealer, 43 Society St.
Darrow, Julius, Carriage Dealer, 43 Society St.
Dart, B. S., Factor, 47 Tradd St.
Davega, Isaac, Attorney, 1 Court House Square
Davenne, Edward, Merchant, Adger's Wharf, res. 66 Tradd St.
Davenport, -----, Pilot, 61 Church St.
Davenport, William, Jr., Wood Factor, 2 Horlbeck's Alley
Davids, A. J., Painter, 73 Queen St.

Davidson, Thomas, Lumber Measurer, 11 South Bay St.
Davidson, William, Planter, 66 Church St.
Davie, Robert, Coach Trimmer, 14 Beaufain St.
Davies, D. W., Conductor, N. Meeting St.
Davis, C. W., Storekeeper, 333 King St.
Davis, Calvin, Bricklayer, 53 Tradd St.
Davis, D. W., Bell Hanger, 104 Meeting St.
Davis, Eliza, Mrs., Seamstress, 26 Mazyck St.
Davis, G. W., Pilot, Longitude Lane
Davis, George Y., Merchant, East Bay St., res. 77 Meeting St.
Davis, Henry, Bell Hanger, 104 Meeting St.
Davis, J., Pilot, 7 Atlantic St.
Davis, Jane, Mrs., Mansion House, 77 Meeting St.
Davis, John, Clerk, 22 Coming St.
Davis, Martha, Mrs., 35 State St.
Davis, Martha, Mrs., St. Philip St.
Davis, N., Bell Hanger, 104 Meeting St.
Davis, Ross, Pilot, 59 East Bay St.
Davis, S., Bell Hanger, 104 Meeting St.
Davis, Solomon, Broker, 5 State St., res. 55 Wentworth St.
Davis, W. H., Merchant, East Bay St., 38 Tradd St.
Dawes, H. P., Broker, 9 State St., res. 22 King St.
Dawson & Blackman, Druggists, 17 Broad St., Joseph Dawson, Joseph Blackman
Dawson, A. V., Attorney, Bee St.
Dawson, C., Mrs. 11 Archdale St.
Dawson, Charles P., 96 Broad St.
Dawson, E. J., Clerk, 118 Meeting St.
Dawson, J. E., Physician, 96 Broad St.
Dawson, James, Laborer, 8 Linguard St.
Dawson, John L., Physician, 60 Church St.
Dawson, -----, Misses, 34 Bull St.
Dawson, S. P., 11 Archdale St.
Dawson, W. H., Bookkeeper, 147 Meeting St., rest. 9 Lynch St.
Day, Fisher, Boarders, 260 King St.
Dayneu, F., Ship Carpenter, 18 Vernon St.
Dearing, William (see Mitchell, E. R. & Co.)
Dearsy, Peter, President St.
Dearsy, Thomas, President St.
Deas, Charles, 113 Tradd St.
Deas, E. H., Physician, 38 East Bay St.
Deas, Henry, Accountant, 113 Tradd St.
Deas, John, Merchant, Hayne St., res. 113 Tradd St.
Deas, Margaret H., Mrs., 3 Friend St.
Deas, -----, Misses, 113 Tradd St.
Deas, Thomas H., Farmer, 37 Wentworth St.
Deas, W. C., Merchant, 3 Friend St.
Debernier, M., Miss, 20 Anson St.
DeBow, John, Blacksmith, Boundary St.
Decamps, A. G., Clerk, 51 King St.
Decamps, Eugene P., Carpenter, 65 Tradd St.
Decamps, John E., Carpenter, 65 Tradd St.
Decamps, Julius L., Carpenter, 65 Tradd St.
Decamps, Laura, Mrs., 65 King St.
DeChoiseul, -----, Count, French Consul, 59 Church St.
Deeden, P., Teacher, 287 King St.
Deery, Ann, Mrs., 2 Williams' Wharf

Dehay, Robert, Clerk, Hanover St.
Dehon, Sarah, Mrs., 37 Meeting St.
Dehon, Theodore, M. D., Planter, 37 Meeting St.
Deigan, Charles, Ship Carpenter, 28 Marsh St.
Dejon, C., Cigar Maker, 58 State St.
Deker, John, Grocer, 61 Tradd St.
Delande, C. W., Clerk, 270 King St.
Delange, J. L., Merchant, East Bay St., res. 6 Clifford St.
Delaunay, Jules, Rev., Teacher, 2 Liberty St.
Deleon, Isabel, Mrs., 1 Wentworth St.
Delky, Martin, St. Philip St.
Della Torre, A., Lumber Merchant, Charlotte St.
Della Torre, P., Attorney, Charlotte St.
Dellettre, M. N., Accountant, Military Hall
Demaly, J., Printer, 104 Tradd St.
Demery, Bernard, Fancy Store, 183 King St., res. 101 King St.
Denck, Joseph, 9 Pitt St.
Dener, Christiana, Mrs., 29 Mazyck St.
Denis, J. A., Confectioner, 114 King St.
Dennis, Isham, Constable, 3 Burns Lane
Dennis, Mary, Mrs., Tailoress, 23 Wentworth St.
Dennison, W. W., Bookkeeper, 41 Boundary St.
Derickson, H., Boundary St.
Desaussure, H. A. & Son, Attorneys, Broad St., H. A. Desaussure, W. G. Desaussure
DeSaussure, C. A., Factor, Adger's Wharf, res. 26 Meeting St.
DeSaussure, H. A., Attorney, 23 Broad St., res. 33 Meeting St.
DeSaussure, H. W., Physician, 31 Meeting St.
DeSaussure, J. B., Factor, Adger's Wharf, res. 33 Meeting St.
DeSaussure, Louis D., Broker, 23 Broad St., res. 33 Meeting St.
DeSaussure, W. G., Attorney, 23 Tradd St., res. 1 Lamboll St.
Desel, C. L., M. D., Planter, N. Pitt St.
Desporte, A., Printer, 98 Queen St.
Dettmyer, -----, cr. Amherst & Nassau Sts.
Deveaux & Fishburne, Factors, Southern Commercial Wharf, J. P. Deveaux, Robert Fishburne
Deveaux, D. H., Scene Artist, 122 King St.
Deveaux, J. P., Factor & Coroner, Southern Wharf, res. Boundary St.
Devermann, H., Clerk, 105 Queen St.
Devineau, E., Dry Goods, 286 King St.
Devineau, S., Seamstress, 349 King St.
Dewar, W. S., Merchant, Adger's Wharf, res. 46 Church St.
Dewees, John, Orphan House.
Dewees, Thomas H., Merchant, East Bay St., res. Orphan House
Dewees, William, Clerk, Orphan House.
Dewing, C., Merchant, 149 Meeting St.
Dewing, Thayer & Co., Straw Bonnets, 149 Meeting St., L. C. Dewing, Emery Thayer, H. Dewing
Dewitt, Gabriel, Clerk, 7 Liberty St.
Dewitt, James S., Boat Builder, 3 Vernon St.
Dexter, F., Mariner, 15 State St.

11

Deye, John, Dyer, 80 King St.
Dibble, P. V., Hatter, 37 Broad St.
Dickinson, -----, Mrs., Boarders, Queen St.
Dickson, George, Bootmaker, 121 Meeting St.
Dickson, Isaac, 186 East Bay St.
Dickson, John, 102 Meeting St.
Dickson, S., Dry Goods, 101 Meeting St.
Dickson, T. C., Ship Carpenter, 21 Beaufain St.
Dickson, Thomas, Capt., Neck Police, Cannon St.
Dieckhoff, C., Judith St.
Dill, Jane E., Mrs., 6 Lamboll St.
Dill, Joseph, Clerk, 6 Lamboll St.
Dill, S. G. W., St. Philip St.
Dillingham, James, Clerk, Hayne St.
Dillingham, Thomas H., Carpenter, 11 Price's Alley
Dingle, William, N. St. Philip St.
Disher, Robert, Butcher, Nassau St.
Divver, Sophia, Mrs., Merchant's Hotel, 290 King St.
Dixon, Isaac, Dry Goods, cr. King & Queen Sts.
Dixon, John, Dry Goods, 196 King St.
Dixon, Robert, Clerk, 196 King St.
Doar, Mary Ann, Mrs., 78 Anson St.
Dobson, O. L., Assessor, 4 Smith's Lane
Donahue, D., Policeman, 6 Smith's Lane
Donahue, H., 22 Market St.
Donald, John, Grocer, 215 East Bay St.
Donbaum, John, Tailor, 39 State St.
Doniphan, E. M., Mrs., 11 Pinckney St.
Donnell, Sarah, Mrs., 17 Pinckney St.
Donovan, H., Clerk, 75 Church St.
Doscher, C. H., Clerk, 28 Smith St.
Doscher, H., Storekeeper, 93 East Bay St., res. 21
  Market St.
Doscher, L., cr. Nassau & Woolf Sts.
Doty, A., Painter, 25 Broad St.
Doucin, P. M., Wharfinger, Boyce's Wharf, res. 214 King
  St.
Dougan, James, Laborer, 126 Queen St.
Dougherty, John, Carpenter, 181 Meeting St.
Dougherty, John, Wood Factor, 17 South Bay St.
Dougherty, Joseph, Grocer, 17 South Bay St.
Dougherty, Joseph, Jr., Ship Carpenter, 17 South Bay St.
Dougherty, Joseph, Washington St.
Dougherty, William, Gas Fitter, 82 Queen St.
Dougherty, William M. & Co., Gas Fitters, 295 King St.,
  W. M. Dougherty, William Browne
Doughty, C. W., Amherst St.
Douglass, Ann, Miss, Dress Maker, 117 Queen St.
Douglass, Campbell, Keeper, St. Andrew's Hall, 78
  Broad St.
Douglass, Caroline, Miss, Dress Maker, 107 Tradd St.
Douglass, J., Tailor, 20 Broad St.
Douglass, John, Clerk, John St.
Dove, Sarah P., Mrs., 7 Mary St.
Dowd, Matthew, Wine Bottler, 32 Anson St.
Dowlin, John, 4 Stoll's Alley
Dowling, -----, Mrs., 116 King St.
Downie, Robert, 80 Church St.
Downie, Thomas W., 86 Church St.
Doyle, John, 30 King St.

Doyle, John, Ship Carpenter, 22 Smith St.
Doyle, Patrick, Mason, 56 Anson St.
Drago, Andrew, Dry Goods, 141 King St.
Drago, Antoine, Dry Goods, 141 King St.
Drake, Miles, Dry Goods, 358 King St.
Drayton, A. R., Bank Officer, 2 Greenhill St.
Drayton, Emma, Miss, 20 King St.
Drayton, Henrietta, Miss, 2 Glebe St.
Drayton, J. S., Pinckney St., Cannonborough
Drayton, -----, Misses, 10 Lamboll St.
Drisden, William, St. Philip St.
Drose, Catherine, Mrs., Dry Goods, 325 King St.
Droutman, -----, Storekeeper, 53 Church St.
Dryer, A., Boundary St.
Dryer, John, Grocer, 66 Beaufain St.
Dubois, Eleanor, Mrs., 86 Queen St.
Dubois, John, Plasterer, 16 Market St.
Duc, Napoleon, Tinner, cr. King & Spring Sts.
Duffus, Alexander, Bookkeeper, 6 Wall St.
Duffus, George, Engineer, 6 Wall St.
Duffus, James A., Clerk, 6 Wall St.
Duffus, S. A., Carpenter, 38 Archdale St.
Duffy, H., 24 Market St.
Dufoe, E., N. Meeting St.
Duggin, John, Laborer, 9 Linguard St.
Dukes, Charlton, King St.
Dukes, F. O., Plasterer, 6 Boundary St.
Dukes, John, Clerk, N. King St.
Dukes, Joseph H., Attorney, 65 Broad St.
Dukes, W. C., Factor, Atlantic Wharf, res. King St., Neck
Dunahon, Michael, Gardener, 78 King St.
Dunbar, John, Mason, 22 Laurens St.
Duncan, A., Machinist, 4 Vernon St.
Duncan, James, 101 East Bay St.
Duncan, L., Physician, 230 King St.
Dunham, C. T. & Co., Wholesale Boots & Shoes, 159
  Meeting St. upstairs, C. T. Dunham, E. W. Cobb, L.
  Faxon
Dunham, C. T., Shoe Merchant, Meeting St., res. cr.
  Anson & Wentworth Sts.
Dunkin, A. H., Attorney, Broad St., res. Vanderhorst St.
Dunkin, B. F., Hon., Chancellor, Vanderhorst St.
Dunlap, James, Hack Driver, 3 Lynch St.
Dunlap, Samuel, Morris St.
Dunlap, W., 225 King St.
Dunn, Charles, Dry Goods, 371 King St.
Dunn, James A., Cabinet Maker, 18 Pinckney St.
Dunn, John, Policeman, 77 Broad St.
Dunn, William, Dry Goods, 371 King St.
Dunning, James, Woolf St
Dunstbseak, William, 13 Queen St.
Dupont, C. McN., Mrs., 23 Wentworth St.
Dupont, F., Upholsterer, 203 King St.
Dupont, -----, Mrs., 3 St. Michael's Alley
Dupre, J., Ann St.
Dupre, J., Mrs., Teacher, 196 East Bay St.
Dupre, James, Measurer, 25 Wall St.
Duquereron, Leopold, Clerk, 19 Tradd St.
Durkin, John, 112 Church St.
Durse, A., Bookbinder, 9 Horlbeck's Alley

12

Durse, L., Clerk, 9 Horlbeck's Alley
Duryea, J. M., 110 Meeting St.
Duryea, James, Carpenter, 225 East Bay St.
Duryea, Mary S., Mrs., 9 Wall St.
Dusenberry, -----, Constable, 76 King St.
Dutrieux, V., Mrs., Baker, 83 East Bay St.
Duval, Anne, Mrs., 4 West St.
Duval, Henry, Engineer, 10 Burns Lane
Duval, J. B., Tinner, 298 King St.
Dwight, J. M., Planter, 56 Wentworth St.
Dye, Harris & Co.
Eager, William, Clerk, 89 Wentworth St.
Earle, James, Mason, 30 Boundary St.
Earle, Ralph, 105 Church St.
Eason, Caroline M., Mrs., Boarders, 2 Glebe St.
Eason, George W., Clerk, 2 Glebe St.
Eason, J. M., Engineer, Drake St.
Eason, -----, Mrs., Amherst St.
Eason, R. H., Mason, 36 Coming St.
Eason, Robert J., Clerk, 2 Glebe St.
Eason, Thomas, Engineer, Nassau St.
East & Riddell, Ladies Shoe Manufactory, 186 King St.,
    William East, J. H. Riddell
East, William, Shoe Maker, 186 King St.
Easterby, George, Clerk, 83 Tradd St.
Easterby, W. H., Clerk, 205 King St.
Eavens, Sabil, Elliott St., Neck
Eckhard, Mary E., Mrs., 31 Meeting St.
Edgerton & Richards, Drapers & Tailors, 32 Broad St.,
    E. W. Edgerton, Frederick Richards
Edgerton, E. W., Tailor, 32 Broad St., res. 3 Orange St.
Edgerton, Eliza, Seamstress, 11 Friend St.
Edmindorff, Aaron, 160 Meeting St.
Edwards, Ann M., Mrs., 26 Wall St.
Edwards, C., Jr., Merchant, 7 Short St.
Edwards, C. L., Bank Officer, Charleston Bank, 2 State
    St.
Edwards, E. H., Mrs., 3 St. Philip St.
Edwards, Edmondston Charles, President, South Carolina
    Insurance Co., res. 8 Legare St.
Edwards, Evan, Clerk, Post Office, 27 Friend St.
Edwards, George, M. D., Planter, 2 Glebe St.
Edwards, George, Planter, 2 Glebe St.
Edwards, J. B., 26 Wall St.
Edwards, J. F., Factor, 26 Wall St.
Edwards, John J., Wharfinger, Central Wharf, 2 State St.
Edwards, L. A., Merchant, 72 Tradd St.
Edwards, Patrick M., Attorney, 13 Legare St.
Edwards, William S., Bookkeeper, 2 State St.
Egleston, G. W., Magistrate, Mary St.
Egleston, James L., Clerk, State Bank, 72 Anson St.
Ehney, Edward, Ship Smith, res. 3 Pinckney St.
Ehney, John, Engineer, 3 Pinckney St.
Ehney, P. M., Customs Office, res. 3 Pinckney St.
Ehrics, C., N. Meeting St.
Elbridge, J., Butcher, N. Meeting St.
Elder, James, Tanner, John St.
Elfe, Albert, Carpenter, 19 Lynch St.
Elfe, Ellen S., Miss, 74 Wentworth St.
Elfe, George, Planter, 2 Court House Square

Elfe, Robert, City Sheriff, 80 Tradd St.
Elfe, William, Customs Officer, 80 Tradd St.
Elford, John, Elizabeth St.
Ellerhorst, H. D., Miller, 6 Market St.
Elliott, B., Mrs., Planter, 10 George St.
Elliott, B. S., Planter, 10 George St.
Elliott, E. A., Mrs., Bakery, 130 King St.
Elliott, G. L., Physician, 10 George St.
Elliott, J. R., Blacksmith, 130 King St.
Elliott, -----, Misses, 36 South Bay St.
Elliott, T. O., Attorney, 14 Meeting St.
Elliott, William, Mrs., 36 South Bay St.
Ellis, B., Mariner, 15 Pinckney St.
Ellis, Joseph, Carpenter, 53 Coming St.
Ellis, W. D., Broker, 7 Wentworth St.
Elmore, F. H., President, Bank of State of S. C.,
    Washington St.
Elmore, J. W., Molder, 6 Boundary St.
Elsworth, F. B., Clerk, 31 Meeting St.
Elsworth, I. S. K., Molder, 21 Concord St.
Elsworth, J. T., Customs Officer, 10 Laurens St.
Ely, Ulysses, Merchant, 29 Meeting St.
Emanuel, N., Dry Goods, 45 Beaufain St.
Emory, J. R., Clerk, Unity Alley
Enderly, F., St. Philip St.
Englatt, William, 15 Queen St.
English, James, Shipwright, 15 South Bay St.
Ennis, James, Morris St.
Enslow, J. L., Cooper, 128 Tradd St.
Enslow, J., N. Meeting St.
Enston, A., Cabinet Maker, 151 King St., res. 118 Queen
    St.
Enston, D., 44 Queen St.
Enston, William, Cabinet Maker, 151 King St., res. 118
    Queen St.
Epping, J. P. M., Druggist, 277 King St.
Epson, J., Mrs., Seamstress, 19 Back Alley
Erickson, C., Carpenter, cr. Elizabeth & Ann Sts.
Erminger, John, Grocer, 1 Boundary St.
Esnard, Peter, 36 King St.
Estill, William, Librarian, Apprentices Hall, res. 9 Back
    Alley
Evans, C. P., Merchant, 37 Broad St.
Evans, Catherine, Mrs., 57 Queen St.
Evans, E., Coach Trimmer, 24 Mazyck St.
Evans, Isaac, Blacksmith, 73 Queen St.
Evans, J. B., Clerk, 41 Wentworth St.
Evans, J., Tailor, 20 Broad St.
Evans, James, 50 Coming St.
Evans, Robert, Turner, 97 Market St.
Eveleigh, Thomas, 95 Church St.
Ewau, John, Jeweller, 131 King St.
Ewau, William, Jeweller, 131 King St.
Faber, J., Planter, cr. Amherst & East Bay Sts.
Fabian, James, Planter, 102 Meeting St.
Fairchild, Daniel, Factor, Patton's Wharf, res. 13 Lynch
    St.
Fairchild, M., Mrs., 26 Marsh St.
Fairchild, Rufus, Tavern Keeper, King St., res. 50
    Wentworth St.

Fairley, James, Laborer, 126 Queen St.
Falk, A., Dry Goods, 265 King St.
Falk, J. L., Dry Goods, 265 King St.
Falk, J. L. & G., Clothing, 265 King St.
Fanning, F. D. & Co., Hats & Straw Goods, 35 Hayne St., F. D. Fanning, A. E. Tweedy
Fanning, F. D., Merchant, Hayne St., res. 2 Maiden Lane
Farr, -----, Drake St.
Farrar, S. S. & Brothers, Wholesale Grocers, 70 East Bay St., S. S. Farrar, J. C. Farrar, C. D. Farrar
Farrar, S. S., Merchant, 1 Hayne St., res. 20 Society St.
Farrell, D., Mason, 3 Philadelphia St.
Farrell, Edward, 104 Meeting St.
Farrelly, Charles, Tavern Keeper, 4 Elliott St.
Farris, A. G., Seaman, 16 Orange St.
Fasbender, Martha, Mrs., Dry Goods, 92 Meeting St.
Fash, Albert, 20 Pinckney St.
Faust, Daniel, Storekeeper, 74 Church St.
Faxon, L. (see Dunham, C. T. & Co.)
Fayolle, -----, Mrs., 82 King St.
Fayssoux, Thomas, Druggist, 31 Broad St., res. 23 Friend St.
Fell, Joseph, Policeman, 11 King St.
Fell, W. W., Mrs., Boarders, 242 King St.
Ferguson, John, 24 Market St.
Ferguson, William, Currier, 20 Queen St.
Ferrara, Manuel, Carpenter, Morris St.
Ferrell, John C., Bar Keeper, 280 King St.
Ferrell, William C., Attorney, Broad St., res. cr. Meeting St. & Horlbeck's Alley
Ferret, J., Miss, 34 Archdale St.
Ferrette, John F., Fruiterer, 41 Market St.
Feugas, -----, Madame, Teacher of Dancing, 70 King St.
Ficken, John F., Grocer, 40 Archdale St.
Fickling, J. G., Mason, 34 Queen St.
Fields, N., Ice House, res. cr. East Bay St. & Adger's Wharf
Figeroux, B., French Teacher, 206 King St.
Fillette, A., Mrs., Dry Goods, 139 King St.
Fillette, -----, Mrs., 12 Pinckney St.
Fink, Alexander, Grocer, 40 King St.
Fink, B. H., Clerk, 369 King St.
Fink, B., N. King St.
Fink, Jacob, Clerk, 40 King St.
Fink, James P., Grocer, 12 Archdale St.
Finkenstadt, G., Grocer, 1 King St.
Finkin, A., Clerk, 11 South Bay St.
Finley, Maria, Mrs., 20 Church St.
Finley, W. P., President, Charleston College, res. N. St. Philip St.
Fishburne, Robert, Factor, Vanderhorst's Wharf, res. 13 South Bay St.
Fisher, Frederick, Shoe Maker, 6 Tradd St.
Fisher, G., 8 Queen St.
Fisher, S. W., Clerk, 232 King St., res. 21 Friend St.
Fisher, Samuel, Bleacher, 252 King St.
Fisher, Susan, Mrs., 69 Meeting St.
Fitch, W. M., Physician, Cumberland St., res. 94 Wentworth St.
Fitts, C., Physician, 26 Hasell St.

Fitts, John, Hanover St.
Fitts, William, Hanover St.
Fitzsimons, B., Saddler, 271 King St.
Fitzsimons, E. P., Mrs., Planter, 26 Hasell St.
Flach, George W., Watch Maker, 27 Anson St.
Flagg, E. B., Physician, 41 Meeting St., res. 15 Archdale St.
Flagg, M. E., Mrs., 15 Archdale St.
Fleming, D. F., Merchant, Hayne St.
Fleming, J. J., Rev., Teacher, Neck High School, Boundary St.
Fleming, John, H., Carpenter, N. Meeting St.
Flinn, Patrick, Laborer, 47 State St.
Flonacher, John, Locksmith, 65 Market St.
Fluray, W., Hanover St.
Flynn, John, Tailor, 19 Church St.
Flynn, Robert, 61 Church St.
Foard, J. W., Shoe Maker, 329 King St., res. 39 King St.
Fogartie, A., Dry Goods, 253 King St., res. 217 King St.
Fogartie, Ann, Miss, Teacher, 24 Wall St.
Fogartie, Edward, Bricklayer, Boundary St.
Fogartie, Samuel, Upholsterer, 160 King St., res. 24 Wall St.
Foley, William, Gardener, 51 Broad St.
Folger, Edward, Packer, 8 Middle St.
Folker, Octavius, John St.
Follin, Gustavus, Tobacconist, 167 Meeting St.
Foot, -----, Mrs., 2 Clifford St.
Forbes, R., Tinner, 24 Tradd St.
Forbes, S. W., Mrs., 56 Meeting St.
Force, B. W., Shoe Merchant, Hayne St., res. 236 King St.
Force, L. M. & B. W. & Co., Wholesale Boots & Shoes, 11 Hayne S., L. M. Force, B. W. Force, J. P. Force, B. Cowley
Force, L. M., Merchant, 11 Hayne St.
Ford, Benjamin, Shoe Dealer, 101 East Bay St., res. 18 Mazyck St.
Ford, John, D., Warren St.
Fordham, Jane, Mrs., 251 East Bay St.
Fordham, Richard, Planter, 81 Church St.
Forrest, John, Rev., Pastor, First Presbyterian Church, 4 Court House Square
Forrest, S., Mrs., 1 Minority St.
Foster, E., Mrs., Washer, 3 Vernon St.
Foster, W. B., Officer, Bank of State of S. C., res. N. Coming St.
Fourgeaud, Eugene, Conductor, 138 Meeting St.
Fourgeaud, Mary, Mrs., 138 Meeting St.
Fowler, Andrew, Rev., 83 Queen St.
Fowler, J. P., Mrs., Dry Goods, 319 King St.
Fowler, J. W., Carpenter, 319 King St.
Fox, Martha, Mrs., 24 Laurens St.
Fraita, Joseph, Fruiterer, 75 Market St.
Frampton, L., Physician, N. King St.
Francis, E., Mariner, 6 Market St.
Francis, Noah, N. St. Philip St.
Francois, Samuel, Clerk, 23 State St.
Frank, A., Cigar Maker, 13 Tradd St.
Fraser, Ann, Mrs., 56 King St.

Fraser, Charles, Artist, 35 King St.
Fraser, Charles P., Boarders, 3 Society St.
Fraser, Frederick E., Clerk, Southern Wharf, 91 Tradd St.
Fraser, John & Co., Factors, Central Wharf, John Fraser, G. A. Trenholm, C. L. Trenholm, T. D. Wagner
Fraser, John, Merchant, Central Wharf, res. 3 Short St.
Fraser, Mary, Mrs., 91 Tradd St.
Fraser, T., 55 Boundary St.
Frederick, P., Rigger, 16 Boundary St.
Frey, Joseph, Piano Tuner, 56 Queen St.
Friedlander, J., 42 Society St.
Friely, N., Woolf St.
Friend, John, Carpenter, America St.
Frierson, James, Clerk, 11 Laurens St.
Frierson, S. M., Mrs., 6 George St.
Fripp, S. H., Mrs., 51 Anson St.
Frohlich, John, Musician, 115 Church St.
Frohnd, F., Tinner, 34 State St.
Froneburger, C. D., Clerk, 118 Meeting St.
Frost, E. H., Merchant, 110 Tradd St.
Frost, Edward, Hon., Judge, 110 Tradd St.
Frost, H. R., Physician, 68 Broad St.
Fuegas, H. P., French Teacher, 70 King St.
Fuller, Benjamin, Planter, 24 Broad St.
Fuller, Oliver, Meeting St.
Fuller, Thomas A., Clerk, 73 East Bay St.
Fulmore, -----, Mrs., Reid St.
Fulmore, R., Factor, Boyce's Wharf, res. 24 Broad St.
Furches, E., Mrs., Nurse, Orphan House.
Furches, M. H., Miss, 34 Hasell St.
Furman, Charles M., Cashier, Bank of State of S. C., 16 Broad St.
Furman, R. I. K., Physician, cr. Meeting & Hudson Sts.
Furman, -----, Tavern Keeper, 17 Elliott St.
Gadsden, A. E., Physician, Charlotte St.
Gadsden, B. C., Planter, 13 Coming St.
Gadsden, C. E., Rt. Rev., Bishop, Protestant Episcopal Church, Charlotte St.
Gadsden, E. F., Miss, 26 Wall St.
Gadsden, Fisher, Officer, Bank of State of S. C., res. 90 Anson St.
Gadsden, J. A., Charlotte St.
Gadsden, James & Co., Factors, North Atlantic Wharf, James Gadsden, C. F. Edwards
Gadsden, James, President, Railroad Co., State St., res. cr. King & John Sts.
Gadsden, James W., Factor, 13 Coming St.
Gadsden, T. N., Broker, State St., res. Church St.
Gaetjens, G., Merchant, 155 East Bay St.
Gage, James, Mariner, 76 Tradd St.
Gaillard & Snowden, Factors, Southern Wharf, P. C. Gaillard, W. E. Snowden
Gaillard, C., Mrs., 185 Meeting St.
Gaillard, Daniel, Mrs., 3 Court House Square
Gaillard, H., Physician, 3 Court House Square
Gaillard, J., Mrs., 11 Archdale St.
Gaillard, P. C., Factor, Southern Wharf, res. 12 Lamboll St.
Gaillard, P. C., Physician, 60 Broad St.

Gaillard, P., Physician, Alexander St.
Gaillard, Theodore, Customs Officer
Galbraith, N., Painter, 72 Market St.
Gallagher, John, Packer, 98 Meeting St.
Galliot, Alexis, Tobacconist, 161 East Bay St.
Galloway, Mary, Miss, Milliner, 181 King St.
Galrich, Joseph, Tailor, 13 Queen St.
Gamage, E., Planter, 65 Broad St.
Gambatti, A., Music Teacher, 88 King St.
Gamble, Samuel, Umbrella Maker, 165 King St.
Gannon, M., Stone Cutter, 5 Horlbeck's Alley
Gannon, Roger, Packer, 130 Church St.
Gantt, J. L., Clerk, 6 Smith St.
Gantt, T. J., Register in Equity, 6 Smith St.
Garden, B., Druggist, 51 Church St.
Garden, E. W., Planter, 8 West St.
Garden, R. H., Clerk, 29 Church St.
Gardner, A. Y., Clerk, 250 King St.
Gardner, J. M., Watch Maker, 250 King St.
Gardner, James, 41 Beaufain St.
Garety, C., Grocer, 22 South Bay St.
Garety, Thomas, Ironmonger, Cumberland St., res. 154 East Bay St.
Garrett, George, Bootmaker, Church St., res. 104 Queen St.
Garrett, -----, Mrs., Milliner, 104 Queen St.
Garrick, Francis, Elliott St., Neck
Garvan, G., Grocer, 44 State St.
Gary, H., Charlotte St.
Gary, J. R., Mrs., N. King St.
Gatchell, E. M. & Co., Druggists, 33 Market St., E. M. Gatchell, M. D., Charles Clarke
Gatchell, E. M., Druggist, 33 Market St.
Gates, Thomas, Butcher, Cannon St.
Gatewood, W. C., Lottery Office, 26 Broad St., res. 19 Legare St.
Gatzen, H., 71 Church St.
Gaugh, A. E., 3 St. Philip St.
Gauthier, F., Professor of Languages, 31 Coming St.
Gayer, William J., Coach Maker, 142 Meeting St., res. N. King St.
Geddes, C., Mrs., 15 Rutledge St.
Geddings, Eli, Physician, N. Meeting St.
Geddings, J. F. M., Physician, N. Meeting St.
Gefkin, H. C., Collector, 79 Meeting St.
George, Reuben, Coming St.
George, Webber, Mary St.
Gerard & Willcocks, Drapers & Tailors, 20 Broad St., P. G. Gerard, Thomas Willcocks
Gerard, P. G., Draper & Tailor, Broad St., res. 113 Broad St.
Gerdes, C. H., Clerk, 32 Archdale St.
Gerdes, J., cr. Boundary & Coming Sts.
Gerdts, C., Boundary St.
Gerdts, H., Grocer, 203 East Bay St.
Gerdts, Herman, Thomas St.
Gervais, Paul T., Jr., Planter, 23 Legare St.
Gervais, Paul T., Rev., 23 Legare St.
Gest, J. L., Clerk, 365 King St.
Gestinger, B. R., Jr., Boiler Maker, Hasell St., res. 12

Boundary St.
Gestinger, B. R., Printer, Cumberland St.
Geyer, R. C., Broker, State St., res. 10 Atlantic St.
Gibbes, A. E., Mrs., 10 George St.
Gibbes, Benjamin, cr. John & Elizabeth Sts.
Gibbes, Caroline S., Mrs., 92 Tradd St.
Gibbes, E. A., Physician, 10 George St.
Gibbes, Henry P., Warren St.
Gibbes, J. E., 10 George St.
Gibbes, J. P., Wharfinger, Magwood's Wharf, res. 2 George St.
Gibbes, James, Ann St.
Gibbes, James S., Merchant, Adger's Wharf, res. 5 Short St.
Gibbes, Lewis R., Professor, Charleston College, res. 5 Boundary St.
Gibbes, R. W., Warren St.
Gibbes, W. G., Merchant, Boyce's Wharf, res. 17 Wentworth St.
Gibbon, G. E., Merchant, Gillon St., res. 9 New St.
Gibbon, George, 9 New St.
Gibbon, John & George E., Commission Merchants, Gillon St.
Gibbon, John, Merchant, Gillon St., res. 24 Broad St.
Gibson, Adam, Charlotte St.
Gibson, Alexander, Merchant, Charlotte St.
Gibson, C. B., Mrs., Seamstress, 15 Back Alley
Gibson, D. C., Attorney, Church St., res. 172 Meeting St.
Gibson, Elizabeth, Mrs., 172 Meeting St.
Gibson, W. H., Wharfinger, Brown's Wharf
Gibson, W. O., 6 Burns Lane
Gidiere, J. M., Dry Goods, 338 King St.
Gilbert, S. & J., Coach Makers, Wentworth St.
Gilchrist, R. B., Hon., District Court Judge, res. 245 East Bay St.
Giles, Robert F., 2 Gibbes St.
Gilfillan, A. E., Mrs., 8 Guignard St.
Gilfus, -----, Baker, 75 Church St.
Gilky, Adams, Clerk, East Bay St., res. 43 Society St.
Gill, John, Bogard St.
Gillespie, A. L., Clerk, Hayne St., res. 147 Meeting St.
Gillett, Ellen, 1 Archdale St.
Gilliland, James, Clerk, Hayne St., res. 3 Society St.
Gilliland, W. D., Merchant, Hayne St., res. 29 Hasell St.
Gilliland, W. H., Merchant, Hayne St., res. 10 Wentworth St.
Gillilands & Howell, Wholesale Dry Goods, 33 Hayne St., W. H. Gilliland, W. D. Gilliland, Sidney Howell
Gilman, A. O., Mrs., Seamstress, 36 Mazyck St.
Gilman, S., Rev., Pastor, Unitarian Church, res. 7 Orange St.
Gilmore, Robert, Baker, 220 King St.
Girardeau, John B., Planter, 2 Beaufain St.
Girardeau, L., Rev., 2 Beaufain St.
Girardeau, -----, Mrs., Boarders, 2 Beaufain St.
Girwan, John, Laborer, 27 State St.
Gissel, H., Grocer, 40 Anson St.
Gist, G. A., N. King St.
Given, W., Shoe Dealer, 359 King St.
Gladden, E., Mrs., 109 Church St.

Gladden, Martha, Mrs., Seamstress, 48 George St.
Gleason, H. B., Boarders, 236 King St.
Gleason, J. E., Musician, 8 Horlbeck's Alley
Gleize, S. A., Mrs., 6 Hasell St.
Glen, D. L., Accountant, 89 Tradd St.
Glen, John E., Shipwright, 22 Savage St.
Glen, John, Officer, Planters & Mechanics Bank, res. Reid St.
Glen, S. H., 89 Tradd St.
Glen, T. C., Clerk, 7 Archdale St.
Glen, William, Physician, Reid St.
Glover & Davis, Factors, Fitzsimons' Wharf, S. Glover, S. L., Gover, W. K. Davis
Glover, Caroline H., Mrs., Teacher, 7 Orange St.
Glover, S. L., Factor, Fitzsimons' Wharf, res. America St.
Godefroy, A., Tailor, 58 State St.
Goff, -----, 130 Church St.
Goldtman, -----, Peddlar, 164 King St.
Golshac, Isaac, Blacksmith, 20 St. Philip St.
Gonnan, John, Policeman, 75 Church St.
Gonzales, B., Merchant, Exchange, res. 4 George St.
Goodman, C. D., Painter, 107 Broad St.
Goodman, M., 1 Queen St.
Goodrich, E. J., Mrs., Boarders, 114 Church St.
Goodrich, Edward, Butcher, Cannon St.
Goodrich, W. T., Butcher, Cannon St.
Goodwin, G. M., Clerk, 5 Liberty St.
Goodwin, Thomas J., Printer, 85 Tradd St.
Goodwin, William, Printer, 85 Tradd St.
Gordon, Alexander, Hardware, 15 Broad St.
Gordon, C., Mrs., Seamstress, 80 Market St.
Gordon, E., Miss, 74 Beaufain St.
Gory, John, 24 Queen St.
Gouldsmith, M., U. S. Deputy Marshal, res. 96 Tradd St.
Gouldsmith, R. H., Nassau St.
Gouldsmith, Richard, Cabinet Maker, 132 Meeting St.
Gourdin, Henry, Merchant, Commercial Wharf, res. 2 Meeting St.
Gourdin, Matthiessen & Co., Commission Merchants, North Commercial Wharf, Henry Gourdin, R. N. Gourdin, F. C. Matthiessen
Gourdin, R. N., Merchant, Commercial Wharf, res. 2 Meeting St.
Gourdin, T. S., Attorney, Law Range, res. 8 Liberty St.
Gourdin, W. A., Accountant, 89 Tradd St.
Goutvegnier, P., Cutler, 43 Queen St.
Gowan, Peter, Watch Maker, 54 Meeting St., res. 8 South Bay St.
Graddick, C. C., Butcher, 28 Boundary St.
Grady, Augustus, 144 King St.
Grady, James, Tailor, 144 King St.
Graeser, C. A., Factor, Central Wharf, res. 309 King St.
Graham, John, Packer, 198 King St.
Granger, C., Charlotte St.
Granger, Henry, Charlotte St.
Granstein, G., Musician, 14 Anson St.
Grant, F. W., Grocer, 112 Meeting St.
Gravely, C., Clerk, 58 East Bay St., res. 68 Queen St.
Gravely, John, Hardware, East Bay St., res. 19 Friend St.
Graves, A. D., Wood Factor, Hasell St., res. 28 Bull St.

Graves, Charles, Bricklayer, 33 Society St.
Graves, D. D., Physician, 4 Friend St.
Gray, A. P., Clerk, 21 Coming St.
Gray, C., Dry Goods, 244 King St.
Gray, Caroline, Miss, Teacher, 26 Society St.
Gray, J. B., Teacher, 26 Society St.
Gray, James F., Teacher, 6 Clifford St.
Gray, James W., Master in Equity, res. 107 Wentworth St.
Gray, M., 23 Hasell St.
Gray, -----, Misses, Teachers, 6 Clifford St.
Grayson, James P., 247 East Bay St.
Grayson, W. J., Customs Collector, 247 East Bay St.
Grayson, W. J., Jr., Physician, 247 East Bay St.
Gready, A. P., Hardware, 29 Pitt St.
Gready, James R., Clothing, cr. King & Wentworth Sts., res. 10 Orange St.
Greaton, John, Inspector, Insurance Co., 8 Broad St., res. 45 Tradd St.
Green & Redmond, Factors, North Commercial Wharf, James F. Green, Thomas Redmond
Green, D., Tailor, 27 State St.
Green, Emily, Mrs., 21 Middle St.
Green, H., Tailor, 27 State St.
Green, James, Merchant, Charlotte St.
Green, Maxwell, Charlotte St.
Green, Patrick, Tailor, 27 State St.
Green, Thomas P., Washington St.
Green, William, Seaman, 11 Tradd St.
Greenhill, -----, Misses, 3 Greenhill.
Greenland, G. A., Mason, 30 Middle St.
Greenland, John, Factor, Patton's Wharf, res. 28 Archdale St.
Greenland, William, 28 Archdale St.
Greer, J. M., Bookseller, 207 King St.
Greer, William, Tavern Keeper, 11 Bull St.
Gregg, Hayden & Co., Jewellers, 232 King St., William Gregg, H. S. Hayden, A. H. Hayden
Gregg, William, Jeweller, 250 King St., res. Boundary St.
Gregorie, F. M., Tailor, Atlantic St.
Gregorie, J. L., Bursar, Citadel.
Greneker, T., Printer, 279 King St.
Griffith, Matilda, Mantuamaker, 24 Burns Lane
Griffiths, Mary J., 41 Wall St.
Griffiths, -----, Mrs., Boarders, 169 Meeting St.
Griggs, Henry S., Teacher, 31 Society St.
Grimball, John B., Planter, South Bay St.
Grimes, L., Ann St.
Grimke, Henry, Attorney, cr. Amherst & East Bay Sts.
Grimke, J. D., Physician, 42 South Bay St.
Grimke, -----, Misses, 13 Savage St.
Grimke, Thomas S., Mrs., 42 South Bay St.
Griner, Ann, Mrs., 10 Pinckney St.
Griswold, Julia, Mrs., 12 Pinckney St.
Gross, John, Clerk, Railroad Depot, Amherst St.
Grote, C., Boundary St.
Grover, H. C., Boundary St.
Grover, John, N. King St.
Groves, E., Mrs., Boarders, 1 Queen St.

Groves, Joseph, Clerk, 153 Meeting St.
Gruber, C., Carpenter, Nassau St.
Gruber, C. J., Pinckney St., Cannonborough
Gruber, C. M., Blacksmith, Sires St.
Gruber, G. H., Clerk, 222 King St.
Gruber, H., Storekeeper, 2 Tradd St.
Gruber, Henry, Carpenter, Sires St.
Gruber, James, Carpenter, Nassau St.
Guenveur, E., Mrs., Storekeeper, 86 Queen St.
Guenveur, Juliette, Miss, China Store, 118 King St.
Guenveur, S. F., Book Binder, 61 Queen St.
Guerard, A., Mrs., 107 Meeting St.
Guerry, A. C., 6 Burns Lane
Guerry, Grandison, Police Officer, 2 Price's Alley
Guerry, H. G., Collector, 17 Bull St.
Guerry, Peter, Clerk, 2 Price's Alley
Guether, N., Baker, 115 Church St.
Guilmette, E. McG., Music Teacher, 1 State St.
Guinemer, A., 279 King St.
Gunnison, J. A., Merchant, 88 East Bay St.
Gunter, F. W., Tobacconist, 20 Boundary St.
Gunther, -----, Mrs., 22 Magazine St.
Gurnep, Mary, Miss, 4 New St.
Guy, J. W., Carpenter, 7 Clifford St.
Guy, John, Mason, 14 Smith St.
Guy, Joseph, Mason, 14 Smith St.
Guy, T. B., Merchant, 118 East Bay St., res. 11 Laurens St.
Gyles, J. A., Magistrate, 18 Broad St., res. 139 King St.
Gyles, -----, Mrs., 82 King St.
Habenich, -----, Grocer, 4 Tradd St.
Hacker, G. S., Agent, Railroad Co., Meeting St., Neck
Hackett, John F., 12 Middle St.
Hackett, L., Mrs., Horlbeck's Alley
Hadeln, C., Clerk, 1 Boundary St.
Hadeln, John Von, Grocer, 29 King St.
Hadler, Adolphus, Saddler, 89 Queen St.
Hagan, J. R., Clerk, 83 East Bay St.
Hagan, R., Boarders, 47 State St.
Hagan, R., Mrs., 10 Clifford St.
Hagan, Thomas, Bar Keeper, 66 Meeting St.
Hagenlocher, H., Dentist, 210 King St.
Haggerty, George, N. Meeting St.
Hagmier, C., Ship Carpenter, 23 South Bay St.
Hagood, J. W., Piano Tuner, 318 King St., res. 251 King St.
Hahnbaum, E. R., Mrs., Teacher, 22 Pitt St.
Haig, Alexander, Thomas St.
Haig, George, Thomas St.
Haig, H. M., Mrs., 20 Meeting St.
Hall, H. & W. P., Factors, Central Wharf
Hall, William, Physician, 263 East Bay St.
Hallonquest, L. D., Attorney, 71 Beaufain St.
Halm, H. H., Grocer, 4 Market St.
Halm, H., Washington St.
Halm, John, Grocer, 19 South Bay St.
Halwerson, Laurence, Mariner, 63 Tradd St.
Ham, William, Engineer, 87 Tradd St.
Hamet, Ripley S., Boarders, 34 Queen St.
Hamilton, A., Coach Trimmer, 111 Meeting St.

Hamilton, James, Coach Trimmer, 111 Meeting St.
Hamilton, Joseph, 4 West St.
Hamilton, L., Miss, Teacher, 36 Chalmers St.
Hamilton, -----, Mason, 102 Church St.
Hamilton, W. N., Accountant, 69 Meeting St.
Hamilton, William, Clerk, 219 King St.
Hamlin, George, Blacksmith, 13 Lynch St.
Hamlin, James, Farmer, 13 Lynch St.
Hamlin, Thomas, Planter, 1 Gadsden St.
Hamlin, William, Printer
Hammerskold, -----, Mrs., Music Teacher, 1 State St.
Hammond, Ogden, Planter, 65 Broad St.
Hammond, -----, Policeman, 44 State St.
Hammond, S., 143 King St.
Hampshire, J., Baker, 100 Meeting St.
Hamson, E., Miss, 6 Liberty St.
Han, Henry, Laborer, 38 King St.
Hanahan, James, Shipwright, 48 King St.
Hanahan, John C., Cooper, 136 King St.
Hanahan, Rippon, 10 Bull St.
Hanahan, Samuel, 48 King St.
Hanch, J. D., Accountant, 30 Laurens St.
Hanckel, C., Rev., Rector, St. Paul's Church, 62
   Boundary St.
Hanckel, M., Physician, 62 Boundary St.
Hanckel, M. S., Physician, 17 Hasell St.
Hanckel, T. M., Attorney, 17 Hasell St.
Hancock, Henry, Laborer, 103 Queen St.
Hands, Jane A., Miss, res. Commercial House
Hanken, J., Washington St.
Hantz, Charles, Bath Keeper, 63 Church St.
Happoldt, Albert, Butcher, Cannon St.
Happoldt, Charles L., Coach Trimmer, 16 Wall St.
Happoldt, Christopher, Farmer, 37 George St.
Happoldt, David, Cannon St.
Happoldt, Edward, Cannon St.
Happoldt, John, Cannon St.
Happoldt, John M., Gunsmith, 45 State St.
Happoldt, William, Cannon St.
Harbers, C. H., N. Meeting St.
Harbers, D., Grocer, 19 Coming St.
Harbers, J. H., Grocer, 19 Coming St.
Harbers, L., Grocer, 19 Coming St.
Harbers, R. F., 10 Coming St.
Harbesson, John, Dry Goods, 350 King St.
Harby, H. J., Blacksmith, Church St., res. 28 Meeting St.
Hare, R. W., Merchant, 39 Hayne St., res. 11 Hasell St.
Harleston, Edward, Customs Officer, 72 Broad St.
Harleston, O., Planter, Pinckney St., Cannonborough
Harleston, -----, Physician, Cannon St.
Harley, T. H., N. King St.
Harling, C., Bootmaker, 5 Queen St.
Harmill, Thomas, Wheelwright, 16 Market St.
Harper, F. M., Printer, 245 King St.
Harper, J. J., Accountant, 245 King St.
Harper, J. M., Clerk, 11 Broad St.
Harral, F., Clerk, 306 King St.
Harral, George, 4 Glebe St.
Harral, H. W., Clerk, 39 Hayne St., res. 4 Glebe St.
Harral, Hare & Co., Saddlery, 30 Hayne St., H. K.

Harral, William Harral, R. M. Hare, P. C. Calhoun
Harral, James, Druggist, 11 Hayne St., res. 46 St. Philip
   St.
Harral, R. L., Druggist, 306 King St.
Harral, William, Saddler, 39 Hayne St., res. 4 Glebe St.
Harrenburg, -----, Grocer, 85 Queen St.
Harris, C. F., Clerk, 309 King St.
Harris, E., Mrs., 16 Horlbeck's Alley
Harris, George, Tailor, 39 King St.
Harris, Issac, Fruiterer, 39 Market St.
Harris, J., Superintendant, Sugar Refinery, 15 Anson St.
Harris, William, 309 King St.
Harrison, D. W., Book Seller, Depository, Chalmers St.
Harrison T. C., Broker, State St.
Harrisson, J. W., Paint Dealer, 72 Meeting St.
Harrisson, John, 72 Meeting St.
Hart, Charles, 46 Market St.
Hart, Francis, Carter, 143 King St.
Hart, H. N., Clerk, 18 Coming St.
Hart, S., Book Seller, King St., res. Aiken's Range
Hart, S. N., Hardware, 216 King St., res. 20 Coming St.
Hartman, J. F., Grocer, Meeting & Boundary Sts.
Hartman, -----, N. St. Philip St.
Hartnett, William, Laborer, 115 Meeting St.
Hartpence, E., Sugar Refiner, 15 Anson St., res. 118
   Church St.
Hartz, Henry, Storekeeper, 192 Meeting St.
Harvey, Isabella, Mrs., 78 Queen St.
Harvey, J., Clerk, 78 Queen St.
Harvey, M. D., Mrs., Dry Goods, 11 Boundary St.
Harvey, Martha, Mrs., 20 Wall St.
Harvey, T. J., Clerk, 78 Queen St.
Harvey, W. O. K., Gas Pipe Dealer, 100 Meeting St.
Haselltine, A. G., Shoe Merchant, 257 King St.
Haselltine, W. H., Shoe Merchant, 257 King St.
Haselltine, William, M., Merchant, Hayne St., res. 1
   Hasell St.
Haseltine, Walton & Co., Boots & Shoes, 257 King St.,
   W. Haseltine, John Walton, A. L. Haseltine
Hashberg, -----, Cap Manufacturer, 101 King St.
Haskett, Jane, Mrs., 9 Middle St.
Haskill, W., Pinckney St., Cannonborough
Haskins, A., Miss, Dress Maker, 39 Montague St.
Hassett, Roger, 110 Meeting St.
Hatch, L. M., Merchant, 118 Meeting St., res. 8 Society
   St.
Hatch, Sarah, Mrs., 76 Anson St.
Hatch, William, Ship Carpenter, 2 Lightwood's Alley
Hatcher, Thomas, 85 Market St.
Hatnalt, L., 120 Church St.
Hauscheldt, Peter, Grocer, 16 Queen St.
Haviland, Harral & Co., Drugs, 25 Hayne St., Robert
   Haviland, James Harral
Hawkesworth, William, Professor, Charleston College,
   69 Broad St.
Hayden, A. H., Jeweller, 250 King St., res. 6 Glebe St.
Hayden, H. S., Jeweller, 250 King St., res. 10 Green St.
Hayden, Mary, Mrs., 1 Magazine St.
Hayford, Ann, Dr.
Hayford, Gardner, Carpenter, 76 Church St.

Hayne, A. P., 77 Meeting St.
Hayne, A. P., Physician, 26 King St.
Hayne, E. P., Mrs., 1 Church St.
Hayne, Edward, William, Clerk, 1 Church St.
Hayne, I. W. (see Peronneau & Hayne)
Hayne, Isaac W., Attorney General, 3 State St., res. 6 Logan St.
Hayne, J. G. U., Clerk, 226 King St.
Hayne, -----, Misses, 25 Meeting St.
Hayne, P., Mrs., Alexander St.
Hayne, R. Y., Mrs., 26 King St.
Hayne, -----, Vanderhorst St.
Hayne, W. A., Attorney, 48 Broad St., res. 26 King St.
Hays, Thomas Hancock, Printer, Chapel St.
Hays, William, Plasterer, Chapel St.
Hazlehurst, G., Washington St.
Head, Amos, Book Seller, 1 Broad St.
Headley, -----, Mrs., Seamstress, 73 King St.
Heath, H., Mrs., 9 Boundary St.
Heath, S., Bee St.
Hebbing, William, 157 East Bay St.
Hecken, J. H., Grocer, 20 Hasell St.
Hedderley, J. B., Brass Founder, 3 East Bay St., res. 9 Vernon St.
Hedley, George, Grocer, 32 Bull St.
Hedley, J. L., Merchant, 165 East Bay St., res. 97 Broad St.
Heffernan, Eliza, Storekeeper, 83 Queen St.
Hefferon, H. J., 128 King St.
Hefferon, John, 128 King St.
Hefferon, M., Miss, Mantuamaker, 128 King St.
Heichel, L., Grocer, 12 St. Philip St.
Heidt, Valentine, Basket Maker, 313 King St.
Heine, H., Clerk, 133 King St.
Heine, W., Tailor, 133 King St.
Heissenbuttel, G., Storekeeper, 101 Church St.
Hele, -----, 261 King St.
Henderson, E., Miss, 10 Smith's Lane
Henderson, J. M. A., Printer, 102 Church St.
Henderson, John, Bookkeeper, 110 Meeting St.
Hendricks, H., Hanover St.
Hendricks, John, Laborer, 14 Beaufain St.
Hendricks, R., Merchant, 169 Meeting St.
Hennessy, Charles, King & John Sts.
Hennessy, J. T., Mason, 12 Wentworth St.
Hennessy, P., Porter, 212 King St.
Hennessy, S., Mrs., Boarders, 12 Wentworth St.
Henry, Ann, Mrs., Tailoress, 3 Vernon St.
Henry, C., Morris St.
Henry, C. W., Factor, Vanderhorst's Wharf, res. 13 Meeting St.
Henry, Edward, Boarders, 112 Meeting St.
Henry, Edward, Clerk, 27 Hayne St.
Henry, Luke, 112 Meeting St.
Henry, Mary, Miss, 269 East Bay St.
Henry, S. W., Auctioneer, King & Clifford Sts., res. 91 Meeting St.
Hensen, Thomas, Teacher, 10 Archdale St.
Herbert, C., Painter, 10 Tradd St.
Herbet, M., Dry Goods, 67 State St.

Herckenwarth, Wragg & Co., Commission Merchants, Adger's South Wharf, L. Herkenwrath, E. L. Wragg
Heriot, B. D., Navy Agent, 9 Central Wharf, res. Beaufain St.
Heriot, B. G., Factor, 9 Central Wharf, res. 3 Glebe St.
Heriot, D. T., Accountant, 9 State St., res. 23 Montague St.
Heriot, Edwin, Teacher, 73 Beaufain St.
Heriot, J. R., Superintendent, Gas Works, 121 Church St., res. 6 Pinckney St.
Heriot, M. E., Mrs., 23 Montague St.
Heriot, O. B., Accountant, 21 King St.
Heriot, T. B., Farmer, 73 Beaufain St.
Heriot, T. S., Accountant, 23 Montague St.
Heriot, W. B., Insurance Agent, 117 East Bay St., res. 3 King St.
Heriot, W. C., Accountant, 9 Central Wharf, res. 73 Beaufain St.
Hernandez, J. J., Clerk, Amherst St.
Hernandez, John, Engineer, Amherst St.
Herricks, D., Mason, 102 Church St.
Herron, John, Clerk, Smith St.
Hertz, Albert E., Clerk, Adger's Wharf, res. 67 King St.
Hertz, Frederick E., Clerk, King & Market Sts., res. 67 King St.
Hertz, Isaac, Clerk, 110 East Bay St., res. 67 King St.
Hervey, George, Merchant, Adger's Wharf, res. 7 Church St.
Herwig, William, Professor of Music, 236 King St.
Hewes, E. E., Engineer, 24 Anson St.
Hewitt, J. H. P., Clerk, 141 Meeting St.
Hewitt, N. A. T., Rev., 80 Broad St.
Hey, Henry, Clerk, 83 Beaufain St.
Heyns, James, Customs Officer, 13 Price's Alley
Heyns, John, Carpenter, 13 Price's Alley
Heyward, Alice J., Mrs., Pitt & Boundary Sts.
Heyward, C. S., Mrs., 34 Wentworth St.
Heyward, Charles, Planter, Chapel St.
Heyward, D., Aiken's Range.
Heyward, Daniel, Planter, 200 East Bay St.
Heyward, G. C., Merchant, 73 East Bay St., res. 42 Bull St.
Heyward, James B., Planter, 90 Broad St.
Heyward, Nathaniel, Planter, 241 East Bay St.
Heyward, T. S. & G. C., Grocers, 73 East Bay Co
Heyward, T. S., Merchant, 73 East Bay St., res. 12 Bull St.
Heyward, Thomas J., Clerk, 1 Legare St.
Heyward, W. H., Planter, 4 Legare St.
Hibler, J. A., Stable Keeper, 93 Church St.
Hickey, Charles, Carver & Gilder, King St., res. 24 Burns Lane
Higgins, Michael, 112 Church St.
Higham, John W., Bootmaker, 29 Queen St.
Higham, Thomas & Co., Commission Merchants, 71 East Bay St., T. Higham, C. N. Hubert
Hilken, Herman, N. Coming St.
Hill, F. C., Artist, 13 Clifford St.
Hill, John, Boatman, 35 Montague St.
Hill, John, Storekeeper, 60 Queen St.

Hill, William, Laborer, Factory, res. 38 Beaufain St.
Hillar, Thomas, Laborer, 55 Coming St.
Hillegas, C., Miss, 5 Back Alley
Hillen, J., Bootmaker, N. King St.
Hills, C. E., Clerk, 258 King St.
Hines, D., Clerk, 4 Market St.
Hines, William, Drayman, 9 Linguard St.
Hinnes, H. F., Clerk, 51 Church St.
Hinrickson, C. F., Grocer, N. King St.
Hitzfeld, John, Grocer, 15 Lynch St.
Hobbes, William, Florist, cr. Meeting St. & Burns Lane
Hockaday, William, Stable Keeper, 3 Chalmers St.
Hodgson, Elizabeth, Mrs., Seamstress, 3 Boundary St.
Hodgson, William, Fisherman, Gadsden's Wharf
Hoff, John C., Stationer, 10 Broad St.
Hoff, Philip, Stationer, 36 Wentworth St.
Hoffman, Henry, Thomas St.
Hogan, Dennis, 32 Queen St.
Hogan, John, Clerk, 11 Elliot St.
Hogan, Martin, 32 Queen St.
Hogan, Patrick, Omnibus Driver, 4 Queen St.
Hogarth, Henry, Cooper, Longitude Lane, res. 40 Church St.
Hogarth, Mary, Mrs., 18 Wall St.
Hoke, F. A., Hotel Keeper, 309 King St.
Holbrook, E. P., Mrs., 1 Greenhill St.
Holbrook, J. E., Physician, 101 Tradd St.
Holbrook, S. H., Accountant, 1 Greenhill St.
Holland, E. C., Wharfinger, Vanderhorst's Wharf, res. 100 Tradd St.
Holland, P. J., Dry Goods, 100 King St., res. 100 Tradd St.
Hollings, B., Clerk, 207 East Bay St.
Hollings, B., Grocer, 207 East Bay St.
Holm, N., Seaman, 6 Stoll's Alley
Holmes, A. F., Customs Officer, 13 East Bay St.
Holmes, A. M., Mrs., 11 Logan St.
Holmes, Ann A., Mrs., 1 Friend St.
Holmes, E. G., Clerk, Charlotte St.
Holmes, E. H., Collector, 13 East Bay St.
Holmes, F. S., Wharfinger, Central Wharf, res. 60 St. Philip St.
Holmes, H. C., 20 King St.
Holmes, H. M., Physician & Planter, 2 Council St.
Holmes, Isaac E., Hon., Member of Congress, res. 13 East Bay St.
Holmes, J. L., Officer, Bank of Charleston, 5 Pitt St.
Holmes, J. W., Carpenter, Railroad, 4 Vernon St.
Holmes, James G., Cashier, Railroad Bank, res. 13 East Bay St.
Holmes, James, Laborer, 212 King St.
Holmes, John, Clerk, 118 Meeting St.
Holmes, John V., Gunsmith, 64 Queen St.
Holmes, Lucy, Mrs., Boarders, 14 Meeting St.
Holmes, Mary S., Mrs., 113 Tradd St.
Holmes, Thomas D., Collector, 84 Tradd St.
Holmes, William H., Planter, Charlotte St.
Holway, Henry, Clerk, 107 Tradd St.
Honour, James L., Mariner, John St.
Honour, John H., Jr., M. D., Penny Post Master, 297 King St.

Honour, John, H., President, Charleston Insurance & Trust Co., 8 Broad St., res. John St.
Honour, Theodore A., Clerk, 222 King St., res. John St.
Honour, Thomas, Book Binder, 11 Beaufain St.
Honour, William E., Book Binder, cr. Meeting St. & Horlbeck's Alley, res. John St.
Hood, Thomas, Printer, 116 King St.
Hopkins, J. A., Cooper, Adger's Wharf, res. 28 Church St.
Hopkinson, E., Clerk, 193 King St.
Hopley, G. A., Merchant, Atlantic St., res. 64 Tradd St.
Hopper, D., 2 King St.
Horan, M., Policeman, 24 State St.
Horlbeck, Daniel, Clerk of Court, 199 Meeting St.
Horlbeck, Edward, Bricklayer, 7 Horlbeck's Alley
Horlbeck, Elias, Physician, cr. Coming & Wentworth Sts.
Horlbeck, Henry, Bricklayer, 199 Meeting St.
Horlbeck, John, Bricklayer, 199 Meeting St.
Horlbeck, M., Mrs., 46 Beaufain St.
Hornberg, J. T., Clerk, 93 East Bay St.
Horry, Ann J., Miss, 69 Broad St.
Horry, E. S., Clerk, 39 Meeting St.
Horry, Mary S., Mrs., 39 Meeting St.
Horry, W. B. S., Planter, 39 Meeting St.
Horsey, F., Mrs., Boarders, 155 East Bay St.
Horsey, Ives & Co., Hats & Caps, 15 Hayne St., T. M., Horsey, Joel Ives, W. Montgomery
Horsey, John R., Clerk, 15 Hayne St., res. 65 Beaufain St.
Horsey, S. G., Clerk, 155 East Bay St.
Horsey, T. M., Merchant, Hayne St., res. Anson St.
Hort, Sarah, Miss, Planter, 257 East Bay St.
Horton, F., America St.
Horton, Thomas, America St.
Horton, Thomas, Tinner, Meeting St., res. 10 Glebe St.
Horton, Victor F., Clerk, 297 King St.
Housman, -----, Storekeeper, 99 East Bay St.
Houston, William, Carpenter, Charlotte St.
Howard, George, 9 Water St.
Howard, H. M., Naval Officer, 259 East Bay St.
Howard, L., Customs Officer, 259 East Bay St.
Howard, M., Policeman, 24 State St.
Howard, Robert, 259 East Bay St.
Howard, S. L., Accountant, Commercial Wharf, 259 East Bay St.
Howard, T. L., Wharfinger, Fitzsimons' Wharf, 259 East Bay St.
Howard, T. M., Gardener, N. King St.
Howe, J. M., Church St.
Howe, Silas, Merchant, 29 Archdale St.
Howell, Sidney S., Merchant, Hayne St., res. 9 Hasell St.
Howland & Taft, Commission Merchants, East Bay Co., B. J. Howland, A. R. Taft
Howland, B. J., Merchant, East Bay St.
Howland, William, Dry Goods, cr. King & Wentworth Sts., res. 21 Lynch St.
Huard, -----, Mrs., Boarders, 59 Church St.
Hubbell, T. C., Miller, Boundary St.
Hubert, C. N., Merchant, 69 East Bay St.

Huchet, E., Merchant, Adger's Wharf, res. 61 Wentworth St.
Huchet, T., Merchant, Adger's Wharf, res. 160 East Bay St.
Hudaff, Henry, Grocer, 19 Wall St.
Huger, A. M., Merchant, East Bay St., res. 52 Meeting St.
Huger, Alfred, Postmaster, 92 Broad St.
Huger, B., Capt., U. S. Navy, 74 Broad St.
Huger, D. E., Hon., Planter, 24 Meeting St.
Huger, D. E., Jr., Broker, 22 Broad St., res. 14 South Bay St.
Huger, Daniel, 61 Coming St.
Huger, E., Warren St.
Huger, F. K., 13 Meeting St.
Huger, John, Planter, 3 Meeting St.
Huger, T. B., U. S. Navy, 92 Broad St.
Huggins, E., Miss, Boarders, 34 Queen St.
Huggins, John, Judith St.
Hughes, Jeremiah, Accountant, 58 East Bay St., res. 26 Savage St.
Hughes, John L., Laborer, 52 King St.
Hughes, -----, Mrs., 2 Beaufain St.
Hughes, Optimus E., Merchant, East Bay St., res. 21 South Bay St.
Hughes, Thomas, Cabinet Maker, 134 Meeting St.
Hull & Knevals, Drapers & Tailors, 143 Meeting St., A. S. Hull, S. W. Knevals
Hull, A. S., Tailor, Meeting St., res. 1 Hasell St.
Hull, S. J., Accountant, Meeting St.
Hume, Robert, Planter, 6 Lynch St.
Hume, Thomas M., Broker, Broad St., res. Thomas St.
Hume, William, M. D., Professor, Citadel, res. Thomas St.
Hummell, William, Apothecary, 31 Broad St.
Hummer, H., Clerk, 50 St. Philip St.
Humphreys, -----, Mrs., 6 Liberty St.
Humphreys, -----, Mrs., Smith St., near Bull St.
Hunt, B. F., Attorney, Broad St., res. 4 Lynch St.
Hunt, B. F., Jr., Attorney, Broad St., res. 4 Lynch St.
Hunt, N., Merchant, 16 Vendue Range, res. 33 Anson St.
Hunt, William M., Physician, 4 Lynch St.
Hunting, W. G., Clerk, 40 Beaufain St.
Huntington, H. L., Clerk, Telegraph Office, res. 63 Meeting St.
Huntoon, C. S., Clerk, 149 Meeting St.
Hurst, C. M., 3 Pinckney St.
Hurst, James, 27 Society St.
Hutchinson, T. L., Hon., Mayor, 27 Meeting St.
Hyams, Henry, Factor, 32 St. Philip St.
Hyams, Moses D., Merchant, East Bay St.
Hyams, Rebecca, Mrs., 42 King St.
Hyams, Solomon, Umbrella Maker, 17 Boundary St.
Hyatt, McBurney & Co., Dry Goods, 29 Hayne Sts., E. Hyatt, William McBurney, J. B. Betts, M. Haseltine
Hyde, Simeon, Merchant, 17 Hayne St., res. 45 Wentworth St.
Hyer, H., Grocer, 152 East Bay St.
Hyer, J. H., Elliott St., Neck
Hyndman, M., Miss, 46 Beaufain St.

Ill, John, Clerk, 161 King St.
Ilsley, Stillman, Clerk, 31 Hayne St.
Inglesby, M. E., Mrs., 5 Orange St.
Inglesby, Mary, Mrs., 37 Tradd St.
Inglesby, W. H., City Treasurer, City Hall, res. 4 Logan St.
Ingraham & Webb, Factors, North Commercial Wharf, G. H. Ingraham, T. L. Webb
Ingraham, D. N., Capt., United States Navy, 8 King St.
Ingraham, George H., Factor, Commercial Wharf, res. 18 Laurens St.
Ingraham, Mary J., Miss, 2 Smith St.
Ingraham, W. P., Planter, 2 Smith St.
Innes, C. M., Clerk, 147 Meeting St.
Irving, Emilius, Physician, 5 Rutledge St.
Irving, J. B., Jr., Clerk, 5 Rutledge St.
Irving, John B., Planter, 5 Rutledge St.
Isaacs, Alexander, Bookkeeper, 288 King St.
Iusti, A., Blacksmith, 31 Queen St.
Ives, Joel (see Horsey, Ives & Co.)
Izard, A. S., Planter, 24 Meeting St.
Izard, Claudia S., Mrs., 29 Legare St.
Izard, Eliza, Mrs., 199 East Bay St.
Izard, R. S., Planter, Broad St.
Jackson, F., Printer, 34 Queen St.
Jackson, George, Tinner, 275 King St.
Jackson, J., Artist, 175 King St.
Jackson, Mary A., Mrs., Milliner, 172 King St.
Jacobi, W. J., Dry Goods, 221 King St.
Jacobs, B. H., Mrs., Boarders, 82 Queen St.
Jacobs, Matthew, Tavern Keeper, 13 Market St.
Jacobs, Myer, Customs Officer, 1 Smith St.
Jacobs, R., Clerk, 209 King St., res. 1 Smith St.
Jacobs, Simon, Storekeeper, 77 Market St.
Jacobs, Washington, Carpenter, 1 Smith St.
Jacobus, P. (see Condict, Jennings & Co.)
Jahn, Edward, Bootmaker, 82 Church St.
James, Henry, Carpenter, 11 Pinckney St.
James, Robert, Printer, 45 St. Philip St.
James, William, Pilot, 11 Pinckney St.
Janes, John, Morris St.
Jaques, G. R., Shoe Dealer, 40 Beaufain St.
Jay, John, N. Coming St.
Jeannerett, J. C., Clerk, Boyce's Wharf, res. Church St.
Jeannerett, J. M. (see Brancroft, James & Co.)
Jeffords, J. H., Sail Maker, 230 King St.
Jeffords, James, Shipsmith, 7 Concord St., res. 19 Wentworth St.
Jeffords, -----, Nassau St.
Jeffords, Samuel, Clerk, 14 Meeting St.
Jeffords, W. G., Clerk, 230 King St.
Jeffries, J., Amherst St.
Jenkins, C. C., Mrs., 7 Lamboll St.
Jenkins, David, Merchant, 147 Meeting St., res. 9 George St.
Jenkins, Henrietta, Mrs., 113 Broad St.
Jenkins, John, Laborer, 47 State St.
Jenkins, Joseph D., Planter, 5 Friend St.
Jenney, R., Saddler, 342 King St.
Jennings, D. (see Condict, Jennings & Co.)

Jerome, Augustus, Confectioner, 39 Wall St.
Jerrens, W., Policeman, 44 King St.
Jervey, James C., Customs Officer, 122 Tradd St.
Jervey, James P., Physician, 13 George St.
Jervey, Lewis, Officer, State Bank, res. 13 George St.
Jervey, Thomas, Washington St.
Jervey, William, Attorney, George St.
Jervis, -----, Mrs., 17 Queen St.
Jesson, H., Merchant, East Bay St.
Jesson, J. A., Grocer, Boundary St.
Jesson, John, Tavern Keeper, 8 Elliott St.
Jessup, Z. R., Shoe Dealer, 142 King St.
Johns, G. W., Engineer, Railroad, res. 347 King St.
Johns, William, Sugar Boiler, 15 Anson St., res. 225 East Bay St.
Johnson & Camfield, Clothing, 197 King St., John J., Johnson, A. W. Camfield
Johnson, A. B., Clerk, 146 East Bay St.
Johnson, Ann, Miss, Teacher, 14 Legare St.
Johnson, Benjamin, N. Coming St.
Johnson, Eleanor, Mrs., 71 Queen St.
Johnson, George (see Lockwood & Johnson)
Johnson, H. L., Clerk, 45 Hayne St.
Johnson, Hollis, Shoe Dealer, 240 King St.
Johnson, J. M. C., Bank of Charleston, res. 23 Pitt St.
Johnson, J., Seaman, 4 Stoll's Alley
Johnson, J. W., Nassau St.
Johnson, James S., Collector, 73 Wentworth St.
Johnson, Jane, Mrs., 229 King St.
Johnson, John, Clothing, 199 King St.
Johnson, Joseph, Druggist, Broad St., res. 107 King St.
Johnson, Joseph, Engineer, 73 Wentworth St.,
Johnson, Joseph, Jr., Merchant, East Bay St., res. 107 King St.
Johnson, -----, Line & America St.
Johnson, Luder, Grocer, 11 Mazyck St.
Johnson, Mary, Mrs., Midwife, 14 Liberty St.
Johnson, -----, Misses, Teachers, 107 King St.
Johnson, Oscar, N. King St.
Johnson, R. A., Bookkeeper, 45 Hayne St.
Johnson, T. W., Tavern Keeper, N. King St.
Johnson, Thomas N., Clerk, 40 East Bay St., res. 107 King St.
Johnson, Thomas, Sires St.
Johnson, William, Factor, Marsh's Wharf, 73 Wentworth St.
Johnson, William, Musician, 63 Church St.
Johnston, A. S., Merchant, East Bay St., res. 193 Meeting St.
Johnston, Benjamin, Umbrella Maker, 327 King St.
Johnston, Crews & Brawley, Dry Goods, 28 East Bay St., A. S. Johnson, A. J. Crews, J. M., Brawley
Johnston, D. P., Mariner, 4 Church St.
Johnston, David C., Physician, 71 Queen St.
Johnston, G. A., Engineer, Union Wharf, res. 183 Meeting St.
Johnston, M. J., Mrs., 20 Anson St.
Johnston, -----, Misses, 26 South Bay St.
Johnston, R., Jr., Grocer, 32 Vendue Range
Johnstone, A. M., Mrs., 27 Legare Sts.

Johnstone, F. W., Planter, 19 Montague St.
Joiner, W., Pinckney St., Cannonborough
Jones, A. C., Clerk, 2 Back Alley
Jones, A. D., Clerk, 56 Meeting St.
Jones, A. H., Clerk, 56 Meeting St.
Jones, A., Steward, Marine Hospital, 2 Back Alley
Jones, C. C., Mrs., Dry Goods, 65 State St.
Jones, E. C., Architect, Broad St., res. 3 Liberty St.
Jones, Edward, Clerk, 39 Archdale St
Jones, Edward, Ship Carpenter, 20 Vernon St.
Jones, J. C., Clerk, 256 King St., res. 3 Liberty St.
Jones, J., Carpenter, 11 Rutledge St.
Jones, John, Bee St.
Jones, John S. & Co., Ship Chandlers, 115 East Bay St., J. S. Jones, D. R. Jones
Jones, Jones, Carpenter, 34 Wentworth St.
Jones, Joseph, 39 Archdale St.
Jones, L., Dry Goods, 72 Market St.
Jones, -----, Misses, 1 Guignard St.
Jones, Paul, Clerk, Bee St.
Jones, Robert, Engineer, Railroad, res. 39 Archdale St.
Jones, Thomas L., Deputy Secretary of State, N. King St.
Jones, William, Carpenter, 11 Rutledge St.
Jones, William H., Mariner, 66 King St.
Jordan, C., Mrs., Seamstress, 40 Tradd St.
Jordan, Edward, Gillon St.
Joseph, -----, Capt., Mariner, 53 Tradd St.
Josephs, E., N., King St.
Josephs, J., Baker, King St., near Boundary St., res. N. King St.
Jowitt, Eliza, Mrs., 115 King St.
Jowitt, John J., Printer, 115 King St.
Joye, D. G., Planter, 45 Church St.
June, Samuel, Tavern Keeper, 24 Elliott St.
Just, George, Wharf Builder, 34 Hasell St.
Kalb, J. H., Baker, N. King St.
Kamlah, H., Tavern Keeper, 15 Vendue Range
Kanapaux, C. E., Attorney, Broad St., res. 19 Smith St.
Kanapaux, Charles, Superintendant, Lucas Mills, 19 Smith St.
Kanapaux, John D., Clerk, 17 Magazine St.
Kanauff, Henry, Carpenter, 37 Meeting St.
Karcher, Michael, Bootmaker, 56 Market St.
Karry, Patrick, Blacksmith, Chalmers St., res. 20 Tradd St.
Kay, Ann, 32 Society St.
Kayal, W., Mariner, 13 Anson St.
KcKenzie, Peter, N. Coming St.
Kean, Eliza, Mrs., 4 West St.
Kean, William, Mariner, 37 East Bay St.
Kearnon, John, 22 Market St.
Keckeley, E. C., M. D., N. Meeting St.
Keckeley, G. W., Engineer, Bennett's Mill, res. 79 Beaufain St.
Keckeley, S., Mrs., Seamstress, 16 Beaufain St.
Keckeley, T. J., Carpenter, 10 Laurens St.
Keenan, James, 22 Market St.
Keenan, W., Engraver, 30 Archdale St.
Kegney, John, Teacher, N. St. Philip St.
Keiffer, John, Leather Dealer, 27 Market St.

Keils, G. M., Wood Factor, Woolf St.
Keils, John H., Grocer, 57 Coming St.
Keip, J. R., Grocer, 6 Rutledge St.
Keith, P. T., Rev., Rector, St. Michael's Church, Hudson St.
Keitt, Frederick, N. King St.
Keitt, J., N. King St.
Kellers, Carsten, Coal Vender, Market St., res. 11 Cumberland St.
Kelly, J. A., Boat Builder, 4 Hard Alley
Kelly, James, Mariner, 84 Queen St.
Kelly, John, Clerk, 42 Meeting St., res. 112 Meeting St.
Kelly Peter, Laborer, 62 State St.
Kelly, Thomas, Bootmaker, 43 Broad St.
Kelly, Thomas, Mason, 27 Montague St.
Kelly, William, Plasterer, 44 St. Philip St.
Kelsey & Deas, Dry Goods, 37 Hayne St., George H. Kelsey, John Deas
Kendrick, J. R., Rev., Pastor, 1st Baptist Church., res. 88 Broad St.
Kenefie, John, Druggist, 43 Queen St., res. 20 Pinckney St.
Kennedy, Andrew, Sires St.
Kennedy, Dennis, N. Smith St.
Kennedy, John J., Tailor, 30 Broad St., res. 21 Meeting St.
Kennedy, John, Laborer, 24 Tradd St.
Kennedy, John, Policeman, 44 Market St.
Kennedy, John, Saddler, 342 King St.
Kennedy, M., Boarders, 43 State St.
Kennedy, Mary, Miss, Milliner, 191 King St.
Kennedy, William, Mariner, 34 Queen St.
Kennie, D. H., Shoe Maker, 186 King St.
Kent & Mitchell, Clothing, 268 King St., W. A. Kent, George H. Mitchell
Kent, Columbus
Kentworth, K., Washington St.
Kenworthy, William, Keeper of Cells, Poor House
Kerigan, Mary, Seamstress, 31 King St.
Kerr, T. J., Merchant, 1 Society St.
Kerrison, C. & E. L., Dry Goods, 209 King St.
Kerrison, Charles, Dry Goods, King & Market Sts., res. 5 New St.
Kershaw, A. E., Mrs., 28 Bull St.
Kessel, John, Carpenter, 4 Beaufain St.
Ketchum & Taylor, Dry Goods, 231 King St., Joel Ketchum, Orrin Taylor
Ketchum, Joel, Dry Goods, 231 King St., res. Laurens & Wall Sts.
Kiddell, A., Clerk, 154 Meeting St.
Kiddell, B., Clerk, 154 Meeting St.
Kiddell, C., Mrs., 3 Court House Square
Kiep, J. H., Grocer, 39 Beaufain St.
Kilroy, P., 30 Market St.
Kimball, J. H., 290 King St.
King, F., Clerk, 18 Boundary St.
King, G. W., Blacksmith, 3 Gillon St., res. 65 Meeting St.
King, George, Boiler Maker, 16 Market St.
King, Henry C., Attorney, 5 St. Michael's Alley, res. 68 Tradd St.

King, John, Laborer, 41 State St.
King, John, Railroad Agent, 42 George St.
King, John, Wheelwright, 26 Chalmers St.
King, Lucinda, Mrs., 63 Meeting St.
King, M., Attorney, 5 St. Michael's Alley, res. 14 George St.
King, M. C., Planter, 14 George St.
King, Mitchell C., Physician, 14 George St.
King, N. S., Wig Maker, 185 King St.
King, Samuel, Officer, Planters & Mechanics Bank, 8 State St.
King, W. A., Mrs., 7 Chalmers St.
King, W. S., Editor, Courier, 111 East Bay St., res. 26 Broad St.
Kingdom, T. Pinckney, Cannonborough
Kingman, Eliab J., Penny Post, 297 King St.
Kingman, John, Boarders, 297 King St.
Kingman, K., Mrs., 1 Wentworth St.
Kingman, M. G., Clerk, 93 Church St.
Kings, G. W., Brass Workers, 109 Meeting St.
Kings, H. W., Wig Maker, 109 Meeting St.
Kinloch, George, Merchant, 233 East Bay St.
Kinloch, -----, Millwright, 15 Bull St.
Kinloch, R. A., Physician, 233 East Bay St.
Kinloch, Samuel, Aiken's Range
Kinloch, Thomas, Aiken's Range
Kinney, Thomas, Farrier & Tavern Keeper, California House, 88 Church St.
Kinsley, Peter A., Shoe Maker, 120 Church St.
Kinsman, H. W., Storekeeper, 80 Meeting St.
Kirk, Mary A., Mrs., 8 Magazine St.
Kirker, James, N. King St.
Kirkpatrick, John & Co., Factors, South Atlantic Wharf
Kirkwood & Knox, Shipwrights, Gadsden's Wharf, William Kirkwood, W. P. Knox
Kirkwood, William, Shipwright, Gadsden's Wharf, res. 3 Laurens St.
Kitchins, James C., 105 Church St.
Kittel, Joseph, Merchant, King St., res. 31 Anson St.
Kittleband, John, 115 Tradd St.
Kittleband, S., Mrs., Boarders, 279 King St.
Klaus, Henry, Bootmaker, 38 Queen St.
Klebere, -----, Policeman, 22 St. Philip St.
Kleinbech, J. D., Grocer, 7 Inspection St.
Kleinbech, J. H., Clerk, 7 Inspection St.
Klinck, John, Grocer, Broad & Church Sts., res. 71 Coming St.
Kline, J. C., Syrup Maker, 106 Wentworth St.
Klink & Wickenberg, Grocers, Broad & Church Sts., John Klink, F. R. Wickenberg
Klinkwood, Henry, Radcliffe St.
Klumek, H., Clerk, 39 State St.
Knapp, A., Peter W., N. St. Philip St.
Knaps, A., Shoemaker, 69 Wentworth St.
Knauar, Peter, Cabinet Maker, 143 King St.
Knee, Harman, Grocer, 38 Church St.
Knee, -----, Mrs., Milliner, 38 Church St.
Knepley, S., Blacksmith, 73 Queen St.
Knevals, S. W. (see Hull & Knevals)

23

Knevin, Patrick, Butcher, Cannon St.
Knight, J. D., Capt., U. S. Navy, Elizabeth St.
Knobloch, William, Baker, 19 Boundary St.
Knowles, E., Mrs., Milliner, 202 King St.
Knox, Walter, Mrs., 16 Green St.
Knox, William, Shipwright, Gadsden's Wharf
Knust, G., Collector, 33 Coming St.
Koegel, L., Clerk, 123 Meeting St.
Koennecker, Albert, Grocer, Elizabeth & John Sts.
Kohne, Eliza, Mrs., 98 Broad St.
Kohnke, C. F., Grocer, 61 Boundary St.
Konig, John H., Grocer, 65 Queen St.
Kopman, J., N., King St.
Korber, G. H., Grocer, 8 Lynch St., res. 12 Rutledge St.
Kornarens, John, Grocer, Nassau St.
Kracker, F. C. C., Pinckney St.; Cannonborough
Kremar, -----, N. Meeting St.
Krous, G., Clerk, 26 Anson St.
Kruger, C., 85 Queen St.
Kuffner, A., N. King St.
Kugley, W. F. A., 36 Mazyck St.
Kunhardt, W. W., Attorney, St. Michael's Alley, res.
   Wentworth St.
Kunhardt, William, Port Warden, 5 Wentworth St.
Kurth, C., Policeman, 105 Broad St.
Kusee, H., Grocer, 12 Mazyck St.
Kyhe, W., N. St. Philip St.
La Barbice, -----, Church St.
Labatat, Isadore, Portrait Painter, 54 Boundary St.
Laborde, Ann, Mrs., Boarders, 72 Beaufain St.
Laborde, J. B., Clerk, East Bay St.
Labrere, -----, Mrs., 14 Coming St.
LaBruce, -----, Mrs., Drake St.
Lacassagne, E., Hair Worker, 148 King St.
Lachicotte, Julius, Cooper, Chisolm's Mill
Lachicotte, Philip, Engineer, Chisolm's Mill
Lacoste, A. T. J., Rigger, 16 Vernon St.
Ladaveze, J. V., Dry Goods, 146 King St.
Ladson, J. H., Factor, Southern Wharf, res. 4 Meeting St.
Ladson, James H. & Co., Factors, Southern Wharf, J. H.
   Ladson, William C. Bee
Ladye, W., Nassau St.
Lafande, Louisa, Mrs., 160 East Bay St.
Lafar, D. B., Cooper, Vendue Range, res. 54 Queen St.
Lafar, D. X., Student of Divinity, 54 Queen St.
Lafar, J., Engineer, Nassau St.
Lafar, -----, Mrs., 2 Clifford St.
Lafar, William, Clerk, 48 Meeting St.
Laffan, James, Seaman, 7 Smith's Lane
Laffiteau, A., Clerk, Union Wharves, res. 192 King St.
Lafitte, E. & Co., Steam Boat Agents, Fitzsimons'
   Wharf, E. Lafitte, J. B. Lafitte
Laidler, William, Collector, Courier, 10 Savage St.
Lake, Nicholas, Ship Joiner, 22 Laurens St.
Lalane, A., Tobacconist, 46 East Bay St.
Lalane, J., 46 East Bay St.
Lalane, Peter B., Officer, Bank of Charleston, 118 King
   St.
Lamb, David, Physician, 191 Meeting St.
Lamb, J. T., Clerk, 191 Meeting St.

Lamb, James, Merchant, 191 Meeting St.
Lamb, -----, Mrs., 2 Price's Alley
Lambert & Brother, Carpet Store, 219 King St.
Lambert, Charles, Carpet Dealer, 219 King St., res. 77
   Wentworth St.
Lambert, Patrick, President St.
Lambert, Walter, Clerk, 219 King St.
Lambly, -----, Capt., N. Coming St.
Lamotte, W. J., Printer, 68 Meeting St.
Lance, Archibald, Accountant, 29 Friend St.
Lance, F. L., Physician, 29 Friend St.
Lance, Francis, Clerk of Council, 29 Friend St.
Lance, John, U. S. Army, 29 Friend St.
Landershine, D. P., Ship Carpenter, Marsh's Wharf, res.
   1 Marsh St.
Landreth, D. M., Seedsman, 285 King St.
Landreth, Robert, Bar Keeper, 93 Market St.
Lane, E. H., Merchant, 309 King St.
Lane, J. C., Clerk, 41 Hayne St.
Lane, W. G., Merchant, 1 George St.
Langley, W., 35 Queen St.
Lanneau, Basil, Clerk, 116 East Bay St., res. 7 Pitt St.
Lanneau, Fleetwood, Merchant, 14 Hayne St., res. 43
   Coming St.
Lanneau, Mary, Mrs., 183 Meeting St.
Lapenne, J. J., Dry Goods, 336 King St.
Lapenne, J. N., Dry Goods 336 King St.
Lapenne, Philip, Tinner, 61 Queen St.
Larkin, C., Mrs., Boarders 126 Church St.
Larkin, M., Mrs., Boarders 36 Queen St.
Larousseliere, T. H., Upholsterer, 166 King St., res. 10
   Liberty St.
Lassan, H., Grocer, 18 Pitt St.
Latitte, E., Merchant, Fitzsimons' Wharf, res. 5 Pinckney
   St.
Latitte, John B., Steam Boat Agent, Fitzsimons' Wharf,
   res. 138 Meeting St.
Laurens, E. R., Master in Equity, Broad St., res. 194 East
   Bay St.
Laurens, John, Planter, 194 East Bay St.
Laurens, Joseph, Cabinet Maker, 52 St. Philip St.
Laurens, K. S., Planter, 7 East Bay St.
Laurens, M. H., Mrs., Planter, 23 Lynch St.
Laurens, R. C., 23 Lynch St.
Laux, M., Bootmaker, 38 Queen St.
Laval, William J., Clerk, Comptroller, Fire Proof
   Building, res. Elizabeth St.
Laval, William, U. S. Treasurer, Fire Proof Building,
   res. 1 George St.
Lawson, M., Commission Merchant, Fitzsimons' Wharf,
   res. 13 East Bay St.
Lawton, John, Police Officer, 20 Queen St.
Lawton, Joseph & Co., Dry Goods, 40 East Bay St., J.
   Lawton, W. Naylor, T. P. Smith, A. M. Huger
Lawton, R. B., 20 Queen St.
Lawton, W. C., Carpenter, 92 Church St.
Lawton, W. S., Factor, East Bay St., res. 236 King St.
Lawton, William M., Factor, 13 Southern Wharf, res. 17
   Rutledge St.
Layde, Jesse, Cannon St.

Lazarus, B. D., Merchant, Wentworth & Smith Sts.
Lazarus, G., Customs Officer, 84 Wentworth St.
Lazarus, J. E. P., Clerk, 20 Coming St.
Lazarus, Joshua, President, Gas Company, 121 Church St., res. Laurens St.
Lazarus, Michael, 12 Montague St.
Lea, Charles, Pilot, 53 East Bay St.
Lea, John C., Pilot, 53 East Bay St.
Lea, W. P., Jr., Pilot, Longitude Lane
Lea, William P., Pilot, 53 East Bay St.
Leach, R. M., Clerk, 2 Wall St.
Leader, Mary, Mrs., 8 Clifford St.
Leary, D., Gillon St.
Leaumont, de R., 30 Broad St.
Leaumont, Henry, 2 Minority St.
Lebby, E., Mrs., 8 Middle St.
Lebby, N. H., 15 Tradd St.
Lebby, William, Machinist, Hasell St., res. 15 Wentworth St.
Lebleux, Ann, Mrs., 86 Queen St.
Leckie, Clark, Umbrella Maker, 165 King St.
Leckie, David, Accountant, N. Meeting St.
Leckie, Robert, Umbrella Maker, 165 King St.
Leclare, -----, Mrs., 32 Boundary St.
Leclear, C., Mrs., 12 Magazine St.
Lee, Ann, Mrs., 51 Queen St.
Lee, Ann, Mrs., Monthy Nurse, 84 King St.
Lee, Benjamin, Alexander St.
Lee, Charles F., Elliott St.
Lee, F., Alexander St.
Lee, Henry, 28 Queen St.
Lee, John C., Grocer, 32 Archdale St.
Lee, John, Hotel Keeper, Broad St., res. 78 Tradd St.
Lee, Joseph T., Teacher, 44 Pitt St.
Lee, K., Mrs., 44 Pitt St.
Lee, Sarah, Mrs., Beaufain St.
Lee, T., Alexander St.
Lee, W. H., Clerk, City Court, 21 Smith St.
Lee, William, Carpenter, 112 Meeting St.
Leeman, William, Confectioner, 40 Queen St.
Legare, J. B., Attorney, 14 New Sts.
Legare, J. B., Planter, 19 Hasell St.
Legare, J. Davidson, Thomas St.
Legare, James, Factor, Commercial Wharf, res., 107 Broad St.
Legare, James, Warren St.
Legare, Joshua, Painter, 9 Marsh St.
Legare, S. J., Clerk, 10 New St.
Legare, Solomon, Planter, 103 Tradd St.
Legé, J. G., Clerk, 97 King St.
Legé, -----, Madame, 116 King St.
LeGras, C., Clerk, Adger's Wharf, res. 59 Church St.
Lehartz, C., Cooper, 83 Beaufain St.
Lehre, Thomas, Alexander St.
Leitch, James, Clerk, 24 Savage St.
Leitch, W. Y., Dry Goods, King St.
Leite, J. C., N. Meeting St.
Leland & Brother, Merchants, Commercial Wharf
Leland Brothers & Co., Commission Merchants, North Commercial Wharf, Joseph Leland, David Leland,
Thomas Trout
Leland, Dexter, Teacher, 33 King St.
Leland, John A., Teacher, Citadel
Leman, E., Washington St.
Leman, M., Bookkeeper, 7 Gadsden St.
Leman, -----, Nassau St.
Leman, William, Clerk, N. Meeting St.
Lenord, Edward, 8 Linguard St.
Leon, Israel, Clothing, 310 King St.
Leonard, James, Drayman, 14 Market St.
Leopold, F., N. Meeting St.
Leprince, A., Dry Goods, 192 King St.
Leprince, John, Tinner, 298 King St.
Lequeux, B., Wood Factor, Gadsden's Wharf, res. 5 Burns Lane
Lesby, Lewis B., Doughty St.
Lesesne, H. D., Attorney, 8 St. Michael's Alley, res. 14 Green St.
Lesesne, W. J., Teacher, 64 Church St.
Lessman, Augustus, Baker, 115 Church St.
Lester, A. H., Clerk, 147 Meeting St.
Levin, M., 317 King St.
Levin, N., Customs Officer, 47 Wentworth St.
Levitt, W., Seaman, 8 Bedon's Alley
Levy, Elias, Gauger, 8 Lightwood's Alley
Levy, I. C., East Bay St.
Levy, L. L., 174 Meeting St.
Levy, M., A., John St.
Levy, Moses, Boarders, 3 Tradd St.
Levy, R. R., Carpenter, 8 Lightwood's Alley
Lewis, H. P., Bookkeeper, Boyce's Wharf
Lewis, Isaac, 7 Society St.
Lewis, John, Bookkeeper, 154 King St.
Lewis, S. A., Mrs., 8 Rutledge St.
Lieure, P., Clerk, 69 Church St.
Lightbourne, E. B., Mrs., 21 St. Philip St.
Limehouse, Robert J., Clerk, 35 Montague St.
Limehouse, Robert, Tradd St.
Lincoln, William, Bowling Saloon, Meeting St., res. 91 Market St.
Lindergreen, Charles, Nassau St.
Lindow, A., Grocer, 2 King St.
Lindsay, G. W., Accountant, Accommodation Wharf, res. 8 Guignard St.
Lindsay, J. L., Accountant, East Bay St., res. 8 Guignard, St.
Lindsay, J., Painter, N. King St.
Lindsay, John T., Clerk, 155 E. Bay St.
Lindsay, William, Accountant, 29 Broad St., res. 8 Guignard St.
Lines, Robert, John St.
Ling, Philip, Ice House, Church St.
Ling, Robert, Mrs., 21 Bull St.
Ling, Samuel, Seaman, 124 Queen St.
Lining, Charles, Clerk, Bennett's Mill, res. 24 South Bay St.
Lining, E. B., Jr., Bank of Charleston, res. Drake St.
Lining, Eda, Drake, St.
Linley, Rebecca, Mrs., Mantuamaker, 42 King St.
Linn, George, Cart Driver, 9 Back Alley

Linn, John, Drayman, 9 Back Alley
Linstead, A., N., Meeting St.
Lips, William, Bootmaker, 12 Meeting St.
Lissak, G. B., Cap Maker, 328 King St.
Litshgi, Alban, 14 Anson St.
Little, George & Co., Clothing, 269 King St.
Livingston, Jane, Mrs., 57 Anson St.
Livingston, John, Alexander St.
Livingston, P., Mrs., 6 Water St.
Lloyd, A., Tinner, 352 King St.
Lloyd, -----, Carpenter, 4 Horlbeck's Alley
Lloyd, Mary, 14 Chalmers St.
Lloyd, William, Broker, Broad St., res. 61 Meeting St.
Lochin, Daniel, Sugar Refiner, Anson St., res. 180 East
    Bay St.
Locke, B. C., Merchant, East Bay St., res. 12 George St.
Locke, E. H., Merchant, East Bay St., res. Meeting St.
Locke, G. A., Merchant, 167 East Bay St.
Locke, G. B. & Son, Commission Merchants, 66 East
    Bay St., G. B. Locke, E. H. Locke
Locke, G. B., Merchant, East Bay St., res. 12 George St.
Lockwood & Johnson, Machinists, Patton's Wharf,
    Joshua Lockwood, George Johnson
Lockwood, Caroline D., Mrs., 73 Broad St.
Lockwood, Joshua W., Engineer, Concord St., 222 res.
    73 Broad St.
Lockwood, S. L., Physician, 73 Broad St.
Lockwood, T. P., Jr., Attorney, 14 St. Michael's Alley,
    res. 379 King St.
Lockwood, T. P., Sr., Teacher, Orphan House, res. 379
    King St.
Lode, H. B., Grocer, 1 Market St.
Loftus, Patrick, 4 Linguard St.
Logan, E. H., Rev., 373 King St.
Logan, George, Physician, 5 Liberty St.
Logan, William, Librarian, Charleston Library, 373 King
    St.
Lonergan, James, 106 Meeting St.
Long, A. K., Gas Pipe Dealer, 100 Meeting St.
Long, J. H., Grocer, 102 Tradd St.
Long, Peter, Painter, 13 Elliott St.
Long, R. A., 14 Mazyck St.
Lonigan, William, 125 Church St.
Loper, H. G., Officer, Railroad Bank, 19 Broad St.
Lopez, David, Builder, 28 George St.
Lopez, M., 13 College St.
Lord, Capers, Blacksmith, 9 Marsh St.
Lord, J. F. M., Mason, 24 Vernon St.
Lord, J., N. St. Philip St.
Lord, Samuel, Merchant, East Bay St., res. 18 Society St.
Lore, Henry, Clerk, 67 Meeting St.
Loryea, Isaac, 7 Market St.
Loryea, Isaac, Clothing, 69 Market St.
Loud, John, 309 King St.
Loud, P. H., 309 King St.
Love, Charles, Saddler, Broad St., res. 96 Tradd St.
Lovegreen, A. A., Dry Goods, 370 King St.
Lovell, -----, Misses, Teachers, 26 Church St.
Lowndes, A. D., Mrs., 3 Friend St.
Lowndes, Charles T., Planter, 39 East Bay St.

Lowndes, Elizabeth B., Mrs., Planter, 7 King St.
Lowndes, Margaret M., Mrs., 2 Legare St.
Loyall, L. C., N. St. Philip St.
Lubbs, P. S., Tobacconist, 263 King St.
Lubking, L., Storekeeper, 1 Tradd St.
Lucas & Co., Merchants, North Commercial Wharf, T.
    B. Lucas, P. J. Barbot
Lucas, Benjamin, Mason, 4 Savage St.
Lucas, -----, Clerk, 54 Market St.
Lucas, E., Pinckney St.
Lucas, Henry, Lucas St.
Lucas, John, Mason, 4 Savage St.
Lucas, R. H., Pinckney St., Cannonborough
Lucas, T. B., Merchant, Pinckney St., Cannonborough
Lucas, W., Sr., Pinckney St.
Lucinder, W., 60 Meeting St.
Ludecus, E., Mrs., Worsted Dealer, 188 King St.
Luden, C., Clerk, 53 Market St.
Luers, F., Shoemaker, 28 Anson St.
Luhrsteadt, Henry, Baker, 115 Church St.
Lukin, Henry, N. King St.
Lutelman, H., 78 Anson St.
Lyall, Henry L., 4 Mazyck St.
Lynass, M., Dry Goods, 212 King St.
Lynch, F. C., Tailor, 91 Market St.
Lynch, J. G., Printer, 10 Stoll's Alley
Lynch, P. A., Rev., D. D., 80 Broad St.
Lyon, John, Clerk, 5 Liberty St.
Lyon, Oliver, 102 Meeting St.
Lyons, J., Dr., N. King St.
Lyons, M., 6 Linguard St.
Macbeth, Robert, Clerk, Market, 5 Smith St.
MacBeth, Charles, Attorney, Law Range, res. 7 Legare
    St.
MacBeth, James, Cotton Broker, Exchange Wharf, res.
    30 Broad St.
Macer, Henry, Clerk, 65 Queen St.
Mack, P., President St.
Mackery, William, Clerk, 14 Queen St.
Mackey, A. G., Physician, 55 Beaufain St.
Mackey, -----, Boarders, 261 King St.
Mackie, Margaret, Mrs., 75 Broad St.
Mackie, Octavius, Engineer, Railroad, res. 75 Broad St.
Mackintosh, David, Ship Carpenter, Gadsden's Wharf,
    res. 96 Beaufain St.
Macklin, Mary, Mrs., Dress Maker, 117 Queen St.
Magrath, A. G. & E., Attorneys, Broad St.
Magrath, A. G., Attorney, Broad St., res. Thomas St.
Magrath, E., Attorney, Broad St., res. Thomas St.
Magrath, John, Bee St.
Magrill, Joseph, Seaman, 119 King St.
Maguire, D., Dry Goods, 362 King St.
Magwood, Charles, Merchant, Magwood's Wharf, res. 9
    Smith St.
Magwood, James, Planter, 2 Gadsden St.
Magwood, Simon, N. St. Philip St.
Maher, Mary A., Dry Goods, 31 State St.
Maher, Michael, Policeman, 98 Meeting St.
Mahoney, J., Clerk, 13 Broad St.
Mahoney, John, Blacksmith, 20 Middle St.

Main, A. R., 46 Anson St.
Mair, James, Laborer, 6 Coming St.
Malcolm, James, Policeman, 30 King St.
Mallar, F., Tailor, 12 Pitt St.
Mallen, Edward, Dry Goods, 85 Market St.
Mallet, Frederick, Confectioner, 19 Mazyck St.
Mallory, H., Seaman, 101 Meeting St.
Mallory, L., Clerk, 101 Meeting St.
Mallory, Sarah, Mrs., Boarders, 101 Meeting St.
Malone, T. W., Attorney, 23 Mazyck St.
Malony, John, 32 Queen St
Malony P., 32 Queen St.
Man, John, Mason, 23 Boundary St.
Manigault, A. H., Mrs., 12 Meeting St.
Manigault, A. M., Factor, John St.
Manigault, Charles, Planter, 6 Gibbes St.
Manigault, E., Planter, John St.
Manigault, H. H., Planter, 12 Meeting St.
Manigault, H., Planter, Drake St.
Mansfield, L., 12 Linguard St.
Manson, G. R., Ship Carpenter, 4 Marsh St.
Manson, Mary, Mrs., 66 Anson St.
Margart, George, Farmer, Reid St.
Margart, J. H., 178 Meeting St.
Marhar, Thomas, 22 Pinckney St.
Marion, John, Confectioner, 289 King St.
Marion, -----, N. Coming St.
Marley, John E., Conductor, Charlotte St.
Marsh, James, Jr., Shipwright, Concord St., res 5 Hasell
    St.
Marsh, James, Sr., Shipwright, 4 Concord St., res. 138
    East Bay St.
Marshall, A. W., Rev., Pastor, St. John's Chapel, res. 94
    Broad St.
Marshall, John, Alexander St.
Marshall, -----, Misses, 94 Broad St.
Marshall, Samuel, Alexander St.
Marshall, T. M., Clerk, 288 King St.
Martin, Charlotte, Mrs., 264 E.Bay St.
Martin, Henry, Joiner, 5 Hard Alley
Martin, Isaac, Shoe Dealer, 187 East Bay St.
Martin, J. C., 24 Hasell St.
Martin, J. J., Merchant, 29 Coming St.
Martin, Jacob, Blacksmith, 46 Wentworth St., res. 29
    Coming St.
Martin, Lewis V., Bricklayer, N. Coming St.
Martin, Robert, Factor, Boyce's Wharf, res. Charlotte St.
Martin, Starr & Walter, Factors, Boyce & Co. Wharf,
    Robert Martin, E. P. Starr, E. W. Walter
Martin, Thomas, Bricklayer, N. Coming St.
Martin, Thomas, Magistrate, East Bay St., res. 20 George
    St.
Martin, W. A., Engineer, Railroad, 347 King St.
Martin, W., Laborer, 24 Tradd St.
Martin, W. M., Insurance Agent, 9 Broad St., res. 24
    Hasell St.
Martin, W. S., 29 Coming St.
Martin, William, Broker, 6 Stoll'sAlley
Martin, William, Charlotte St.
Marting, J. B., 11 Back Alley

Martins, F. W., Tailor, 77 Church St.
Marty, A., Shoe Maker, 70 State St.
Mashburn, E., Wharfinger, 24 Boundary St.
Mashburn, J. H., Customs Officer, 24 Boundary St.
Massot, H., Mary St.
Maston, V., Mrs., Dress Maker, 155 King St.
Matheson & Simons, Commission Merchants, 114 East
    Bay St., M. P. Matheson, K. L. Simons
Matheson, E., Mrs., 19 Laurens St.
Matheson, M. P., Merchant, 26 Hasell St.
Mathews, E. W., Factor, Vanderhorst's Wharf, res. 13
    Short St.
Mathews, G., Physician, 31 East Bay St.
Mathews, J. F., Planter, 31 East Bay St.
Mathews, J. R., Planter, 31 East Bay St.
Mathews, Jane, Mrs., 5 Orange St.
Mathews, S., 340 King St.
Mathews, Thomas D., Clerk, 43 Anson St.
Matta, A., Showman, 34 Market St.
Matthiessen, C., Druggist, 42 Queen St., res. 139 King
    St.
Matthiessen, C. F., 8 Church St.
Matthiessen, F. C., Merchant, Commercial Wharf, res. 8
    Church St.
Matthiessen, William, Clothing, 139 East Bay St., res. 14
    Wentworth St.
Maull, Charles, Millinery, 126 King St.
Maull, Philip, Carpenter, Sires St.
Maxey, Samuel T., Brick Layer, Duncan St.
Maxey, Virgil, Clerk, 17½ South Bay St.
May, J. W., Attorney, Broad St., res. 62 Queen St.
May, John, Cabinet Maker, 62 Queen St.
May, John, Clerk, 10 Queen St.
Mayer, H., Druggist, N. King St.
Mazyck, C. B., Mrs., 26 George St.
Mazyck, P. W., Painter, 74 Meeting St., res. 20
    Washington St.
Mazyck, T. F., 26 George St.
Mazyck, William, Factor, Chapel St.
McAlister, Charles, Dry Goods, 339 King St.
McAnally, E., Miss, Teacher, 107 Tradd St.
McAnally, E., Mrs., Dress Maker, 107 Tradd St.
McAndrew, James, Policeman, 5 South Bay St.
McAndrew, Patrick, Grocer, 5 South Bay St.
McBride, A., 176 East Bay St.
McBride, M., Broker, 1 Chalmers St.
McBride, P., Auctioneer, 22 Vendue Range
McBurney, William, Merchant, 9 Hayne St., res. 29
    George St.
McCabe, James, Engineer, 6 Guignard St.
McCabe, John, Sugar Refiner, 180 East Bay St.
McCaddon, J. S., Shoe Dealer, 136 King St.
McCaffrey, James, Bar Keeper, 5 Princess St.
McCall, B., Clerk, 48 Church St.
McCall, J. P., 17 Mazyck St.
McCall, M., Mrs., 56 Broad St.
McCall, -----, Misses, 1 Logan St.
McCalrey, Patrick, Laborer, 62 State St.
McCan, John, Laborer, 60 State St.
McCarter & Allen, Booksellers, 116 Meeting St., J. J.

McCarter, T. P. Allen
McCarter, J., Clerk, 326 King St.
McCarter, James J., Book Seller, 116 Meeting St., res. 14
Hasell St.
McCarthy, D. L., Clothing, 193 East Bay St.
McCarthy, John, 126 Church St.
McCartney, John, 33 Boundary St.
McCartney, Samuel, 15 Broad St.
McCay, -----, Misses, Teachers, 8 Friend St.
McClannerhand, C., Clerk, 127 King St.
McClung, C., Clerk, 155 East Bay St.
McClure, -----, Printer, 32 Tradd St.
McClure, Thomas H., Bootmaker, 15 Queen St.
McClure, William, Washington St.
McCollum, James, Jailor, 19 Magazine St.
McCollum, John
McConnel, J., 105 Church St.
McCormack, James, 26 Market St.
McCoy, S., Painter, 34 Queen St.
McCrady & Caldwell, Attorneys, Chalmers St., E.
McCrady, W. S. Caldwell
McCrady, Edward, District Attorney, U. S. Court House,
Chalmers St., res. 20 Anson St.
McCrady, J. W., 68 King St.
McCready, J. B., 172 King St.
McCready, W. T., Customs Officer, 172 King St.
McDermed, Duncan, Machinist, 1 Washington St.
McDermed, R., Machinist, Gadsden's Wharf, res. 6
Wharf St.
McDermot, James, Clerk, 350 King St.
McDoal, James, Tinner, 126 Church St.
McDoe, James, Baker, 6 Coming St.
McDonald, D., Accountant, 3 Logan St.
McDonald, John, Daguerreotypist, 143 King St.
McDonald, M., Mrs., 52 King St.
McDonald, Patrick, Policeman, 52 King St.
McDougal, -----, 264 King St.
McDougal, David, Engineer, Chisolm's Mill
McDowall, A. & Co., Dry Goods, 32 East Bay St., A.
McDowall, W. G. Mood
McDowall, Andrew, Merchant, East Bay St., res. 8
Meeting St.
McDowall, J. S., Clerk, 200 King St.
McDowall, John, John St.
McDowall, R. H., Clerk, 32 Coming St.
McDowall, W. H., Pilot, 8 Stoll's Alley
McDowall, William, Clerk, 185 Meeting St.
McDowall, William, John St.
McElheran, W. C., Blacksmith, 24 Wentworth St.
McElmoyle, -----, Mrs., King St.
McGary, P., Bootmaker, 9 Tradd St.
McGee, Hall T., Merchant, 5 Boyce's Wharf, res. 372
King St.
McGentry, T., Sugar Refiner, 180 East Bay St.
McGilvray, J. G., Accountant, 10 Atlantic St.
McGinlay, Samuel, Blacksmith, 15 Price's Alley
McGinn, Jane, Mrs., Fruiterer, 52 King St.
McGinnis, -----, Blacksmith, Chalmers St., res. 87 King
St.
McGovern, Ann, Mrs., 20 South Bay St.

McGrath, Thomas, 4 Linguard St.
McGuines, James, Laborer, 60 State St.
McGuira, -----, Mrs., Monthly Nurse, 76 King St.
McGuira, Robert, Omnibus Driver, 76 King St.
McGuire, James, 22 Market St.
McGuire, James, Dry Goods, 94 Anson St.
McGuire, M., Mrs., Fruiterer, 65 King St.
McHugh, F. Q., Attorney, 49 Beaufain St.
McHugh, P., Bar Keeper, 125 East Bay St.
McIahn, J., Tavern Keeper, 22 Elliott St.
McInnis, Joseph, Charlotte St.
McIntosh, David N. (see Adger, James & Co.)
McIntyre, Peter, 32 Market St.
McIntyre, S. C., Daguerreotypist, 309 King St.
McKean, James, Clerk, 26 Archdale St.
McKee, Abel, Joiner, 6 Market St., res. 16 Pinckney St.
McKegan, John, Blacksmith, 189 Meeting St.
McKenna, Francis, Painter, 106 King St.
McKenzie, A., Saddler, 99 Church St.
McKenzie, Cadow & Co., Dry Goods, 82 East Bay St.,
B. F. Mckenzie, William Cadow, H. M., McKenzie
McKenzie, -----, Clerk, 261 King St.
McKenzie, G. T., Saddler, 99 Church St.
McKenzie, James, Clerk, 27 St. Philip St.
McKenzie, John, 88 Church St.
McKenzie, John, N. Coming St.
McKenzie, R. B., Saddler, 99 Church St.
McKewen, E., Mrs., Seamstress, 78 Beaufain St.
McKinney, Christopher, Officer, Bank of Charleston, 55
Queen St.
McLaren, James, Miller, 8 Wharf St.
McLarty, Edward, Mariner, 63 King St.
McLaughlin, T. Pinckney, Cannonborough
McLean, J., Carpenter, 79 Queen St.
McLeish, A., Machinist, 4 Cumberland St.
McLeish, James, Machinist, Gadsden's Wharf, res. 1
Inspection St.
McLeish, -----, Mrs., 44 Tradd St.
McLeish, W., Storekeeper, 82 Church St.
McLeon, Frances, Mrs., 56 St. Philip St.
McMahan, N., Tavern Keeper, 20 Elliott St.
McMan, Robert, Laborer, 4 Longitude Lane
McManis, J., Drayman, 11 Chalmers St.
McManus, John, Drayman, 92 Anson St.
McManus, Thomas, Grocer 20 South Bay St.
McMaster, Elizabeth, Dry Goods, 364 King St.
McMillan, J., Boarders, 27 Queen St.
McMillan, J. W., Printer, Mercury Office, res. East Bay
St.
McMillan, T. J., Ship Carpenter, 107 Church St.
McMillan, Thomas, Wood Factor, 115 Tradd St.
McNamara, D., Laborer, 75 Church St.
McNamara, L., Policeman, 74 Church St.
McNamee, Mary, Mrs., Boarders, 44 Queen St.
McNeal, Mary, Mrs., Storekeeper, 142 Tradd St., res. 2
Savage St.
McNeil, E. S., Mrs., 30 Middle St.
McNeill, -----, Mrs., Milk Vender, 25 King St.
McNeill, Neil, Customs Officer, 54 Broad St.
McNellage, John, Sail Maker, Atlantic Wharf, res. 7

Hasell St.

McNellage, M., Mrs., 41 Beaufain St.

McOwen, Patrick, Merchant, Adger's Wharf, res. 37 St. Philip St.

McOwen, Robert, Wharfinger, Adger's Wharf, res. 37 St. Philip St.

McOwen, Seth, Atlantic Wharf, res. 37 St. Philip St.

McPhalen, B., Laborer, 1 St. Michael's Alley

McPherson, James, Mrs., 255 East Bay St.

McPherson, John, Mrs., 255 East Bay St.

McPherson, -----, Mrs., Planter, 255 East Bay St.

McPherson, S., Mrs., Nurse, Orphan House

McQueen, Donald, Bookkeeper, 1 Hayne St., res. 23 Laurens St.

McRugh, -----, Carpenter, 88 Church St.

Meacher, G. W., Gas Pipe Fitter, 72 Meeting St.

Mead, S., Mrs., Boarders, 46 Queen St.

Meadow, E., Mrs., Milliner, 324 King St.

Mealy, John, 19 St. Philip St.

Medicis, M., Cigar Maker, 4 Hard Alley

Meers, S., Ship Carpenters, Marsh St.

Megler, Jacob, Shoemaker, 70 State St.

Mehrtens, C. L., Grocer, Washington St.

Mehrtens, F., Grocer, Coming & Vanderhorst Sts.

Mehrtens, J. C., Grocer, 7 St. Philip St.

Meissner, E., Grocer, 107 Tradd St.

Meissner, H., Grocer, 134 Tradd St.

Melehers, F., Painter, 287 King St.

Memminger & Jervey, Attorneys, Broad St., C. G. Memminger, William Jervey

Memminger, C. G., Attorney, 92 Meeting St., res. 102 Wentworth St.

Menale, John, Boundary St.

Mencengnyer, C. F., North St. Philip St.

Mendenhall, M. T., Ordinary, Fire Proof Building, res. 81 Meeting St.

Menude, Alexander, Cannon St.

Meredith, Richard, Dry Goods, 335 King St.

Meredith, William, Reid St.

Merritt, T. B., 28 Pitt St.

Mertens, J., Grocer, Gadsden's Wharf

Mertens, William, Clerk, 6 Rutledge St.

Messervey, P., Wragg Square

Metz, F., Mary St.

Meyer, A., Clerk, 320 King St.

Meyer, B. H., Grocer, 51 State St.

Meyer, C., Shoemaker, 53 State St.

Meyer, F. C., Clothing, 273 King St.

Meyer, H., Druggist, 369 King St.

Meyer, J. C., Clerk, 320 King St.

Meyer, John D., Grocer, 320 King St.

Meyer, John, Dry Goods, 304 King St.

Meyer, John Jacob, Bootmaker, 38 Queen St.

Meyer, Lewis, Shoe Maker, 57 Wentworth St.

Meyer, M., Storekeeper, 320 King St.

Meyer, Naser, Cooper, Adgar's Wharf, res. 41 King St.

Meyer, O., Shoemaker, 186 Meeting St.

Michel, A. N., Silversmith, 136 Meeting St.

Michel, John, Jr., N. St. Philip St.

Michel, John, Magistrate, East Bay St., res. N. St. Philip St.

Michel, Myddleton, Physician, 74 Queen St.

Michel, R. F., Physician, 74 Queen St.

Michel, William, Physician, 74 Queen St.

Middleton & Co., Factors, Vanderhorst's Wharf, Thomas Middleton, Charles Henry

Middleton, C. H., Physician, 44 South Bay St.

Middleton, H. A., Planter, 44 South Bay St.

Middleton, H., Planter, Boundary St.

Middleton, N. R., Planter, 26 Pitt St.

Middleton, O. H., Planter, 3 New St.

Middleton, R. Izard, Planter

Middleton, T., Factor, Vanderhorst's Wharf, res. 6 Meeting St.

Middleton, William, Planter, 39 Broad St.

Mierhoff, H., Grocer, 50 St. Philip St.

Mignot, T., Mrs., Confectioner, 174 King St.

Mikel, Jane E., Mrs., 17 Meeting St.

Mikel, Joseph, Dry Goods, 145 King St.

Milan, John, Laborer, 4 Clifford St.

Miler, D., Clerk, 309 King St.

Miles, E. R., Teacher, 12 Coming St.

Miles, Henry, Elliott St., Neck

Miles, James W., Rev., 12 Coming St.

Miles, Sarah B., 12 Coming St.

Miles, William P., Professor, Charleston College, 12 Coming St.

Millar, R. S., Baker, 131 Meeting St.

Millen, J. E., 9 Stoll'sAlley

Miller, A. E., Printer, Broad St. res, 43 Tradd St.

Miller, Ann, Miss, 65 Coming St.

Miller, C., Bootmaker, 119 King St.

Miller, E., Engineer, 50 Queen St.

Miller, E., Merchant, 309 King St.

Miller, Francis, Clerk, Vanderhorst St.

Miller, Henry, Cigar Maker, 176 East Bay St.

Miller, J. A., 101 East Bay St.

Miller, J. Claudius, Clerk, King & Hasell Sts., res. 15 College St.

Miller, J. D., Accountant, Commercial Wharf, res. 50 Queen St.

Miller, J. D., Printer, 9 Stoll's Alley

Miller, J. H., Shoe Maker, 56 Anson St.

Miller, Jacob, Rope Maker, Vanderhorst St.

Miller, James, Collector, 9 Laurens St.

Miller, John C., Mary St.

Miller, John, Carter, 28 Laurens St.

Miller, L. A., Sail Maker, 42 State St.

Miller, Louis, Grocer, 3 South Bay St.

Miller, M. A., Miss, Teacher, 36 Chalmers St.

Miller, Samuel D., Rope Maker, Vanderhorst St.

Miller, Samuel S., Printer, East Bay St., res. 7 Wall St.

Miller, William, Officer, Bank of the State of S. C., res. Hudson St.

Milligan, E., Amherst St.

Milliken, E. P., Merchant, 162 Meeting St.

Milliken, J. B., 162 Meeting St.

Milliken, Thomas, Planter, 162 Meeting St.

Milliken, William, Merchant, 155 East Bay St., res. 243 East Bay St.

Millington, R., Seaman, 31 Tradd St.
Mills, Clark, Artist, 9 Atlantic St.
Mills, N. N., 12 Atlantic St.
Mills, O. & Co., Corn Merchants, corner East Bay St. & Commercial Wharf, O. Mills, E. M. Beach
Mills, Otis, Corn Merchant, East Bay St., res. 36 Meeting St.
Milne, Andrew, Planter, 18 Rutledge St.
Milnor, G. H., Auctioneer, Vendue Range
Minnis, Robert, Plumber, 193 East Bay St.
Minturn, J. & Co., Steam Cotton Press, Union Wharf
Mintzing, H. C., Grocer, 159 King St.
Mintzing, J. M., Grocer, 159 King St.
Miot, A., 8 Bull St.
Miot, C. H., 8 Bull St.
Miot, H., Mrs., 124 Church St.
Miscally, Daniel, Carpenter, Marsh St.
Miscally, M., Miss, 6 Orange St.
Miscally, W. J., Engineer, 7 Marsh St.
Misdorff, James, Mariner, 24 Savage St.
Missroon, Henry, Merchant, Adger's Wharf, res. 77 Tradd St.
Missroon, J., 2 East Bay St.
Missroon, W., Clerk, 21 Broad St.
Mitchel, A. D., Mrs., Planter, 98 Wentworth St.
Mitchel, A. R., Cotton Presser, Longitude Lane, res. 15 Meeting St.
Mitchel, C., Mrs., 166 Meeting St.
Mitchel, Charles, Boat Builder, 16 Market St.
Mitchel, Charles T., Merchant, Boyce's Wharf, res. 15 Meeting St.
Mitchel, E., Jr., Accountant, Evening News, res. 58 Coming St.
Mitchel, E., Physician, 11 Smith St.
Mitchel, F. M., Clerk, 98 Wentworth St.
Mitchel, G. B., Teacher of Music, 201 King St.
Mitchel, G. H., Clothing, 270 King St.
Mitchel, H. W., Clerk, 15 Anson St., res. 98 Wentworth St.
Mitchel, J. D., Clerk, 42 East Bay St., res. 100 Wentworth St.
Mitchel, J. S., Physician, Society St., res 148 Meeting St.
Mitchel, Nelson, Attorney, St. Michael's Alley, res. 166 Meeting St.
Mitchel, T. C., Clerk, 58 Coming St.
Mitchel, Theodore, Bricklayer, 8 West St.
Mitchel, William, Millwright, 8 West St.
Mitchell & Mure, Commission Merchants, corner Boyce's Wharf & East Bay St., Charles T. Mitchell, Robert Mure
Mitchell, E. R. & Co., Steam Cotton Press, Longitude Lane, E. R. Mitchell, William Dearing
Mitchell, George H. (see Kent & Mitchell)
Mixer, Daniel, Charleston Hotel
Moeberg, B., Storekeeper, 29 Market St.
Moffett, Andrew, Dry Goods, King St., res. 198 East Bay St.
Moffett, John, Merchant, East Bay St., res. Society St.
Moise, A. H., Ship Carpenter, 24 Mazyck St.

Moise, Aaron, Officer, Bank of South Carolina
Moise, Abraham, Attorney, 3 Courthouse Square, res. 1 College St.
Moise, Abraham, Jr., Assistant Cashier, Bank of Charleston, res. 43 Beaufain St.
Moise, H. L., Mrs, Teacher, 6 Bull St.
Moise, Isaac, Merchant, 6 Bull St.
Moise, P. A., Clerk, Hayne St., res. 24 Beaufain St.
Moise, T. J., Clerk, East Bay St. res. 24 Beaufain St.
Moland, M., Drayman, 9 Linguard St.
Molen, D., Coach Painter, 30 Wentworth St.
Moncreif, J., Cooper, 41 Queen St.
Monefeldt, W. S., Dentist, 243 King St.
Monk, J. P., Tavern Keeper, 38 Elliott St.
Monpoey, Honore, Planter, 40 Bull St.
Montandon, Ellen, 144 East Bay St.
Montgomery, A. W., Tailor, 35 Queen St.
Montgomery, Andrew, Watch Maker, 27 George St.
Montgomery, Charles, 27 George St.
Montgomery, R. C., Fruiterer, 17 Market St.
Montgomery, W. (see Horsey, Ives & Co.)
Mood, E. M., Pump Maker, Wentworth St., res. 26 Coming St.
Mood, James R., Physician, George St., res. 293 King St.
Mood, John, Carpenter, Cannon St.
Mood, John, Jeweller, 293 King St.
Mood, William G., Merchant, 32 East Bay St., res. 75 Beaufain St.
Moody, G. W., Clerk, 155 East Bay St.
Moody, J. G., Officer, Railroad Bank
Moody, W. M., Jr., Bookkeeper, Charleston Hotel
Moore, B. F., Patent Maker, Railroad Depot, res. 3 Gadsden St.
Moore, -----, Carpenter, 34 Queen St.
Moore, D. (see Cameron, G. & H. Co)
Moore, Frances, Mrs., 32 Savage St.
Moore, G. A., Printer, Courier Office, res. 56 King St.
Moore, G. R., 14 Burns Lane
Moore, James, Clerk, 30 Pinckney St.
Moore, -----, Misses, 32 Savage St.
Moore, -----, Seamstress, 85 East Bay St.
Moore, W. B., Dry Goods, 68 Market St.
Moorehead, James, Grocer, 26 Archdale St.
Morall, John F., Clerk, 2 Beaufain St.
Moran, -----, Dr., Cannon St.
Morang, Mary, Miss, 68 King St.
Mordecai, B., Broker, State St., res. 49 Wentworth St.
Mordecai, M. C., Merchant, East Bay St., res. 4 Meeting St.
Mordecai, T. W., Broker, 4 State St.
Moreland, Andrew, Lumber Merchant, 7 South Bay St.
Morello, J. B., Fruiterer, 129 King St.
Morello, James, Fruiterer, 129 King St.
Morello, N., Fruiterer, 129 King St.
Morgan, Benjamin, Customs Officer, 4 Price's Alley
Morgan, Benjamin, Mariner, 16 Middle St.
Morgan, J. B., Mariner, 11 Middle St.
Morris, Dominic, Tinner, 59 Broad St.
Morris, Henry, Officer, Planters & Mechanics Bank, Charlotte St.

Morris, John, Cooper, Gadsden's Wharf, res. 4 Inspection St.
Morris, Joseph C., 290 King St.
Morris, M. J., Mrs., Council St.
Morris, Patrick, Laborer, 47 State St.
Morris, William, Cooper, Bennett's Mill, res. 5 Vernon St.
Morris, William, Cooper, Bennett's Mills, res. 4 Inspection St.
Morris, William, Laborer, 47 State St.
Morrisson, Elizabeth, Mrs., 38 South Bay St.
Morrisson, S., 22 Broad St.
Morrisson, Thomas, 120 Church St.
Mortimer, Jackson, Washington St.
Mortimer, S. H., Secretary, Charleston Insurance & Trust Co., 8 Broad St., res. Drake St.
Mortimer, Thomas H., Washington St.
Morton, Courtney & Co., Hardware, 31 Hayne St., W. R. Morton, W. C. Courtney, G. B. Tennent
Moses, -----, Amherst St.
Moses, Isaiah, 33 St. Philip St.
Moses, L., 6 Horlbeck Alley
Moses, L. J., Clerk, Chapel St.
Moses, M. J., 3 Princess St.
Moses, Reuben, 104 Meeting St.
Moses, Solomon, Deputy Sheriff, 47 Wentworth St.
Mosimann, W. J., Printer, 8 Pinckney St.
Motet, Edward, Merchant, Adger's Wharf, res. 13 Archdale St.
Motta, S. M., Mrs., Dry Goods, 101 King St.
Motte, H. E., Miss, 8 Savage St.
Motte, J. Ward, Lumber Merchant, 88 Beaufain St.
Mottet, E. (see Roger, T. J. & Co.)
Moultrie, James, Physician, 14 Montague St.
Mousseau, Adolphus, Carpenter, Mary St.
Mousseau, L., Mrs., 17 Wall St.
Mouzon, Charles, 4 St. Philip St.
Mouzon, L. H., Collector, 103 Church St.
Mowry & Son, Commission Merchants, 68 East Bay St., S. Mowry, Jr., Lewis D. Mowry
Mowry, E. C., Attorney, 175 Meeting St.
Mowry, Edward, Merchant, Boyce & Co. Wharf
Mowry, Lewis, Merchant, East Bay St., res. 7 Hasell St.
Mowry, S., Jr., Merchant, East Bay St., res. 175 Meeting St.
Muckenfuss, B. S. D., Lumber Merchant, Beaufain St., res. President St.
Muckenfuss, C., Miss, 1 Montague St.
Muckenfuss, H. W., Lumber Merchant, Beaufain St., res. 86 Wentworth St.
Muckenfuss, Henry, Mason, 86 Wentworth St.
Mudge, S., Merchant, 101 Meeting St.
Muir, Asa J., Printer, 6 Hard Alley
Muir, -----, Mrs., Boarders, 24 Broad St.
Mullan, Sarah, Miss, 52 King St.
Muller, F. M., Mrs., 83 Tradd St.
Muller, H., Grocer, 7 Pinckney St.
Muller, N., Rev. Pastor, German Church, res. 57 King St.
Muller, T. D., Physician, 83 Tradd St.
Mullings, D., Pilot, 34 Church St.

Mullings, H. A., Pilot, 101 East Bay St.
Mullings, J., Jr., Pilot, 34 Church St.
Mullings, J., Pilot, 34 Church St.
Mullings, W., Pilot, 34 Church St.
Mullins, Charles, 20 Pinckney St.
Mulry, William, 17 Wall St.
Mulvanie, -----, Mariner, 2 Stoll's Alley
Munro, Brewster & Dunkin, Attorney, Meeting St., R. Munro, C. R. Brewster, A. H. Dunkin
Munson, Albert, Dealer in Straw Goods, 124 Meeting St.
Murcreef, A. S., Bricklayer, 71 Queen St.
Murden, -----, Misses, Teachers, 34 Society St.
Mure, Robert, Merchant, Boyce's Wharf, res. 86 Church St.
Murphy, Francis, 181 East Bay St.
Murphy, J., Carpenter, 41 Queen St.
Murphy, James, Porter, 56 State St.
Murphy, Joseph, 96 Meeting St.
Murphy, Peter, Drayman, 53 Tradd St.
Murphy, T., Laborer, 9 Tradd St.
Murray, Charles, 53 King St.
Murray, James, Bootmaker, 41 King St.
Murray, James L., 18 South Bay St.
Murray, James, Plasterer, 70 Market St.
Murray, Joseph, Teacher, 103 Queen St.
Murray, L. M., Seaman, 18 South Bay St.
Murray, P. & W., Hatstore, 13 Broad St.
Murray, Patrick, Laborer, 13 Pitt St.
Murray, W. C., Merchant, 26 East Bay St., res. 2 South Bay St.
Murrell, J., 23 Middle St.
Murrell, James H., Bookkeeper, Courier Office, res. 20 Savage St.
Murthy, James, Laborer, 59 Beaufain St.
Musso, -----, Fruiterer, 35 Market St.
Mustard, D., Machinist, Hasell St., 6 Laurens St.
Myddleton, F., Pilot, 16 Tradd St.
Myer, A., Collector, 90 Meeting St.
Myer, C., Boundary St.
Myer, H., Storekeeper, 320 King St.
Myer, Henry, Clerk, 6 Archdale St.
Myer, P. F., Clerk, 224 King St.
Myerhoff, B., Boundary St.
Myers, C., Miller, N. King St.
Myers, J., Miller, Boundary St.
Myers, James, Boiler Maker, 12 Boundary St.
Myers, John, Coach Maker, 4 Vernon St.
Myers, Joseph, Cigar Maker, 101 King St.
Myers, M., Aiken's Range
Myers, M. D., Grocer, 64 Meeting St.
Myers, -----, Meeting & Reid Sts.
Myles, J., Vanderhorst St.
Nabb, John, Assistant Harbor Master, 72 Church St.
Nachmann, A., Iron Dealer, 39 Beaufain St.
Nagle, P., N. St. Philip St.
Nance, F., Bookkeeper, 12 Wentworth St.
Napp, -----, Clerk, 104 Church St.
Naser, Frederick, 16 Coming St.
Nash, John, Baker, 60 King St.
Nash, William, Baker, 183 East Bay St.

Nathan, Asher, Cabinet Maker, 253 King St., res. 30 St. Philip St.

Nathan, Moses, Coach Maker, Meeting & Wentworth Sts., res. 30 St. Philip St.

Nathans, Levy, N. King St.

Nathans, N., N. King St.

Nayel, Vincent, Baker, 97 King St.

Naylor, John, Fisherman, 30 King St.

Naylor, William, Merchant, 40 East Bay St., res. 46 Beaufain St.

Neal, Philip, 89 Church St.

Neal, W., Carpenter, 96 Meeting St.

Neckles, ----, Mrs., 132 Tradd St.

Neibuhr, John P., Druggist, 70 Broad St., res. 17 Friend St.

Nelson, A., Mrs., 166 Meeting St.

Nelson, F., Clerk, 38 Coming St.

Nelson, Isaac, Planter, 38 Coming St.

Nelson, S. A., Clerk, 101 Meeting St.

Nelson, William, 20 Pinckney St.

Nelson, William, Tavern Keeper, 19 Berresford St.

Nesbit, Douglas, Accountant, 3 Logan St.

Neuffer, -----, Grain Merchant, East Bay St., res. 5 Liberty St.

Neufville, B. S., Accountant, 52 Anson St.

Neufville, -----, Mrs., 30 Tradd St.

Neuman, Philip, Lumber Merchant, 22 Montague St.

Newbold & Locke, Grocers, 57 East Bay St., S. Newbold, B. C. Locke

Newbold, Samuel, Grocer, 65 East Bay St.

Newman, Nick, Line St.

Newton, H., Cannon St.

Newton, William, Cannon St.

Newton, William, Jr., Cannon St.

Neyle, Mary J., Mrs., 3 Legare St.

Nherden, C., Grocer, 2 Laurens St.

Nicholson, J., Clerk, 44 Broad St.

Nickerson, T. S., Clerk, Charleston Hotel

Nicklin, J., Painter, 102 Church St.

Nicola, A., Shoemaker, 69 Wentworth St.

Nicols & Gibbs, Shipping Merchants, Boyce & Co. Wharf, James C. Nicols, W. G. Gibbs

Ninemeister, E., Clerk, 309 King St.

Ninitz, A., Grocer, 65 East Bay St.

Nixon, J. B., Printer, Broad St., res. 42 Wentworth St.

Nolan, Thomas, 48 Market St.

Norman, G. A., 121 Meeting St.

Norris, James C., Master, Work House, res. 11 Lynch St.

Norris, Thomas, 11 Lynch St.

North, E., Miss, 107 Tradd St.

North, Edward, Physician, 29 Meeting St., res. 79 Meeting St.

North, K., Shoemaker, 69 Wentworth St.

Northrop, C. B., Attorney, Broad St., res. 50 King St.

Norton, Jabez, Officer, Bank of Charleston, res. 115 Queen St.

Norwood, Thomas, Pinckney St., Cannonborough

Nowell, John, 54 Broad St.

Nowell, John L., Planter, N. Bay St.

Oakes, Z. B., Broker, 7 State St., res. 72 Queen St.

Oakley, R. S., Druggist, 150 King St.

Oates, E., Clerk, 234 King St.

Oates, George, Bookseller, 234 King St.

Oates, James, Carpenter, Liberty St., res. 41 Queen St.

Oberhausser, John, Druggist, 128 Church St.

Obreclt, Frances, Midwife, 29 Anson St.

Obreclt, John, Shoemaker, 29 Anson St.

Odena, J. E., Saddler, 302 King St.

Odena, P., Saddler, 302 King St.

Oeland, D., 6 Archdale St.

Oelrich, Charles, Piano Maker, 201 King St., res. 78 Wentworth St.

Oetjen, C., Miller, Boundary St.

Oetjen, Henry, Miller, Coming & Radcliffe Sts.

Oetjen, J. D., Baker, 17 Tradd St.

Offaman, -----, 2 Glebe St.

Ogeman, John, Clerk, 87 Broad St.

Ogier, E., Miss, 12 Pinckney St.

Ogier, T. O., Physician, 37 East Bay St., res. 33 East Bay St.

Ogilvie, J. T., Clerk, 15 Broad St., res 21 Broad St.

Ogilvie, Matthew, Hardware, 21 Broad St., res. 5 Logan St.

Ohlrogge, P., N. King St.

Olandt, John, 4 Market St.

Oldenburg, Henry, Grocer, 47 King St.

Oldenbuttel, Henry, Grocer, 67 Tradd St.

Oldenbuttel, W., Tailor, 333 King St.

Oldendorff & Briggman, Dry Goods, 26 Anson St., Frederick Oldendorff, William Briggman

Oldendorff, F., Grocer, 26 Anson St.

Olfers, J. B., Porter, 146 East Bay St.

Oliphant, E., 3 George St.

Oliver, B., Mrs., Vender of Milk, 23 King St.

Oliver, G., Mariner, 22 Boundary St.

Oliver, Joseph H., Carver & Gilder, 23 King St.

Olten, C., Grocer, 18 Tradd St.

Oneale, James, Carpenter, 20 Magazine St.

Oneale, Patrick, Cannon St.

Oppenheim, H. W., King & Hudson Sts.

Oppenheim, J. H. & Brother, Wholesale Grocers, 100 East Bay St., J. H. Oppenheim, Samuel H. Oppenheim

Oppenheim, J. H., Merchant, 102 East Bay St., res. N. Meeting St.

Oppenheim, Samuel, King & Hudson Sts.

Osborn, George, Seaman, 113 East Bay St.

Osgood, G. E., Engineer, 68 State St.

Ostendorff, J. H., Grocer, 87 East Bay St.

Ostendorff, J. M., Grocer, 95 East Bay St.

Osterholtz, D., Thomas St.

Otten, D., Clerk, 1 Coming St.

Otten, J., Grocer, 63 Market St.

Ottolengui, A., 1 Pinckney St.

Ottolengui, J., Auctioneer, 28 Vendue Range, res. 1 Pinckney St.

Outon, J., Mrs., Milk Vender, 19 Back Alley

Owens, Alexander, Cannon St.

Owens, Samuel, Laborer, 56 Beaufain St.

Owens, Stephen, Clerk, Hayne St., res. 48 Beaufain St.

Owens, William, Clerk, 349 King St.

Oxlade, Thomas, Painter, 2 Queen St.
Oxlade, Thomas, Watch Maker, Broad St., res. 16
  Middle St.
O'Bannan, Augustus, 15 Montague St.
O'Brien, Patrick, Carpenter, 69 State St.
O'Brien, Peter, Clerk, 222 King St., res. 59 King St.
O'Brien, S., Carpenter, 44 Queen St.
O'Brien, Thomas, Stable Keeper, 28 Chalmers St.
O'Callahan, D., 116 Church St.
O'Connell, L., 80 Broad St.
O'Donnell, Patrick, Mason, 5½ King St.
O'Dott, Vincent, 36 Queen St.
O'Ferrel, John, 9 Queen St.
O'Gorman, Peter, 111 Church St.
O'Hanlon, Eliza, Mrs., Seamstress, 2 Archdale St.
O'Hara, Daniel, Mariner, 11 Anson St.
O'Hara, H., Laborer, 24 Tradd St.
O'Hara, John, 36 Queen St.
O'Hara, John, Physician, 43 East Bay St.
O'Hara, M., Mrs., 18 Montague St.
O'Hear, James F., Ordinary's Office, Fire Proof Building
O'Hear, James, Factor, Southern Wharf, res. Vanderhorst
  St.
O'Leary, Daniel, Boat Builder, 14 Vernon St.
O'Neill, B., Merchant, 177 East Bay St.
O'Neill, C., Printer, 104 Meeting St.
O'Neill, H., Saddler, 41 Queen St.
O'Neill, J. F., Student, 80 Broad St.
O'Neill, James, Shoemaker, 98 Meeting St.
O'Neill, John F., Grocer, East Bay & Queen Sts., res. 34
  Chalmers St.
O'Neill, P., Rev., St. Patrick's Church, res. 377 King St.
O'Neill, R., Shoemaker, 98 Meeting St.
O'Reilly, James, Printer, 225 East Bay St.
O'Reilly, Patrick, 4 Wentworth St.
O'Sullivan, James, Storekeeper, 181 East Bay St.
O'Sullivan, T. F., Printer, 21 Wall St.
O'Weir, J. D., Mrs., Boarders, 102 Church St.
Pacault, -----, Cabinet Maker, 63 Church St.
Paine, James, Capt., Police, res. 2 Mazyck St.
Paine, N. R., Officer, Union Bank, res. 8 Green St.
Palacei, Olivia, Mrs., 26 Laurens St.
Palmeltis, J., Hanover St.
Palmer, Floyd, Clerk, 3 Tradd St.
Palmer, J., Customs Officer, 22 Church St.
Palmer, J. W., Merchant, 104 Meeting St.
Palmer, Richard, 26 Market St.
Palmer, W. S., Bricklayer, 60 Meeting St.
Palmer, W. S., Carpenter, 104 Meeting St.
Panknin, Charles, Druggist, 123 Meeting St.
Pansin, E., Dry Goods, 153 King St.
Pardon, A., Morris St.
Parisot, -----, Mrs., 7 Water St.
Parker, Ann G., Milliner, 200 King St.
Parker, B. J., Clerk, Railroad Depot, res. 6 George St.
Parker, C. R., Surveyor, 1 Friend St.
Parker, Charles, City Surveyor, 14 Lamboll St.
Parker, G., Mrs., 1 Short St.
Parker, J. S., Collector, 13 Back Alley
Parker, -----, Miss, Seamstress, 11 Clifford St.

Parker, P., Chapel St.
Parker, Robert, Charlotte St.
Parker, S. D., Clerk, Railroad Depot, res. 6 George St.
Parker, Thomas, Carpenter, 75 Church St.
Parker, Thomas E., Merchant, 14 Lamboll St.
Parker, W. McKensie, Planter, 117 Broad St.
Parker, W. S., Carpenter, 60 Meeting St.
Parker, William R., N. Meeting St.
Parsell, W. N., Furniture Store, 314 King St.
Passailaigue, E., N. St. Philip St.
Passailaigue, U., St. Philip St.
Patrick, J. B., Dentist, 231 King St.
Patrick, Julia, Mrs., Chapel St.
Patrick, Philip, Accountant, 107 Church St.
Pattani, Joseph, Fruiterer, 17 Market St.
Patterson & Stock, Commission Merchants, North
  Atlantic Wharf, J. L. Patterson, J. Y. Stock
Patterson, G. L., N. St. Philip St.
Patterson, James, Merchant, Atlantic Wharf, res. 54
  Broad St.
Patterson, John, Bootmaker, 29 Broad St.
Patterson, S. H., Inspector of Boilers, 9 Wentworth St.
Patterson, W. P., Carpenter, 31 Wentworth St.
Patterson, William, Bookkeeper, Church St.
Patterson, William, Painter, 60 Queen St.
Patton, James, Gilder, 4 Beaufain St.
Patton, William, Merchant, Patton's Wharf, res. 16
  Laurens St.
Paty, James, Mariner, 6 Unity Alley
Paul & Brown, Grocers, corner Broad & Church Sts.,
  Dunbar Paul, George Brown
Paul, Dunbar, Grocer, 47 Broad St., res. 20 New St.
Paul, Joseph, Cannon St.
Pauls, Frederick, Grocer, 15 King St.
Pauls, H., Grocer, 44 King St.
Paxton, W. Y. & Co., Editors, Evening News, W. Y.
  Paxton, B. G. Pringle
Paxton, W. Y., Editor, Evening News, 56 Wentworth St.
Payne, E. T., Radcliffe St.
Payne, J. S., Planter, 19 Friend St.
Payne, R. K., Surveyor, Hampstead St.
Payne, S., Mrs., 38 Wentworth St.
Payne, T., Capt., U. S. Navy, Radcliffe St.
Peah, H., Engineer, Elliott St.
Pease, H. W., Clerk, 9 Queen St
Pease, J. F., Bar Keeper, 195 King St.
Pecare, Myer, Clerk, 334 King St.
Peck, Edward, Painter, 41 Queen St.
Peckover, William, Tavern Keeper, 5 Market St.
Pelerine, A., Clerk, 294 King St.
Pelerine, S., Mrs., Mantuamaker, 294 King St.
Pelot, W. M., Teacher, N. Meeting St.
Pelzer, A. P., Physician, N. Boundary St.
Pelzer, F., Merchant, N. King St., res. President St.
Pelzer, George S., Physician, Chapel St.
Pemberton, E., Mrs., 38 Archdale St.
Pendarvis, John, N. Coming St.
Pendergrast, Edward, Clerk, 52 King St
Pennal, J. K., Grocer, 359 King St.
Penniman, James, Clerk, 297 King St.

Pennington, S. M., Mrs., 34 Hasell St.
Pepper, A. M., Planter, N. King St.
Pepper, L. L., N. Coming St.
Perey, Ann, Mrs., 8 Mazyck St.
Perkins, Caroline, 20 Berresford St.
Perkinson, -----, Queen St.
Peronneau & Hayne, Attorneys, Law Range, H. W.
Peronneau, I. W. Hayne, W. H. Peronneau
Peronneau, H. W., Attorney, Broad St., res. 93 Tradd St.
Peronneau, -----, Misses, 40 South Bay St.
Peronneau, W. H., Attorney, Broad St., res. 2 Legare St.
Perry, A. S., Clerk,193 East Bay St.
Perry, John, Cannon St.
Perry, Julia, Mrs., Milliner, 2 St. Philip St.
Perry, M. A., Mrs., Teacher, 48 Bull St.
Perry, Mary, Mrs., 366 King St.
Perry, William, Officer, Customs, 45 Market St.
Pesson, M. L., Mrs., Hair Braider, 57 Queen St.
Pestla, David, Tailor, 24 Queen St.
Pete, A., Storekeeper, 7 Market St.
Peterman, D., 16 Queen St.
Peterman, D., Boundary St.
Peterman, Henry, Clerk, 4 Inspection St.
Peters, H., Grocer, 28 Smith St.
Peters, James, Officer, Railroad Bank, 59 Tradd St.
Peters, John, Henrietta St.
Peterson, C., Seaman, Lightwood's Alley
Peterson, John, 2 Williams' Wharf
Petigru & Lesesne, Attorneys, St. Michael's Alley, J. L.
Petigru, H. D. Lesesne
Petigru, Daniel, Attorney, St. Michael's Alley, res. 103
Broad St.
Petigru, James L., Attorney, St. Michael's Alley, res. 103
Broad St.
Petigru, Thomas, Capt., U.S. Navy, 30 Bull St.
Petit, Anna, Mrs., Seamstress, 57 Church St.
Petit, Charles, N. Meeting St.
Petit, E., Confectioner, 194 King St.
Petit, Julius, Tinner, 298 East Bay St.
Petit, N. F., Tinner, 62 Market St.
Petsch, Alexander, Engineer, Factory, res. Elizabeth St.
Petsch, Julius, Engineer, 2 Vernon St.
Petsch, W., Engineer, Elliott St.
Pety, James, Seaman, 6 Longitude Lane
Peurifoy, A., Druggist, 367 King St.
Pfaud, Augustus, Clerk, 60 King St.
Pflammer, George, 13 Queen St.
Phelps, F. L., Bookkeeper, 3 Stoll's Alley
Phillips, Charlotte, Mrs., Milk Vender, 27 King St.
Phillips, Edward, Rev., 44 Beaufain St.
Phillips, John, Attorney, Church St., res. 158 Meeting St.
Phillips, L., 310 King St.
Phillips, -----, Mrs., Seamstress, 85 East Bay St.
Phillips, Otis, Corn Merchant, East Bay & Market Sts.,
res. 16 New St.
Phillips, S. L., 310 King St.
Phillips, St. John, Physician, 44 Beaufain St.
Phin, -----, 58 Meeting St.
Phin, A. C., Farmer, 7 Liberty St.
Phinigan, George, Mariner, 12 Market St.

Phynney, J. J., Printer, 69 Coming St.
Picanet, -----, Mrs., 7 State St.
Pierce, George, Carpenter, 15 Smith St.
Pierce, Phineas, Keeper, Ice House, Meeting St., res. 110
Meeting St.
Pierce, Richard, Blacksmith, 15 Smith St.
Piercon, -----, Mrs., 30 Tradd St.
Pierson, Ann, Mrs., 20 Bull St.
Pierson, James W., Clothing, 199 King St.
Pinckney, Charles, Customs Officer, res. 3 St. Philip St.
Pinckney, H. L., Jr., Teacher, High School, Warren St.
Pinckney, H. L., Tax Collector, Fire Proof Building, res.
3 St. Philip St.
Pinckney, H., Miss, 199 East Bay St.
Pinckney, Hopson, Officer, State Bank, res. 76 Queen St.
Pinckney, L., Mrs., Planter, 31 Pitt St.
Pinckney, Mary Jane, Miss, 28 King St.
Pinckney, R. Q., Civil Engineer, 34 Meeting St.
Pinckney, Roger, Jr., 28 King St.
Pinckney, Roger, Sr., 28 King St.
Pinckney, Thomas, Mrs., 74 Broad St.
Pink, -----, Mrs., 132 King St.
Plane, William A., Customs Officer, res. 35 East Bay St.
Platt, -----, Mrs., 44 Tradd St.
Plein, H., Storekeeper, 80 Beaufain St.
Ploger, F. H., Bootmaker, 119 King St.
Plumeau, Margaret, Mrs., 86 King St.
Poincignon, A., 11 Queen St.
Poincignon, E., Tinner, 11 Queen St.
Polack, M., N. King St.
Polant, O., Bar Keeper, 15 Vendue Range
Police, Francis, 78 Church St.
Polock, J. B., Plasterer, 32 St. Philip St.
Poole, J., Clerk, 234 King St.
Pooser, M. H., Officer, Neck Police, Amherst St.
Pope, J. J., Attorney, Broad St., res. 8 Liberty St.
Poppenheim, J. F., Planter, Washington St.
Porcher, C., Miss, 103 Wentworth St.
Porcher, C., Mrs., Planter, 199 East Bay St.
Porcher, E. P., Physician, 30 Wentworth St.
Porcher, F. A., Professor, Charleston College, res. 79
Meeting St.
Porcher, F. J., Factor, Adger's Wharf, res. 119 Church
St.
Porcher, F. Y., Physician, 119 Church St.
Porcher, -----, Misses, 34 South Bay St.
Porcher, P. J., Broker, 25 Broad St., res. 28 South Bay
St.
Porcher, Peter, Physician, 49 Church St.
Porter, A. A., Rev., Pastor, Third Presbyterian Church,
res. 20 Montague St.
Porter, J. A., Rev., Pastor, Bethel Church, Boundary St.
Porter, N. M., Grocer, 222 King St. res. 10 Montague St.
Porter, R. H., Mariner, 6 Longitude Lane
Porter, W. D., City Attorney, Broad St., res. 1 Pitt St.
Porter, William L., 10 Montague St.
Post, Reuben, Rev., Pastor, Circular Church, 22 Meeting
St.
Powell, J., Piano Tuner, 242 King St.
Powell, J. V., Carpenter, 102 Church St.

Powell, J. V., Mrs., Teacher, 102 Church St.
Poyas, J., Ship Carpenter, 12 Wentworth St.
Poyas, James, Planter, Aiken's Range
Poyas, William, 29 Mazyck St.
Poznanski, G., Rev. Rabbi, Synagogue, res. 93 Broad St.
Pratt, Elizabeth, Mrs., 19 Laurens St.
Pratt, G. L., Engineer, 15 Anson St., res. 225 East Bay St.
Pregnall, Henry, Carpenter, 16 Rutledge St.
Prentiss, M., 10 Tradd St.
Pressly, B. C., Attorney, Church St., res. 11 George St.
Pressly, M. J., Miss, 34 George St.
Preston, James, Merchant, East Bay St., res. 66 Queen St.
Preston, John, Grocer, 97 Church St.
Prevost, Joseph, Wharf Owner, Accommodation Wharf, res. 12 Hasell St.
Price, Alfred, Hardware Merchant, 12 Hayne St., res. 59 Meeting St.
Price, Mary, Planter, 59 Coming St.
Price, T. P., Mrs., 59 Meeting St.
Prigge, C., Grocer, Elizabeth St.
Prince, E. L., N. Meeting St.
Prince, Edward, Clerk, 108 King St.
Prince, G., Druggist, 330 King St.
Prince, H., Fisherman, 36 Market St.
Prince, H., Meeting St.
Prince, Sarah, Mrs., 108 King St.
Prince, Sarah, Mrs., Dry Goods, 244 East Bay St.
Prince, William, 108 King St.
Pringle, B. G., Editor, Evening News, res. 6 Montague St.
Pringle, E. J., Attorney, Church & Broad Sts., res. 9 King St.
Pringle, E. P., Miss, 160 Meeting St.
Pringle, H., Boundary St.
Pringle, J. St. J., Thomas St.
Pringle, James R., Merchant, Adger's Wharf, res. 9 Legare St.
Pringle, John J., U. S. Navy, 9 King St.
Pringle, Motte A., Clerk, Adger's Wharf, res. 9 King St.
Pringle, R. A., Shoe Merchant 30 East Bay St., res. 6 Montague St.
Pringle, S. M., Mrs., 6 Montague St.
Pringle, W. A. & E. J., Attorneys, Broad & Church Sts.
Pringle, W. Alston, Attorney, Church & Broad Sts., res. Meeting St.
Pringle, W. B., Planter, 9 King St.
Prioleau, Martha, Miss, 164 Meeting St.
Prioleau, P. G., Mrs., Planter, 164 Meeting St.
Prioleau, T. B., Jr., Physician, Washington St.
Prioleau, Thomas G., Physician, Washington St.
Prior, John, Porter, 42 Market St.
Prior, Seth T., Clerk, 165 Meeting St., res. 13 Wall St.
Pritchard, C. C., Physician, 150 East Bay St.
Pritchard, C. H., Rev., Pastor, Trinity Church, Pinckney St.
Pritchard, E. E., Clerk, 217 East Bay St.
Pritchard, E., Mrs., 34 Wentworth St.
Pritchard, Paul, Shipwright, 1 Gibbes St.
Proctor, Mary S., Mrs., 14 South Bay St.

Proctor, William, Accountant, East Bay St. res. 25 Wentworth St.
Proughton, -----, Seaman, 2 Stoll's Alley
Pundt, John, Clerk, 40 Anson St.
Purse, Benjamin, Cooper, Lucas' Mill, 29 Boundary St.
Purse, James S., Upholsterer, 267 King St.
Purse, Robert S., Upholsterer, 9 Pinckney St.
Pyatt, John F., Planter, Meeting & Charlotte Sts.
Pyatt, Joseph, Planter, Meeting & Charlotte Sts.
Pyatt, M. H., Mrs., Planter, Meeting & Charlotte Sts.
Quackenbush, P. L., Grocer, 116 Church St.
Quail, John, Clerk, 4 Clifford St.
Quash, C., Miss, 4 College St.
Quash, H. H., Mrs., 2 College St.
Quigley, Charles, Bootmaker, 295 King St.
Quigley, E., Rev. 80 Broad St.
Quigley, Thomas, Student, 80 Broad St.
Quin, Eliza, Mrs., Seamstress, 103 King St.
Quin, Michael, Bricklayer, 20 Tradd St.
Quin, Patrick, Laborer, 13 St. Philip St.
Quintan, John, Merchant, 25 King St.
Quintin, Susan, Mrs., Teacher, 71 Tradd St.
Raad, Jane, Mrs., Boarders, 54 Market St.
Rabb, Jacob, Pump Maker, 8 Market St., res. 12 Society St.
Rabuski, T., Portrait Painter, 64 Market St.
Radcliffe, John T., Scavenger, 7 College St.
Radcliffe, Maria, Mrs., Nurse, 7 College St.
Rain, -----, Mrs., Seamstress, 26 State St.
Ralls, F., Farrier, 36 Pinckney St.
Rambert, J., Carpenter, 34 Queen St.
Ramsden, John, Mariner, 27 King St.
Ramsey, E., Mrs., 3 Wall St.
Ramsey, James, Physician, Coming St., res. 3 Wall St.
Ramsey, -----, Misses, Broad St.
Ramsey, W. F., Physician, East Bay St., res. 10 New St.
Randles, Thomas, Storekeeper, 20 Market St.
Ranken, J., Tavern Keeper, 14 Elliott St.
Rantin, A., Clerk, Bennett's Mill, res. 18 Society St.
Rantin, J. M., Druggist, N. King St.
Rasch, B., Grocer, 85 Queen St.
Raveneau, H., Clerk, 139 Beaufain St.
Ravenel, A. F., Merchant, 2 East Bay St.
Ravenel, Brother & Co., Merchants, 16 East Bay St., John Ravenel, William Ravenel, A. F. Ravenel
Ravenel, C., Mrs., 56 Broad St.
Ravenel, Daniel, President, Planters & Mechanics Bank, res. 23 East Bay St.
Ravenel, F. G., Merchant 2 East Bay St.
Ravenel, Henry, President, Union Bank, res. 114 Tradd St.
Ravenel, James, Factor, 23 East Bay St.
Ravenel, John, Merchant, East Bay St., res. 2 East Bay St.
Ravenel, St. Julien, Physician, 79 Church, res. 2 East Bay St.
Ravenel, Susan W., Mrs., 65 Meeting St.
Ravenel, William, Merchant, East Bay St., res. 9 East Bay St.
Ravina, J. D., Professor of Languages, 51 Beaufain St.

Raworth, E. F., Engineer, Railroad, res. Mary St.
Raworth, H. B., Engineer, Railroad, res. 12 Liberty St.
Raymond, H. H., Attorney, 2 Water St.
Rayne, Paul, Dry Goods, 162 King St.
Raze, A. P., Saddler, 41 Queen St.
Read, J. Harleston, Planter, 4 Rutledge St.
Read, James W., Planter, 4 Rutledge St.
Rebb, Lewis
Rebman, C., Bootmaker, 158 King St.
Rebman, J., Bootmaker, 158 King St.
Rechtglen, H., Tailor, 25 Tradd St.
Redfern, Edward, Harness Maker, 125 Church St.
Redfern, John, 45 St. Philip St.
Redmond, Thomas (see Green & Redmond)
Redmond, W. S., Merchant, Commercial Wharf, res. 77
   Meeting St.
Reed, Asa, 360 King St.
Reed, H., Charlotte St.
Reed, Henry, Tavern Keeper, 28 Elliott St.
Reed, J. P., Dry Goods, N. King St.
Reeder, M. B., Merchant, 86 Wentworth St.
Reeder, Oswell, Merchant, N. King St.
Reedy, Mary, Mrs., Boarders, 99 Queen St.
Reeves, M. L., Professor of Music, N. King St.
Reeves, Patrick, 32 Queen St.
Reicke, George, Grocer, 348 King St.
Reicke, Gerd, Grocer, 195 East Bay St.
Reid, A., Accountant, 72 East Bay St., res 113 King St.
Reid, George B., Cashier, Bank of South Carolina, 18
   New St.
Reid, James, Accountant, 19 Archdale St.
Reihnken, George, Tailor, 133 King St.
Reiley, William, Bookmaker, 1 Clifford St.
Reine, H., Drake St.
Rene, A. P., Bookkeeper, 18 Queen St.
Rene, B., Carpenter, N. Coming St.
Renncker, John H., Grocer, 134 King St.
Renner, C., Clerk, 2 Middle St.
Rentz, M., Mrs., Seamstress, John St.
Requar, Joseph, Painter, 58 State St.
Reynolds, A., Mrs., 51 Anson St.
Reynolds, G. N., Jr., Coach Maker, 85 Meeting St., res.
   Hasell St.
Reynolds, George N., Coach Maker, 85 Meeting St.
Reynolds, J. A., Right Rev., Bishop, Roman Catholic
   Church, 80 Broad St.
Reynolds, R. F., Coach Maker, 85 Meeting St.
Reynolds, T. Caute, 85 Meeting St.
Rhett, B. S., Merchant, East Bay St., res. Pinckney St.,
   Cannonborough
Rhett, Benjamin, Attorney, America St.
Rhett, Charles, Attorney, America St.
Rhett, J. S. & Son, Attorneys, Broad St.
Rhett, James S., Attorney, America St.
Rhett, W., Attorney, America St.
Rians, Peter, Sexton, Scotch Church, res. 2 Whim's
   Court
Ricardo, John, Clerk, 23 State St.
Ricardo, Joseph, Tavern Keeper, 115 East Bay St.
Ricards, C. W., Clerk, 33 Boundary St.

Rice, Alexander G., Attorney, 43 East Bay St.
Rice, F., Blacksmith, 49 State St.
Rice, H. S., Shipping Officer, 85 East Bay St., res.
   Longitude Lane
Rice, J. W., Clerk, 16 Hasell St.
Rice, William, Hon., Recorder, City Court, 9 Lamboll St.
Rich, John, Wheelwright, N. King St.
Richards, F., Merchant Tailor, 32 Broad St., res. 112
   Wentworth St.
Richards, G. R., Ship Blacksmith, 251 East Bay St.
Richards, J. W., Artist, 11 Wall St.
Richards, -----, Mason, 102 Church St.
Richardson, C. Y., Bell Hanger, 89 Meeting St.
Richardson, F. D., Attorney, 20 Broad St., res. 53
   Wentworth St.
Richardson, J. C. E., Bell Hanger, 89 Meeting St.
Richardson, J. K., 2 Linguard St.
Richbourg, James, Cannon St.
Ricter, Joseph, Blacksmith, 20 St. Philip St.
Riddell, J. H., Shoemaker, 186 King St.
Riddell, J. S., Clerk, 226 King St.
Riggs, J. S., Jr., Broker, 1 Chalmers St., res. 122 Queen
   St.
Riggs, J. S., Saddler, 130 Meeting St.
Riggs, Samuel, Clerk, Railroad, 130 Meeting St.
Righton, E., Mrs., Milliner, 5 Water St.
Righton, John M., Customs Officer, res. 1 Middle St.
Riker, David, Engineer, Elliott St.
Riker, Robert, Engineer, Cannon St.
Riley, Thomas, Factor, Southern Wharf, res. 77 Meeting
   St.
Riley, William, Stationer, 41 Broad St.
Rineke, John, Clerk, 263 King St
Ring, Conrad, Auctioneer, Vendue Range, res. 30 Savage
   St.
Ring, D. A., 30 Savage St.
Rinker, C. F., Policeman, 104 King St.
Rinker, E., Miss, Milliner, 200 King St.
Rinker, John M., Customs Officer, res. 1 Middle St.
Riols, B., 48 Wentworth St.
Ripley, B. H., Physician, 7 George St.
Ripley, N. F., Lamp Store, 262 King St.
Ripley, S. P., 7 George St.
Riva, A., Shoemaker, 104 Meeting St.
Rivers, Montgomery, Teacher, 41 Church St.
Rivers, W. B., Dentist, 269 King St.
Rivers, W. H., Printer, 269 King St.
Rivers, W. J., Teacher, 182 Meeting St.
Rivers, William T., Accountant, 53 Queen St.
Riviere, J. P., 174 King St.
Roach, E. A., Mrs., 11 Society St.
Roach, M. C., Mrs., 20 Montague St.
Robb, James, Grocer, 198 King St., res. 204 King St.
Robb, W., Bookkeeper, East Point Mill, res. 204 King St.
Roberts, A. J., Printer, 23 Tradd St.
Roberts, D., 93 Church St.
Roberts, F, Seaman, 2 Lightwood's Alley
Roberts, J. S., Shoe Dealer, 233 King St.
Roberts, -----, Mrs., Milliner, 191 King St.
Roberts, -----, Teacher, 21 College St.

Robertson & Blacklock, Factors, 18 East Bay St.,
  Alexander Robertson, John F. Blacklock
Robertson, Alexander, Factor, 27 East Bay St.
Robertson, David, Pinckney St., Cannonborough
Robertson, F. M., Physician, 18 Hayne St., res. 1 Maiden
  Lane
Robertson, George, Cotton Broker, Fitzsimons' Wharf,
  res. 1 Meeting St.
Robertson, James F., Clerk, 23 Hayne St.
Robertson, James, Merchant, Vanderhorst's Wharf, res.
  37 Church St.
Robertson, John, Line St.
Robertson, John, N. Meeting St.
Robertson, Joseph, N. St. Philip St.
Robertson, L. F., Attorney, Broad St., res. 118 Meeting
  St.
Robertson, S. B., Miss, 2 Bull St.
Robertson, W. A., Accountant, 21 Society St.
Robertston, J., Hudson St.
Robin, M. E., Dry Goods, 42 Queen St.
Robins, Anthony, Fruiterer, 9 Market St.
Robinson & Caldwell, Factors, North Atlantic Wharf,
  James K. Robinson, John M. Caldwell
Robinson, Alexander, 7 Broad St.
Robinson, Allen, Pilot, 19 Meeting St.
Robinson, G. O., Merchant, 12 Wentworth St.
Robinson, George O. & Co., Laces & Ribbons, 237 King
  St., G. O. Robinson, D. G. Tenney
Robinson, Henry, Pinckney St., Cannonborough
Robinson, James K., Factor, Atlantic Wharf, res. Judith
  St.
Robinson, John, 18 Wall St.
Robinson, John, Mrs., Judith St.
Robinson, Randal, Clerk, Bank of Charleston,
  Cannonborough
Robinson, Richard, Pinckney St., Cannonborough
Robinson, Simon, Clerk, Bank of Charleston,
  Cannonborough
Robinson, Stephen T., Cashier, Planters & Mechanics
  Bank, Judith St.
Robinson, William, N. St. Philip St.
Robson, J. N., Clerk, cr. Meeting & Wentworth Sts.
Robson, -----, Mrs., Boarders, cr. Meeting & Wentworth
  Sts.
Roddy, Martin, Grocer, 9 Queen St.
Roderigo, P., Cigar Maker, 174 East Bay St.
Rodgers, E. H. & Co., Country Store, North King St., E.
  H. Rodgers, F. P. Pelzer
Rodgers, E. H., N. King St.
Rodgers, Thomas L., Superintendent, Bennett's Mill,
  Bull St.
Rodgers, Z., Rev., 98 Wentworth St.
Rodrigues, B. A., Dentist, 93 Meeting St.
Roempke, -----, Mrs., 57 Tradd St.
Roger, T. J. & Co., Commission Merchants, Adger's
  Wharf, T. J. Roger, E. Mottet, T. Huchet
Roger, Thomas, Merchant, Adger's Wharf, res. 13
  Archdale St.
Rogers, James, Wheelwright, N. Meeting St.
Rogers, John., Line St.

Rogers, L., N. Meeting St.
Rogers, Margaret E., 6 Orange St.
Rogers, S. B., Jeweller, 156 King St.
Rogers, Simon, Locksmith, 121 King St.
Rogers, Thomas, Merchant, 91 Wentworth St.
Rogers, W., Clerk, 41 Tradd St.
Rohde, Dedrick, Grocer, 124 Tradd St.
Romaine, Albert, 114 Church St.
Romer, H. C., N. St. Philip St.
Rooseveldt, H. L., Merchant, Hayne St., res. 116
  Meeting St.
Roosevelt, Hyde & Clark, Hardware, 13 Hayne St., H. L.
  Roosevelt, Simeon Hyde, Robert A. Clark
Roper, B. D., Jr., Attorney, St. Michael's Alley, res. 25
  Legare St.
Roper, B. D., Planter, 25 Legare St.
Roper, M. J., Planter, 25 Legare St.
Roper, Martha, Mrs., Planter, 7 East Bay St.
Roper, Richard, Factor, Commercial Wharf, res. 3
  Legare St.
Roper, Thomas, Planter, 25 Legare St.
Rose, -----, 64 Meeting St.
Rose, Arthur G., Cashier, Bank of Charleston, res. 9
  Rutledge St.
Rose, E. A., Mrs., 347 King St.
Rose, Emanuel, Cigar Maker, 66 State St.
Rose, Hugh, Planter, 17 Legare St.
Rose, James, President, Railroad Bank, 17 Legare St.
Rose, John A., Carpenter, 7 Minority St.
Rose, John, Columbus St.
Rose, Joseph, Cigar Maker, 66 State St.
Rose, L. A., Mariner, Hard Alley
Rose, -----, Misses, Pinckney St., Cannonborough
Roselorum, -----, 12 Stoll's Alley
Rosenbaum, John, Clerk, 32 Pitt St.
Rosenfeldt, J., Rev., Rabbi, Synagogue, Wentworth St.,
  res. 18 Beaufain St.
Rosenthall, Isaac, Broker, 101 King St.
Ross, A., Mrs., 269 East Bay St.
Ross, C., Miss, 41 George St.
Ross, Charles, Mariner, 20 Queen St.
Ross, James, Customs Officer, 54 Broad St.
Ross, James, Port Warden, 8 Legare St.
Ross, John, Mary St.
Ross, M., Miss, 41 George St.
Ross, W. N., 4 Motte's Lane
Roteman, D., Clerk, 35 Anson St.
Rotureau, Charles, 104 Meeting St.
Rotureau, Jane, Mrs., 2 Friend St.
Rotureau, Peter, Accountant, 2 Friend St.
Roulain, A., Coach Manufacturer, 135 Meeting St., res. 5
  Glebe St.
Roumillat, A., Confectioner, Broad St.
Rouphing, J., Tailor, 168 King St.
Rouse, C., Carpenter, 6 Boundary St.
Rouse, William, Jeweller, 183 King St.
Rout, Eliza, Miss, 118 King St.
Roux, F. L., Accountant, 5 Beaufain St.
Roux, L. P., 290 King St.
Roux, -----, Misses, 6 Liberty St.

Rowand, R., Factor, 58 Tradd St.
Roye, N. A., Tinner, 7 Queen St.
Ruberan, G., Clerk, 140 King St.
Ruddock, A., Carpenter, 81 King St.
Ruddock, T. D., Teacher of Music, 4 Orange St.
Rudolph, Jane M., Church St.
Ruger, -----, Mrs., 7 Water St.
Rumph, G. H., Grocer, 44 Anson St.
Rumph, H., N. Meeting St.
Runcken, H., 71 Church St.
Runkle, M., Clerk, 29 State St.
Russ, John, Ship Carpenter, 16 Washington St.
Russell, A. J., Miss, 34 Hasell St.
Russell, J., 18 Tradd St.
Russell, John, Bookseller, 256 King St., res. 3 Liberty St.
Russell, -----, Mrs., 97 Market St.
Russell, Sarah, Mrs., Dress Maker, 51 Queen St.
Rutherford, -----, Mrs., Water St.
Rutjec, J., Music Teacher, 37 Queen St.
Rutledge, Caroline, Mrs. 14 Lamboll St.
Rutledge, E. C., U. S. Navy, 101 Tradd St.
Rutledge, H., Dr., Vanderhorst St.
Rutledge, H. P., Mrs., Planter 101 Tradd St.
Rutledge, Sarah, Miss, 199 East Bay St.
Rutledge, T., Planter, Vanderhorst St.
Ryan, D. T., 309 King St.
Ryan, H., Mrs., 21 Middle St.
Ryan, H., Printer, 32 Tradd St.
Ryan, J. S., Broker, 36 Broad St., res. 19 King St.
Ryan, J. S., Joiner 106 Wentworth St.
Ryan, James, Laborer 106 Meeting St.
Ryan, John, 4 Linguard St.
Ryan, John, 64 King St.
Ryan, L., 42 Church St.
Ryan, Matthew, President St.
Ryan, Thomas, Broker, 12 State St., res. 46 King St.
Ryan, W. B., Broker, 12 State St., res. 46 King St.
Ryan, William, Store Keeper, 96 Church St.
Ryers, John, Mariner, 24 Burns Lane
Ryla, Peter, 94 Meeting St.
Sachtleben, A., Teacher, 14 Society St.,
Sage, William, Clerk, 30 Pinckney St.
Sahlman, Herman, Grocer, 4 Middle St.
Sahlman, Herman, Grocer, Meeting & Reid Sts.
Salinas, A., Broker, State St., res. 58 Meeting St.
Salinas, S. H., Mrs., Boarders, 58 Meeting St.
Saltar, T. R., Joiner, Mary St.
Salter, H., Tavern Keeper, 9 Bedon's Alley
Saltus, F. W., Clerk, Central Wharf, res. 25 Mazyck St.
Salvo, C., Fruiterer, 88 King St.
Salvo, G., Painter, 164 King St.
Samson, Joseph, Deputy Sheriff, 96 Tradd St.
Samson, Samuel, Merchant, 96 Tradd St.
Sanders, C. M., Printer, 56 St. Philip St.
Sanders, G. W., Bricklayer, 56 St. Philip St.
Sanders, J. J. T., Carpenter, 56 St. Philip St.
Sanders, Joseph, Bricklayer, N. Pitt St.
Sanders, Joseph, Mason, 5½ King St.
Sanders, Mary F., Mrs., 56 St. Philip St.
Sanders, T. L., Bricklayer, N. Pitt St.

Sanders, W., Carpenter, Thomas St.
Sandtrue, F. C., Painter, 117 Meeting St.
Santon, J., Boundary St.
Sass, Jacob K., Officer, Bank of Charleston, 34 Society St.
Sass, Ludwig, Sexton, 159 East Bay St.
Sass, Washington, Cabinet Maker, 53 Queen St.
Sauls, John, 32 Queen St.
Saunders, S., Barber, 49 Broad St.
Savage, George, Mrs., 36 South Bay St.
Savage, Sarah H., Miss, 34 Savage St.
Sawyer, -----, 260 King St.
Sawyer, J. B., Meeting St.
Sawyer, John, 272 King St.
Saylor, L., Mrs., 15 Meeting St.
Scanlan, C. A., Ship Smith, 7 Concord St., res. 19 Wentworth St.
Schacte, John, Grocer, King & Vanderhorst Sts.
Schad, John, Bootmaker, 56 Market St.
Scheckner, Charles, Musician, 93 Queen St.
Scheib, M., Tailor, 92 Meeting St.
Scherferee, A., Cabinet Maker, 164 King St.
Schirmer, Jacob F., Cooper, Commercial Wharf, res. 124 King St.
Schirmer, W. H., Cooper, 46 Queen St.
Schlechtren, Flora, Mrs., Boarders, 29 State St.
Schmidt, -----, Clerk, 39 Beaufain St.
Schmidt, H., Grocer, 18 Atlantic St.
Schmidt, J. H., Keeper, Masonic Hall, 268 King St.
Schmidt, J. W., Physician, Cumberland St., res. 67 Church St.
Schnaars, -----, Grocer, 11 King St.
Schnahan, T. F., 62 Wentworth St.
Schneider, N. B., Boarders, 33 Queen St.
Schnierle, John, Planter, 21 Pitt St.
Schnierle, William, 309 King St.
Schniple, William, Baker, 183 East Bay St.
Scholks, G., Boundary St.
Schonboe, F. L., Police Officer, 41 Society St.
Schonewan, H. G., Grocer, 18 Boundary St.
Schoolbred, J., N. Coming St.
Schrague, Dedrick, N. Coming St.
Schreck, C., Store Keeper, 31 Tradd St.
Schreiner, J. H., Bacon Merchant, Atlantic Wharf, res. 231 East Bay St.
Schrenck, H., Musician, 31 Tradd St.
Schrenck, H., Painter, 31 Tradd St.
Schroder, Fitz, Clerk, 8 Lynch St., res. 12 Rutledge St.
Schroder, H., Dry Goods, 291 King St.
Schroder, H. J., Grocer, 32 Meeting St.
Schroder, H. W., Attorney, Broad St., res. 24 George St.
Schroder, Henry, 7 St. Philip St.
Schroder, J., Grocer, 47 Market St.
Schroder, J., Grocer, 62 Anson St.
Schroder, John, N. St. Philip St.
Schroder, John, Sail Maker, 184 Meeting St.
Schroder, M. & Sussdorff, Straw Goods, 141 Meeting St., M. Schroder, G. Sussdorff
Schroder, William, Grocer, 69 Market St.
Schroder, William, Grocer, Market St., res. 184 Meeting

St.
Schu, David, Sexton, 58 Broad St.
Schulken, F., Grocer, 209 East Bay St.
Schulken, H., Clerk, 209 East Bay St.
Schultz, George, N. St. Philip St.
Schultz, H., Clerk, Aiken's Range
Schultz, Philip, Bogard St.
Schwarly, -----, Clerk, 66 Wentworth St.
Schwart, Henry, 4 Market St.
Schweitzer, O., Jeweller, 335 King St.
Schwing, Charles, Grocer, 39 St. Philip St.
Scott, E. C., Bookkeeper, Mercury Office, res. 44 Society St.
Scott, Edwin, 2 Glebe St.
Scott, Ellis, 14 Pinckney St.
Scott, Jane, Mrs., 2 Magazine St.
Scott, M. J., 14 Pinckney St.
Scott, M. J., Mrs., Hair Dresser, 161 King St.
Scott, Margaret, Mrs., 7 Pinckney St.
Scott, Morgan, Shoemaker, 8 Tradd St.
Screven, R. E., Merchant, Atlantic Wharves, res. 33 Meeting St.
Seabrook, E., Elliott St., Neck
Seabrook, W., Elliott St., Neck
Seabrook, William, Planter, 16 South Bay St.
Seagle, T. J., Clerk, 11 Hayne St.
Sealy, J. W., Jeweller, 5 Liberty St.
Sealy, Joseph, Jeweller, 271 King St.
Seba, C. F., Grocer, 14 Queen St.
Sebring, Edward, President, State Bank, res. Boundary St. Continued
Seckendorff, -----, Dry Goods, 145 King St.
Seckler, -----, Spring St.
Seedorff, H. C., Grocer, Elizabeth St.
Segar, John, Grocer, 4 Inspection St.
Seigling, John, Jr., Attorney, Court House Square, res. 227 King St.
Seigling, John, Music Store, 227 King St.
Seignous, C. W., Coach Maker, Meeting St., res. 366 King St.
Seignous, E. P., Turner, 173 Meeting St.
Seigwald, Mary, Mrs., 10 Burns Lane
Seimsen, Theodore, Tavern Keeper, 159 East Bay St.
Seixas, D. C., Clerk, 4 Society St.
Seixas, R. C., Mrs., 4 Society St.
Seixas, S. D., 4 Society St.
Selle, E., Mrs., Milliner, 200 King St.
Selps, John, Chapel St.
Sergeant, George, Shoe Dealer, 89 Market St.
Sernicer, Jacob, Sires St.
Serucke, Edward, Grocer, 89 Queen St.
Serupe, F., Clerk, 47 Market St.
Service, S. H., Miss, Nurse, 11 Friend St.
Seyle, Charles C., Clerk, Mazyck St.
Seyle, F. O., Engineer, Mazyck St.
Seyle, John, Carpenter, 14 Bull St.
Seyle, Samuel, Master, Poor House, Mazyck St.
Seymour, Ann, Mrs., 37 King St.
Seymour, R. W., Attorney, Meeting St., res. 7 Back Alley
Seymour, S., Miss, Milliner, 30 Mazyck St.

Seymour, T. S., Teacher, 69 Coming St.
Shackelford & Graeser, Factors, Central Wharf, F. R. Shackelford, C. A. Graeser
Shackelford, F. R., Factor, 7 Central Wharf, res. 10 Hasell St.
Shackelford, J. M., Merchant, East Bay St., res. 43 Church St.
Shackelford, J., N. Coming St.
Shaffer, A., 112 Queen St.
Shaffer, F. J., Attorney, Boundary St.
Shaffer, Frederick, Carpenter, Boundary St.
Sharlock, Alexander, Constable, 64 Meeting St.
Shaw, James, Seeds Store, 163 King St.
Shea, George, Tailor, 346 King St.
Sheckard, Mary, Mrs., 14 Coming St.
Shecut, L. A., Accountant, Central Wharf, res. 27 Mazyck St.
Sheller, Charles, Cabinet Maker, 304 King St.
Shelton, C. M., Clerk, 15 Hayne St.
Shelton, Isabel, Miss, 9 Clifford St.
Shelton, -----, Mrs., 20 Society St.
Shepherd, John J., Saddler, 34 Coming St.
Shepherd, William, Saddler, 40 Coming St.
Sheppard, T. C., Wharfinger, Boyce Wharf, res. 233 East Bay St.
Sheridan, Patrick, Bootmaker, 74 Tradd St.
Sheridan, Patrick, Sugar Refiner, 16 Anson St.
Sherman, Sim, N. St. Philip St.
Shier, Alfred, Ship Joiner, 1 Lynch St.
Shier, C. P., Butcher
Shiffer, H. W. & Co., India Rubber, 276 King St.
Shiffer, H. W., Store Keeper, 146 Meeting St.
Shine, Dennis, Fruiterer, 169 King St.
Shingler, Thomas, Alexander St.
Shingler, W. P., Alexander St.
Shingler, William S., Sheriff, Charleston District, Alexander St.
Shirer, George, N. King St.
Shirer, J. B., N. King St.
Shirer, John, 72 Church St.
Shirer, M., Clerk, N. King St.
Shockney, Mary, Mrs., 138 Queen St.
Shoemaker, J. S., Clerk, 226 King St.
Shokes, George, Hanover St.
Shokes, H., Hanover St.
Shokes, John, Hanover St.
Shokes, William, Hanover St.
Shoolbred, -----, Mrs., Planter, Vernon St.
Shubrick, E. T., U. S. Navy, 39 Meeting St.
Shubrick, Hester, Mrs., 12 Savage St.
Shuckman, L., Worsted Dealer, 249 King St.
Siddons, Joseph, Cabinet Maker, 128 Meeting St.
Sifly, Henry, 18 Friend St.
Sigwald, C. B., Bookkeeper, 22 Cumberland St.
Sikke, Richard, 73 Market St.
Silcox, D. H., Cabinet Maker, 234 King St., res. Magazine St.
Silcox, James, Cabinet Maker, 224 King St.
Silliman, Eliza, Mrs., 21 Cumberland St.
Silliman, H. K., 21 Cumberland St.

Simmons, A., Mariner, 29 Cumberland St.
Simons, A., 270 King St.
Simons, A., Clerk, 9 Hayne St.
Simons, C. W., Mary St.
Simons, Eliza, Mrs., 34 Savage St.
Simons, Elizabeth, Mrs., 156 East Bay St.
Simons, Harris, Radcliffe St.
Simons, J. C., Paints & Oil, 226 King St.
Simons, J., Planter, 69 Anson St.
Simons, J. Ward, Rev., Assistant Minister, St. Stephen's, Hudson St.
Simons, James, Attorney, Broad St., res. Mary St.
Simons, Maurice, Mrs., 80 Tradd St.
Simons, Sarah Ruth, Mrs., 97 Tradd St.
Simons, -----, Seaman, 6 Tradd St.
Simons, T. G. & Sons, Factors, Vanderhorst's Wharf, T. G. Simons, T. G. Simons, Jr., -----Simons
Simons, T. Y., Jr., Teacher, High School, 49 Tradd St.
Simons, T. Y., Physician, 49 Tradd St.
Simons, W. F., Painter, 45 Queen St.
Simons, W. M., Physician, 110 Meeting St.
Simonton, James R., Accountant, 267 East Bay St.
Simonton, John, Clerk, 267 East Bay St.
Simpson, J., Dry Goods, 59 Wentworth St.
Simpson, James, Mariner, 18 South Bay St.
Simpson, Lydia, Mrs., 4 Guignard St.
Simpson, M. M., Dry Goods, 59 Wentworth St.
Simpson, -----, Misses, Teachers, 59 Wentworth St.
Sims & Dulin, Factors, Central Wharf
Sims, J. T., Merchant, Central Wharf, res. 18 Smith St.
Sinclair, M., Mrs., 193 Meeting St.
Sinclair, M., Mrs., 34 Tradd St.
Sires, Francis, Elliott St., Cannonborough
Sires, Peter, Elliott St., Cannonborough
Slawson, H., Merchant, 8 Archdale St.
Slawson, T. N., Engineer, Railroad, 347 King St.
Slosser, M., State St.
Slowman, John, 52 Wentworth St.
Slowman, -----, Misses, Music Teachers, 52 Wentworth St.
Sluter, Maria, Mrs., 37 George St.
Small, Jacob, Baker, 193 King St.
Small, R., Mrs., Boarders, 5 Liberty St.
Small, Robert, Clerk, 5 Liberty St.
Small, W. C., Clerk, 288 King St., res. 297 King St.
Smallwood, W., Seaman, 98 Queen St.
Smart, Ann, Mrs., 69 Market St.
Smelie, -----, Misses, 99 King St.
Smetzer, Charles, Butcher, Thomas St.
Smetzer, Lewis, Engineer, Thomas St.
Smith & Coffin, Factors, Adger's North Wharf, W. Mason Smith, George N. Coffin
Smith, A. P., Soda Water Maker, 166½ King St., res. 49 Broad St.
Smith, Aaron C., Cashier, Union Bank, 14 State St.
Smith, Andrew, Molder, 3 Wharf St.
Smith, Ann F., Mrs., 98 East Bay St.
Smith, B. F. & Co., Ship Chandlers, 76 East Bay St., B. F. Smith, R. F. Smith
Smith, B. F., Merchant, 76 East Bay St., res. Meeting & John Sts.
Smith, Benjamin, Meeting & John Sts.
Smith, Charles, Clerk, Fitzsimons' Wharf, res. 13 Lynch St.
Smith, Charlotte, Mrs., 11 Legare St.
Smith, Edward, Merchant, Smith's Wharf, res. 8 Atlantic St.
Smith, Eliza, Miss, 48 George St.
Smith, Eliza, Mrs., 15 Montague St.
Smith, Eliza, Mrs., Mantuamaker, 2 Philadelphia St.
Smith, Fowler, 66 Market St.
Smith, G., Shoe Dealer, 354 King St.
Smith, H., 12 Stoll's Alley
Smith, J. J. P., Planter, 18 Meeting St.
Smith, J. R., Merchant, 15 Wentworth St.
Smith, James, Assistant Clerk, Market, 32 Society St.
Smith, James E., Officer, Union Bank, 87 Wentworth St.
Smith, James, Judith St.
Smith, Jane, Mrs., 4 Coming St.
Smith, John, Clerk, St. Philip's Church, 10 Magazine St.
Smith, Joseph T., Boat Builder, 24 Marsh St.
Smith, L., Clerk, 87 Tradd St.
Smith, Lewis, Tavern Keeper, 13 Elliott St.
Smith, M. G., Mrs., 64 Broad St.
Smith, M., Mrs., 34 South Bay St.
Smith, N. A., Clerk, 361 King St.
Smith, P. F., Teacher, 54 Wentworth St.
Smith, Quentin, Hosier, 41 Wall St.
Smith, R. C., Union Wharf
Smith, R. F., Clerk, 76 East Bay St., res. Meeting & John Sts.
Smith, R., Mrs., 18 Meeting St.
Smith, Rebecca A., Miss, 200 King St.
Smith, Richard, Messenger of Council, 79 Broad St.
Smith, S. A., Miss, Boarders, 69 Broad St.
Smith, S., Mrs., 255 East Bay St.
Smith, Sarah, Mrs., Seamstress, 5 Clifford St.
Smith, Sebastian, Laborer, 52 King St.
Smith, T. A., Tailor, 37 Queen St.
Smith, T. M., Ship Carpenter, 18 Middle St.
Smith, T. O., Clerk, 3 Hayne St., res 75 Wentworth St.
Smith, T. P., Merchant, 40 East Bay St., res. 82 Beaufain St.
Smith, W. B., Engineer, 32 Society St.
Smith, W. H., Blacksmith, 17 Berresford St.
Smith, W. J., Officer of Customs, Charlotte St.
Smith, W. M., Factor, Adger's Wharf, res. Meeting St.
Smith, W., Washington St.
Smith, Whitefoord, Rev., Pastor, Cumberland Church, 9 Society St.
Smith, William, 28 Queen St.
Smith, William, Mariner, 1 Hard Alley
Smith, William, Washington St.
Smith, William Wragg, Planter, 11 Legare St.
Smith. W. B., Merchant, East Bay St., res. 79 Broad St.
Smithys, John, 105 Church St.
Smyth, John, Cabinet Maker, 152 King St.
Smyth, Thomas, Rev., D. D., Pastor, 2d Presbyterian Church, Spring St.
Smyzer, Henry, Ship Joiner, 219 East Bay St., res. 67

Anson St.
Sneckenburger, A., Confectioner, N. King St.
Snowden, W. E., Factor, Southern Wharf, res. 204 East Bay St.
Snowdenburg, A., N., King St.
Sollee, H., Brown's Wharf, res. 20 George St.
Sollee, H., Mrs., 65 Church St.
Solomons, J. R., Dentist, 93 Meeting St.
Solomons, M., N. St. Philip St.
Solomons, Rebecca, Mrs.,101 King St.
Somers, E., Dry Goods, 334 King St.
Somers, John, Sail Maker, 12 Elliott St.
Soope, Hugh, 4 Clifford St.
Soubiates, Peter, Mariner, 178 East Bay St.
Souterigger, J., Shoemaker, 6 Tradd St.
Sparnick, H., Customs Officer, 21 Queen St.
Spear, George, 309 King St.
Spear, J. E. & Co., Jewelry & Silverware, 235 King St., J. E. Spear, J. C. Wood
Spear, James E., Jeweller, 235 King St.
Spear, Rachel, Mrs., 12 Hasell St.
Spear, W. W., Rev., Rector, Grace Church, Bull St.
Specht, F., Shoemaker, 69 Wentworth St.
Speissegger, E. C., Clerk, 9 Pinckney St.
Speissegger, J. W., N. Meeting St.
Speissegger, L. P., Piano Tuner, 41 Queen St.
Speissegger, T. C., Grocer, 9 Pinckney St.
Speissegger, T., Tivoli Garden
Speissegger, W. W., 9 Pinckney St.
Spelman, Andrew, Grocer, 45 Market St.
Spencer, A., Engineer, Railroad, 271 King St.
Spencer, Catherine, Mrs., Mantuamaker, 42 King St.
Spencer, G. W., Clerk, Hayne St., res. 271 King St.
Spencer, M., Mrs., Boarders, 271 King St.
Spencer, Margaret, Mrs., Seamstress, 39 Wentworth St.
Spencer, Seth, Broker, State St., res 271 King St.
Spinkear, Martin, Grocer, 25 Savage St.
Sprague, D. F. (see Woodruff, P. D. & Co.)
Sprague, J. W., Clerk, 4 Hayne St.
Sprigg, Ross, East Bay St., Neck
Spring, Alexander, Teacher, 244 King St.
Springer, J. M., 37 King St.
Springer, Mary, Mrs., 37 King St.
Springs, R., Clerk, 45 Hayne St.
Squires, Nelson, Elliott St., Neck
Sreag, Antonio, Seaman, 2 Pitt St.
St. Amand, J. P., Merchant, Hayne St., res. N. King St.
St. Amand, M. W., Secretary, South Carolina Insurance Co., res. 22 Beaufain St.
Stafford, John, Tinner, 65 State St.
Stagg, John, Wheelwright, Archdale St., res. 37 Montague St.
Stall, F., Butcher, Thomas St.
Stallgrass, H., Storekeeper, 47 Church St.
Stanley, Ann, Mrs., 38 Beaufain St.
Stapleton, C., Mrs., Storekeeper, 16 Chalmers St.
Starr, E. P., Factor, Boyce's Wharf, res. 100 Wentworth St.
Steedman, Thomas, Customs Officer, N. Coming St.
Steedman, William, Vanderhorst St.

Steel, E., Mrs., 48 Bull St.
Steel, Walter, Hat Store, 308 King St., res. 39 Coming St.
Steen, Thomas, Hotel Keeper, 290 King St.
Stein, Francis, Watch Maker, 62 Meeting St.
Stein, J. F., Mariner, 15 Water St.
Steinmeyer, F., Clerk, 29 Anson St.
Steinmeyer, J. F., Carpenter, Boundary St.
Steinmeyer, J. H., Lumber Merchant, 100 Beaufain St.
Steinmeyer, John, Fireman, Railroad, res. 13 Smith St.
Stell, Elizabeth, Mrs., 7 Smith's Lane
Stelley, Susan, Mrs., Clear Starcher, 11 Princess St.
Stelling, E., 15 Market St.
Stelling, H., 15 Market St.
Stelling, Henry, Policeman, 77 Broad St.
Stelling, John, Grocer, 96 East Bay St.
Stellor, Peter, Seaman, 3 Wharf St.
Stender, Conrad, N. King St.
Stender, Henry, N. King St.
Stephens, W., Radcliffe St.
Stevens & Betts, Hardware, 80 East Bay St., Joel Stevens, F. J. Betts
Stevens, J. R., Clerk, 18 Wentworth St.
Stevens, James, Bookkeeper, Central Wharf, res. 197 Meeting St.
Stevens, Joel., Hardware, 80 East Bay St., res. 51 Tradd St.
Stevens, M. S., Mrs., 4 South Bay St.
Stevens, R. S., Mrs., 17 St. Philip St.
Stevens, Susan M., Mrs., 17 Coming St.
Stewart, D., Painter, 88 Queen St.
Stewart, Jane, Mrs., 5 Greenhill St.
Stewart, R. L., Officer, Bank of Charleston, 11 Pitt St.
Stewart, Robert H., Vanderhorst St.
Stewart, Samuel, Carpenter, 16 Rutledge St.
Stewart, W. J. H., Mrs., 21 Concord St.
Stewart, William, Printer, East Bay St.
Stiffens, William, Grocer, 25 College St.
Stilling, H., Grocer, 21 Market St.
Stillman, Alfred, Clerk 297 King St.
Stillman, James, Customs Officer, 20 Society St.
Stimmerman, Albert, Clerk, 18 Bull St.
Stimmerman, Henry, Grocer, 18 Bull St.
Stinebeck, A., Clerk, 12 Wentworth St.
Stock, Ann S., Miss, 108 Tradd St.
Stock, J. Y., Merchant, Atlantic Wharves, res. 11 Montague St.
Stockdeck, F., Painter, 164 King St.
Stocker, Henry, Clerk, 101 Broad St.
Stocker, James M., Auctioneer, Accommodation Wharf, res. 101 Broad St.
Stocking, D. L., Clerk, 14 Meeting St.
Stoddard, H. & Wood, Shoes, 21 Hayne St., H. Stoddard, A. B. Wood
Stokes, E. R., Bookbinder, 104 Church St.
Stone, R. G. (see Brown & Stone)
Stone, William, Clerk, 101 Meeting St.
Stoney, C. F., Druggist, King St., res. 26 Hasell St.
Stoney, E. G., Customs Officer, 81 Broad St.
Stoney, E., Mrs., 26 Hasell St.

Stoney, S. D., Clerk, 26 Hasell St.
Stoney, T., 26 Hasell St.
Stopplebein, L. E., City Measurer, 13 Bull St.
Stow, Margaret, Mrs., Keeper of Court House, Broad St.
Stoy, J. W., Book Store, 258 King St.
Strain, James, Mariner, 109 Wentworth St.
Strain, Mary A., Mrs., Washer, 4 Magazine St.
Street, H. T. & Brothers, Commission Merchants, 64
    East Bay St., H. T. Street, Gustavus Street
Street, H. T., Merchant, East Bay St., res. 8 Society St.
Street, Thaddeus, Merchant, Boyce's Wharf, res.
    Columbus St.
Stretinger, Belton, 4 Beaufain St.
Stringer, Mary E., Mrs., Storekeeper, 8 Wall St.
Strobel, B. M., Merchant, 147 East Bay St., res 249 East
    Bay St.
Strobel, Daniel H., Clerk, 18 Liberty St.
Strobel, John, 35 St. Philip St.
Strobel, M. D., Accountant, Atlantic Wharves, res. 249
    East Bay St.
Strobel, Robert, Pinckney St., Cannonborough
Strobel, S., Mrs., Back Alley
Strobel, Sarah, Mrs., 18 Liberty St.
Strohecker, H. F., Hardware, Meeting St., res. 8 Glebe
    St.
Strohecker, J. L., Lumber Factor, 31 Montague St., res.
    81 Beaufain St.
Stroller, -----, Carpenter, 34 Queen St.
Strong, George, Woolf St.
Strong, N., 294 King St.
Strong, P., 294 King St.
Stroub, G., Carpenter, 14 Burns Lane
Stuart & Harper, Factors, North Atlantic Wharf
Stuart, James B., Merchant, Atlantic Wharf, res. 5
    Meeting St.
Sturgis, Mary, 265 East Bay St.
Sturken, Herman, Tailor, 104 King St.
Stuthard, W., Doughty St.
Styer, Henry, Carpenter, Motte's Lane
Suares, A., Cabinet Maker, 340 King St.
Suares, B., Tailor, Middle St.
Suares, J. E., Cabinet Maker, 340 King St.
Sulaff, C., Clerk, 85 Queen St.
Sullivan, John, Laborer, 12 Linguard St.
Sullivan, Mary T., Mrs., 72 Anson St.
Sullivan, T. J., Rev., 80 Broad St.
Surtis, Thomas, Mariner, 15 State St.
Sussdorff, G. (see Schroder, M. & Sussdorff)
Sutcliffe, James, Line St.
Sutton, Ellen, Mrs., Milliner, 132 King St.
Sutton, M., Policeman, 7 Smith's Lane
Sweegan, M., Grocer, 61 State St.
Sweeny, Bernard, 22 Market St.
Sweeny, Morgan, Laborer, 30 Queen St.
Sweeny, Thomas, Book Binder, 76 Anson St.
Swift, T. B., Police Officer, 6 Tradd St.
Swinton, E. A., Boundary St.
Swinton, William H., Boundary St.
Syers, Joseph, Carpenter, 114 Wentworth St.
Symes, John, Nassau St.

Symes, T. B., Hanover St.
Symes, W. L., Nassau St.
Symmes, -----, Mrs., 130 Church St.
Taber, W. R., Teller, Bank of State of S. C., res.
    Radcliffe & Coming Sts.
Taft, A. R., Merchant, East Bay St., res. 29 Laurens St.
Taft, Davis, Clerk, 150 Meeting St.
Talleyrand, N., Bar Keeper, 115 East Bay St.
Talvande, -----, Madame, Teacher, 14 Legare St.
Tanswell, Martha, Mrs., Seamstress, 95 Queen St.
Taylor, Ann T., Mrs., 6 King St.
Taylor, J., Conductor, Railroad, 43 St. Philip St.
Taylor, James H., Auctioneer, Vendue Range, res. 16
    Hasell St.
Taylor, James M., Clerk, 225 King St.
Taylor, John, 4 Linguard St.
Taylor, John J., N. Coming St.
Taylor, M. S., Mrs., 6 Lamboll St.
Taylor, -----, Misses, 1 Burns Lane
Taylor, -----, Misses, 44 Coming St.
Taylor, Orrin, Dry Goods, 231 King St., res. 20 Beaufain
    St.
Taylor, R., Printer, 101 Meeting St.
Taylor, Richard, N. Meeting St.
Taylor, Robert R., 6 Lamboll St.
Taylor, Thomas B., Accountant, East Bay St., res. 297
    King St.
Taylor, Thomas R., Shoe Dealer, 241 King St.
Taylor, William M., Accountant, Southern Wharf, res.
    Mansion House
Teague, J. M., N. King St.
Teape, Elizabeth, Miss, Storekeeper, 94 Meeting St.
Teasdale, Richard, Clerk, Railroad, res. Wragg Square
Techen, -----, Boundary St.
Teigen, John, Cannon St.
Telfer, Robert, Gauger, 6 Mazyck St.
Tenhet, Isabella, Dry Goods, 6 Anson St.
Tennent, E. S., Physician, 60 Anson St.
Tennent, G. B., Merchant, 8 Hayne St., res. 4 South Bay
    St.
Tennent, J. S., Officer, Planters & Mechanics Bank, res.
    60 Anson St.
Tennent, William, Planter, 60 Anson St.
Tenney, D. G., Merchant, 12 Wentworth St.
Tenney, S., Clerk, 12 Wentworth St.
Ternoe, J., Gas Fitter, 41 Queen St.
Terry, J. W., Tailor, 32 George St.
Thackum, F., Clerk, 21 Broad St., res. 34 Broad St.
Thackum, T., Carpenter, 101 Meeting St.
Thames, John, Clerk, 231 King St., res. Boundary St.
Thaos, Henry, Tavern Keeper, 9 Elliott St.
Tharin, E. C., Auctioneer, Vendue Range, res. Charlotte
    St.
Thayer, Ebenezer, Teacher, 77 Broad St.
Thayer, Emery, Merchant, 157 Meeting St., res. 146
    Meeting St.
Thayer, Mary, Miss, 11 Logan St.
Thayer, T. H., Broker, 18 Broad St., res. 76 Broad St.
Thayer, T. H., Jr., Broker, 34 Broad St., res. 76 Broad St.
Thee, J. H., Grocer, Amherst St.

Theus, S. B., Mrs., 47 Beaufain St.
Thierman, H., Merchant, Fitzsimons' Wharf, rs. 208 King St.
Thomas, H., Laborer, Kirkland's Alley
Thomas, J. M., Carpenter, 48 Broad St.
Thomas, James, Seaman, 32 Church St.
Thomas, Mary, Mrs., 56 Anson St.
Thomas, S. J., Collector, 48 Broad St.
Thomas, Stephen, Bookkeeper, Meeting St., res. 3 Wentworth St.
Thomas, William, Stone Cutter, 11 Tradd St.
Thompson, A., Tailor, 95 Meeting St.
Thompson, Francis, Seaman, 39 King St.
Thompson, George, Mason, 10 Glebe St.
Thompson, Hannah, Mrs., 1 Bull St.
Thompson, Henry, Mason, 100 Meeting St.
Thompson, James P., Printer, 10 Market St.
Thompson, Jane, Mrs., 7 Laurens St.
Thompson, -----, Mrs., 63 Coming St.
Thompson, N., Painter, 66 Broad St.
Thompson, T., Furniture Dealer, 292 King St.
Thompson, -----, Tavern Keeper, 7 Elliott St.
Thompson, Thomas, 17 Queen St.
Thompson, W. H., Mariner, 20 Pinckney St.
Thompson, William, Brick Layer, 39 George St.
Thomson, Charles, Mariner, 73 Church St.
Thomson, John, Seedsman, 264 King St.
Thomson, P. B., Tavern Keeper, 95 Market St.
Thomson, Theodore, Bootmaker, 87 Church St.
Thrower, James, Policeman, 1 St. Philip St.
Thurston, Emily, Mrs., 45 Anson St.
Tibbetts, Ann, Mrs., 48 George St.
Tidyman, Philip, Dr., Planter, 1 Ladson's Court
Tiedeman, J. F., Grocer, Elizabeth St.
Tiedeman, Otto, Grocer, Boundary St.
Tieman, John, 290 King St.
Tiernay, James, Laborer, 118 Church St.
Tietgen, D., Clerk, 67 Tradd St.
Tighy, Joseph, N. King St.
Tilson, Rebecca, Mrs., Boarders, 102 Meeting St.
Timbrook, Emily, Miss, 6 Berresford St.
Timmons, F. R., Physician, 4 Smith's Lane
Timmons, G. C., 4 Smith's Lane
Timmons, J. D., Clerk, 290 King St.
Timmons, W. L., Hardware, East Bay St., res. Smith St.
Timrod, T., Mrs., 108 King St.
Tindell, Thomas, Fisherman, 78 King St.
Tinken, H., Boundary St.
Tinken, J., Chapel St.
Tinkham, E., Miss, 32 Wentworth St.
Tinsley, Samuel, Reid St.
Titheradge, William, Rigger, 187 East Bay St.
Tobias, A., Auctioneer, 86 East Bay St., res. 96 Wentworth St.
Tobias, A., Clerk, East Bay St., res. 22 Beaufain St.
Tobias, Isaac, 95 Broad St.
Tobias, J. L., Clerk, 86 East Bay St., res. 96 Wentworth St.
Tobias, Joseph, Fisherman, McBride's Alley
Tobias, Virginius, Attorney at Law, 95 Broad St.

Todd, James, Tailor 10 Linguard St.
Tomlinson, Joseph, Merchant, 3 Hayne St., res. 92 Wentworth St.
Tomlinson, R., Saddler, Meeting St., res. 16 Liberty St.
Tomsdon, E., Painter, 28 Anson St.
Toohel, Daniel, 32 Queen St.
Toomer, H. L., Planter, Meeting & Ann Sts.
Toomer, H. V., Physician, Chapel St.
Toomer, John, Physician, Meeting & Ann Sts.
Topp, C., Clerk, 180 King St.
Torch, J. D., Grocer, 146 East Bay St.
Torlay, John, N. King St.
Torlay, Joseph, N. Meeting St.
Torlay, M. F., Mrs., Dress Maker, 117 Queen St.
Torlay, M., N. Meeting St.
Tornlaus, J., Nassau St.
Torrey, -----, Misses, 8 New St.
Torrington, Martha, Mrs., Store Keeper, 23 Friend St.
Toulry, M., Bootmaker, 17 Queen St.
Toussigger, Eliza, Mrs., 20 Water St.
Townsend, Arnold & Co., Dry Goods, 45 Hayne St., William H. Townsend, R. C. Townsend, Isaaac Townsend, C.
Trapier, B. F., Physician, 53 Meeting St.
Trapier, Mary E., Miss, 6 Logan St.
Trapier, Paul, Rev., 37 Meeting St.
Trapier, W. H., N. Meeting St.
Trapmann, Lewis, Merchant, 20 East Bay St., res. 100 Broad St.
Traxler, David, Shoe Dealer, 360 King St.
Tree, A., Miss, Seamstress, 80 Market St.
Trenhold, C., Merchant, Fitzsimons' Wharf, res. 19 Rutledge St.
Trenholm, E. L., Merchant, Central Wharf, res. Pinckney St., Cannonborough
Trenholm, G. A., Merchant, Central Wharf, res. Pinckney St., Cannonborough
Trescott, Edward, Planter, Vanderhorst St.
Trescott, George, Mariner, 15 Friend St.
Trescott, Henry, Cashier, State Bank, 4 Anson St.
Trieste, J., Dry Goods, 85 Market St.
Tron, A. W., Jeweller, 187 King St.
Trott, E. M., Mrs., 71 King St.
Trotti, Caroline, Mrs., 35 Tradd St.
Trouche, -----, Mrs., 21 Queen St.
Trout, T. B., Wharfinger, Southern Wharf, res. 22 Beaufain St.
Trout, Thomas, Merchant, Commercial Wharf, res. 94 Wentworth St.
Troy, T., President St.
Truesdale, David, Tavern Keeper, 28 Queen St.
Trull, D. C., Carpenter, 69 King St.
Trumbo, C. H., Mason, 55 Tradd St.
Trumbo, Henry, 11 Wall St.
Trupp, John, Judith St.
Tryest, M., Clothing, Market St., res 143 King St.
Tucker, J. H., Planter, Drake St.
Tunis, Mary, Mrs., Boarders, Vanderhorst's Wharf
Tunno, -----, Mrs., 25 Church St.
Tunno, Sarah E., 35 Church St.

Tupper & Son, Commission Merchants, Brown's Wharf, Tristram Tupper, Samuel Y. Tupper

Tupper, James, Attorney, 52 Broad St.

Tupper, S. Y., Merchant, Brown's Wharf, res. 52 Tradd St.

Tupper, Tristram, Merchant, Brown's Wharf, res. 52 Tradd St.

Turnbull, Andrew, Planter, 94 Broad St.

Turnbull, Anna, Mrs., 1 Logan St.

Turnbull, James, 22 Water St.

Turnbull, R. J., 94 Broad St.

Turnbull, W. O., Clerk, 5 Liberty St.

Turner, Richard, Clerk, 18 Hayne St., 15 St. Philip St.

Tuttle, G. W., Baker, 366 King St.

Tweedy, A. E. (see Fanning, F. D. & Co.)

Tweedy, W. H., Clerk, 159 Meeting St.

Tweedy, W. H., Clerk, 21 Society St.

Tylee, N., Clerk, 123 E. Bay St., res. 28 State St.

Tyler, P., Miss, 2 Price's Alley

Tyrrell, J. M., Clerk, 155 East Bay St.

Ufferhardt, W., Clerk, 140 King St.

Uhl, W., Portrait Painter, 216 King St.

Uts, John, Printer, 115 King St.

Uttermahl, M. O., Mrs., 12 Burns Lane

Valentine, J., 42 King St.

Valentine, S., 42 King St.

Valentine, S., Carpenter, 103 Meeting St.

Valleau, H. J., Clerk, 33 Beaufain St.

Van Hahn, John, Thomas St.

Van Horten, V. H., N. King St.

Vanderhorst, John, Chapel St.

Vanderhorst, L., Chapel St.

Vanderlieth, E., Tailor, 8 Queen St.

Vanderzee, H. (see Wiley, Banks & Co.)

Vandohlen, A., Grocer, 189 East Bay St.

Vandohlen, C., Grocer, 189 East Bay St.

Vandulken, John, Grocer, 8 Wall St.

Vandyck, -----, Mrs., Teacher, Horlbeck's Alley

Vanglahn, H., Clerk, Gadsden's Wharf

Vanglahn, M., Grocer, 1 Coming St.

Vanhollen, H. W., Grocer, 29 Anson St.

Vannoy, John, Clerk, 5 Burns Lane

Vanwinkle, John, Variety Store, 308 King St.

Vapour, John, 6 Tradd St.

Vardell, William, Clerk, Vanderhorst St.

Varner, Henry, Policeman, 28 Mazyck St.

Vedding, J. D., Tavern Keeper, 2 Elliott St.

Veitch, W., Apothecary, Duncan St.

Vellet, J. C., Grocer, 36 Elliott St.

Venning, H. M., Lumber Merchant, Gadsden's Wharf, res. 17 Society St.

Venning, Jonah, Charlotte St.

Vennon, E. W., Planter, 1 Greenhill St.

Vente, E., Physician 15 Beaufain St.

Vernon, Henry, Carpenter, 44 Bull St.

Vernon, Mary, Mrs., 44 Bull St.

Vernon, W. H., Accountant, 1 Greenhill St.

Veronee, Samuel, Clerk, Railroad, N. Meeting St.

Veronee, W. B., Tinner, 63 State St.

Veronee, William, Tinner, 63 State St.

Vesey, T. M., Laborer, 5 Archdale St.

Vial, Joseph, Fruiterer, 95 King St.

Vickman, H., Morris St.

Vidal, Joseph, 3 Minority St.

Vierfelder, Samuel, Bootmaker, 73 Meeting St.

Vincent, D. B., Mariner, Church St. & St. Michael's Alley

Vincent, H. E. & Son, Ship Chandlers, 75 East Bay St., H. E. Vincent, Sr., H. E. Vincent, Jr.

Vincent, H. E., Jr., Ship Chandler, 75 East Bay St.

Vincent, H. E., Ship Chandler, 75 East Bay St.

Vinkleman, August, Line St.

Vinro, Sarah, Mrs., Midwife, 30 Pinckney St.

Vintilleer, F., Clerk, 2 King St.

Vinyard, John, Planter, Nassau St.

Vogalsank, Gerd, Grocer, 27 Bull St.

Volger, B., Tobacconist, 341 King St.

Vollante, C., 114 Church St.

Vollers, Hanke, Clerk, 11 King St.

Vollers, John, Clerk, 134 King St.

Von Behn, -----, Grocer, 18 State St.

Von Dohlen, A. & C., Grocers, 189 East Bay St.

Von Eitzen, D., Grocer, 35 Anson St.

Von Hollen, H. W., Grocer, 82 Anson St.

Von Hollen, Jacob, Clerk, 82 Anson St.

Von Kolnitz, H., N. St. Philip St.

Vonglahn, F., Clerk, 230 King St.

Vonglahn, H., Dry Goods, 230 King St.

Voorhies, Maria, Mrs., Seamstress, 63 Tradd St.

Vulcan, F., N. St. Philip St.

Wagener, John A., Editor, 67 Broad St.

Wagner, George, 261 East Bay St.

Wagner, Samuel J., Customs Officer, 114 Queen St.

Wagner, Theodore, Merchant, Central Wharf, res. 261 East Bay St.

Wahlckan, Lewis, Fruiterer, 45 Market St.

Wald, T., Hanover St.

Walden, Henry, N. Coming St.

Waldron, G. Z. & Co., Clothing, 273 King St., G. Z. Waldron, T. A. Waldron

Waldron, G. Z., Clothing, 273 King St.

Walker & Duffus, Steam Cotton Press, Dewees' Wharf, Walker, George H. Duffus

Walker & James, Printers, 101 East Bay St., Joseph Walker, R. James

Walker, David A., Stone Cutter, 133 Meeting St.

Walker, E. J., Accountant, Pitt St.

Walker, G., Shoe Store, 168 King St.

Walker, G. W., Clerk, 208 East Bay St.

Walker, H. D., Carpenter, 18 Magazine St.

Walker, H. P., Attorney, 63 Meeting St., res, 54 Tradd St.

Walker, J. E. & Brothers, Stone Cutters, 141 Meeting St., James E. Walker, William S. Walker, David A. Walker

Walker, James E., Stone Cutter, 133 Meeting St.

Walker, James M., Attorney, St. Michael's Alley, res. 13 New St.

Walker, James, Merchant, 179 East Bay St., res. 155 East Bay St.

Walker, John C., Clerk, 101 East Bay St., res. 155 East

Bay St.

Walker, Joseph, Stationer, 101 East Bay St., res. Hasell St.

Walker, M. C., Mrs., 208 East Bay St.

Walker, R. T., Clerk, 208 East Bay St.

Walker, Thomas, Tailor, 143 King St.

Walker, William, N. Meeting St.

Walker, William S., 5 Logan St.

Walker, William S., Stone Cutter, 133 Meeting St.

Wallace & Evans, Dry Goods, 320 King St., Thomas Wallace, Charles P. Evans

Wallace, Andrew, 52 Market St.

Wallace, Cranmore, Rev., Minister, St. Stephen's Chapel, 195 East Bay St.

Wallace, Thomas, Dry Goods, 318 King St., res. 364 King St.

Wallace, William, Carpenter, 9 Price's Alley

Wallace, William N., Carpenter, 22 Wall St.

Wallis, E., Shoemaker, 9 Friend St.

Wallis, Robert, Clerk, 60 King St.

Walpole, Thomas H., Accountant, Mansion House

Walter, E. Wilmot, Merchant, Boyce's Wharf, res. 7 Meeting St.

Walter, George H., Clerk, 24 Anson St.

Walter, Jerry, Auctioneer, Vendue Range, res. 2 Glebe St.

Walter, William, Clerk, Meeting St.

Walton, J. M., Merchant, 257 King St., res. 79 Mazyck St.

Waltonden, S., Watch Maker, 359 King St.

Wanerky, W., Pinckney St., Cannonborough

Ward, C. A., Cabinet Maker, 1 Clifford St.

Ward, Daniel, Mrs., 24 Smith St.

Ward, John, Wharfinger, Adger's Wharf, res. Pitt St.

Ward, Mary, Mrs., 18 Liberty St.

Ward, -----, Misses, Teachers, 19 George St.

Wareham, John, Sailmaker, 40 State St.

Waring, C. S., Miss, 25 Lynch St.

Waring, H. S., Physician, 57 Meeting St.

Waring, M. A., N. St. Phililp St.

Waring, P. H., Planter, 10 Gadsden St.

Waring, T. D., Mason, 5 Gadsden St.

Waring, Thomas, Auditor, Railroad Co., res. 5 Gadsden St.

Waring, Thomas R., Officer, Bank of State of S. C., res. Cannon St.

Warnken, H. G., Bootmaker, 53 King St.

Warnken, J., Clerk, 4 Tradd St.

Warren, B., Druggist, Hayne St., res. 10 Boundary St.

Warren, S., Mrs., Seamstress, 137 East Bay St.

Washington, -----, Misses, 2 Legare St.

Waterbury, William, 27 Market St.

Waterman, C., Grocer, 20 State St.

Waterman, Z., Grocer, 20 State St.

Waters, Richard, Tavern Keeper, 115 Meeting St.

Waters, William, Clerk, 4 Gadsden St.

Waters, William, Clerk of Market, 124 Church St.

Waties, Julius P., Customs Officer, 17 Archdale St.

Watson, Ann, Mrs., 9 West St.

Watson, D., Mariner, 36 Tradd St.

Watson, J. R., Barber, 278 King St.

Watson, Stephen, Merchant, 9 Archdale St.

Watts, -----, Mrs., Milliner, 191 King St.

Waugh, William, 114 Church St.

Wayne, D. G., Carpenter, N. St. Philip St.

Wear, John, Shoemaker, 47 Meeting St.

Webb & Rice, Shipping Office, 85 East Bay St., M.

Webb, H. S. Rice

Webb, Daniel C., Pinckney St., Cannonborough

Webb, T. L., Factor, Southern Wharf, res. Cannon St.

Webb, W. L., Clerk, Pinckney St., Cannonborough

Webb, W. R., Boat Builder, 14 Middle St.

Webb, Walter, Gardener, 40 King St.

Webber, John, Ship Joiner, 17 Pinckney St.

Webber, Peter, 13 Queen St.

Weber, A., Bootmaker, 54 Broad St.

Weber, John, Bootmaker, 119 King St.

Weber, M., Mrs., 60 Anson St.

Weed, -----, Mrs., Teacher, 87 King St.

Wehmann, F., Grocer, 105 Broad St.

Weiring, C. W., 104 Queen St.

Welbroe, John, Grocer, 6 Archdale St.

Welch & Honour, Bookbinders, Meeting & Horlbeck's Alley, S. B. Welch, W. E. Honour

Welch, John, Carpenter, Woolf St.

Welch, John, Policeman, 40 Market St.

Welch, L. M., Shoe Dealer, 66 Market St.

Welch, M. C., Hanover St.

Welch, Michael, Morris St.

Welch, Michael, Pinckney St., Cannonborough

Welch, Samuel B., Bookbinder, Meeting St. & Horlbeck's Alley, res. 9 Smith's Lane

Welch, Thomas, Carpenter, 96 Meeting St.

Welch, W., Woolf St.

Welch, William, Bookbinder, 1 St. Philip St.

Welling, Edward, Carpenter, N. Meeting St.

Welling, Samuel, Carpenter, Nassau St.

Wells, R. T., Blacksmith, 100 Meeting St.

Welsman, James, Merchant, Boyce's Wharf, res. 2 Church St.

Welsman, James T., Merchant, Vanderhorst's Wharf, res. 16 Church St.

Wendelken, Carsten, Grocer, Line St.

Wendelken, Martin C., Grocer, Line St.

Wenderken, Martin, Clerk, 7 Pinckney St.

Wendleken, M., Sugar Refiner, 15 Anson St., res. 29 Anson St.

Werner, C., Blacksmith, 49 State St.

Werner, D., Clerk, 135 King St.

Werson, L., Plasterer, 24 Magazine Sst.

Wesner, E. A., Mrs., 4 Friend St.

West, Charles H., Ship Chandler, 77 East Bay St., res. 3 Church St.

West, Preston, Stable Keeper, 83 Meeting St., res. 97 Queen St.

Westendorff, C. P. L., Clerk, Mercury Office, res. 8 Anson St.

Westerland, C. F., Mariner, Longitude Lane

Weyman, A. C., Mrs., 63 Beaufain St.

Weyman, -----, Misses, Teachers, 38 George St.

Wharton, Edwin, Woolf St.
Wharton, Thomas, Woolf St.
Wheeler, G., Drake St.
Whilden, B., 68 Queen St.
Whilden, Joseph, Clerk, 16 Magazine St.
Whilden, L. E., Mrs., Boarders, 68 Queen St.
Whilden, William G., Clerk, 16 Magazine St.
Whiskeman, M., Mrs., Worsted Dealer, 188 King St.
Whitaker, D. K., Attorney, King St.
Whitaker, -----, Mrs., N. St. Philip St.
White, Alonzo J., Broker, 27 Broad St., res. 40 Meeting St.
White, Charles C., Mariner, 71 Meeting St.
White, Edward B., Architect, 42 Meeting St.
White, Edward, Carpenter, Kirkland's Alley
White, J. B., Attorney, 21 Legare St.
White, J. K., Broker, 16 State St.
White, James, Lamplighter, 29 Montague St.
White, Jane, Mrs., John St.
White, John, Confectioner, 301 King St.
White, Joseph, Confectioner, 301 King St.
White, Joseph, Dry Goods, 267 King St.
White, Joseph H., Factor, Boyce's Wharf, res. 46 Boundary St.
White, -----, Mrs., Teacher, 44 Wentworth St.
White, O. A., Physician, 21 Legare St.
White, Robert, Cabinet Maker, 347 King St.
White, William J., Miller, Bennett's Mills, res. 1 Wentworth St.
Whitehead, John, Engineer, Railroad, res. 6 Anson St.
Whitesides, Mary, Mrs., 22 Wall St.
Whitesone, Peter, Clerk, 297 King St.
Whiting, E. M., Turner, Boundary St.
Whiting, William, 116 Church St.
Whitney, C. G., 23 Cumberland St.
Whitney, C. N., Tallow Chandler, N. King St.
Whitney, F. C., Tallow Chandler, N. King St.
Whitney, Mary A., Mrs., 23 Cumberland St.
Whitney, P. L., 12 Smith's Lane
Whitney, T. A., Collector, 12 Horlbeck's Alley
Whittemore, C., Tallow Chandler, Radcliffe & St. Philip Sts.
Whittemore, L. S., Mrs., 63 Meeting St.
Whitty, Otto, Clerk, 225 East Bay St.
Whyte, Joseph, Teacher, 6 Mazyck St.
Wickenberg, F. R. (see Klink & Wickenberg)
Wickenburg, -----, Grocer, 44 Broad St.
Wiebens, F., Drayman, Gadsden's Wharf
Wiebens, H., Grocer, Gadsden's Wharf
Wiedemyer, F., Fruiterer, 59 Market St.
Wienges, Conrad, Clerk, 14 Water St.
Wienges, E., Nassau St.
Wienges, G. W., Clerk, 22 Burns lane
Wienges, H. W., Clerk, 276 King St.
Wienges, Jacob, 19 Pitt St.
Wienholtz, F., Tavern Keeper, 18 Elliott St.
Wienholtz, J. P., Boarders, Exchange St.
Wieschussen, D., Boundary St.
Wightman, J., Painter, 27 Broad St.
Wightman, John T., 96 Meeting St.

Wightman, W. M., Rev., D. D., Editor, Southern Christian Advocate, Meeting & Henrietta Sts.
Wilbur, W. W., Auctioneer, 176 King St.
Wild, John, Clerk, 73 King St.
Wild, Maria, Dry Goods, 73 King St.
Wildman, N. H. & Co., Hats & Caps, 161 Meeting St., N. H. Wildman, D. A. Ambler
Wildman, N. H., Hats, 161 Meeting St.
Wiley, Banks & Co., Dry Goods, 41 Hayne St., I. M. Wiley, H. R. Banks, W. G. Lane, H. Vanderzee, E. H. Lane
Wiley, James, Grocer, 373 King St.
Wiley, -----, Mrs. Atlantic St.
Wiley, Samuel, Grocer, 361 King St.
Wiley, W. J., Accountant, 16 Green St.
Wilkenning, J. H., Grocer, 59 Market St.
Wilkes, John Planter, 13 Meeting St.
Wilkie, G. W., Customs Officer, 14 Horlbeck's Alley
Wilkie, Octavious, 8 Liberty St.
Wilkie, W. B., Mrs., Boarders, 8 Liberty St.
Wilkins, -----, 261 King St.
Wilkins, B. C., Clerk, 11 Lamboll St.
Wilkins, E. B., Mrs., 11 Lamboll St.
Wilkinson, H. B., 66 Queen St.
Wilkinson, J. W., Attorney, Broad St., res. 24 Meeting St.
Willcocks, Thomas (see Gerard & Willcocks)
Willcox, Louisa, Mrs., Milliner, 157 King St.
Willcox, Thomas, Tailor, 20 Broad St., res. 157 King St.
Willhangen, -----, Policeman, 30 Church St.
Williams & Butler, Commission Merchants, East Bay St. & Brown's Wharf, John Williams, Richard Butler
Williams, C., Mrs., 19 Beaufain St.
Williams, Dorcas, Mrs., Seamstress, 52 Beaufain St.
Williams, E. H., Coal Dealer, East Bay St., res. 10 Beaufain St.
Williams, G. P., Clerk, 19 Beaufain St.
Williams, G. W., Rigger, State St.
Williams, H. H., Hatter, 1 Liberty St.
Williams, Henry, Dry Goods, N. King St.
Williams, -----, Miss, 9 Church St.
Williams, S. K., Baker, N. King St.
Williams, T. W., Pattern Maker, 70 Market St.
Williams, W. B., Merchant, Central Wharf, res. 6 King St.
Williamson, J. D., Rev., Pastor, Universalist Church, 66 Queen St.
Williamson, John, Bailiff, N. King St.
Willie, Charles, Variety Store, 208 King St.
Williman, C., Jr., Clerk, 71 East Bay St., res. 70 Tradd St.
Williman, Jacob, Attorney, 5 St. Michel's Alley, res. 43 East Bay St.
Willington, A. S. & Co., Editors, Courier, A. S. Willington, R. Yeadon, W. S. King
Willington, A. S., Editor, Courier, 50 Meeting St.
Willis, Henry, Broker, Broad St., res. Line St.
Willis, Henry, Jr., Broker, Broad St., res. Line St.
Willis, J. G., Shoe Dealer, 182 King St.
Wilmans & Co., Hardware, Hayne St., A. F. Williams, A.

H. Price, H. A. Block

Wilmans, H. F., Merchant, 23 Hayne St., res 6 Hasell St.

Wilson, A. B., N. St. Philip St.

Wilson, A. B., Radcliffe St.

Wilson, Agnes, Teacher, 90 Wentworth St.

Wilson, Charity, Mrs., 17 Hasell St.

Wilson, E. C., Mrs., Mantuamaker, 46 Society St.

Wilson, E. L., 6 Clifford St.

Wilson, E., Mrs., Monthly Nurse, 90 Wentworth St.

Wilson, Henry, Policeman, 17 Tradd St.

Wilson, Hugh, Planter, Elliott St., Neck

Wilson, Isaac M., Accountant, 18 East Bay St., res. 85 Broad St.

Wilson, Isabel, Miss, 65 Meeting St.

Wilson, J. B., Clerk, Post Office, res. 10 New St.

Wilson, J., N. King St.

Wilson, J., N. Meeting St.

Wilson, James, Clerk, 60 King St.

Wilson, James M., Merchant, Hayne St., res 6 New St.

Wilson, John, Elliott St., Neck

Wilson, Joseph, Clerk, 90 Wentworth St.

Wilson, Mary, 113 Queen St.

Wilson, -----, Mrs., 15 Queen St.

Wilson, Samuel, Physician, 10 New St.

Wilson, Thomas, Ship Carpenter, 6 Tradd St.

Wilson, W. H., 15 Church St.

Wing, Robert, Clerk, 121 King St.

Winsey, W., Lucas St.

Winslow, Edward, Agent, Steam Packets, 17 West St.

Winthrop, Frederick, Merchant, Adger's Wharf, res. 95 Tradd St.

Winthrop, Henry, Physician, 95 Tradd St.

Winthrop, John, Wood Factor. South Bay St., res. 107 Meeting St.

Winthrop, Joseph A., Factor, Adger's Wharf, res. 99 Tradd St.

Wise, Alfred, Painter, 66 Broad St., res. 3 Mazyck St.

Wish, Eliza, Mrs., Tailoress, 24 St. Philip St.

Wiskerman, E. & F. Ludikens, Worsted Goods, 255 King St.

Witcofskey, William, Tailor, 9 friend St.

Witeschiens, C., Grocer, 25 College St.

Witherby, Joel, Shoe Dealer, 290 King St.

Withers, Caroline, Mrs., 15 Savage St.

Withington, P., Iron Dealer, 34 Mazyck St.

Witt, P. F., Shoemaker, 176 East Bay St.

Witterhann, M., Store Keeper, 19 Market St.

Wittpenn, F., Seedsman, 331 King St

Witz, John, Clerk, 65 Coming St.

Wohlers, John C., Clerk, 30 Coming St.

Wolf, Ann, Mrs., Washer, 49 Meeting St.

Wolf, W., 94 Meeting St.

Wood, A. B., Clerk, 21 Hayne St.

Wood, Charles, Jeweller, 233 King St.

Wood, G. P., Boatman, 22 Anson St.

Wood, G. W., Shoe Dealer, 257 King St.

Wood, George, Clerk, 233 King St.

Wood, George, Grocer, 81 Market St., res. 24 Cumberland St.

Wood, I., N. St. Philip St.

Wood, Mary, Mrs., Seamstress, 124 Queen St.

Wood, Samuel, Painter, 27 St. Philip St.

Woodman, Peter, Miller, Bennett's Mills, res. 8 Washington St.

Woodruff, John, Druggist, Hayne St., res. 48 Church St.

Woodruff, P. D. & Co., Commission Merchants, corner Hayne & Church Sts., P. D. Woodruff, D. F. Sprague

Woodruff, P. D., Grain Merchant, 4 Hayne St., res. 21 Pickney St.

Woods, P., Clerk, 136 King St.

Woody, J. T., Blacksmith, Railroad, res. 13 Burns Lane

Woolfe, Isaac, Dry Goods, 317 King St.

Worthman, H., Elliott St., Neck

Worthman, H., N. Coming St.

Wotherspoon, R., Cotton Broker, East Bay St., res. 70 Church St.

Wotten, Henry, Mason, 5 Burns Lane

Wraeden, B., N. Coming St.

Wragg, E. L. (see Herckenwarth, Wragg & Co.)

Wragg, E., Miss, 11 Legare St.

Wragg, T. L., Merchant, Alexander St.

Wragg, William T., Physician, 66 Wentworth St.

Wredon, Henry, Grocer, 7 Pinckney St.

Wright, C. F., Mrs., Dry Goods, 122 King St.

Wright, D., 290 King St.

Wright, H., Mrs., Dry Goods, 178 King St.

Wright, Robert S., Plasterer, N. St. Philip St.

Wulbern, H., Grocer, 54 State St.

Wyld, Vincent, Boiler Maker, Gadsden's Wharf, res. 3 Inspection St.

Yates, E. A., Mrs., 9 Church St.

Yates, F. W., Clerk Vanderhorst's Wharf, res. 11 New St.

Yates, F. W., Officer, Bank of S. C., res. 11 New St.

Yates, J., Customs Officer, 21 Church St.

Yates, J. D., State Treasurer, Fireproof Building, res. 9 Church St.

Yates, J. L., Accountant, 5 Water St.

Yates, J. L., Clerk, Accommodation Wharf, res. 11 New St.

Yates, Jeremiah, Mrs., 21 Church St.

Yates, Martha, Mrs., 122 King St.

Yates, W. B., Rev., Pastor, Mariners' Church, 25 East Bay St.

Yates, W., N. King St.

Yates, W., Shoe Dealer, 359 King St.

Yeadon & McBeth, Attorneys, Law Range, R. Yeadon, C. MacBeth

Yeadon, R., Attorney, Law Range, res. 56 Wentworth St.

Yeadon, S. V., N. Coming St.

Yeadon, William, Col., Powder Receiver, Powder Magazine

You, Dandridge C., 8 Archdale St.

Young, C. D., Merchant, 6 State St.

Young, James, Mariner, 2 Archdale St.

Young, T. J., Rev., Assistant Minister, St. Michael's, 5 Smith's Lane

Young, William, Clerk, 33 Church St.

Zachariah, J., Dry Goods, 147 King St.

Zager, H., Thomas St.

Zeagler, M. W., 179 Meeting St.
Zealy, Joseph, Officer, Union Bank, 13 Rutledge St.
Zeche, H., Cannon St.
Zeche, W., Cannon St.
Zylstra, J. P., Clerk, 59 Broad St.
Zylstra, John, 114 Church St.

The 1852 Directory

J. H. Bagett, who is not listed in this volume, published *Directory of the City of Charleston for the Year 1852. Containing the Names, Occupation, Place of Business & Residence of the Inhabitants Generally, With Other Information of General Interest* (Charleston: Edward C. Councell, 1851). The directory has 5,848 entries. Boundary Street had been renamed Calhoun Street by this time. In addition, the area above Calhoun Street had been annexed into the city. The four old wards were below Calhoun and the four new ones above that street. The lower wards were divided by Queen Street one way (east-west) and Meeting Street the other (north-south). The four upper wards were divided by Amherst, Woolf and Cannon streets (east-west) and King Street (north-south). The directory does not indicate free persons of color.

Abbott, George, Paint, Oil & Lamp Dealer, 97 East Bay St.
Abbott, -----, Mrs., Milliner & Dress Maker, 43 Wentworth St.
Abrahams, A. H., Merchant, 38 State St.
Abrahams, Elias, 94 Queen St.
Abrahams, J. M., Silk Dyer & Scourer, 15 St. Philip St.
Abrahams, -----, Tailor, 39 Archdale St.
Abrams, Abram, Machinist, 30 Tradd St.
Abrams, Alexander, Factor, Dewee's Wharf, res. 33 St. Philip St.
Adams, A., Seaman, 11 Middle St.
Adams, Alexander, Clerk, 220 King St.
Adams, E. L., Factor, Adger's Wharf, res. cr. Smith & Bull Sts.
Adams, -----, Mrs., 120 King St.
Adams, W. S., Bricklayer & Stove Dealer, 34 Broad St., res. 82 Wentworth St.
Addison & McIntosh, Ship Builders, Marshal Wharf
Addison, Alexander, St. Philip St., Ward 6
Addison, George, Watchmaker, 185 East Bay St.
Addison, J. S., Ship Builder, Marshal's Wharf, res. 26 Marsh St.
Addison, James, Wood Factor, 9 South Bay St., res. 15 South Bay St.
Addison, John, Ship Carpenter, St. Philip St., Ward 6
Addison, William, Mechanic, 26 Beaufain St.
Adger, J. E., Hardware Dealer, 54 East Bay St., res. 200 East Bay St.
Adger, J. R., Pastor, Anson St. Church, res. 247 East Bay St.
Adger, James & Co., Cotton Merchants, Adger's Wharf
Adger, James, Cotton Merchant, Adger's Wharf, res. King St., Ward 7
Adger, James, Jr., Cotton Merchant, Adger's Wharf, res. King St., Ward 7
Adger, Robert, Cotton Merchant, Adger's Wharf, res. King St., Ward 7
Adger, W. & J. E., Hardware Dealers, 54 East Bay St.
Adger, W., Hardware Dealer, 54 East Bay St., res. Charlotte St.
Adicks, John, Bootmaker, King St., Ward 5

Adkins, S., Pilot, 57 East Bay St.
Adsden, Martha, 52 Coming St.
Affanassieffe, D., Paint Dealer, 37 Coming St.
Agnew, James, Wheelwright, King St., res. Reid St.
Agrill, S., Mrs., Calhoun St.
Ahrens, C. D., Grocer, 165 King St.
Ahrens, Henry, Clerk, 57 Coming St.
Ahrens, John, Clerk, 19 Wall St.
Aiken, J. D., Attorney, St. Michael's Alley, res. cr. Charlotte & Alexander Sts.
Aiken, William, Planter, Edisto Island, res. cr. Elizabeth & Judith Sts.
Aimar, C. P., Accountant, 244 King St., res. 30 Archdale St.
Aimar, G. W., Clerk, 31 Broad St., res. 30 Archdale St.
Ainger, E., Mrs., 39 Tradd St.
Albergotti, T. E., 48 Church St.
Albergotti, T. W., Confectioner, 366 King St.
Albergotti, W., Clerk, Meeting St., res. 48 Church St.
Albers, Frederick, Drayman, Woolf St.
Albright, G., Tailor, 37 Queen St.
Albright, -----, Mrs., Midwife, 27 Anson St.
Albright, N., Grocer, 19 South Bay St.
Alburn, John, Clerk, 66 Beaufain St.
Alderson, J. F., Door, Sash & Blind Maker, Council St., res. cr. Council & Tradd Sts.
Alexander, G. H. T., Clerk, 30 East Bay St., res. 19 State St.
Alexander, H. D., Clerk, Union Bank, 106 Church St.
Alexander, H., Mrs., Calhoun St., Ward 5
Alexander, J. D., Clerk & Notary, Bank of State of South Carolina, res. Calhoun St., Ward 6
Alexander, J., Physician, Calhoun St., Ward 5
Alexander, R. N., Clerk, 25 Vendue Range, res. 48 Bull St.
Alexander, S., Rigger, 45 King St.
Alexander, Samuel, Harbor Master, 89 East Bay St., res. cr. Bull & Lynch Sts.
Alexander, Thomas, 12 East Bay St.
Alfs, C., Castor Oil Manufacturer, King St., Ward 5
Allan, Alexander, Carpenter, Rutledge St., Ward 8
Allan, -----, Mrs., Milliner, Rutledge St., Ward 8
Allason, Thomas, Saddler & Harness Dealer, 293 King St.
Allemong, A. A., Attorney, 17 Broad St., res. 61 Meeting St.
Allen, T. P., Bookseller & Stationer, 116 Meeting St., res. 5 Society St.
Allerd, Thomas, Clerk, 280 King St.
Allers, C., Grocer, Calhoun, Ward 5
Alley, J. B. P., Cabinet Maker, 62 Queen St., res. 80 King St.
Allison, G., Bootmaker, 87 Church St.
Alston, C., Mrs., 7 East Battery St.
Alston, Catharine, 20 Burns Lane
Alston, Charles, Planter at Waccamaw, res. 15 East Battery St.
Alston, R. A., Clerk, 143 Meeting St., res. Commercial Hotel
Alston, William, Planter at Waccamaw, Ashley St.

Ambler, D. A., Hatter, 161 Meeting St., res. Charleston Hotel
Amell, A. M., Proprietor, Sailors Home, 8 Market St.
Amlox, -----, Bootmaker, 38 Queen St.
Amme, D. A., Grocer, 22 St. Philip St.
Amme, H., Tailor, 17 Queen St.
Ancrum, Hasell, Planter, Mary St.
Anderson, A. C., Clerk, cr. King & Market Sts., res. Victoria Hotel
Anderson, A. L., Clerk, 1 Hayne St., res. Meeting St.
Anderson, A. T., Accountant, 54 East Bay St., res. 236 King St.
Anderson, A., Tavern Keeper, 30 State St.
Anderson, Daniel, Coachmaker, Jasper's Corner
Anderson, Robert, Accountant, 20 Cumberand St., res. 48 Meeting St.
Anderson, W. H., Physician, 13 Hasell St., res. 22 Society St.
Andrews, A. O., Factor, 27 Hasell St.
Andrews, J. J. J., Clerk, 24 Vendue Range, cr. Society & Meeting Sts.
Angel, R., Mrs., Private Boarding, Carolina Hotel
Angele, James, Fruiterer, 4 Guignard St.
Angres, John, Tailor, 99½ East Bay St.
Angus, John, Milk Seller, Nassau St.
Angus, Thomas C., Butcher, Nassau St.
Annely, A. L., Miss, 8 Rutledge St.
Annely, A. M., Miss, 8 Rutledge St.
Ansell, F., Cabinet Maker, 296 King St.
Ansell, H. O., Clerk, 110 East Bay St., res. 279 King St.
Ansell, John, Cabinet Maker, res. 296 King St.
Anthony, J., Mrs., King St., Ward 5
Apela, D., Grocer, cr. King & Reid Sts.
Apeler, J. F., Grocer, Chapel St.
Apler, -----, Cabinet Maker, 4 Beaufain St.
Archer, Benjamin, Coach Trimmer, 47 St. Philip St.
Arlay, James, America St.
Arms, -----, Miss, 18 George St.
Armstrong, A., Clerk, Hayne St., res. 17 Middle St.
Armstrong, A. D., Clerk, 31 Hayne St., res. Wentworth St.
Armstrong, D. F., Clerk, 155 East Bay St., res. Charlotte St.
Armstrong, J. A., Clerk, 133 Meeting St., res. Market St.
Armstrong, James, Clerk, 35 Hayne St., res. Market St.
Armstrong, L., Saddler, 47 Coming St.
Armstrong, W. G., Accountant, Bennett's Mills, res. Charlotte St.
Armstrong, William, Clerk, 35 Hayne St., res. Market St.
Arnau, Michael, Blacksmith, Calhoun St., res. Washington St.
Arner, J. J., Clerk, 238 King St., res. 102 Church St.
Arnholder, William, Gas Fitter, 16 Beaufain St.
Arnold, F., Bootmaker, 100 Meeting St.
Arnold, John, Stone Cutter, 11 Tradd St.
Arnold, L., Mrs., 15 Smith St.
Arnold, R., Blacksmith, 129 Church St., 7 College St.
Arnold, Thomas, Printer, 66 Queen St.
Arnot, William, Painter, 29 Broad St.
Artman, John, Coach Maker, 5 Archdale St.

Artope, G. P., Superintendent, Bennett's Mills, res. Bennett's Mills
Ash, H., Hatter, 149 King St.
Ashby, A., Miss, 2 West St.
Ashby, E., Mrs., Dressmaker, 159 King St.
Ashby, H., Mrs., Private Boarding, 43 East Bay St.
Ashby, L. P., Printer, 159 King St.
Ashe, John S., Col., 23 Meeting St.
Ashton, William, Watch Maker, 210 King St.
Aspinwall, Albert, Tailor, Henrietta St.
Astle, George, Milk Seller, 84 King St.
Atkinson, C., Commission Merchant, 2 Central Wharf, res. Mansion House
Atkinson, Thomas, Coming St.
Aubert & Soyer, Confectioners, 285 King St.
Aubert, L. M., Confectioner, 285 King St.
Austin, Robert, Broker, 10 State St., res. Planters Hotel
Aveilhe, P. A., Commission Merchant, 171 East Bay St., res. George St.
Avery, L., Accountant, 157 Meeting St., res. Victoria Hotel
Awls, -----, Misses, 8 George St.
Axson, A., Mrs., 33 King St.
Axson, C. H., Magistrate, 63 Broad St., res. 6 King St.
Axson, H. T., Clerk, 24 Hayne St., res. 17 Meeting St.
Axson, J. W., Clerk, 35 Hayne St., 17 Meeting St.
Axson, S. E., Ship Carpenter, 33 King St.
Axson, W. J., Clerk, Commercial Wharf, res. 17 Meeting St.
Babcock, T. C., Clerk, 259 King St., res. 236 King St.
Babcock, W. H., Medical Student, Planters Hotel
Babcock, W. R., Bookseller & Stationer, 259 King St., res. Planters Hotel
Babson, -----, Mrs., 55 State St.
Bachman, J., Pastor, Lutheran Church, Rutledge St., Ward 6
Backes, F., Watchmaker, 82 Meeting St.
Backus, F. & Co., Dry Goods, 192 King St.
Backus, F., Dry Goods, 192 King St.
Bacon, J. C. S., Clerk, 192 King St., res. 159 King St.
Bacon, J. W., Dry Goods, 192 King St.
Bacot, R. D., Clerk, 26 East Bay St., res. 61 Coming St.
Bacot, R. W., Factor, 13 Southern Wharf, cr. King & Tradd Sts.
Bacot, T. W., Mrs., cr. King & Tradd Sts.
Badenhoys, H., Clerk, Rutledge & Spring Sts.
Badger, Mary, Mrs., 116 King St.
Baer, Charles, Bathing House, 63 Church St.
Bagget, J. H., Publisher, City Directory, Merchants Hotel
Bahntege, F. W., Grocer, cr. Calhoun & Alexander Sts.
Bahntege, H., Grocer, 76 Church St.
Bailey, David, Attorney, 77 Broad St., res. Hudson St.
Bailey, Gerard, 50 Meeting St.
Bailey, J. A., Grocer, 98 East Bay St., res. Planters Hotel
Bailey, J. G., Clerk, 219 King St., res. Merchants Hotel
Bailey, M., Mrs., 49 Calhoun St.
Bailey, R. S., Physician, Hudson St.
Bailey, S. M., Clerk, cr. East Bay St. & Commercial Wharf
Bailey, Samuel, Seaman, Bedon's Alley

Bailing, -----, Mrs., Wragg Square
Bakeman, J. C., Grist Miller, Market St., res. St. Philip St., Ward 6
Baker, B. E., Clerk, 42 East Bay St., res. 20 King St.
Baker, E. B., Clerk, 159 Meeting St., res. 94 Tradd St.
Baker, E. B., Engineer, King St., Ward 6
Baker, F. A., Plasterer, Coming St.
Baker, H. F., Packet Agent & Coal Dealer, 120 East Bay St., res. 19 Smith St.
Baker, H. Harned, Commissioner of Deeds, 281 King St.
Baker, H. Hern, Clerk, 181 East Bay St., res. Lamboll St.
Baker, R. B., Planter, Ashley River, res. 8 Lamboll St.
Baker, R. S., Pastor, St. Mary's Church, res. 62 Wentworth St.
Baker, Robert, Planter, 249 King St.
Baker, T. E., Tavern Keeper, Market & Meeting Sts., res. King St.
Ball, E., Mrs., 25 Lynch St.
Ball, Isaac, 30 Society St.
Ball, John, Planter, Cooper River, res. cr. Vernon & East Bay Sts.
Ball, W. J., Planter, Cooper River, res. cr. Vernon & East Bay Sts.
Ballard, John, Carpenter, Hanover St.
Ballard, Joseph, Accountant, Standard Office, res. 75 King St.
Bancroft, E. W., Dry Goods,143 meeting St., res. Charleston Hotel
Bancroft, Edward, Commission Merchant, 15 Coming St.
Bancroft, Goodwin & Dawson, Commission Merchants, 94 & 96 East Bay St.
Bancroft, J. & Co., Commission Merchants, 94 & 96 East Bay St.
Bancroft, J. K., Clerk, 253 & 255 King St.
Bancroft, James, Commssion Merchant, 15 Coming St.
Bancroft, James, Jr., Commission Merchant, 15 Coming St.
Bancroft, W. G., Dry Goods, 253 & 255 King St., res. Charleston Hotel
Banks, H. L., Mrs., 9 Short St.
Banks, H. R., Dry Goods, 41 Hayne St., res. 75 Wentworth St.
Banks, W. L., Clerk, 41 Hayne St., res. 9 Short St.
Barber, F. C., Broker, 116 Church St.
Barbot, A. A., Engineer, res. 41 East Bay St.
Barbot, A., Commission Merchant, 41 East Bay St.
Barbot, A., Jr., Engineer, 41 East Bay St.
Barbot, A. O., Engineer, 41 East Bay St.
Barbot, C. D., Clerk, 4 Broad St., res. 41 East Bay St.
Barbot, L. J., Clerk, 46 Broad St., res. 41 East Bay St.
Barbot, P. G., Accountant, Commercial Wharf, 41 East Bay St.
Barfield, J. S., Clerk, 235 King St., res. 9 Franklin St.
Bargman, P., Grocer, Rutledge St.
Barh, L. N., Commission Merchant, Adger's Wharf, res. America St.
Barker & Wardlaw, Factors & Commission Merchants, Atlantic Wharf
Barker, H. C., Mrs., 20 Coming St.
Barker, S. G., Factor & Commission Merchant, Atlantic Wharf, res. cr. Glebe & Wentworth Sts.
Barker, Theodore, 70 Wentworth St.
Barksdale, M., Miss, 18 Hasell St.
Barnet, Juliet, Mazyck St.
Barns, James, Butcher, John St.
Barns, Thomas, Railroad Conductor, Columbus St.
Barnwell, B. S., Clerk, cr. King & Market Sts., res. Mazyck St.
Barnwell, Edward, Jr., Factor, 3 Southern Wharf, res. cr. Meeting St. & Price's Alley
Barnwell, J. L., Clerk, cr. King & Market Sts., res. Mazyck St.
Barnwell, Nathaniel, Factor, 19 Vanderhorst's Wharf, res. 43 E. Bay St.
Barnwell, William, Pastor, St. Peter's Church
Barrader, Joseph, Railroad Engineer, 14 Beaufain St.
Barre, John, Spirits Dealer, 23 Market St., res. 24 George St.
Barren, Joseph, Carpenter, 37 Montague St.
Barrette, R., Clerk, 177 King St., res. 76 King St.
Barron, Francis, Carpenter, 5 Montague St.
Barron, Joseph, Wheelwright, Calhoun St., Ward 5
Barrot, Jacob, Planter, Drake St.
Barrow, David, Clerk, 16 East Bay St., res. 2 Magazine St.
Barrows, J. E., Carpenter, 26 Mazyck St.
Barry, John Dry Goods, King St., Ward 6
Bartels, William, Tailor, 18 Calhoun St.
Barth, W. H. C., Clerk, 109 East Bay St., res. 7 Liberty St.
Bartless, W. H., Commission Merchant, 4 Vendue Range, res. Spring St.
Bartlett, F. C., Boots & Shoes, 283 King St., res. Coming St., Ward 6
Bartlett, H., Boots & Shoes, 283 King St., res. Coming St., Ward 6
Bartlett, J. L., Rev., 77 Wentworth St.
Bartlett, William, America St.
Barton, A. J., Clerk, 89 Beaufain St., res. 116 Wentworth St.
Barton, J., Physician, 54 Tradd St.
Bascon, Q., Upholsterer, Coming St., Ward 6
Bass, J. A., Clerk, 135 Meeting St., res. Commercial Hotel
Bass, Margaret, Coming St., Ward 6
Basset, O., Printer, 38 Coming St.
Batchelder, J., Pile Driver, 147 East Bay St., res. King St.
Bates, E., Engineer, 72 Church St.
Bates, Edwin, Clothier, 118 Meeting St., res. Pavilion Hotel
Bates, J., Miss, Teacher, 14 Church St.
Bates, J. R., Clerk, 135 Meeting St., res. Merchants Hotel
Bates, M., Miss, Teacher, 14 Church St.
Battersby, Joseph, Commission Merchant, Adger's Wharf
Baum, J. A., Accountant, 286 King St.
Baum, J. P., Leather & Findings, 286 King St.
Baussang, Francis, Fruiterer, 78 King St.
Baxtell, R. R., Mrs., 12 Church St.

Baxter, -----, Mrs., King St., Ward 6
Beach, E. M., Grain Dealer, cr. East Bay St. &
Commercial Wharf, res. Meeting St.
Beach, J. S., Bookseller & Stationer, 5 Hayne St., res.
Bee St.
Beach, W. H., Fancy Goods, 19 Hayne St., res.
Charleston Hotel
Beamer, Charlotte, St. Philip St., Ward 6
Beattie, Ann, Mrs., Cannon St.
Beaudrot, Joseph, Gunsmith, 45 State St., res. 1
Cumberland St.
Beaufort, A., Bootmaker, 94 Meeting St.
Beazley, W. B., Dry Goods, 349 King St.
Becher, F. H., Accountant, 14 Liberty St.
Beckett, W. L., Clerk, 253 King St., res. 49 Beaufain St.
Beckman, A., Coming St.
Beckman, C. J., Grist Miller, 61 Market St., res. St.
Philip St.
Beckman, Charles, Clerk, Railroad, Radcliffe St.
Beckman, J. C., Grist Miller, 61 Market St., res. John St.
Beckman, J. F., Attorney, Court House Square, res.
Calhoun St., Ward 6
Beckman, J. O., Clerk, Calhoun St., Ward 6
Beckman, John, Laborer, Rutledge St., Ward 8
Bee & Tylee, Ship Chandlers, 123 East Bay St.
Bee, Benjamin, Finisher, Rutledge St., Ward 6
Bee, G. W., Clerk, 76 East Bay St., res. 8 Beaufain St.
Bee, Henry, Laborer, King St., Ward 6
Bee, J. B., Outdoor Clerk, State Bank, res. 8 Beaufain St.
Bee, J. J., Carpenter, Cannon St.
Bee, J. M., Collector & Notary, State Bank, res. 8
Beaufain St.
Bee, J., Mrs., Rutledge St., Ward 6
Bee, J. P., Wharfinger, 6 Southern Wharf, res. 4 Orange
St.
Bee, J. R., Ship Chandler, 123 East Bay St., res. 8
Beaufain St.
Bee, R. R., Cooper, Adger's Wharf, res. cr. Legare &
South Bay Sts.
Bee, Richard, Blacksmith, Rutledge St., Ward 6
Bee, W. C., Factor, 13 Southern Wharf, res. 108 Tradd
St.
Bee, W. H., Sea Captain, 33 King St.
Bee, William, Finisher, Rutledge St., Ward 6
Beesley, James, Tavern Keeper, 20 Queen St.
Beesley, John, Tailor, King St.
Behan, Thomas, Gardener, Spring St.
Behling, E. F., Tavern Keeper, cr. Elliott & East Bay Sts.
Behrans, F. W., Tailor, 93 King St.
Behre, H., Grocer, cr. St. Philip & Warren Sts.
Behre, Henry, Shopkeeper, Radcliffe St.
Beisner, H., Grocer, 66 Beaufain St.
Bekotter, W., Bootmaker, 73 Meeting St., res. 28 Market
St.
Belin, A. H., Planter, Georgetown District, res. 93 Broad
St.
Belitzer, J., Clothier, 265 King St.
Bell, David, Accountant, Merchants Hotel, res. 6 Broad
St.
Bell, J. L., Cooper, cr. East Bay St. & Boyce's Wharf,

res. 71 Meeting St.
Bell, Samuel, Pilot, 57 Tradd St.
Bell, Sarah, Dressmaker, 2 Green St.
Bell, William, Pilot, 73 East Bay St.
Bell, William, Planter, St. Thomas' Parish, res. 38
Society St.
Bellinger, H., Mrs., 10 Bull St.
Bellinger, John, Physician, 11 College St.
Belser, L., Mrs., 20 Friend St.
Benford, Mary J., Spring St.
Benjamin, S. A., Clothier, under America Hotel
Bennett, C. G., Printer, 109 Church St.
Bennett, E. S., Physician, 23 Rutledge St.
Bennett, J. B., Printer, 109 Church St.
Bennett, J. S. K., Assistant Teller, Union Bank, res.
Charlotte St.
Bennett, S. P., Lumber Measurer, 98 Beaufain St.
Bennett, T. B., Superintendent, Sawmills, Calhoun St.
Bennett, Thomas, Steam Sawmill, west end of Calhoun
St.
Bennett, W. J., Rice Mill, East Bay St., res. 28 Montague
St.
Bensch, Charles, Tavern Keeper, 143 King St.
Bense, John, Laborer, Anson St.
Benson, W. G., Auctioneer, Morris St.
Benthan, Emeline, Pastry Cook, 49 St. Philip St.
Bentschner, J., Clerk, 265 King St.
Bergman, A., Trader, Spring St.
Berlin & Nathans, Grocers, King St., Ward 6
Berlin, R., Grocer, King St., Ward 6, res. King St., Ward
5
Bernard, A. W., Planter, Combahee, res. 6 Legare St.
Bernard, C., Mrs., Milliner, 257 King St.
Berrie, C. J., Clerk, 300 King St., res. 65 King St.
Berry, Francis, Clerk, 18 Broad St., res. 47 Calhoun St.
Berry, M., Mrs., res. 47 Calhoun St.
Berry, M., Steamship Captain, 127 King St.
Berry, Thomas, Clerk, 143 East Bay St., res. 47 Calhoun
St.
Bessent, A. W., Clerk, 246 King St., res. cr. Meeting &
Market Sts.
Betsel, J. M., Coachmaker, Cumberland St.
Bettison, Elizabeth, 15 Mazyck St.
Betts, Charles, Presiding Elder, Calhoun St., Ward 6
Betts, E. C., Clerk, 155 Meeting St., res. 21 Cumberland
St.
Betts, J. B., Francy Goods, 135 Meeting St., res. 21
Cumberland St.
Betts, W. H., Hardware, 80 East Bay St.
Beverson, J. G., Clerk, 13 Beaufain St., res. 11 Beaufain
St.
Beylot, Francis, Cook, Nassau St.
Bia, H., Clerk, 25 Broad St., res. 99½ East Bay St.
Biance, A., Bootmaker, 57 Church St.
Bicaise, Ann, Mrs., Private Boarding, 225 East Bay St.
Bicaise, B. P., Gunsmith, 50 State St.
Bicaise, M. Ann., Mantuamaker, Calhoun St., Ward 5
Bicaise, P. P., Gunsmith, 50 State St.
Bickley, J. C., Clerk, 68 East Bay St., res. Vanderhorst
St.

Bickley, John, Planter, Vanderhorst St.
Billings, J., Mrs., Williams Row
Bilton, George, Tailor, 9 Tradd St.
Bing, Gordon, Carter, Coming St., Ward 6
Bing, John, Tailor, Morris St.
Bing, Robert, Tailor, Morris St.
Bingley, C. W., 253 East Bay St.
Bingley, D. P., Clerk, 41 Hayne St., res. 253 East Bay St.
Binns, John, Proprietor of Drays, Hanover St.
Birch, C. A., Mrs., 12 Coming St.
Bird, C. H., Clerk, 225 King St., res. 16 Coming St.
Bird, Cooper, Wood Factor, Bennett's Mill, 100 Wentworth St.
Bird, J. S. & Co., Fancy & Military Goods, 225 King St.
Bird, J. S., Fancy and Military Goods, 225 King St.
Bird, William, Jr., Ship Carpenter, 100 Wentworth St.
Bird, William, Ship Builder, 23 South Bay St., 100 Wentworth St.
Biren, J. K., Cooper, Elizabeth St.
Birnie & Ogilvie, Hardware, 21 Broad St.
Birnie, William, President of Bank of South Carolina, res. Smith St.
Bischoff, A., Grocer, 163 East Bay St.
Bischoff, H., Grocer, 55 East Bay St.
Bischoff, J., Grocer, 5 King St.
Bishop, Henry, Clerk, 50 St. Philip St.
Bisken, H., Clerk, 80 Beaufain St.
Bissell, J. B., Clerk, 147 Meeting St., res. 36 Wentworth St.
Bissell, T. L., Clerk, 155 Meeting St., res. 36 Wentworth St.
Bize, R. B., Farmer, Woolf St.
Black, A. F., Wood Factor, Southern Wharf, 9 Savage St.
Black, A. W., Notary Public, 91 East Bay St., res. 11 Savage St.
Black, D., Mrs., Baker, 189 King St.
Black, E. J., Clerk, 91 East Bay St., res. Queen St.
Black, Ed, Assistant Clerk, Bank of South Carolina, res. 10 Water St.
Black, F. C., Commission Merchant, 11 Exchange St., res. 41 Wentworth St.
Black, G. W., Mason, 29 Society St.
Black, H. C., Clerk, cr. King & Market Sts., res. 236 King St.
Black, S. C., Clerk, 11 Exchange St., res. 41 Wentworth St.
Black, S., Mrs., Shopkeeper, 41 King St.
Black, Thomas, 29 Society St.
Blacklock, J. F., Factor, cr. East Bay St. & Vanderhorst's Wharf, res. 4 Bull St.
Blackman, James, Clerk, Railroad, 22 Beaufain St.
Blackman, Joseph, Druggist, 17 Broad St., res. 22 Beaufain St.
Blackman, S., Mrs., 22 Beaufain St.
Blackwood, B. G., Clerk, 54 East Bay St., res. Commercial Hotel
Blackwood, H., Mrs., 28 Pitt St.
Blackwood, J. C., Clerk, Brown's Wharf, res. 8 Montague St.
Bladen, B., Plasterer, 30 Tradd St.

Blain, J. E. A., Clerk, Atlantic Wharf, res. 120 Queen St.
Blain, N. T., Mrs., Teacher, 120 Queen St.
Blair, -----, Mrs., Teacher, Meeting St., Ward 5
Blair, W. McN., Clerk, 154 East Bay St., res. Meeting St., Ward 5
Blake, J. A., Clerk, 76 East Bay St., res. 10 Water St.
Blake, J., Mrs., cr. Thomas & Warren Sts.
Blake, John, Carpenter, Calhoun St., Ward 5
Blake, Peter, Porter, 181 East Bay St.
Blanchild, Ed, Carpenter, Radcliffe St.
Blanchild, S., Carpenter, Coming St., Ward 5
Bland, James, Carpenter, Henrietta St.
Blanding, -----, Mrs., 2 Logan St.
Blanding, O., Attorney, 11 Broad St., res. 2 Logan St.
Blanding, W., Attorney, 34 Broad S., res. 2 Logan St.
Blank, Mary, Mantuamaker, Coming St., Ward 6
Blank, William, Carpenter, 6 Middle St.
Blanmyer, William, Planter, St. John's Parish, res. 273 East Bay St.
Bliss, T. W., Tinner, 109 Meeting St., res. 11 Horlbeck Alley
Blohme, J. C., Grocer, 66 Meeting St.,
Blondo, E., 70 Anson St.
Bloom, H., Confectioner, 16 King St.
Blueto, John, Constable, 8 Orange St.
Blum & Cobia, Auctioneer & Commission Merchant, 26 Vendue Range
Blum, F. C., Lumber Factor, 98 Beaufain St., res. St. Philip St., Ward 6
Blum, J. Andrew, Teacher, Mary St.
Blum, J. Charles, Auctioneer & Commission Merchant, 26 Vendue Range, res. 6 Beaufain St.
Blya, Patrick, Dry Goods, King St., Ward 5
Blyding, C., Accountant, 26 Hayne St. cr. Market & King Sts.
Boag, C. L., Clerk, 24 Vendue Range, res. 24 George St.
Boag, T. G., Clerk, Atlantic Wharf, res. 24 George St.
Bobbs, Elizur, Henrietta St.
Bocken, H., Grocer, 59 Market St.
Boerin, Mary, 81 Wentworth St.
Boerro, E., Fruiterer, 60 Market St.
Boesch, J. U., Coppersmith, 18 Market St.
Boesch, N., French Dyer, 80 King St.
Boggs, Robert, Clerk, 25 Hayne St., res. 236 King St.
Bohlts, M., Mrs., Grocer, 24 Archdale St.
Boils, H. L., Teacher, Wentworth St., res. 23 Pinckney St.
Boinest, M., Mrs., 46 Queen St.
Bolger, H. M., Cabinet Maker, King St., Ward 5
Bolger, T. W., Harness Maker, King St., Ward 5
Boll, A. M., Spring St.
Bolles, J. H., Clerk, 251 King St., res. 249 King St.
Bollman, B., Clerk, 16 Vendue Range, res. 1 Horlbeck Alley
Bollman, D., 22 St. Philip St.
Bollman, H., Grocer, 320 King St.
Bolzhoz, Theodore, Molder, 20 Middle St.
Bomar, -----, Proprietor, Commercial Hotel, cr. Queen & Church Sts.
Bonck, Henry, Nurse, Hospital, Poor House

Bonfield, L., Bootmaker, 102 Queen St.
Bonneau & Mazyck, Shipping Merchants, 7 Boyce & Co. Wharf
Bonneau, A., Miss, 5 Friend St.
Bonneau, E., Miss, 5 Friend St.
Bonneau, F. N., Shipping Merchant, 7 Boyce & Co. Wharf, res. 106 Tradd St.
Bonneau, M., Miss, 5 Friend St.
Bonnell, Jacob, Wheelwright, 6 Atlantic St.
Bonnell, John, 6 Atlantic St.
Bonnell, John, Iron Merchant, Boyce & Co. Wharf, res. 84 Wentworth St.
Bonnell, Thomas, Commission Merchant, 13 Exchange St., res. 6 Atlantic St.
Bonner, John, Carpenter, 302 King St.
Bonnoit, J. F., Clerk, 259 King St., res. cr. King & Calhoun Sts.
Bontheneau, C., Bond & Register Clerk, Custom House
Bonymaster, -----, 58 Meeting St.
Boon, W. J., Bricklayer, Bee St.
Boone, J. S., Attorney, 20 Broad St., res. 10 Middle St.
Boothe, William, 10 Magazine St.
Bordenave, John, Tobacconist, 103 East Bay St., res. 28 Middle St.
Boring, W. H., Tobacconist, King St., Ward 7
Born, W. I., Bricklayer, Bee St.
Borneman, F., Engraver, 271 King St.
Bose, Peter, Clerk, 192 King St.
Bostwick, Ed, Attorney, 9 Broad St., res. 13 South Bay St.
Bouge, E., Mrs., 38 George St.
Boultan, Peter, 118 King St.
Bounetheau, E. W., Magistrate, 34 Broad St.
Bours, T. B., Dry Goods, 40 East Bay St., res. 41 Church St.
Bouse, John, Carpenter, Paine Court
Bowen, M., Mrs., 24 South Bay St.
Bowers, J. A., Line St.
Bowie, J. S. & L., Dry Goods, 122 Meeting St.
Bowie, J. S., Dry Gods, 122 Meeting St., res. 22 Hasell St.
Bowie, J. Sheridan, Clerk, 122 Meeting St., res. 22 Hasell St.
Bowie, L., Dry Goods, 122 Meeting St., res. 13 Hasell St.
Bowie, Robert, Clerk, 122 Meeting St., res. 22 Hasell St.
Bowls, A., 65 Calhoun St.
Bowman, E. L., Mrs., 30 Pitt St.
Bowman, G. A., Accountant, 30 Broad St., res. 3 Franklin St.
Bowman, M., Mrs., 30 Pitt St.
Bowrie, H. J., Bootmaker, 25 Beaufain St., res. 85 Wentworth St.
Boyce, Jerome, Drayman, 63 Anson St.
Boyce, John, Drayman, Ann St.
Boyland, P., Clerk, cr. Meeting & Market Sts.
Boyling, Patrick, Laborer, 24 Tradd St.
Boylston, H., Jr., Clerk, 1 Hayne St., res. King St., Ward 5
Boylston, H., Physician, King St., Ward 5

Boylston, J. R., Dry Goods, 1 Hayne St., res. King St., Ward 5
Bradford & Patton, Factors & Commission Merchants, Accommodation Wharf
Bradford, J. B., Factor & Commission Merchant, Accommodation Wharf, res. Huntsville, Ala.
Bradford, W., Blacksmith, Gillon St., res. Vernon St.
Bradley, C. P., Farmer, Sires St.
Bradley, J. C., Tavern Keeper, Four Mile House, res. Sires St.
Brady, C., Mrs., 11 Calhoun St.
Brady, E., Mrs., 11 Calhoun St.
Brady, F., Grist Mill, 17 Bull St., res. 12 Archdale St.
Brady, John, Clerk, Brown's Wharf, res. 122 Church St.
Brady, M., Mrs., 11 Calhoun St.
Brady, Patrick, Dry Goods, 74 King St.
Brady, Patrick, Wood Factor, Smith's Wharf, res. Church St.
Braidman, Henry, Laborer, Meeting St., Ward 7
Brailsford, J. M., Physician, 37 East Bay St., res. 15 Church St.
Brailsford, R. M., Physician, Cannon St.
Brailsford, W. R., Commission Merchant, 4 Gillon St., res. 1 Orange St.
Brailsord, -----, Mrs., Cannon St.
Branan, Thomas, Drayman, 13 Marsh St.
Branch, J. L., Clerk, 116 East Bay St., res. Broad St.
Brandes, Peter, Pussly St.
Branford, C. G., Coachmaker, Mary St.
Brant, C. W., Ship Carpenter, 2 Washington St.
Brant, H. F., Confectioner, 299 King St
Brant, Thomas, Mechanic, 92 Anson St.
Brawley, J. H., Dry Goods, 181 East Bay St.
Brawley, J. M., Clerk, 181 East Bay St., res. 256 King St.
Bredenberg, C. F., Grocer, cr. Calhoun & St. Philip Sts.
Bredenberg, J. H., Grocer, 87 King St.
Breeden, Benjamin, Grocer, cr. Coming & Cannon Sts.
Breen, Michael, Finisher, Meeting St., Ward 5
Breese, W. C., Teller, Bank of South Carolina, res. 3 Maiden Lane
Breiver, M., Mrs., 6 Liberty St.
Brener, William, Grocer, cr. Cannon & Smith Sts.
Brenon, Luke, Guardman, 73 King St.
Bresnan, J. T., Clerk, King St., res. 5 Liberty St.
Brett, James, Contractor, Radcliffe St.
Brewster, C. R., Attorney, 65 Meeting St., res. Vanderhorst St.
Bridges, John, Sea Captain, 5 State St.
Brigcoft, A., Bootmaker, 119 King St.
Briggs, David, Planter, 86 Tradd St.
Bright, James, Cooper, 211 East Bay St., res. Calhoun St.
Brisbane, A. H., Professor of Belles Lettres, Citadel Academy
Brisbane, William, Planter, 20 Pitt St.
Brisinden, H. J., Professor of Music, 99 Wentworth St.
Bristoll, A., Tailor, 9 Horlbeck Alley
Bristoll, E., Mrs., Private Boarding, 9 Horlbeck Alley
Bristoll, J. A., Clerk, 228 King St.
Bristoll, J. D., Clerk, 232 King St.
Bristoll, T. M., Boots & Shoes, 232 King St.

54

Bristoll, W. B., Boots & Shoes, 228 King St.
Britton, C., Printer, Meeting St.
Britton, H., Mrs., Shopkeeper, 44 King St.
Britton, R. A., Printer, 44 King St.
Broadford, David, Upholsterer, 120 King St.
Broadford, Frances, 5 Tradd St.
Broadford, John, Bootmaker, 120 King St.
Brock, H. C., Clerk, 220 King St.
Brodie, E., Clerk, Broad St., res. Merchants Hotel
Brodie, Furman, Clerk, cr. Vanderhorst & St. Philip Sts.
Brodie, J. K., Clerk, cr. Vanderhorst & St. Philip Sts.
Brodie, J. W., Lumber Factor, Broad St., res. 115 Queen St.
Brodie, R. H., Planter at Goose Creek, res. 45 Coming St.
Brodie, Robert, Lumber Factor, Broad St., res. 158 East Bay St.
Brodie, Thomas, Tailor, 21 Calhoun St.
Brookbanks, W., Gasfitter, 6 Liberty St.
Broom, James, Wharfinger, Atlantic Wharf
Brosna, D., Tavern Keeper, Market St.
Broughton, A. T., Clerk, Post Office, res. 8 New St.
Broughton, M., Mrs., 37 Society St.
Broughton, M., Mrs., 51 Wentworth St.
Broughton, W. W., Clerk, 253 King St., res. 49 Beaufain St.
Brown & Stone, Crockery, 147 Meeting St.
Brown & Strobel, Ship Grocers, 147 East Bay St.
Brown, A. H., Attorney, 30 Broad St., res. Greenhill St.
Brown, A. L., Watchmaker, 236 King St.
Brown, A. McD., Accountant, 153 East Bay St., res. 8 Glebe St.
Brown, A., Mrs., 39 Society St.
Brown, A. P., Attorney, 30 Broad St.
Brown, A. S., Clerk, 232 King St.
Brown, B. F., Crockery, 147 Meeting St., res. 154 Meeting St.
Brown, C., Mrs., 26 Coming St.
Brown, C. P., Teacher, Archdale St., res. 49 Anson St.
Brown, Charles, Coffee Shop, 9 Queen St.
Brown, E. G., Fancy Goods, 26 Hayne St., res. Charleston Hotel
Brown, E. T., Clerk, 116 Meeting St., res. 49 Anson St.
Brown, E. W., Builder & Contractor, 6 Coming St.
Brown, G. B., Clerk, 218 King St., res. 2 Society St.
Brown, G. H., Clerk, 147 Meeting St., res. cr. Beaufain & St. Philip St.
Brown, G. W., Commission Merchant, Brown's Wharf, 8 Montague St.
Brown, George, Clerk, 253 King St., res. Queen St.
Brown, H. N., Clerk, 243 King St., res. 26 Coming St.
Brown, J. B., Engineer, 2 Society St.
Brown, J., Caps, 317 King St.
Brown, J., Clerk, cr. King & Market Sts., res. King St.
Brown, J. D., Superintendent, Public Seminary, Rutledge St., Ward 8
Brown, J. K., Planter at Goose Creek, res. 49 Anson St.
Brown, J. M., Planter, 43 Church St.
Brown, J., Mrs., Private Boarding, 4 Beaufain St.
Brown, J. P., Clerk 147 Meeting St., res. Coming St.

Brown, J. W., Clerk, Southern Wharf, res. 106 Church St.
Brown, J. W., Ship Grocer, 147 East Bay St., res. 2 George St.
Brown, James, Public Weigher, Market St., res. 4 Beaufain St.
Brown, John, Clerk, Railroad, Vanderhorst St.
Brown, John, Sawyer, 2 Philadelphia St.
Brown, M., Mrs., 23 Coming St.
Brown, M., Mrs., 9 Clifford St.
Brown, M., Mrs., Seamstress, Coming St., Ward 6
Brown, Malcolm, Bootmaker, St. Philip St., Ward 6
Brown, P. W., Tinner, Hanover St.
Brown, R. E., Factor, Southern Wharf, 43 Church St.
Brown, R. McO., Clerk, 221 King St., res. 26 Coming St.
Brown, Robert & Co., Factors, Southern Wharf
Brown, S., Mrs., 17 Pitt St.
Brown, Sarah, 14 Magazine St.
Brown, Scott, Carpenter, 24 Coming St.
Brown, T., Barber, 61 Church St., res. Mary St.
Brown, T., Butcher, 87 Market St.
Brown, W. S., Dentist, 49 Anson St.
Brown, W. W., Carpenter, cr. Meeting & Mary Sts.
Brown, William, 41 Tradd St.
Browne, R. C., Grain Dealer, cr. East Bay St. & Commercial Wharf, res. 41 Tradd St.
Brownell, M. J., Mrs., 136 Queen St.
Brownfield, J. W., Planter in Sumter District, res. 26 Magazine St.
Browning, A. F., Dry Goods, cr. King & Market Sts., res. 3 Pitt St.
Browning, C. H., Clerk, cr. King & Market Sts., res. 13 Bull St.
Browning, H., Mrs. 13 Bull St.
Bruggeman, H., Bootmaker, 333 King St.
Brugman, Peter, Dentist, 14 Smith St.
Brunkards, William, Mechanic, 59 Tradd St.
Bruns, H., Grocer, 55 Anson St.
Bruns, H. M., Teacher, High School, res. 11 Pitt St.
Bruns, N., Scissors Grinder, 58 State St.
Bruns, R. T., Accountant, Central Wharf, cr. Wentworth & Pitt Sts.
Brunson, C. H., Grocer, Rutledge St.
Brush, D., Clerk, cr. Meeting & Woolf Sts.
Bryan, E. B., Legare St.
Bryan, G. S., Attorney, 26 Broad St., res. 27 Church St.
Bryan, J. M., Hardware dealer, 349 King St.
Bryan, John, Custom House Officer, res. Bee St.
Bryan, Jonathan, Paying Teller, Planters & Mechanics Bank
Bryan, T. A., Factor & Commission Merchant, 3 Boyce's Wharf, res. 65 Broad St.
Buchanan, C., Tailor, 1 Queen St.
Buck, Henry, Baker, 4 Wall St.
Buckelhoff, -----, Grocer, 89 Queen St.
Buckholder, J., Laborer, Williams Row
Bucking, J. H., Painter, Williams Row
Buckley, J., Merchant Tailor, 82 Meeting St.
Bucklin, John, Laborer, 1 Washington St.
Buckner, A. F., Mason, 86 Queen St.

Budd, T. G., Commission Merchant, 76 East Bay St., res. 21 Anson St.
Buhre, D., Tavern Keeper, Line St.
Buhre, J. F., Grocer, cr. Anson & America Sts.
Buise, G. & H., Attorneys, St. Michael's Alley
Buist, C. B., Attorney, rear Court House
Buist, G., Attorney, St. Michael's Alley, res. 3 Rutledge St.
Buist, H., Attorney, St. Michael's Alley, res. 3 Rutledge St.
Bull, E., Coopersmith, cr. East Bay & Market Sts., res. cr. East Bay St. & Williams Wharf
Bull, W. Izard, Planter in St. Andrew's Parish, res. 100 Broad St.
Bulow, T. L., Planter in St. Andrew's Parish, res. cr. Cannon & King Sts.
Bulwinkle, D., Grocer, 105 Queen St.
Bulwinkle, D., Grocer, cr. Nassau & Mary Sts.
Bulwinkle, D., Grocer, cr. Ann & Elizabeth Sts.
Bulwinkle, F., Grocer, 101 Church St.
Bulwinkle, H., 31 Coming St.
Bulwinkle, H., Grocer, cr. Charlotte & Elizabeth Sts.
Bulwinkle, John, Grocr, 2 King St.
Burch, R. T., Clerk, 18 Broad St., res. 49 East Bay St.
Burckmyer & Moffet, Commission Merchants, 78 East Bay St.
Burckmyer, C. L., Commission Merchant, 14 Hayne St., res. 13 Coming St.
Burckmyer, J. A., Commission Merchant, 98 East Bay St., res. 13 Coming St.
Burckmyer, J. C., Commission Merchant, 78 East Bay St., res. 22 Society St.
Burckmyer, J. G., Clerk, 78 East Bay St., res. 22 Society St.
Burdell, E., Mrs., Chapel St.
Burdell, F. M., Clerk, Railroad, Calhoun St., Ward 6
Burdell, Robert, Mechanic, Chapel St.
Burdell, T. J., Clerk, 306 King St., res. 9 Franklin St.
Burdell, T. S., Clerk, Atlantic Wharf, res. Chapel St.
Burger, S. J., Clothier, 273 King St., res. 63 Beaufain St.
Burgess, J. S., Printer, 11 New St.
Burgess, S. E., 11 New St.
Burie, J., Printer, 23 Anson St.
Burke, A. B., Physician, 5 St. Philip St.
Burke, A. J., Printer & Stationer, 40 Broad St., res. 23 Tradd St.
Burke, Edmund, Guardman, 80 Queen St.
Burke, G. R., Clerk, 149 Meeting St.
Burke, J., Clerk, Meeting St., res. 75 Church St.
Burke, James, Dry Goods, 136 King St.
Burke, James, Laborer, 64 Queen St.
Burke, John, Clerk, Railroad, Meeting St., Ward 5
Burke, L. & T., Dry Goods, 204 King St.
Burke, L., Dry Goods, 204 King St., res. 27 Friend St.
Burke, Michael, Porter, 143 Meeting St., res. 35 Queen St.
Burke, Samuel, Boat Builder, Market Wharf, res. 33 Wall St.
Burke, T., Dry Goods, 204 King St., res. 27 Friend St
Burkely, John, Engineer, 27 Anson St.

Burleigh, W. H., Clerk, 51 Broad St., res. State St.
Burn, Henry, Planter in St. Andrew's Parish, res. Cannon St.
Burn, T. A., Wharfinger, Vanderhorst's Wharf, res. 17 Coming St.
Burn, William, Planter in St. Andrew's Parish, res. Cannon St.
Burner, C., Grocer, 39 Beaufain St.
Burner, C., Jr., Clerk, 39 Beaufain St.
Burner, J., Clerk, 108 East Bay St.
Burnham, R. W., Druggist, 343 King St.
Burnham, William, Machinist, Laurens St.
Burns, D. M., Clerk, 47 Broad St.
Burns, E., Blacksmith, Mary St.
Burns, James, Laborer, King St., Ward 5
Burns, John, Porter, 145 Meeting St., res. 32 Queen St.
Burns, John, Rice Dealer, 127 East Bay St., res. 31 King St.
Burns, M. A., 10 West St.
Burns, O. J., Clerk, 268 King St.
Burnside, James, Clerk, 54 East Bay St., res. Queen St.
Burrows, Charles, Carpenter, 20 Church St.
Burrows, E. G., Clerk, Commercial Hotel, res. 51 East Bay St.
Burrows, Frederick, Pilot, 20 Church St.
Burrows, Henry, Engineer, 20 Church St.
Burrows, J. T., Carpenter, 20 Church St.
Burrows, -----, Pilot, 51 East Bay St.
Burrows, S. L., Clerk, 2 Southern Wharf, res. 54 East Bay St.
Bury, George, Blacksmith, Williams Row
Busch, S., Grocer, 83 Beaufain St.
Busch, T. D., Grocer, Calhoun St., Ward 5
Bushee, J. J., Carpenter, 26 Queen St., res. Wentworth St.
Butler, A. R., Clerk, Adger's Wharf, res. Elizabeth St.
Butler, B. G., Clerk, Adger's Wharf, res. Elizabeth St.
Butler, C. T., Jeweller, 115 King St., res. Wentworth St.
Butler, J. W., Clerk, 84 East Bay, res. 17 Wentworth St.
Butler, John, Dry Goods, King St., Ward 8
Butler, R. M., Commission Merchant, 84 East Bay St., res. 17 Wentworth St.
Butler, W. B., Clerk, Adger's Wharf, res. Elizabeth St.
Butler, W. R., Upholsterer, 177 King St., res. 104 Queen St.
Butler, William, Bootmaker, 83 Queen St.
Butterfield, A., Clerk, Pavilion Hotel
Butterfield, H. L., Proprietor, Pavilion Hotel
Butters, Charles, Clerk, 237 King St., res. 236 King St.
Butts, John, Drayman, Woolf St.
Buzby, G. W., Bricklayer, 24 Bull St.
Byrean, John, Meeting St., Ward 5
Byrne, John, Packer, 145 Meeting St., res. Church St.
Byrns, G., Bootmaker, 25 State St.
Byrns, J. B., Bootmaker, 62 State St.
Byrns, R., Bootmaker, 25 State St.
Cadow, William, Dry Goods, 82 East Bay, res. Planters Hotel
Cadren, Joseph, Shoemaker, King St., Ward 5
Cageney, John, Teacher, cr. St. Philip & Radcliffe Sts.

Cahal, M. C., Laborer, Cannon St.
Cain, D. J., Physician, 20 Wentworth St
Cain, William, Planter, St. John's, res. Coming St., Ward 6
Calder, Alex, Clerk, 26 Vendue Range, res. 2 Friend St.
Calder, James, Cabinet Maker, 78 Meeting St.
Calder, James, Jr., Clerk, 82 East Bay St., res. Meeting St.
Calder, William, Dry Goods, 246 & 248 King St., res. 246 King St.
Caldwell, A. P., Auction & Commission Merchant, 25 Vendue Range, res. 74 Meeting St.
Caldwell, E. A., Clerk, Central Wharf, res. Carolina Hotel
Caldwell, J. & Son, Upholsterers, 310 King St.
Caldwell, J. M., Factor & Commission Merchant, Atlantic Wharf, res. Judith St.
Caldwell, J. W., Ship Broker, 89 East Bay St., res. 61 Wentworth St.
Caldwell, James, Upholsterer, 310 King St.
Caldwell, John, Factor, 10 Central Wharf, res. Columbia
Caldwell, John, Jr., Clerk, 155 East Bay St., res. 310 King St.
Caldwell, John, Upholsterer, 310 King St.
Caldwell, R. & A. P., Auction & Commission Merchants, 25 Vendue Range
Caldwell, R. & J. & Co., Factors, 10 Central Wharf
Caldwell, R. W., Telegraph Operator, cr. Meeting & Market Sts.
Caldwell, Richard, Auction & Commission Merchant, 25 Vendue Range, res. 63 Wentworth St.
Caldwell, Robert, Factor, 10 Central Wharf, res. Mansion House
Call, John, Laborer, 12 Philadelphia St.
Caloit, J. M., Blacksmith, Reid St.
Calvitt, John, Blacksmith, Reid St.
Caly, James, Cooper, 9 Marsh St.
Cambers, J. S., Atlantic Wharf, res. Planters Hotel
Cambridge, S., Bootmaker, 73 Meeting St.
Cameron, Archibald, Engineer & Machinist, Marsh St.
Cameron, G. & H., Crockery & Glass, 145 Meeting St.
Cameron, G. S., 145 Meeting St., res. Charleston Hotel
Cameron, H. P., 145 Meeting St., res. Charleston Hotel
Cameron, McDermid & Mustard, Engineers & Machinists, foot of Hasell St.
Cameron, Susan, 21 Mazyck St.
Caminade, F., Turner, 21 Pinckney St.
Caminade, H., Mechanic, 24 Pinckney St.
Caminade, H., Mrs., Private Boarding, 21 Pinckney St.
Cammer, M. J., Mrs., 94 Beaufain St.
Campbell, F., Livery Stables, 36 Pinckney St., res. 40 Coming St.
Campbell, J., Attorney, 40 Broad St., res. 84 Beaufain St.
Campbell, J. M., Physician, 89 Broad St.
Campbell, J. S. G., Carpenter, 46 Bull St.
Campbell, John, Clothier, 66 Market St.
Campbell, John, Pastor, St. Philip's Church, res. 1 Short St.
Campbell, Joseph, Farmer, Cannon St.
Campbell, L. J., Barber, King St., Ward 6

Campbell, Owen, Bricklayer, 349 King St.
Campbell, W. M., Accountant, 28 Vendue Range, res. 155 East Bay St.
Campsen & Ellerhorst, Grain Dealers, 6 Market St.
Campsen, George, Boot Maker, 129 Meeting St., res. 140 King St.
Campsen, H., Dry Goods, 140 King St., res. Calhoun St.
Campsen, J., Grain Dealer, 6 Market St.
Canale, A., Fruiterer, 11 Market St.
Candler, E., Naval Store, 69 East Bay St.
Cane, Alfred, Tobacconist, 6 Broad St.
Cannady, A., Clerk, 184 East Bay St., res. Meeting St.
Cannady, E., Carpenter, 16 Horlbeck Alley
Cannady, James, Clerk, 137 East Bay St., res. Broad St.
Canning, C., Printer, 24 Church St.
Cannon, C. A., Mrs., St. Philip St., Ward 8
Cannon, George, Dry Goods, 312 King St.
Cannon, J., Sea Captain, Hanover St.
Cannon, T. W., Machinist, St. Philip St., Ward 8
Canter, R., Mrs., 8 Calhoun St.
Cantwell, Thomas, Laborer, 7 King St.
Capers, Charles, Cannon St.
Capers, W., Bishop, St. Philip St., Ward 6
Capers, W. G., Clerk, Post Office, 106 Church St.
Capters, T. F., Broker, Broad St., res. 12 Legare St.
Carberry, J. B., Accountant, 14 Hayne St., res. Charlotte St.
Carberry, John, Clerk, Atlantic Wharf
Carby, -----, Mrs., 24 Tradd St.
Cardoza, Isaac, Weigher, Custom House, 204 East Bay St.
Cardoza, J. N., Editor, Evening News, 249 King St.
Cares, H., Mrs., Meeting St., res. Ward 5
Carew & Heart, Publishers, Mercury, 121 East Bay St.
Carew & Hopkins, South Carolina Shoe Factory, cr. King & John Sts.
Carew, Hamilton, Clerk, 4 Vendue Range, res. Washington St.
Carew, J. E., Editor, Washington St.
Carey & Couturier, Druggists, 35 Broad St.
Carey, E. M., Druggist, 35 Broad St.
Carey, Thomas, Laborer, 64 Queen St.
Carleghan, William, Dry Goods, 73 Church St.
Carlisle, -----, Mrs., 10 Wall St.
Carmalt, J. W., Accountant, 97 East Bay St., res. Carolina Hotel
Carmand, F., Turner, 188 Meeting St.
Carmand, H., Mrs., 86 Queen St.
Carney, Peter, Porter, 153 East Bay St.
Carninghan, John, Pilot, 71 Tradd St.
Carpender, M., Mrs., Cannon St.
Carpender, W. S., Planter, King St.
Carr & Flynn, Drapers & Tailors, 30 Broad St.
Carr, C. C., Draper & Tailor, 30 Broad St., 31 Meeting St.
Carr, J., Printer, 183 King St.
Carr, John, Dry Goods, King St., Ward 6
Carr, John, Laborer, 74 Tradd St.
Carr, M., Mrs., 112 Queen St.
Carrere, M. E., Physician, Radcliffe St.

57

Carrere, W. G., Wharfinger, Adger's Wharf, res. 1
    Orange St.
Carrington, W., Watchmaker, 266 King St., res. 107
    Wentworth St.
Carroll, A., Fireman, Line St.
Carroll, Alex, Assistant Editor, Courier, res. Pavilion
    Hotel
Carroll, B., Livery Stabler, 126 Meeting St.
Carroll, B. R., Teacher, King St., Ward 5
Carroll, Ed, Clerk, 306 King St.
Carroll, J., Shoe Manufacture, 65 Anson St.
Carroll, P., Blacksmith, 16 Mazyck St.
Carroll, Patrick, Plasterer, 178 Meeting St.
Carroll, T., Bootmaker, 65 Anson St.
Carson, D. A., Factor, Boyce & Co. Wharf, res. 5 Hasell
    St.
Carson, Elisha, Factor, Boyce & Co. Wharf, res. 25
    Laurens St.
Carson, F., Clerk, 38 Church St.
Carson, Harlee & Co., Factors, 5 Boyce & Co. Wharf
Carson, J. M., Factor, Boyce & Co. Wharf, res. 25
    Laurens St.
Carson, John, Farmer, Ann St.
Carson, M., 15 West St.
Carson, W. J., Clerk, Boyce & Co. Wharf, res. 25
    Laurens St.
Carson, William, Planter, 90 Tradd St.
Carsten, A., Clerk, Coming St., Ward 6
Carsten, E. H., City Scavenger, 24 Montague St.
Cart, E., Mrs., 26 Bull St.
Cart, F. G., Clerk, Adger's Wharf, res. Calhoun St.
Cart, Francis, Clerk, Calhoun St., Ward 6
Cart, L., Mrs., 26 Bull St.
Carter, A., Bookseller, 163 Meeting St.
Carter, J., Mrs., Grist Mill, 48 Queen St.
Carter, J. W., Clerk, cr. East Bay St. & Commercial
    Wharf, res. 48 Queen St.
Carter, John, Carpenter, 48 Queen St.
Carter, Nelson, Druggist, 153 Meeting St., res.
    Charleston Hotel
Carter, T. M., Auction & Commission Merchant, 30
    Vendue Range, res. Rutledge St., Ward 5
Cartman, Thomas, Clerk, 212 King St.
Carvalho, S. N., Daguerreotypist, 167 Meeting St., res.
    Calhoun St.
Casey, H., 19 Franklin St.
Caskin, Henry, Laborer, Line St.
Caskin, John, Carpenter, America St.
Cassidy, C., Grocer, St. Philip St., Ward 6
Cassidy, John, Bricklayer, St. Philip St., Ward 6
Cassidy, John, Seaman, 24 Mazyck St.
Cassin, W. M., Tinner, 2 Queen St.
Castallon, Thomas, Shopkeeper, 5 Tradd St.
Castens, G. H., Clerk, cr. East Bay & Elliott Sts.
Casy, John, Clerk, 125 East Bay St.
Caufield, James, Accountant, 135 East Bay St.
Caulier, George, Physician, 12 Queen St.
Causse, R., Clerk, 254 King St., res. 279 King St.
Cay & Aveilhe, Commission Merchants, 171 East Bay
    St.

Cay, A. A., Clerk, 171 East Bay St., res. cr. Meeting &
    George Sts.
Cay, J. A., Accountant, 171 East Bay St., res. cr. Meeting
    & George Sts.
Cay, J. E., 171 East Bay St., cr. Meeting & George Sts.
Ceaf, Thomas, Laborer, 24 Tradd St.
Chafee, C. H., Clerk, 179 East Bay St., res. 121 Queen
    St.
Chafee, N. U., Flour Inspector, Queen St., res. 121
    Queen St.
Chafee, O. J., Commission Merchant, 179 East Bay St.,
    res. 15 George St.
Chamberlain & Bancroft, Dry Goods, 143 Meeting St.
Chamberlain, C. V., 143 Meeting St., res. Charleston
    Hotel
Chambers & White, Factors, Atlantic Wharf,
Chambers, Ann, Sires St.
Chambers, B. R., Clerk, 135 Meeting St., res. 11 George
    St.
Chambers, Thomas, Bootmaker, res. 7 Burns Lane
Champlin, John, Mason, 23 Franklin St.
Champlin, Oliver, Accountant, 28 Magazine St.
Champlin, S., Coastwise Inspector, Custom House, res.
    28 Magazine St.
Chandler, M., Mrs., Radcliffe St.
Chandler, T. P., Deputy Sheriff, Charlotte St.
Channel, William, Carpenter, Coming St., Ward 6
Chapin, B. A., Mechanic, Columbus St.
Chapin, Charles, Bookbinder, 101 Meeting St.
Chapin, L., Coachmaker, 40 Wentworth St., res. cr. King
    & Market Sts.
Chaplin, B., Carpenter, 29 Church St.
Chaplin, -----, Mrs., 31 Wentworth St.
Chaplin, W. J., Clerk, 283 King St., res. Church St.
Chapman, J. C., Clerk, 215 King St.
Chapman, James, Commission Merchant, Exchange St.,
    res. 4 Water St.
Chapman, Perry, Pilot, 1 Atlantic St.
Chapman, Samuel, Grist Mill, 14 Tradd St.
Chapman, Thomas E., Commission Merchant, Exchange
    St., res. 4 Water St.
Chapman. R. B., Commission Merchant, Exchange St.,
    res. 4 Water St.
Charke, G. E., 151 Meeting St., res. Charleston Hotel
Charlotte, M. D., Printer, 53 East Bay St.
Chartland, C., Mrs., 9 Wall St.
Chase, P. A., Clerk, 142 King St., res. 96 Queen St.
Chase, P. S., Clerk, 142 King St., res. 96 Queen St.
Chase, T. P., Wharfinger, Union Wharves, res. 96 Queen
    St.
Chazal, E. C., Mrs., 48 Anson St.
Chazal, Ellen, Mrs., 48 Anson St.
Chazal, J. P., Physician, 32 Hasell St.
Cheesborough E. R. & Brother, Brokers & Auctioneers,
    6 State St.
Cheesborough, E. R., 6 State St., res. Broad St.
Cheesborough, J. B., 6 State St., res. Broad St.
Cheesborough, J., Transfer Clerk, Bank of Charleston,
    res. 4 Wentworth St.
Cheesborough, -----, Mrs., 18 Church St.

Cheney, E., Jr., 99 East Bay St.
Cheney, -----, Mrs., Private Board, 99 East Bay St.
Cherling, C., Bootmaker, 5 Queen St.
Cherol, Thomas, Tailor, Cannon St.
Cherrell, Ed, Milliner, 183 King St.
Cheves, C. M., Planter at Savannah, res. 44 South Bay St.
Chew, T. R., Blacksmith, 3 Market St.
Chewing, Charles, Grocer, 39 St. Philip St.
Chichester, E. V., Clerk, 25 Hayne St., res. 236 King St.
Chichester, L., Clerk, 161 Meeting St., res. Charleston Hotel
Childs, J., Mrs., Vanderhorst St.
China, Thomas J., Clerk, 273 King St., res. Merchants Hotel
Chisolm, Alex, Rice Mill, west end of Tradd St., res. 119 Broad St.
Chisolm, George, 13 South Bay St.
Chisolm, H. L., Clerk, Atlantic Wharf, cr. Mill & Rutledge Sts.
Chisolm, J., Mrs., 45 Anson St.
Chisolm, -----, Mrs., 77 Beaufain St.
Chisolm, O., Broker & Auctioneer, 33 Broad St., res. 17 Savage St.
Chisolm, R. B., Clerk, 71 East Bay St., res. Rutledge St., Ward 6
Chisolm, R., Rutledge & Mill Sts.
Choate, H. E., Clerk, 19 Vendue Range, res. 104 Tradd St.
Choate, S. M., Mrs., 104 Tradd St.
Choate, T., Clerk, 84 East Bay St., res. 104 Tradd St.
Chrest, John, Bootmaker, 73 Meeting St.
Chrietzburg, C., Mrs., 17 Beaufain St.
Chrietzburg, J. R., Clerk, Central Wharf, res. King St.
Chrietzburg, R. S., Carpenter, 60 Wentworth St.
Chrietzburg, Thomas, Mechanic, 26 Beaufain St.
Christiansen, J., Grocer, 180 King St.
Christie, David, Blind, Cannon St.
Chroder, John, Grocer, St. Philip & Cannon Sts.
Church, C. A. D., Bricklayer, 27 St. Philip St.
Church, J. F., Plumber, 20 Broad St.
Church, M., Mrs., 27 St. Philip St.
Clacius, C., Clerk, 13 Central Wharf, res. 208 King St.
Clagett, Thomas, Broker & Auctioneer, 7 State St., res. 120 Tradd St.
Clagett, W. H., Dry Goods, Calhoun St.
Clagett, William, Clerk, 122 Meeting St., res. Charleston Hotel
Clarison, J. C., Clerk, King St., res. St. Philip St., Ward 6
Clarke, C., Druggist, 33 Market St.
Clarke, Francis, Tavern Keeper, 337 king St.
Clarke, H. B., Dry Goods, 213 King St.
Clarke, Henry, Planing Mills, 89 Beaufain St., res. 87 Beaufain St.
Clarke, J. M., Turner, 19 Mazyck St.
Clarke, John, Porter, 1 Hayne St., res. 27 Wentworth St.
Clarke, Joseph, Engineer, 28 Mazyck St.
Clarke, Pringle, Planter on Ashepoo River, res. 160 Meeting St.
Clarke, R. A., Hardware, 133 Meeting St., res. 11 George

St.
Clarke, Richard, Port Warden, 11 Church St.
Clarke, S. S. & G., Fancy Goods, 151 Meeting St.
Clarke, S. S., 151 Meeting St., res. Charleston Hotel
Clarksons & Mey, Factors and Commission Merchants, Accommodation Wharf
Clarksons, R. H., Accommodation Wharf, res. 4 Smith St.
Clarksons, T. B., Accommodation Wharf, res. 4 Smith St.
Clarksons, W. N., Physician, 83 Tradd St.
Claucy, M. A., Mrs., Warren St.
Claussen, J. C. H., Baker, 183½ East Bay St.
Clayton, E. J., Engineer, 6 Liberty St.
Clayton, W. C., Printer, cr. Anson & Wentworth Sts.
Cleapor, C. W., Clerk, 110 East Bay St., res. 55 Calhoun St.
Cleapor, J. W., 55 Calhoun St.
Cleaveland, J. A., Druggist, 215 King St.
Cleaveland, W. L., Druggist, 215 King St.
Cleiland, J. M., Clerk, Vendue Range, 6 Queen St.
Cleiland, S., Mrs., 6 Queen St.
Clemon, J. L., Tinner, 48 East Bay St.
Clemont, J. P., Superintendent of Streets, res. Amherst St.
Clifford, L. C., Planter at Pon Pon, res. Warren St.
Clifton, A. J., 76 Church St.
Close, L. P. H., Dry Goods Dealers, 340 King St., res. Merchants Hotel
Clyde, T. E., Grocer, 88 Meeting St.
Clysen, -----, Misses, Milliners, 82 King St.
Cobb, E. W., Boots & Shoes, 141 Meeting St., res. Horlbeck Alley
Cobia, Henry, Auctioneer & Commission Merchant, 26 Vendue Range, res. 88 Wentworth St.
Cobia, -----, Mrs., Teacher, Meeting St., Ward 7
Coburn, Peter, Carpenter, St. Philip St., Ward 6
Cochran, J. C., Bookkeeper, South West Railroad Bank, res. Cannon St.
Cochran, James, Laborer, 20 Middle St.
Cochran, Patrick, Laborer, 44 Tradd St.
Cochran, T. B., Teacher, High School, King St., Ward 5
Cochran, Thomas, Rutledge St., Ward 6
Cochran, W. S., Teller, South West Railroad Bank, res. Cannon St.
Cock, Rudolph, Sailmaker, 7 Magazine St.
Cockran, James, Pastor, 80 Broad St.
Coffay, F. A., Shoes, 187 East Bay St., res. 35 State St.
Coffey, Jeremiah, 22 Tradd St.
Coffey, Jeremiah, Jr., Laborer, 22 Tradd St.
Coffey, M., Mrs., 9 Tradd St.
Coffin, G. M., Factor, Adger's Wharf, res. 86 Broad St.
Coffin, Thomas, Planter, St. Helena, res. 7 Rutledge St.
Cogdell, C. S., Clerk, Bank of the State of South Carolina
Cogdell, G. B., Mill St.
Cogdell, R. W., 65 Broad St.
Coglan, M., Mrs., 36 Mazyck St.
Cogswell, H., Clerk, 14 Hayne St., res. 25 Philip St.
Cohen, A. E., Clerk & Librarian, M. L. A., 4 Society St.

Cohen, A. N., Jr., Commission Merchant, 157 East Bay St., res. 55 King St.
Cohen, Bell, Miss, 116 King St.
Cohen, D. D., Jr., Clerk, cr. King & Market Sts., res. Chapel St.
Cohen, D. D., Planter, Ashley River, res. Chapel St.
Cohen, H., Warren St.
Cohen, I. S., Auctioneer & Commission Merchant, 29 Vendue Range, res. 15 Society St.
Cohen, J. H., Clerk, 157 East Bay St., res. 46 Meeting St.
Cohen, J. H., Clerk, 29 Hayne St., res. Horlbeck Alley
Cohen, J. J., Factor & Commission Merchant, Central Wharf, res. Smith St.
Cohen, Jacob, Broker & Auctioneer, 29 Broad St., res. 12 Friend St.
Cohen, -----, Mrs., Fruiterer, 71 Market St.
Cohen, N. A., Dry Goods, 157 East Bay St., res. 46 Meeting St.
Cohen, P., 6 Wentworth St.
Cohen, P. M. & Co., Druggist, 29 Hayne St.
Cohen, P. M., Druggist, 29 Hayne St., res. 4 Society St.
Cohen, -----, Rev. Mr., Pastor, Woolf St. Church, res. 297 King St.
Cohen, Samuel, Peddler, 116 King St.
Cohn, L., Accountant, 157 East Bay St., res. 55 King St.
Cohn, L., Dry Goods, 159 King St., res. 55 King St.
Cohrs, C. H., Clerk, 82 East Bay St., res. Victoria Hotel
Colburn & Holland, Dry Goods, cr. King & Broad Sts.
Colburn, J. H., Clerk, 244 King St., res. 135 Queen St.
Colburn, J. S., cr. King & Broad Sts.
Colcock, J. & Co., Factors, Commercial Wharf
Colcock, John, 2 Orange St.
Colcock, R. H., 2 Orange St.
Colcock, R. W., Superintendent, Citadel Academy
Colcock, S. H., Clerk, 114 East Bay St., res. Church St.
Cole, Agnes, 15 Pitt St.
Cole, E. M., Mrs., 258 King St.
Cole, G. F., Music Store, 175 King St.
Cole, John, Seaman, Bedon's Alley
Coll, Patrick, Bootmaker, 95 Meeting St., res. 4 Anson St.
Collins, J. N., Teacher, 86 Anson St.
Collins, M., Mrs., Private Boarding, Linguard St.
Collins, -----, Mrs., 86 Anson St.
Collins, -----, Mrs., Dressmaker, 124 Church St.
Collins, T., Bootmaker, King St., Ward 6
Collins, W., Laborer, Coming St., Ward 6
Colman, George, Clerk, 217 King St., res. 18 Mazyck St.
Colman, H. W., Dry Goods, 217 King St., res. 18 Mazyck St.
Colson, A., Gas Fitter, 4 Horlbeck Alley
Colson, Charles, Dry Goods, 27 Middle St.
Colson, Thomas, Carpenter, 4 Horlbeck Alley
Comier, Alex, Boiler Maker, 22 Washington St.
Comier, Charles, Molder, 22 Washington St.
Comier, Ervin, Boiler Maker, 22 Washington St.
Comier, Francis, Ship Chandler, 22 Washington St.
Commins, John, Shoes & Hats, 274 King St.
Commins, Michael, Clerk, 274 King St., res. 269 King St.

Comstock, D. B., Accountant, 122 Meeting St., res. 236 King St.
Comwell, Amelia L., Dressmaker, 12 Smith St.
Conder, W., Tailor, 24 Queen St.
Condict, Jennings & Co., Saddlery, 157 Meeting St.
Condict, S. H., Saddlery, 157 Meeting St.
Condy & Son, Broker & Auctioneer, 9 State St.
Condy, P., Broker & Auctioneer, cr. Rutledge & Bee Sts.
Condy, T. D., Broker & Auctioneer, cr. Rutledge & Bee Sts.
Cone, -----, Mrs., 98 Broad St.
Conly, B., Laborer, 12 Horlbeck Alley
Conly, James, Clerk, 179 King St.
Connell, P. O., Laborer, Clifford St.
Conner, H. W., Clerk, Central Wharf, res. 9 Meeting St.
Conner, H. W., President, South Carolina Railroad, 9 Meeting St.
Conner, James, Attorney, St. Michael's Alley, res. 9 Meeting St.
Conner, John, Laborer, St. Philip St.
Conner, M., Mrs., Calhoun St., Ward 6
Conner, William, Gunsmith, 34 Wentworth St.
Conroy, William, Clerk, 145 Meeting St.
Conturier, J. R. E., Druggist, 35 Broad St., res. 21 King St.
Cook, G. S., Daguerreotypist, 235 King St., res. 236 King St.
Cook, J. A., Grocer, cr. King & Mary Sts.
Cook, J. R., 4 Gadsden St.
Cook, Jacob, Grocer, King St., Ward 5
Cook, Thomas C., Dry Goods, 347 King St.
Cook, W., Clerk, 308 King St., res. Wentworth St.
Cooper & Rivers, Attorneys, 49 Broad St.
Cooper, A., Mrs., 38 Wentworth St.
Cooper, G. W., Attorney, 49 Broad St., res. 4 Franklin St.
Cooper, R. T., Porter & Ale Bottler, King St., Ward 6
Copes & Black, Cotton Press, 91 Church St.
Copes, J., Cotton Press, 91 Church St., res. Rutledge St., Ward 6
Corbet, John, 23 Lynch St.
Corbet, John, Laborer, 7 Burns Lane
Corbet, -----, Miss, 24 South Bay St.
Corbot & Brothers, Dry Goods, 322 King St.
Corbot, H. D., Dry Goods, 322 King St.
Corbot, J. N., Dry Goods, 322 King St.
Corbot, James, Dry Goods, 322 King St.
Corbot, -----, Mrs., 24 South Bay St.
Corby, E. R., Blacksmith, Hampden court
Corby, John, Blacksmith, 110 Meeting St.
Corby, John, Hampden Court
Corcoran, Carter, cr. Cannon & Smith Sts
Corcoran, J. M., Accountant, 147 East Bay St., res. 65 Beaufain St.
Corcoran, Patrick, Cattle Dealer, Doughty St.
Corcoran, T., Mrs., Dry Goods, cr. Cannon & Smith Sts.
Corcoran, Thomas, Laborer, Columbus St.
Corcoran, Timothy, Conductor, South Carolina Railroad, Mary St.
Cordas, George, Grocer, 56 Anson St.

Cordis, John, 207 East Bay St.
Cordray, Thomas, Hard Alley
Cords, A. C., Baker, 45 Calhoun St.
Cords, George, Varnisher, Spring St.
Cords, J. J., Grocer, 7 Cumberland St.
Cords, Ralph, Butcher, Henrietta St.
Cords, T., Tavern Keeper, 55 Market St.
Corkel, T. M., Printer, East Bay St.
Corkle, Edward, East Bay St.
Corkle, William, Laborer, Bedon's Alley
Corkrell, Thomas, Grocer, 180 East Bay St.
Corneps, F., Tavern Keeper, Exchange St.
Corneps, H., Tavern Keeper, Exchange St.
Correa, Joseph, Fruiterer, 53 Market St., res. Tradd St.
Corregan, P., Dry Goods, 78 Church St.
Corregan, P. M., Clerk, 43 Hayne St., res. 195 East Bay
St.
Corrie, S. J., Clerk, 1 Hayne St., res. Pavilion Hotel
Corrie, W. C., Clerk, 69 East Bay St.
Cors, H., Baker, King St., Ward 5
Cosgrove, J., Fruiterer, 65 Market St.
Cosrie, B., Tavern Keeper, Vendue Range
Cotchett, C. E., Engineer, 9 Society St.
Cotchett, G. M. J., Clerk, Adger's Wharf, res. 9 Society
St.
Cotchett, George, Adger's Wharf, res. 9 Society St.
Cotton, E., Mrs., Mantuamaker, 39 Wall St.
Counceil, E. C., Printer & Bookseller, 119 East Bay St.,
res. cr. East Bay St. & Longitude Lane
Course, Henry, Machinist, Sires St.
Courtenay & Tennant, Hardware, 35 Hayne St.
Courtenay & Wienges, Booksellers & Stationers,
opposite Post Office
Courtenay, E. S., Import Inspector, Custom House
Courtenay, J., Stone Cutter, 112 Queen St.
Courtenay, S. G., Green St.
Courtenay, W. A., Clerk, Beaufain St.
Courtenay, W. C., 35 Hayne St. & 38 Broad St.
Covelay, Jeremiah, Mason, Archdale St.
Covert, H. C., Clerk, 101 East Bay St., res. 3
MagazineSt.
Covert, T. W., Clerk, 120 Meeting St., res. 3 Magazine
St.
Cowperthwait, E. R., Furniture, 251 King St., res. 76
Beaufain St.
Cox, D., Butcher, 40 Calhoun St.
Cox, S. K., Pastor, Methodist Protestant Church, 6 Wall
St.
Cox, W. H., Grocer, 184 East Bay St.
Crafts, George J., Planter, St. Andrew's Parish, res. 60
Broad St.
Crafts, W., Clerk, 101 East Bay St., res. 10 Broad St.
Cramer, G. W., Mechanic, 19 Pinckney St.
Crane, David, Coach Trimmer
Crane, J. G., Dry Goods, 1 Hayne St., res. Charleston
Hotel
Crane, L., Clerk, 165 Meeting St., res. Pavilion Hotel
Crane, R., Miss, 11 Broad St.
Cranston, E., Wharfinger, Union Wharf, res. Mazyck St.
Craven, R. H., Carpenter, King St., Ward 5

Creighton, James, Planter at Pon Pon, res. Rutledge St.,
Ward 6
Creighton, John, Clerk, Rutledge St.,Ward 6
Creighton, -----, Mrs., Rutledge St., Ward 6
Cres, Abbot, Laborer, St. Philip St., Ward 8
Crews, A. J., Dry Goods, 181 East Bay St., res. 17
George St.
Crews, E. B., Auctioneer & Commission Merchant, 19
Vendue Range, res. 1 Smith St.
Crews, Michael, Steam Boat Captain, Pritchard St.
Crip, A., Miss, 41 Meeting St.
Crip, C., Miss, 41 Meeting St.
Croft, M. E., Mrs., Seamstress, 7 Longitude Lane
Croft, S. E., Mrs., Private Boarding, 204½ King St.
Croft, T. M., Accountant, 179 East Bay St., res. 44
Wentworth St.
Croghan, Michael, Laborer, America St.
Croghan, O., Blacksmith, 21 Queen St.
Croghan, Stephen, Laborer, Bedon's Alley
Cromlay, Daniel, Bootmaker, 80 Queen St.
Cromwell, Samuel, Professor of Music, 15 Franklin St.
Crosby, Mary, Meeting St., Ward 5
Cross, Franklin, Ship Chandler, 15 Friend St.
Cross, Henry, Mason, 15 Friend St.
Cross, M. W., Mechanic, 106 Church St.
Cross, Sarah, 42 St. Philip St.
Cross, W., Accountant, 9 Middle St.
Crouch, C. W., Teacher, Calhoun St., res. Smith St.,
Ward 4
Croush, -----, Mrs., 34 Queen St.
Cruikshank, Samuel, Tanner, 22 Queen St., res. Hanover
St.
Cudworth, J., Import Inspector, Custom House, res. 20
Hasell St.
Culbert, James, Police Office, King St., Ward 7
Culbert, John, Clerk, King St., Ward 7, res. America St.
Culbert, William, Cotton Dresser, America St.
Cullinwe, P., Dry Goods, 360 King St.
Cummings, J. A., Clerk, 312 King St.
Cummings, J. B., Accountant, cr. Broad & Church Sts.,
res. Wentworth St.
Cummings, Thomas, Rigger, 73 East Bay St.
Cunnings & Robertson, Attorneys, Charleston Library
Cunningham, A., Mrs., Henrietta St.
Cunningham, Andrew, Contractor & Builder, St. Philip
St., Ward 6
Cunningham, John, Attorney, Charleston Library
Cunningham, Richard, Henrietta St.
Curly, Stephen, Bootmaker, 56 State St.
Current, E., Gilder, 154 King St.
Currie, Alex, Carpenter, 24 Bull St.
Currier, G. L., 237 King St.
Curry, C., Mrs., Shop Keeper, 7 Tradd St.
Curtis, C., Miss, 11 Calhoun St.
Curtis, E., Carpenter, 9 Franklin St.
Curtis, E., Mrs., 11 Calhoun St.
Curtis, James, Carpenter, Rutledge St.
Curtis, W., Paint, Oil & Lamp Dealer, 137 East Bay St.
Custa, -----, Mrs., Dry Goods, 10 King St.
Cuyler, S. G., Clerk, 229 King St., res. 269 King St.

Dacosta, Antonius, Professor of Music, 17 Broad St.
Dacosta, W. P., Millwright, 108 Queen St.
Dadin, L. A., Jeweler, 155 King St.
Dadin, L. H., Jeweler, 155 King St., res. 148 King St.
Dagett, W. L., Printer, King St.
Dagget, L. W., Machinist, 11 Horlbeck Alley
Dagget, Thomas, Mechanic, 25 Society St.
Daggett, Shepherd, Carpenter, 11 Horlbeck Alley
Dagner, Charles, Ship Chandler, 26 Washington St.
Dail, E., Carpenter, 1 Queen St., res. King St.
Dalbis, J. L., Grocer, 152 East Bay St.
Dalglish, W., Bricklayer, 17 Pinckney St.
Dallas, W., Bootmaker, 56 Meeting St., res. 96 East Bay St.
Dallrick, E., Mrs., Upholsterer, 160 King St.
Daly, E., Boots & Shoes, 306 King St., res. Merchants Hotel
Daly, John, Boots & Shoes, 326 King St., res. Merchants Hotel
Daly, Michael, Laborer, 20 Pinckney St.
Daly, W., Clerk, Poor House, 95 Queen St.
Dana, W. C., Rev., Pastor, Central Church, res. 19 Laurens St.
Dand, Ed, Clerk, 115 East Bay St.
Daniel, John, Fireman, South Carolina Railroad, Sires St.
Daniel, N. W., Engineer, South Carolina Railroad, 26 St. Philip St.
Daniel, S. B., Tailor, 13 Anson St.
Daniels, F., Pilot, 72 Church St.
Dansman, -----, Mrs., Baker, 90 King St.
Dappray, J. E., Dentist, King St., Ward 8
Darby, F., Coppersmith, 67 East Bay St., res. 325 King St.
Darby, J. T., Clerk, 279 King St., res. Marion St.
Darby, O. A., Teacher, Marion St.
Darby, W., Carpenter, 50 Beaufain St.
Darcy, Peter, Porter, 153 East Bay St.
Darcy, T. K., Painter, 112 Queen St.
Darr, H. L., Printer, 23 Society St.
Dart, A., Mrs., 47 Tradd St.
Dart, Thomas, Accountant, Accommodation Wharf, res. 236 King St.
Dart, William, Painter, Coming St., Ward 6
Davant, J. L., Clerk, Commercial Wharf
Davega, C., Medical Student, 150 East Bay, res. 92 Wentworth St.
Davega, G., Mrs., 92 Wentworth St.
Davega, Isaac, Attorney, Court House Square, res. 92 Wentworth St.
Davenport, R. L., Bookbinder, cr. Church & Market Sts.
Davey, Robert, Coach Maker, 14 Beaufain St.
David, R. L., Dry Goods, 265 King St.
Davidson, W., Planter, Louisiana, res. 66 Church St
Davis, C. H., Bricklayer, 114 King St.
Davis, D., Locksmith & Bell Hanger, 329 King St., res. Warren St.
Davis, Ed, Private Boarding, Mansion House
Davis, G. Y., Commission Merchant, cr. East Bay St. & Boyce Wharf, res. cr. Meeting & Queen
Davis, Isaac B., Accountant, Accommodation Wharf, res.

cr. St. Philip & Beaufain Sts.
Davis, J., Mrs., 36 Tradd St.
Davis, J. S., Accountant, cr. King & Market Sts, res. 260 King St.
Davis, John, Clerk, 40 East Bay St., res. Vanderhorst St.
Davis, Moses, Printer, 3 Tradd St.
Davis, -----, Mrs. & Son, Private Boarding, Mansion House
Davis, -----, Mrs., cr. Pitt & Vanderhorst Sts.
Davis, Nathan, Mechanic, 115 Meeting St.
Davis, R. C., Sea Captain, 56 Church St.
Davis, T. G., Attorney, 20 Broad St., res. Vanderhorst St.
Davis, W. H., Clerk, 74 East Bay St., res. 36 Tradd St.
Davis, W. R. Commission Merchant, Central Wharf, res. 3 Glebe St.
Daws, ------, Carpenter, Coming St., Ward 8
Dawson & Blackman, Druggist, 17 Broad St.
Dawson, C., Miss, 38 Bull St.
Dawson, C. P., 96 Broad St.
Dawson, E.J., Clerk, 116 Meeting St., res. Pavilion Hotel
Dawson, F., Clerk, Post Office, 25 Anson St.
Dawson, J., Commission Merchant, 94 & 96 East Bay St., res. 25 Anson St.
Dawson, J. Ed, M. D., 96 Broad St.
Dawson, J. L., M. D., 48 Tradd St.
Dawson, Joseph, Druggist, 17 Broad St., res. 25 Anson St.
Dawson, S. P., 3 Meeting St.
Dawson, Tobias, Bricklayer, St. Philip St., Ward 6
Dawson, W. H., Jr., Clerk, Adger's Wharf, 9 Lynch St.
Dawson, W., Mrs., 3 Meeting St.
Day, D. F., Clerk, 133 Meeting St., res. 260 King St.
Day, Fisher, Private Boarding, 260 King St.
Day, W. B., Clerk, Post Office, res. 3 Friend St.
Day, W. H., Coach Trimmer, 1 Montague St.
Dearcy, Thomas, Gardener, President St.
Deas, A., Miss, Dressmaker, 77 King St.
Deas, Eliza C., Charlotte St.
Deas, Henry, cr. Tradd & Council Sts.
Deas, Jane, Mantuamaker, Coming St., Ward 6
Deas, T. H., 39 Wentworth St.
DeBow, B. F., Agent, Debow's Review, cr. Broad & East Bay Sts., res. 6 Broad St.
DeBow, John, Blacksmith, Calhoun St., Ward 5
DeBuse, William, Clerk, Columbus St.
Decamps, E., Cabinet Maker, 65 King St.
Decamps, J., Carpenter, 65 King St.
Decamps, P. E., Cabinet Maker, 65 King St.
DeChoiseul, M., French Consul, 30 Broad St.
DeGafferelly, J. C., Conductor, South Carolina Railroad, Rutledge St., Ward 8
DeHay, R. H., Police Officer, Cannon St.
DeHay, William, Watchmaker, King St.
Dehon, T., Dr., Planter, Ashpoo, res. 37 Meeting St.
DeHyams, M. D., Shipper, 79 East Bay St.
Delahay, J. B., Sea Captain, 4 Horlbeck Alley
Delamps, A. G., Clerk, 70 East Bay St., res. 156 East Bay St.
DeLand, C. W., Dry Goods, 229 King St., cr. King & Wentworth Sts.

Delange, J. L., Commission Merchant, 112 East Bay St., res. Queen St.
Delaunay, J. P., Professor, 50 Wentworth St.
DeLeaumont, H., Accountant, Adger's Wharf, 2 Minority St.
DeLeon, H., Clerk, Treasury Office, 119 Queen St.
Della Torre, A., Steam Saw Mill, Washington St., Ward 6
Denck, Joseph, Music Teacher, 17 Friend St.
Deneau, T. E., Clerk, 141 Meeting St., res. 2 Liberty St.
Dener, C., Mrs. 29 Mazyck St.
Dener, George, Farmer, Christ Church Parish, 29 Mazyck St.
Denis, G. A., Confectioner, 41 Archdale St.
Denkirk, W. M., Clerk, 123 Meeting St.
Denney, -----, Mrs., 52 Queen St.
Denoon, D. H., Printer, 63 Broad St.
Dentrieau, V., Mrs., 10 Beaufain St.
Dereef, R. E., Jr., Wood Factor, Dereef's Wharf
Dereef, R. E.,Wood Factor, Dereef's Wharf
Derry, W. C., Clerk, 135 Meeting St., res. Charleston Hotel
Desasussure & Son, Attorneys, 23 Broad St.
Desaussure, C. A., Insurance Agent, 35 East Bay St., res. 26 Meeting St.
Desaussure, H. A., Attorney, 23 Broad St., res. 33 Meeting St.
Desaussure, H. W., M. D., 77 Meeting St.
Desaussure, J. B., Factor, Adger's Wharf, res. 32 Meeting St.
Desaussure, L. D., Broker, 23 Broad St., res. 33 Meeting St.
Desaussure, W. G., Attorney, 23 Broad St., res. 31 East Bay St.
Desel, Charles, Planter, Goose Creek, res. Pitt St., Ward 6
Desportes, Eliza, Vanderhorst St.
Desverney, Francis, Livery Stable, cr. Broad & Friend Sts., res. 5 Magazine St.
DeTreville, E., Attorney, 20 Broad St., res. Rutledge St.
Devea, D. H., Painter, 122 King St.
Deveau, J. P., Factor, 29 Vanderhorst's Wharf, res. cr. Amherst & Hanover Sts.
DeVega, Isaac, Attorney, Court House Square, cr. Broad & Meeting Sts.
Deveneau, A., Wheelwright, 349 King St.
Deveneau, E., Dry Goods, 304 King St.
Deveneer, Peter, Proprietor of Drays, Mary St.
Deveraux, N., Cooper, 170 Meeting St.
Devie, J. H., French Dyer, 89 King St.
Dewar, -----, Mrs., 39 Church St.
Dewees, John, Planter, Alexander, St.
Dewees, W., Clerk, 71 East Bay St., res. Alexander St.
Dewing & Thayer, Fancy Goods, 119 Meeting St.
Dewing, H., Fancy Goods, 119 Meeting St.
Dewing, L., Fancy Goods, 119 Meeting St.
Dewire, James, Pattern Maker, Meeting St., Ward 5
DeWitt, G., Farmer, 10 Beaufain St.
Dexler, -----, 6 Tradd St.
Dibble, A. C., Mrs., Private Boarding, 219 King St.

Dibble, P. V., Hatter, 37 Broad St.
Dibble, S. W., Clerk, 16 East Bay St., res. 219 King St.
Dick, Henry, Clerk, 67 Tradd St.
Dickinson, Eliza, Coming St., Ward 6
Dickson, S. H., Professor, Medical College, res. Hudson St.
Dieckhoff, C., Grocer, Judith St.
Dienstback, W., Bootmaker, 111 East Bay St.
Dierressen, W., Grocer, cr. Coming & Morris Sts.
Dill, Ervin, Fireman, Coming St., Ward 8
Dill, J. T., Factor, 13 Southern Wharf, res. cr. Beaufain & Wilson Sts.
Dill, S. G. W., Constable, Coming St., Ward 8
Dillingham, James, Clerk, 43 Hayne St., res. 179 King St.
Dinaman, C., Carpenter, King St., Ward 5
Dinkins, T. J., Clerk, cr. King & Market Sts.
Dishbrow, W. W., Clerk, 238 King St.
Disher, E., Mrs., Meeting St., Ward 5
Disher, George, Grocer, 105 Broad St.
Disher, Robert, Butcher, Nassau St.
Disman, Cornelius, Laborer, Morris St.
Divine, John, Mason, 74 Beaufain St.
Divine, Michael, Mason, 74 Beaufain St.
Divine, Thomas, Mason, 74 Beaufain St.
Divver, J. B., Clerk, cr. King & Market Sts., res. Beaufain St.
Divver, Joseph, Clerk, 300 King St., res. Beaufain St.
Divver, S., Mrs., Beaufain St.
Dixon, T. E., Ship Carpenter, 21 Beaufain St.
Dixon, Thomas, Tallow Chandler, King St., Ward 6
Doar, Marquis, Blacksmith, Hanover St.
Dobson, O. L., Mrs., 4 Smith Lane
Docille, William, Baker, King St., Ward 6
Dodd, William, Carpenter, Sires St.
Dom, William, Grocer, 20 State St.
Donald, John, Shopkeeper, 53 King St.
Donnell, B. W., Carpenter, cr. Laurens & Washington Sts.
Donnohoe, D., Hardware, 52 King St.
Donoonay, Patrick, Mason, 22 Queen St.
Doogan, Patrick, Mason, 22 Queen St.
Dooly, John, Laborer, Woolf St.
Dora, William, Baker, 351 King St.
Dorbaum & Amme, Tailors, 17 Queen St.
Dorbaum, C., Tailor, 17 Queen St.
Dorin, A., Carpenter, 22 Queen St.
Dorman, J. W., Clerk, 85 Market St.
Dorrell, John, Carpenter, Whims Court
Dorrill, A., Lumber Merchant, cr. Beaufain & Lynch Sts., res. Bee St.
Dortie, W. T., Clerk, Fitzsimons' Wharf, res. 12 Wentworth St.
Dotterer, H. E., Clerk, 1 Hayne St., res. America St.
Dotterer, T. D., Machinist, America St.
Dotterer, Thomas, Finisher, America St.
Doty, A., Sign & Ornamental Painter, 38 Broad St., res. 137 King St.
Doucin, P. M., Wharfinger, Boyce & Co. Wharf, res. 84 Beaufain St.

Dougherty, John, Wood Factor, 19 South Bay St.
Dougherty, Joseph, Grocer, 17 South Bay St., res. 19 South Bay St.
Dougherty, W. M. & Co., Gasfittting & Lamps, 292 King St., res. 19 St. Philip St.
Dougherty, W. M., Gasfitting & Lamps, 292 King St., res. 19 St. Philip St.
Doughty, Charles, Time Keeper, America St.
Douglas, A. M., Clerk, 4 Vendue Range, res. Washington St.
Douglas, C., Jr., Clerk, 47 Broad St.
Douglas, C., Miss, Shopkeeper, 53 King St.
Douglas, C., St. Andrew's Hall, Broad St.
Douglas, E. C., Clerk, 300 King St., res. Washington St.
Douglas, Hannah, St. Philip St., Ward 6
Douglas, J. F., Clerk, Atlantic Wharf, res. Washington St.
Douglas, John, Clerk, Washington St.
Douglas, Mary, 4 Wilson St.
Douglas. G. S., Accountant, 25 Hayne St., res. 236 King St.
Dowd, Martin, Bottler, 32 Anson St.
Dowie, George, Accountant, 1 Hayne St., res. King St.
Dowling, E., Mrs., 116 King St.
Dowling, John, Grocer, 38 Market St.
Dowling, Joseph, Painter, 11 Tradd St.
Downey, F. F., Clerk, Vanderhorst's Wharf, res. 24 Savage St.
Downey, M. A., Mrs., 24 Savage St.
Downing, M., Guardman, 74 Tradd St.
Downing, M., Mrs., 2 Pitt St.
Downing, R., 68 Church St.
Doyle, Jeremiah, Clerk, cr. Broad & Church Sts., res. 22 Tradd St.
Drago, A., Fruiterer, 70 Market St.
Drago, B., Mrs., Dry Goods, 141 King St.
Drake, G. W., Commission Merchant, Atlantic Wharf, res. Huntsville, Ala.
Drake, Miles, Dry Goods, 358 King St.
Drandy, Benjamin, Shoemaker, Columbus St.
Drayton, A. R., Discount & Transfer Clerk, Southwest Railroad Bank, 58 Tradd St.
Drayton, Charles, Planter, St. Andrew's Parish, res. Coming St., Ward 6
Drayton, H. B., Mrs., Ladson Court
Drayton, J. G., Pastor, St. Andrew's Parish, res. 42 South Bay St.
Drayton, J. S., Coming St., Ward 6
Drayton, M., Mrs., Coming St., Ward 6
Drayton, T. H. M., Planter, St. John's Parish, res. Coming St., Ward 6
Dreier, E., Clerk, 7 St. Philip St.
Dreier, O., Grocer, 31 Tradd St.
Droutman, J., Dry Goods, Church St.
Druber, Charles, Carpenter, Hanover St.
Drummond, John, Bootmaker, 55 Broad St.
Drummond, N., Engineer, 55 Broad St.
Dryer, D., Grocer, 43 Wall St.
Dryer, William, Drayman, Williams Row
Duboise, E., Mrs., 86 Queen St.
Duboise, John, Plasterer, 24 Washington St.

Duc, H. A., Tinner, cr. King & Spring Sts.
Duchne, D., Drayman, cr. Columbus & King Sts.
Duffus, A. W., Accountant, 137 Meeting St., res. 13 Lynch St.
Duffus, Ann, Mrs., 13 Lynch Lane
Duffus, G. H., Cotton Press, Dewees' Wharf, res. 13 Lynch St.
Duffus, J. A., Express Agent, 3 Hayne St., res. 71 Beaufain St.
Duffus, J. J. W., Clerk, 31 Hayne St., res. 71 Beaufain St.
Duffus, Samuel, Carpenter, 40 Beaufain St.
Dufort, A., Gunsmith, King St., Ward 8
Dufort, J., Tinner, Meeting St., Ward 7
Duggen, James, Watchmaker, Savage St.
Dukes, Francis, Plasterer, 12 East Bay St.
Dukes, J. H., Attorney, 61 Broad St.
Dukes, J. R., Factor & Commission Merchant, Atlantic Wharf, res. King St., Ward 5
Dukes, M. M., Mrs., St. Philip St., Ward 8
Dukes, T. C., Clerk, Atlantic Wharf, King St., Ward 5
Dukes, W. C. & Son, Factor & Commission Merchant, Atlantic Wharf
Dukes, W. C., Factor & Commission Merchant, Atlantic Wharf, res. King St., Ward 5
Dulin, Rice, Factor & Commission Merchant, Central Wharf, res. 189 Meeting St.
Dunavant, A. J., Commission Merchant, Atlantic Wharf, res. Chester District
Duncan, A., Boiler Maker, King St., Ward 6
Duncan, Catherine, Seamstress, Coming St., Ward 8
Duncan, L. C., Clerk, 143 Meeting St., res. 35 St. Philip St.
Duncan, W., Clerk, 105 East Bay St., res. Broad St.
Dunham, C. T. & Co., Boots & Shoes, 141 Meeting St.
Dunham, C. T., Boots & Shoes, 141 Meeting St., res. 11 Horlbeck Alley
Dunkin, A. H., Attorney, 65 Meeting St., res. Warren St.
Dunkin, B. F., Judge, Court of Equity, res. Warren St.
Dunlap, James, 3 Lynch St.
Dunlap, Samuel, Chandler, Woolf St.
Dunlap, W. C., 359 King St.
Dunlap, W. M., Guardman, 7 Magazine St.
Dunn & Duryea, Clothiers, 238 King St.
Dunn, C., Dry Goods, King St., Ward 6
Dunn, J., Tavern Keeper, 96 Church St.
Dunn, James, Coachsmith, King St.
Dunn, John, City Constable, 93 Queen St.
Dunn, John, Clerk, cr. Beaufain & Lynch Sts., res. 128 Queen St.
Dunn, Samuel C., Clothier, 20 Hayne St.
Dunn, Samuel C., Clothier, 238 King St.
Dunn, William, Dry Goods, 371 King St.
Dunning, James, Butcher, Reid St.
Dupont, D., Upholsterer, 203 King St.
Dupont, F., Upholsterer, 203 King St.
Dupont, M., Mrs., Teacher, 27 Wall St.
Dupree, John, Engineer, 84 Queen St.
Dupree, Joseph, Carpenter, cr. King & Spring Sts.
Dupree, -----, Mrs., Teacher, 27 Wall St.
Duquercron, F. H., Clerk, Central Wharf, 96 Tradd St.

Durose, A., Bookbinder, Vanderhorst St.
Duryea, J. M., Private Boarding, cr. Meeting & Market
Sts.
Duryea, John, Clothier, 238 King St.
Duryea, M. A. S., Mrs., 9 Wall St.
Duryea, R. S., Clerk, 84 Church St., res. 110 Meeting St.
Dusenberry, George, State Constable, 53 Tradd St.
Duval, E. A., Tinsmith, 298 King St.
Duval, J. B., Tinner, 298 King St.
Duval, L. A., Tinner, 298 King St.
Dwight, C., Mrs., Pastry Cook, 72 King St.
D'Antignac, William, Factor, Accommodation Wharf
Eager, W. M., Clerk, 1 Hayne St., res. Meeting St.
Earle, J., Bricklayer, 30 Calhoun St.
Eason, C. D., Mrs., Private Boarding, 2 Glebe St.
Eason, G. W., 2 Glebe St.
Eason, J. M. & Brothers, Engineers & Machinists, cr.
Columbus & Nassau Sts.
Eason, J. M., Engineer & Machinist, cr. Columbus &
Nassau Sts., res. Drake St.
Eason, R. H., Bricklayer, 30 Calhoun St.
Eason, R. J., Auctioneer, Vendue Range, res. 2 Glebe St.
Eason, T. D., Engineer & Machinist, cr. Columbus &
Nassau Sts., res. America St.
Easterby, George, 82 Tradd St.
Easterby, S. D., 106 Church St.
Easterby, W. H., Clerk, 213 King St., res. 106 Church St.
Easton, G. L., Sea Captain, 14 Friend St.
Eaton, Charles, Stone Cutter, 38 Market St.
Eberle, Charles, Upholsterer & Manufacturer, 205 King
St.
Eckhard, M. E., Mrs., 31 Society St.
Eden, John, Engineer, 37 Market St.
Edes, D. B., Clerk, cr. Meeting & Market Sts.
Edgerton & Richards, Drapers & Tailors, 32 Broad St.
Edgerton, E. S., Clerk, 32 Broad St., res. 3 Orange St.
Edgerton, E. W., Draper & Tailor, 32 Broad St., res. 3
Orange St.
Edmondston, Charles, President, South Carolina
Insurance Co., 109 East Bay St., res. 8 Legare St.
Edmondston, H., Clerk, cr. King & Market Sts., res. 8
Legare St.
Edmondston, L. A., Port Warden, res. 72 Tradd St.
Edmondston, T., 8 Legare St.
Edwards, C. L., Porter, Bank of Charleston, res. State St.
Edwards, Evan, Clerk, Post Office, 7 Logan St.
Edwards, F. M., Clerk, Central Wharf, res. 7 Logan St.
Edwards, J. B., 26 Wall St.
Edwards, J. F., Factor, 62 East Bay St., res. 26 Wall St.
Edwards, J. J., Clerk, 10 Central Wharf
Edwards, Morris, Carpenter, 29 Beaufain St., res. 19
College St.
Edwards, W. S., Collecting Clerk, Bank of Charleston,
res. 8 Legare St.
Egan, John, Shopkeeper, 61 King St.
Egleston, G. W., Attorney & Magistrate, 53 Broad St. &
King St., Ward 6, res. Warren St.
Egleston, J. L., Transfer & Discount Clerk, State Bank,
res. 72 Anson St.
Egleston, T. R., Clothier, 27 Hayne St., res. Commercial

Hotel
Ehlies, N., Grocer, 107 Tradd St.
Ehney, Edwin, Blacksmith, 12 Pinckney St.
Ehney, J. J., Molder, 12 Pinckney St.
Ehney, P. M., Coastwise Inspector, Custom House, res.
12 Pinckney St.
Ehricks, H., Grocer, cr. Meeting & Mary Sts.
Elbridge, James, Proprietor of Drays, Meeting St., Ward
7
Elder, W. T., Tanner, John St.
Elfe, Albert, Carpenter, 19 Lynch St.
Elfe, Eleanor, Dressmaker, 31 Montague St.
Elfe, Maria, Charlotte St.
Elfe, R. L., Barber, 28 Broad St.
Elfe, Robert, City Sheriff, 1 Middle St.
Elfe, W., Import Inspector, Custom House, 236 King St.
Elford, F. P., Wharfinger, Vanderhorst's Wharf, res. 17
Coming St.
Elfred, J. R., Proprietor of Drays, Elizabeth St.
Elleran, E., Mrs., Milliner, 146 King St.
Ellerhorst, H. D., Dry Goods, 192 King St.
Ellerhorst, W., Grain Dealer, 6 Market St.
Elliott, Gibbs, Dr., Planter, 10 George St.
Elliott, Thomas O., Attorney, 61 Broad St., res. 2 Glebe
St.
Ellis, Joseph, Carpenter, Rutledge St., Ward 8
Elmore, James, Molder, 12 East Bay St.
Elsworth, F. B., Collector, 31 Society St.
Elsworth, J. T., Gauger, Custom House, res. cr. Laurens
& Marsh Sts.
Elwig, Amelia, 55 Coming St.
Elwig, William, Carpenter, 19 West St.
Emanuel, Joel, 45 Beaufain St.
Emanuel, Nathan, 45 Beaufain St.
Emery, J. R., Clerk, South Carolina Railroad, res. Unity
Alley
Emmen, Loder, Clerk, 24 Archdale St.
Engelberg, M., Tailor, 71 Market St.
England, M., Mrs., 10 Orange St.
England, William, Clerk, 10 Orange St.
Englert, W., Private Boarding, 43 Market St.
English, James, Builder & Contractor, 15 South Bay St
English, James, Jr., 15 South Bay St.
Enslow & Bell, Coopers, cr. East Bay St. & Boyce's
Wharf
Enslow, J. A., Importer, 110 East Bay St., res. Meeting
St., Ward 5
Enslow, J. L., Cooper, cr. East Bay St. & Boyce's Wharf,
res. Tradd St.
Enston, Alfred, Cabinet Maker, 99 Queen St.
Enston, Daniel, Cabinet Maker, 118 Queen St.
Enston, W. & Co., Cabinet Makers, 169, 171 & 173 King
St.
Enston, William, Cabinet Maker, 118 Queen St.
Epping, J. P. M., Druggist, 227 King St.
Erickson, C., Wood Builder, Smith's Wharf
Ervin, John, Dr., 5 Rutledge St.
Ervin, W. F., Surveyor General, Fireproof Building, res.
Sumter District
Estill, W., Bookbinder, 5 Lynch St.

Estill, W., Jr., Printer, King St.
Evans, B. F., Clerk, 101 East Bay St., res. Meeting St.
Evans, C., Mrs., 57 Queen St.
Evans, E., Mrs., America St.
Evans, G. W., Factor Accommodation Wharf, res. 2 Hasell St.
Evans, J. B., Clerk, 35 Hayne St., res. Wentworth St.
Evans, James, Tailor, 67 Broad St.
Evans, R., Miss, Teacher, 373 King St.
Evans, R., Tavern Keeper, 97 Market St.
Evans, Samuel, Boiler Maker, Elizabeth St.
Evans, Sellers, Carpenter, Coming St., Ward 8
Evans, W. E. & Co., Factor, Accommodation Wharf
Evans, W. E., Factor, Accommodation Wharf, res. 2 Hasell St.
Evans, W., Private Boarding, 373 King St.
Eveleigh, Thomas, Private Boarding, 297 King St.
Ewan, John, Silverware Store, 127 King St.
Ewan, W. H., Silverware Store, 127 King St.
Ewart, J., Clerk, Central Wharf, res. 106 church St.
Ewbank, Henry, Hardware, 155 Meeting St., res. 17 Smith St.
Ewing, M., Mrs., Private Boarding, 269 King St.
Ezekiel, P., Watchmaker, 61 Broad St., res. 89 Church St.
Faber, A. M., Mrs., Alexander St.
Fabin, William, Seaman, 83 Queen St.
Fairchild, B., Factor, Bell's Wharf, 111 Wentworth St.
Fairchild, Rufus, Music Store, 210 King St., res. cr. King & Beaufain Sts.
Fairly, Arthur, Clerk, 41 Broad St., res. 22 Cumberland St.
Falk, Abraham, Clothier, 265 King St.
Falk, I. L. & Co., Clothiers, 265 King St.
Faman, Mary, Henrietta St.
Fanning, F. D. & Co., Hats & Caps, 31 Hayne St.
Fanning, F. D., Hats & Caps, 31 Hayne St., res. 2 Maiden Lane
Farnum, O., Grocer, 189 East Bay St.
Farrar, C. D., Grocery Merchant, 70 East Bay St., res. 28 Society St.
Farrar, J. C., Grocery Merchant, 70 East Bay St., res. 28 Society St.
Farrar, S. S. & Brothers, Grocery Merchants, 70 East Bay St.
Farrar, S. S., Grocery Merchant, 70 East Bay St., res. 28 Society St.
Faulkernon, Isaac, Clerk, 5 Hayne St.
Faust, M., Mrs., 21 Middle St.
Favor, Joseph, Planter, Pon Pon, res. Charlotte St.
Fayssoux, T., Druggist, 31 Broad St., res. 4 Orange St.
Fedhazke, E., Bootmaker, 5 Queen St.
Feehan, C. F., Miss, 61 Anson St.
Feehan, James, Porter, Hayne St., res. King St., Ward 5
Fees, G., Watchmaker, 187 King St.
Felis, B., Cigar Maker, 68 State St.
Fennick, John, Tailor, 7 Beaufain St.
Ferette, Mary, 5 Calhoun St.
Ferguson, Emeline, 35 George St.
Ferguson, J. H., Accountant, 145 Meeting St., res.

Planters Hotel
Ferguson, W. C., Currier, 22 Queen St.
Ferira, Jason, Carpenter, Morris St.
Ferrell, J. J., Accountant, 19 Hayne St., res. 23 St. Philip St.
Ferrell, Michael, Mechanic, 23 St. Philip St.
Ferrell, Thomas, Mechanic, 23 St. Philip St.
Ferrette, Adeline, 15 College St.
Ferrette, J. F., Fruiterer, 41 Market St.
Ferrette, J., Miss, 34 Archdale St.
Ferry, W., Carpenter, Beaufain St.
Fiberoux, B., 206 King St.
Ficken, J. F., Grocer, 13 Beaufain St.
Ficklin, E. S., Mrs., 7 Short St.
Ficklin, James, Clerk, 19 Hayne St., res. 7 Short St.
Ficklin, W. B., Attorney, 63 Broad St., res. 7 Short St.
Fickling, J. J., Bricklayer, 30 Tradd St.
Fiegre, Julius, Hatter, 164 King St.
Fields, Nathan, Proprietor, Charleston Ice House, cr. Adger's Wharf & East Bay St.
Figeroux, B., Mrs., Milliner, 206 King St.
Figney, Abraham, Drayman, 7 Bull St.
Fillette, A., Madame, Dry Goods, 139 King St.
Fillette, Theo, Clerk, 29 Hayne St., res. 139 King St.
Fimkensteadt, G., Grocer, 1 King St.
Fincken, -----, Grocer, 11 South Bay St.
Finckle, J. O., Cotton Spinner, Columbus St.
Fink, A. & Co., Tavern Keepers, Exchange St.
Fink, A., Tavern Keeper, Exchange St.
Fink, B. H., Druggist, 369 King St.
Fink, H., Laborer, St. Philip St., Ward 8
Fink, P. J., Clerk, 123 Meeting St.
Finlayson, -----, Clerk, 75 East Bay St.
Finley, E., Mrs., 7 Atlantic St.
Finley, W. P., President, Charleston College, 12 Montague St.
Finn, E., Laborer, 1 Washington St.
Finnegan, J., Sea Captain, 12 Market St.
Finnegan, John, Tailor, 188 King St., res. 21 Franklin St.
Firth, H. D., 5 Mazyck St.
Fishburn, Robert, Planter, St. Paul's Parish, 257 East Bay St.
Fisher, F., Bootmaker, 6 Tradd St.
Fisher, John, Dry Goods, 209 East Bay St.
Fisher, John, Tailor, Meeting St.
Fisher, S., Mrs., Milliner, 252 King St.
Fisher, S., Planter, Summerville, res. 252 King St.
Fisher, S. W., Clerk, 248 King St., res. 21 Friend St.
Fitch, W. M., M. D., 78 Meeting St., cr. Wentworth & Pitt Sts.
Fitz, John, Blacksmith, Hanover St.
Fitz, William, Blacksmith, Hanover St.
Fitzgerald, M., Laborer, 26 State St.
Fitzpatrick, A. F., Clerk, 80 East Bay St., res. 52 Tradd St.
Fitzpatrick, P., Clerk, 100 East Bay St., res. 52 Tradd St.
Fitzsimons, B., Saddler & Harness Maker, 282 King St.
Fitzsimons, C., M. D., 26 Hasell St.
Fitzsimons, E., Mrs., 26 Hasell St.
Fitzsimons, R. T., Saddler & Harness Maker, 282 King

St.

Flack, G. W., Watchmaker, 40 Anson St.

Flagg, C. B., Attorney, 59 Meeting St., res. 15 Archdale St.

Flagg, E. B., M. D., 15 Archdale St.

Fleeken, Frederick, Laborer, Woolf St.

Fleming, D. F. & Co., Boots & Shoes, 43 Hayne St.

Fleming, D. F., Boots & Shoes, 43 Hayne St., res. Charleston Hotel

Fleming, James, Laborer, 20 Tradd St.

Fleming, Robert, Candy Manufacturer, 269 King St.

Fleming, William, Clerk, cr. King & Market Sts., res. King St.

Flinn, James, Clerk, 54 East Bay St., res. 29 Church St.

Flinn, John, Clerk, 54 East Bay St., res. 29 Church St.

Flinn, Martin, Guardman, America St.

Flinn, Michael, 129 East Bay St.

Flood, J., Clerk, 116 Church St.

Fludd, J. S., Clerk, Central Wharf, res. Spring St.

Fludd, -----, Mrs., Spring St.

Flynn, J. T., Draper & Tailor, 30 Broad St., res. New St.

Fobb, William, Clerk, 264 King St.

Fogartie, A., Clerk, 253 King St., res. 59 Beaufain St.

Fogartie, A., Mrs., Teacher, 23 Wall St.

Fogartie, Ed, Bricklayer, Calhoun St., Ward 6

Fogartie, S., Accountant, 23 Wall St.

Fogartie, S., Mrs., 31 George St.

Folger, -----, Packer, 8 Middle St.

Folker, E. G., Clerk, South Carolina Railroad, Radcliffe St.

Folker, Octavus, Clerk, Vanderhorst St.

Folker, P. H., Teacher, Cannon St.

Follin, G., Tobacconist, 169 Meeting St., cr. Meeting & Society Sts.

Fonda, D. A., Clerk, 234 & 236 King St.

Foote, C., Mrs., 113 King St.

Foran, J. J., Clerk, 181 East Bay St., res. 231 E. Bay St.

Forbes, R., Tin Plate Worker & Tin Roofer, 22 Tradd St.

Force, B. W. & J. P. & Co., Boots & Shoes, 21 Hayne St.

Force, B. W., Boots & Shoes, 21 Hayne St., res. 1 Hasell St.

Force, J. P., Boots & Shoes, 21 Hayne St., res. Augusta, Ga.

Ford, B., Boots & Shoes, 99¾ East Bay St., res. Ashley St.

Ford, C. H., Miss, 7 MacBride's Lane

Ford, F. A., Attorney, 41 Broad St., res. 97 Broad St.

Ford, J. D., Student, 23 Broad St., res. 97 Broad St.

Ford, Lewis, Carver, 92 Queen St.

Ford, W. H., Student, 97 Broad St.

Fordham, R., Church St.

Fordham, W. R., Livery Stables, Chalmers St., res. Meeting St., Ward 5

Foren, J. J., Clerk, 361 King St.

Forest, John, Pastor, First Presbyterian Church, res. rear of Court House

Forest, S., Mrs., 94 Wentworth St.

Forrest, Francis, Bootmaker, St. Philip St., Ward 6

Forrester, A., Engineer, 58 Anson St.

Forsyth, W. C., Clerk, 350 King St., res. 30 Burns Lane

Fosket, Alex, Mail Contractor, St. Philip St., Ward 6

Fosket, S. A., Mrs., Dressmaker, St. Philip St., Ward 6

Foster, Charles, Clerk, 37 Hayne St., res. 72 Wentworth St.

Foster, W. B., Clerk, Bank of the State of South Carolina, res. 72 Wentworth St.

Fowle, G. M. & Co., Commission Merchants, Vanderhorst's Wharf

Fowle, G. M., Commission Merchant, Vanderhorst's Wharf

Fowler, A. D., Clerk, 244 King St., res. 83 Queen St.

Fowler, Joseph, Seaman, 68 Queen St.

Fowler, William, Sailor Boarding, Bedon's Alley

Fox, M., Mrs., 22 Laurens St.

Fox, Sarah, 38 St. Philip St.

Fox, William, Wharfinger, Fitzsimons' Wharf, res. 22 Laurens St.

Frahna, F., Coopersmith, 34 State St.

Francis, B., Shoemaker, 171 East Bay St.

Francis, G. M., Saddler, 344 King St.

Francis, John, Barber, 316½ King St.

Francois, S., Clerk, 23 Market St.

Franklin, Linguard, cr. King & Ann Sts.

Fraser, A., Clerk, 13 Exchange St., res. 30 Tradd St.

Fraser, Charles, 35 King St.

Fraser, J. E., Factor & Commission Merchant, 1 Southern Wharf, res. 91 Tradd St.

Fraser, John & Co., Factor & Commission Merchant, Central Wharf

Fraser, John, Factor & Commission Merchant, Central Wharf, res. 3 Short St.

Fraser, John J., Conductor, South Carolina Railroad, 273 King St.

Fraser, John, Tailor, 16 St. Philip St., res. Radcliffe St.

Fraser, M., Mrs., 91 Tradd St.

Fraser, Samuel, Bootmaker, 2 Archdale St., res. Beaufain St.

Fraser, W. S., Clerk, Fire Proof Building, res. Meeting St., Ward 5

Frazer, C. P., Warm Bath Establishment, 67 Meeting St.

Frazer, J. M., Accountant, 213 King St., res. 67 Meeting St.

Fredsberg, J. M., Clerk, 20 East Bay St.

Freeman, J., Mrs., America St.

Freeman, W., Seaman, 7 Longitude Lane

Freer, Isaac, Clerk, Rutledge St., Ward 8

French, Henry, Overseer, Charleston Factory, Line St.

French, John, Clerk, 40 East Bay St., res. Planters Hotel

Frender, E., Butcher, Woolf St.

Frey, Joseph, Clerk, 210 King St., res. 50 Queen St.

Frierson, E., Miss, 11 Burns Lane

Fripp, J. A., 1 Lamboll St.

Froeliah, N., Conductor, South Carolina Railroad, Woolf St.

Froneberger, Caleb, Boots & Shoes, 165 Meeting St., res. Charleston Hotel

Frost, E. D., Clerk, Adger's Wharf, res. 110 Tradd St.

Frost, E. H., Clerk, Adger's Wharf, res. 110 Tradd St.

Frost, Edward, Judge, 110 Tradd St.

Frost, H. R., M. D., 68 Broad St., res. 70 Broad St.

Frost, Thomas, Attorney, St. Michael's Alley, res. 110 Tradd St.

Fryer, E., Mrs. Music Teacher, 27 Broad St.

Fryer, W. DeB., Accountant, 250 King St., res. 27 Broad St.

Fuller, Benjamin, Planter, St. Andrew's Parish, 24 Broad St.

Fuller, John, Guardman, Spring St.

Fuller, M., Mrs., Paine Court

Fuller, R., Clerk, cr. King & Market Sts., res. 204 King St.

Fuller, T. A., 52 Calhoun St.

Fulmer, John, Woolf St.

Furman, C. M., President, Bank of South Carolina, res. above bank

Furman, R. K., Planter, Daniel's Island, res. 9 Archdale St.

Furst, Daniel, Carpenter, Bedon's Alley

Gadsden, Benjamin, Planter, Goose Creek, res. 11 Coming St.

Gadsden, F., Porter & Outdoor Clerk, Bank of the State of South Carolina, res. Meeting St.

Gadsden, James & Co., Factors, 62 East Bay St.

Gadsden, James, Factor, 62 East Bay St., res. Ann St.

Gadsden, James, Factor, Commercial Wharf, res. Coming St.

Gadsden, P., Bishop, Charleston District, Alexander St.

Gadsden, Richard, Farmer, Meeting St., Ward 7

Gadsden, T. N., Broker, Chalmers St., res. 5 Church St.

Gaetjens, G., Spirit Dealer, 104 East Bay St., res. 39 Broad St.

Gafry, John, Clerk, 45 Hayne St., res. Market St.

Gage, James, Sea Captain, 98 Queen St.

Gaillard & Snowden, Factors & Commission Merchants, 6 Southern Wharf

Gaillard, A., Mrs., 3 Meeting St.

Gaillard, A. P., Planter, St. Andrew's Parish, res. Smith's Lane

Gaillard, E., Mrs., 13 Pitt St.

Gaillard, E., Mrs., Ann St.

Gaillard, F. P., Clerk, Central Wharf, res. 19 State St.

Gaillard, P. C., Factor & Commission Merchant, 6 Southern Wharf, res. Smith Lane

Gaillard, P. C., M. D., 60 Broad St.

Gaillard, S., Mrs., Court House Square

Gaillard, T. P., Clerk, 24 Vendue Range, res. Court House Square

Galagher, D., Clerk, Planters Hotel

Galdman, L. A., Butcher, 24 St. Philip St.

Gall, R. W., Clerk, 253 King St., cr. Wentworth & King Sts.

Gallagher, D., Tinner, King St., Ward 6

Gallaway, M., Miss, Milliner, 181 King St.

Galliot, Alexis, Cigar Manufacturer, 161 East Bay St.

Galy, Arthur, 36 Anson St.

Gamage, Edward, 30 Society St.

Gambatti, A., Music Teacher, 88 King St.

Gamble & Son, Jewellers, 185 King St.

Gamble, James, Jeweller, 185 King St.

Gamble, Richard, Jeweler, 185 King St.

Gamble, Samuel, Clerk, 179 King St.

Gannon, -----, Mrs., Private Boarding, 42 State St.

Gannon, R., Dry Goods, 130 Church St.

Gannon, T., Bar Keeper, Planters Hotel

Gant, Edward, Factor & Commission Merchant, Accommodation Wharf, res. cr. Coming & Warren Sts.

Gant, Huff & Gant, Factors & Commission Merchants, Accommodation Wharf

Gant, J. L., Factor & Commission Merchant, Accommodation Wharf, res. cr. Coming & Warren Sts.

Gant, R. S., Clerk, 82 East Bay St., res. 185 East Bay St.

Gant, T. J., Register in Equity, Court House

Ganthier, F., Teacher, Citadel Academy, Cannon St.

Garbon, A., Grocer, Charlotte St.

Garden, B., Druggist, 162 King St.

Garden, E., Mrs., Rutledge St., Ward 6

Garden, R. H., Accountant, 45 Hayne St., res. 10 Middle St.

Gardner, A. Y., Clerk, 250 King St.

Gardner, Elias, King St., Ward 6

Gardner, J. M., Watchmaker, 250 King St., res. 15 Broad St.

Gardner, Maria, St. Philip St., Ward 6

Garrette, G., Bootmaker, 75 Church St., res. 104 Queen St.

Garrette, J. W., Clerk, 167 Meeting St., res. 104 Queen St.

Garrette, John, Planter, Charlotte St.

Garrette, -----, Mrs., Private Boarding, 104 Queen St.

Garrette, Samuel, Tailor, St. Philip St., Ward 8

Garrick, F., Blacksmith, Spring St.

Garrity, B., Grocer, 5 South Bay St.

Garrity, C., Grocer, 22 South Bay St.

Garrity, Thomas, Porter, 139 Meeting St., res. 32 Queen St.

Gary, E., Mrs., King St., Ward 7

Gates, Thomas, Butcher, Cannon St.

Gatewood, W. C., 17 Legare St.

Gaugan, A. E., Warren St.

Gayer, W. J., Coachmaker, 142 Meeting St., res. 146 Meeting St.

Gayser, B., Mrs., 43 Archdale St.

Geddes, C., Mrs., Planter, 14 Rutledge St.

Geddings, Eli, Physician, 16 George St.

Gehis, J. H., Commission Merchant, 32 Vendue Range, res. 28 Queen St.

Geiger, P., Mechanic, 121 Meeting St.

Geissel, H., Grocer, cr. Concord & Hasell Sts.

Genther, N., Baker, 4 Wall St.

George, John, Clerk, 40 East Bay St.

George, Reuben, Engineer, Railroad, Sires St.

George, Wiley, Mason, 58 Queen St.

Gerard, P. G., 23 Franklin St.

Gerdis, E., Grocer, cr. Ashley & Doughty Sts.

Gerdts, C. H., Grocer, 43 Archdale St.

Gerdts, H., Grocer, 203 East Bay St.

Gervais, J. L., Dr., Planter, St. John's Parish, res. Rutledge St., Ward 6

Gervais, Paul T., Jr., Planter, St. John's Island, res. 23 Legare St.

Gervais, Paul T., Rev., 23 Legare St.
Gibbon, G., 9 New St.
Gibbon, G. E., Commission Merchant, Gillon St., res. 94 Broad St.
Gibbon, J. & G. E., Commission Merchants, Gillon St.
Gibbon, John, Commission Merchant, Gillon St., res. 23 Broad St.
Gibbs, B. S., cr. John & Elizabeth Sts.
Gibbs, E. A., Dr., 10 George St.
Gibbs, E. C., Mrs., 9 Short St.
Gibbs, H. P., Medical Student, 66 Tradd St.
Gibbs, J. B., Accountant, Adger's Wharf, res. 83 Broad St.
Gibbs, J. B., Wharfinger, Atlantic Wharf, res. 83 Broad St.
Gibbs, J. Reeves, Clerk, 56 East Bay St., res. 66 Tradd St.
Gibbs, J. S., Coal Yard, Patton's Wharf, 46 Calhoun St.
Gibbs, J. S., Commission Merchant, Adger's Wharf, 5 Short St.
Gibbs, Lewis, Professor, Charleston College, res. 51 Calhoun St.
Gibbs, Mary, Mantuamaker, 25 St. Philip St.
Gibbs, W. G., Commission Merchant, Boyce & Co. Wharf, res. 29 Friend St.
Gibbs, W. H., 92 Tradd St.
Gibson, A. E., Accountant, Atlantic Wharf, res. Alexander St.
Gibson, Alexander, Alexander St.
Gibson, C. B., Mrs., 21 Franklin St.
Gibson, D. C., Attorney, 84 Church St., res. 172 Meeting St.
Gibson, E., Mrs., 172 Meeting St.
Gibson, J. R., Clerk, 43 Hayne St., res. 1 Hasell St.
Gibson, W. C., Freight Collector, 2 Glebe St.
Gibson, William, Columbus St.
Gidiere, John, Music Teacher, 338 King St.
Gidiere, Joseph, Clerk, 338 King St.
Gidiere, M., Dry Goods, 338 King St.
Gilbert & Chapin, Coach Makers, 35 & 40 Wentworth St.
Gilbert, S. H., Printer, Church St.
Gilbert, E. M., 35 & 40 Wentworth St., res. 249 King St.
Gilbreth, N. M., Painter, 94 Market St.
Gilchrist, J. M., Broker & Auctioneer, 10 State St.
Gilchrist, James, Assistant Clerk, Bank of South Carolina
Gilchrist, R. B., U. S. Judge, Chalmers St., res. 245 East Bay St.
Gilchrist, R. C., Attorney, Chalmers St., res. 245 East Bay St.
Gill, John, Carpenter, Spring St.
Gillespie, A. O., Dry Goods, 37 Hayne St., res. Charleston Hotel
Gillilands, Howell & Co., Dry Goods, Hayne St.
Gillilands, James, Dry Goods, Hayne St., res. Society St.
Gillilands, W. D., Dry Goods, Hayne St., res. 29 Hasell St.
Gillilands, W. H., Dry Goods, Hayne St., res. 24 Hasell St.
Gilman, C., Mrs., Columbus St.

Gilman, S., Pastor, Unitarian Church, 7 Orange St.
Ginane, James, Wheelwright, King St., Ward 5
Ginard, Dennis, Drayman, King St., Ward 5
Giradeau, M. T., Mrs., 50 Broad St.
Girardeau, C., Medical Student, 50 Broad St.
Girardeau, E. F., Clerk, west end of Montague St., res. 28½ Montague St.
Gist, B. H., St. Philip St., Ward 6
Gist, J. L., Clerk, 288 King St., res. 26 Marsh St.
Gitsinger, B. R., City Inspector, 22 Cumberland St.
Gitsinger, George, Clerk, cr. East Bay St. & Adger's Wharf, res. 22 Cumberland St.
Given, James, Painter, 32 Queen St.
Given, Sarah, Mrs., Coming St., Ward 6
Given, W., Boots & Shoes, 359 King St.
Glade, I. H., Clerk, 29 King St.
Gladen, -----, Mrs., 48 George St.
Glahn, A. Von, Dry Goods, 230 King St.
Glaser, John, Bootmaker, 13 Queen St.
Gleason, E. P., Mrs., Private Boarding, 236 King St.
Gleason, J. E., Professor of Music, 10 Horlbeck Alley
Glen, D. O., Daguerreotypist, 221 King St., res. Beaufain St.
Glen, John, cr. Meeting & Reid Sts.
Glen, M., Mrs., Shopkeepeer, 10 Archdale St.
Glen, T. C., Clothier, 261 King St.
Glen, W. M., M. D., cr. Meeting & Reid Sts.
Glover & Davis, Commission Merchants, Central Wharf
Glover, C. H., Mrs., Teacher, South Carolina Society Hall, res. 7 Orange St.
Glover, G. A., Saddler, Chalmers St., res. 28 Tradd St.
Glover, S. Adam, Clerk, 54 East Bay St., res. 16 Cumberland St.
Glover, S., Commission Merchant, Central Wharf, res. Orangeburg District
Glover, S. L., Commission Merchant, Central Wharf, res. Doughty St.
Glyn, George, Coach Trimmer, Horlbeck Alley
Godefroy, A., Tailor, 58 State St.
Goldsmith, Henry, Clerk, Court House Square, res. 54 Beaufain St.
Goldsmith, J. H., M. D., 98 Tradd St.
Goldsmith, Maurice, Deputy U. S. Marshal, Chalmers St., res. 98 Tradd St.
Goldsmith, N., Nassau St.
Goldstein, J., Jeweller, 153 King St.
Gonfreyville, H., Mrs., Milk Seller, cr. Columbus & Nassau Sts.
Gontvegne, P., Cutler Manufacturer, 43 Queen St.
Gonzalez, B., Commisson Merchant, 15 Exchange St., res. 4 George St.
Goodrich, -----. Mrs., Private Boarding, 80 Market St.
Goodrich, N. E., Butcher, Cannon St.
Goodwin, G. M., Commission Merchant, 94 East Bay St., res. 43 George St.
Goodwin, William M., Printer, 70 Meeting St.
Gordon, Alex, Hardware, 15 Broad St.
Gordon, C., Miss, 6 West St.
Gordon, C. P., Accountant, Ashley St.
Gordon, J. B., Planter, Georgia, res. west end of Calhoun

St.
Gordon, James, Clerk, 349 King St.
Gordon, James, Plumber, 127 Meeting St.
Gordon, John, Butcher, America St.
Gordon, John, Grocer, King St., Ward 5
Gordon, L. C., Accountant, St. Michael's Alley, res. 9
    Friend St.
Gordon, Robert, Bootmaker, cr. Nassau & Mary Sts.
Gorman, James, Laborer, 7 Tradd St.
Gorman, John, Laborer, 7 Tradd St.
Gorman, M., Mrs., 7 Tradd St.
Gorman, Michael, Laborer, 7 Tradd St.
Gosprey, F., Carpenter, Meeting St., Ward 5
Gotgen, John, Grocer, 65 East Bay St.
Gouf, Charles, Bricklayer, Morris St.
Gouldsmith, Rice, Cabinet Maker, 91 Wentworth St.
Gourdin, Henry, Commission Merchant, Commercial
    Wharf., res. cr. South Bay & Meeting Sts.
Gourdin, Matthiesen & Co., Commission Merchants,
    Commercial Wharf
Gourdin, P. G., 43 East Bay St.
Gourdin, R. N., Commission Merchant, Commercial
    Wharf, res. cr. South Bay & Meeting Sts.
Gourdin, T., M. D., 106 Church St., res. 31 East Bay St.
Gourdin, T. S., Attorney, 34 Broad St., res. Alexander St.
Gourdin, W. Allston, Factor, 56 East Bay St., res. 21
    Legare St.
Gowan & Son, Watchmakers, 54 Meeting St.
Gowan, A. H., Watchmaker, 54 Meeting St., res. 8 South
    Bay St.
Gowan, P., Watchmaker, 54 Meeting St., res. 8 South
    Bay St.
Gowan, Sarah, Spring St.
Gowan, Susan, Spring St.
Graddick, Henry, Clerk, South Carolina Railroad, res. 28
    Calhoun St.
Gradick, C. C., Butcher, 28 Calhoun St.
Gradick, C. C., Jr., Clerk, South Carolina Railroad, res.
    28 Calhoun St.
Grady, A. P., Collector, Meeting St., Ward 5
Grady, Augustus, Tailor, 157 East Bay St., res. 144 King
    St.
Grady, James, Tailor, 144 King St.
Grady, Patrick, Drayman, 32 Queen St.
Graham, A. M., Miss, Dressmaker, 222½ King St.
Graham, Daniel, Conductor, South Carolina Railroad,
    res. Marion St.
Graham, John, Clerk, Hayne St., res. 198 King St.
Grainger, Charles, Ship Carpenter, Cannon St.
Granston, George, Bootmaker, 28 Anson St.
Grant, F. W., 176 King St.
Grant, Jane, Brewsters Alley
Grant, Lucinda, Paine Court
Gravely, C., Clerk, 58 East Bay St., res. 28 Broad St.
Gravely, John, Hardware, 58 East Bay St., res. 28 Broad
    St.
Graver, H., Clerk, 87 East Bay St.
Graver, John, Grocer, 357 King St.
Graves, A. D., Factor, Howard's Wharf, 82 Wentworth
    St.

Graves, Charles, 33 Society St.
Graves, D. Des, Planter, Goose Creek, res. 4 Friend St.
Gray, A. H., Painter, 5 Burns Lane
Gray, A. P., Clerk, Fire Proof Building, 21 Coming St.
Gray, Flora, 25 College St.
Gray, H. Y., Clerk, U. S. Court, Chalmers St., res.
    Calhoun St., Ward 6
Gray, J. B., 24 Society St.
Gray, J. F., Teacher, 5 Burns Lane
Gray, J. W., Master in Equity, Fire Proof Building, res.
    88 Beaufain St.
Gray, Jane, 3 Coming St.
Gray, R., Mrs., 3 Coming St.
Grayson, Henry, Clerk, Custom House, res. 64 Tradd St.
Grayson, W. J., Collector, Custom House, res. 64 Tradd
    St.
Grazer, C. A., Factor & Commission Merchant, 13
    Central Wharf, res. 236 King St.
Gready, J. R., Clerk, 253 King St., res. 204 King St.
Greaton, John, Inspector, Charleston Insurance & Trust
    Co., res. 45 Tradd St.
Green & Redmonds, Commission Merchants,
    Commercial Wharf
Green, E., Miss, 30 Tradd St.
Green, J., 12 Chalmers St., res. 10 Chalmers St.
Green, J. F., Clerk, 54 East Bay St., res. Charlotte St.
Green, J. F., Commission Merchant, Commercial Wharf,
    res. Charlotte St.
Green, J. H., Carpenter, America St.
Green, Jacob, Livery Stable, 12 Chalmers St., res. 10
    Chalmers St.
Green, Owen, Tailor, 95 Queen St.
Green, Patrick, Tailor, 19 Anson St.
Green, R. M., Clerk, Commercial Wharf, res. Charlotte
    St.
Green, T. P., Washington St., Ward 5
Green, W. R., Stevedore, Motte's Lane
Greenhill, -----, Mrs., 3 Greenhill St.
Greenland, George, Mason, 30 Middle St.
Greenland, M., Physician, Meeting St., res. 28 Archdale
    St.
Greenleaf, -----, Boiler Maker, 21 Pinckney St.
Greer & White, Tavern Keepers, 280 King St.
Greer, J. M., Bookseller, 207 King St.
Greer, W., Tavern Keeper, 131 East Bay St., res. 15
    State St.
Gregg, Hayden & Co., Jewelry & Silverware, 250 King
    St.
Gregg, William, 250 King St., res. Calhoun St., Ward 6
Gregorie, J. L., Bursar, Citadel Academy
Gregory, A., Cooper, 36 Calhoun St.
Gregory, F. M., Cutler, 143 East Bay St., res. 26 Middle
    St.
Greierson, J. C., Mechanic, 108 East Bay St.
Grierson, J. W., Clerk, 245 King St., res. 79 Wentworth
    St.
Griffitch, M. J., Mrs., 41 Wall St.
Griggs, H. S., Treasurer, Savings Institution, res. 31
    Society St.
Grimbly, J. B., Planter, 6 South Bay St.

Grimke, Henry, Planter, St. Paul's Parish, res. cr.
Amherst & East Bay Sts.
Grimke, John, Physician, 48 St. Philip St.
Grimke, -----, Mrs., 13 Savage St.
Grimke, T. D., Physician, 42 South Bay St.
Grimke, T. S., Mrs., 42 South Bay St.
Griner, A., Mrs., Baker, 10 Anson St.
Groning, Lewis, 249 King St.
Grouver, Michael, Saddler, 302 King St., res. Laurens St.
Groves, E., Mrs., Private Boarding, 1 Queen St
Groves, J. A., Clerk, 153 Meeting St.
Grown, George, Grocer, 47 Broad St.
Gruber, G. H., Clerk, 222 King St., res. Reid St.
Gruver, W., Plasterer, 114 Wentworth St.
Guenebault, Thomas H., Professor of French, 156
Meeting St.
Guenveur, J., Miss, China Dealer, 118 King St.
Guenveur, J. U., Accountant, 118 King St.
Guenveur, S. F., Bookbinder, 118 King St.
Guerard, J. J., Accountant, cr. East Bay St. &
Vanderhorst's Wharf, res. East Bay St.
Guerard, O. J., Planter, St. Peter's Parish, res. Rutledge
St., Ward 6
Guerry, G., 2 Price's Alley
Guerry, P. C., Clerk, 182 King St., res. East Bay St.
Gunnison, J. A., Commission Merchant, 88 East Bay St.,
res. 86 Tradd St.
Gutman, C., Jeweller, 18 St. Philip St.
Guy, James, Carpenter, Clifford St.
Guy, Joseph, Carpenter, Cannon St.
Guy. T. B., Commission Merchant, 106 East Bay St.
Guymer, A., Accountant, East Bay St., res. Coming St.,
Ward 6
Gyles, J. A., Magistrate & Attorney, 18 Broad St.
Habenish, C. F., Grocer, 4 Tradd St.
Hacker, G. S., Car Builder, King St., Ward 7
Hacker, Thomas, Machinist, King St., Ward 7
Hafers, Henry, Proprietor, European Hotel
Hagan, L., Mrs., 10 Clifford St.
Hagood, G. W., Piano Tuner & Repairer, 251 King St.,
res., 318 King St.
Hahn, J. C., Clerk, 6 Market St.
Hahnbaum, E. R., Mrs., 22 Pitt St.
Haig, Alex, Planter, St. Andrew's Parish, res. Ashley St.
Haig, George, Planter, St. Andrew's Parish, res. Rutledge
St., Ward 6
Haig, H. M., Physician, 20 Meeting St.
Haines, George, Laborer, Bedon's Alley
Haines, Isabella, Mrs., Washington St., Ward 5
Halgrave, Nancy, Baker, 30 Meeting St.
Hall, A. M., Accountant, Dewee's Wharf, 10 Liberty St.
Hall, C. G., Clerk, Central Wharf, res. 263 East Bay St.
Hall, Charlotte, 28 Coming St.
Hall, H. & W. P., Commission Merchants, Central Wharf
Hall, H. T., Commission Merchant, Central Wharf, res.
cr. Church & Queen Sts.
Hall, J. A., Clerk, 253 King St., res. Charleston Hotel
Hall, J. J., Furniture, 114 King St.
Hall, Jacob, Fireman, cr. Columbus & Nassau Sts.
Hall, M. S., Mrs., 346 King St.

Hall, -----, Mrs., 16 Liberty St.
Hall, W. P., Commission Merchant, Central Wharf, res.
cr. Church & Queen Sts.
Hall, William, Physician, 263 East Bay St.
Hallaway, R., Porter, Hayne St., res. 70 Beaufain St.
Halsall, W. H., Railroad Conductor, Columbus St.
Halson, William, Porter, 76 East Bay St., res. cr. Church
& Chalmers Sts.
Haly, John, Drayman, King St., Ward 6
Ham, W., Engineer, 94 Church St.
Hamill, Thomas, Wheelwright, 24 Washington St.
Hamilton, A., Coach Trimmer, Meeting St.
Hamilton, Diana, 8 St. Philip St.
Hamilton, Gavin, Carpenter, 6 Queen St.
Hamilton, J., Coachmaker, Meeting St.
Hamilton, J. L., Sea Captain, 9 Queen St.
Hamilton, W. M., Accountant, 80 East Bay St., res.
Meeting St.
Hamlin, Edward, Printer, 23 Concord St.
Hamlin, G., Blacksmith, 111 Wentworth St.
Hamlin, James, Clerk, 74 East Bay St., res. 111
Wentworth St.
Hamlin, John, Coachmaker, 1 Gadsden St.
Hamlin, M., Mrs., 1 Gadsden St.
Hamlin, Moore, Carpenter, 1 Gadsden St.
Hamlin, Thomas, Mason, 1 Gadsden St.
Hammarskold, -----, Architect, 122 East Bay St., res.
Logan St.
Hammond, A. L., Physician, 29 Meeting St.
Hampden, S., Mrs., 12 Orange St.
Hanahan, J. C., Cooper, Adger's Wharf, res. 136 Tradd
St.
Hanahan, James, Ship Carpenter, 48 King St.
Hanckel, C. F., Attorney, 21 Broad St., res. 62 Calhoun
St.
Hanckel, John, Bookkeeper, Bank of the State of South
Carolina, res. Thomas St.
Hanckel, T. M. & C. F., Attorneys, 21 Broad St.
Hanckel, T. M., Attorney, 21 Broad St., res. 17 Hasell St.
Hancker, C. F., Grocer, 20 Anson St.
Hancock, H., Baker, 103 Queen St.
Hannasy, Thomas, Hardware, 38 King St.
Hannington, Thomas, Painter, 32 Queen St.
Happoldt, A. A., Clerk, 137 Meeting St., res. State St.
Happoldt, Albert, Butcher, Cannon St.
Happoldt, B. G., Gunsmith, 45 State St.
Happoldt, C. D., Farmer, Cannon St.
Happoldt, C. L., Coach Trimmer, 16 Wall St.
Happoldt, Edward, Cannon St.
Happoldt, J. H., Gunsmith, 45 State St.
Happoldt, J. M., Gunsmith, 45 State St.
Happoldt, J. P., Clerk, Cannon St.
Happoldt, William, Clerk, Railroad, Cannon St.
Harbers, G. H., Grocer, 19 Coming St.
Harbers, H. F., Grocer, 8 Coming St.
Harbers, J., Clerk, 141 Meeting St., res. cr. Meeting &
Ann Sts.
Harbeson, J. S., clerk, 136 King St.
Harbeson, John, Dry Goods, 350 King St., res. Mary St.
Harbeson, Joseph, Clerk, 204 King St., res. Mary St.

Harbess, C. H., Grocer, cr. Meeting & Ann Sts.
Harby, H. J., Blacksmith, 28 Meeting St.
Harby, Isaac, Clerk, 70 East Bay St., res. 28 Meeting St.
Harby, T. W., Boots & Shoes, cr. King & Calhoun Sts., res. Ridgeville Village
Harden, W. T. R., Dry Goods, 8 Market St.
Hare, R. W., Saddler, 39 Hayne St., res. 11 Hasell St.
Hargrove, John, Slater, 6 Smith St.
Hargrove, Thomas, Spinner, Columbus St.
Harleston, E., Miss, Rutledge St., Ward 6
Harleston, Ed, Measurer, Custom House, res. Rutledge St., Ward 6
Harleston, J., Clerk, 114 East Bay St., res. Rutledge St., Ward 6
Harleston, Lydia, 12 Mazysk St.
Harleston, Summers, Planter, Cannon St.
Harleston, T. C., Charlotte St.
Harlle, Thomas, Factor, Boyce & Co. Wharf, res. Planters Hotel
Harlow, Michael, Laborer, Morris St.
Harms, C., Grist Mill, cr. Coming & Cannon Sts.
Harper, F. M., Printer, 17 Friend St.
Harper, J. M., Clerk, 11 Broad St.
Harrall, Hare & Co., Saddlers, 39 Hayne St.
Harrall, James, Druggist, 25 Hayne St., res. 46 St. Philip St.
Harrall, William, Saddler, 39 Hayne St., res. 4 Glebe St.
Harrersburg, H., Grocer, 16 Archdale St.
Harriman, H., Tanner, Cannon St.
Harris, C. F., Clerk, 54 East Bay St., res. 236 King St.
Harris, H., Bookbinder, 36 Wentworth St.
Harris, J., Fruiterer, 39 Market St.
Harris, John, Factor, Central Wharf
Harrisson, D. W., Bookseller, 17 Chalmers St., res. Queen St.
Harrisson, J. W., Paints & Oils, 72 Meeting St.
Harrisson, James, Bootmaker, 33 Beaufain St.
Harrisson, John, Paints & Oils, 72 Meeting St.
Harron, John, Clerk, Railroad, Smith St., Ward 6
Hart, C., Laborer, 15 King St.
Hart, Eliza, Mantuamaker, Calhount St., Ward 5
Hart, S. N., Hardware, cr. King & Market Sts., res. 197 Meeting St.
Hart, Samuel, Bookseller, 300 King St., res. 7 Aiken Row
Hartman, J. F., Grocer, Meeting St., Ward 5
Hartz, J. H., Grocer, 19 Meeting St.
Harvy, E., Mrs., 23 Wall St.
Harvy, George, 7 Church St.
Harvy, Isabella, Mrs., 78 Queen St.
Harvy, J., Import Inspector, Custom House, res. 78 Queen St.
Hasel, Maria, 25 Clifford St.
Haseltine & Walton, Boots & Shoes, 137 Meeting St.
Haseltine, Albert, Boots & Shoes, 137 Meeting St., res. Charleston Hotel
Haseltine, William, Dry Goods, 37 Hayne St., Charleston Hotel
Haselton, D. B., Machinist, 91 Beaufain St.
Haskell, W. E., Planter, St. Paul's Parish, res. Calhoun

St., Ward 6
Hass, John, Wheelwright, 81 Queen St.
Hasset, James, Laborer, 9 Tradd St.
Hasset, Roger, Mason, 110 Meeting St.
Hastadt, H., Grocer, cr. King & Woolf Sts.
Hatach, G. W., Pressman, Church St.
Hatch, L. M., Commission Merchant, 120 Meeting St., res. 8 Society St.
Hatch, William, Ship Carpenter, 76 Anson St.
Hatcher, Benjamin, Carpenter, Meeting St., Ward 7
Hauck, J. H., Accountant, 30 Laurens St.
Haupt, A. J., Miller, Lucas' Mill
Haupt, J., Miller, Bennett's Mill
Hauscheldt, P., Grocer, 16 Queen St.
Haven, E., Mrs., Dry Goods, 10 Anson St.
Havilland, Harral & Co., Druggist, 25 Hayne St., res. 260 King St.
Hawkesworth, W., Professor, Charleston College, res. 69 Broad St.
Hawkins, J., Rev., 36 Wentworth St.
Hay, A., Seaman, 40 State St.
Hay, R. G., Clerk, 155 Meeting St.
Hay, W. M., Attorney, St. Michael's Alley
Hayden, A. H., Jeweller, 250 King St., res. 6 Glebe St.
Hayden, H. S., Jeweller, 250 King St., res. 10 Green St.
Hayden, Thomas, 11 Lynch St.
Hayer, John, 66 State St.
Hayne, A. B., M. D., 24 King St.
Hayne, A., Miss, 25 Meeting St.
Hayne, A. P., Col., 19 Logan St.
Hayne, E. D., Carpenter, 58 Anson St.
Hayne, E., Mrs., Alexander St.
Hayne, I. W., Attorney General, 30 Broad St., res. 6 Logan St.
Hayne, M., Miss, 25 Meeting St.
Hayne, P., Law Student, Alexander St.
Hayne, W. A., Attorney, 48 Broad St., res. 26 King St.
Hayne, W. D., Mrs., St. Philip St., Ward 6
Hayne, W. E., Clerk, 35 Hayne St., res. 1 Church St.
Hayne, W. E., Mrs., 1 Church St.
Haynsworth, C. D., Clerk, 243 King St., res. cr. Meeting & Market Sts.
Hays, M., Mrs., 26 Queen St.
Hazard, John, Dry Goods, King St., Ward 6
Headly, John, Brass Worker, Hard Alley
Heagan, J. R., Clerk, 193 King St.
Heart, John, Editor, Mercury, 121 East Bay St.
Heath, H., Mrs., 9 Calhoun St.
Heath, Samuel, Engineer, Bee St.
Heckenrath, L. J., Ship & Commission Merchant, Adger's Wharf
Heckman, -----, Accountant, Laurens St., res. Wentworth St.
Hedderly, George, Sires St.
Hedley, Eugenia, 13 West St.
Hedley, J. L., 22 King St.
Heeseman, John, Clerk, 64 Meeting St.
Heesenbutle, G., Grocer, 16 Meeting St.
Hefferon, John, Saddler, 35 Society St.
Hei, E, Grocer, cr. Hanover & Amherst Sts.

72

Heidt, V., House Furnisher, 271 & 315 King St.
Heine, W., Draper & Tailor, 133 King St.
Heins, D., Grocer, 29 Bull St.
Heins, John, Clerk, 12 St. Philip St.
Heins, William, Drayman, 31 Calhoun St.
Heischel, L., Grocer, 12 St. Philip St.
Helinken, C., Grocer, cr. Woolf & Nassau Sts.
Hely, E. M., Miss, Dressmaker, 73 King St.
Hemmet, Sarah, Chapel St.
Henderson, Alexander, Blacksmith, 31 Wentworth St.
Henderson, J. M. D., Printer, 102 Church St.
Hendrix, C. F., Grocer, King St., Ward 6
Hendrix, H. W., Molder, Cannon St.
Hendrix, L. C., Assistant Conductor, South Carolina
 Railroad, St. Philip St., Ward 6
Hendrix, R. E., Commission Merchant, 124 East Bay St.,
 res. Pavilion Hotel
Hendrix, R. F., Clerk, South Carolina Railroad, Cannon
 St.
Henegar, C., Clerk, 137 Meeting St., res. Victoria Hotel
Henken, H., Grocer, King St., Ward 6
Hennesay, C., Shoes & Hats, King St., Ward 6, res. John
 St.
Hennesay, Peter, Porter, 219 King St., 4 Clifford St.
Henry, C. W., Factor, Vanderhorst's Wharf, res. Meeting
 St.
Henry, E., Clerk, 5 Hayne St., res. Charleston Hotel
Henry, E. L., Clerk, 214 King St., res. 3 Liberty St.
Henry, E., Tavern Keeper, Market St., res. 3 Liberty St.
Henry, George, Meeting St., Ward 5
Henry, J. T., Mason, 14 Wentworth St.
Henry, M. C., Carpenter, America St.
Henry, W. S., Machinist, 14 Wentworth St.
Henry, W. T., Clerk, 25 Hayne St., res. 236 King St.
Henshall, C. H., Grocer, 1 Calhoun St.
Herbe, M., Dry Goods, 67 State St.
Herckenrath, Wragg & Co., Ship & Commission
 Merchants, Adger's Wharf
Heriot & Brailsford, Commission Merchant, 4 Gillon St.
Heriot, B. G., Commission Merchant, 4 Gillon St., res.
 86 Beaufain St.
Heriot, D., Mrs., Teacher, cr. Thomas & Radcliffe Sts.
Heriot, Daniel, Clerk, South Carolina Railroad, 23
 Montague St.
Heriot, E. F., Warren St.
Heriot, G. A., Clerk, Atlantic Wharf, 66 Tradd St.
Heriot, J. R., Superintendent, Gas Works, res. 66 Tradd
 St.
Heriot, O. B., Commission Merchant, 20 East Bay St.,
 res. 13 Legare St.
Heriot, R., Mrs., 23 Montague St.
Heriot, W. C., Accountant, Vanderhorst's Wharf, res. 71
 Beaufain St.
Heriot, W. J., Clerk, Gas Works, 66 Tradd St.
Heriot, W. B., Underwriter, 4 Broad St., res. 5 King St.
Hernandez, J. M., Clerk, 243 King St., res. East Bay St.
Hernholm, A., Fruiterer, 333 King St.
Heron, George, Commission Merchant, 11 Central
 Wharf, res. Mansion House
Heron, Nicholas, Judith St.

Herrin, W. B., Carpenter, 31 Bull St.
Hersey, C. W., Clerk, 229 King St., res. 82 Queen St.
Hertisch, B., Bootmaker, 13 Queen St.
Hertz, A. E., Accountant, Adger's Wharf, res. King St.
Hertz, F. E., Accountant, cr. King & Markets Sts., res. 67
 King St.,
Hertz, J. E., Clerk, 110 East Bay St., res. Queen St.
Hertz, T. E., 67 King St.
Hervy, C. L., Clerk, 153 Meeting St., res. 8 Liberty St.
Herwig, W., Worsted Dealer, 239 King St., res. 249 King
 St.
Heslope, W., Clerk, 91 Church St.
Hess, Jacob, Spring St.
Hevy, -----, Mrs., Teacher, 111 Church St.
Hewess, Elias, Engineer, 10 Anson St.
Hewit, G. W., Clerk, 18 Vanderhorst St., res. 13 Lynch
 St.
Hewit, O. H. P., Clerk, 26 Hayne St., res. Pavilion Hotel
Hey, Henry, Clerk, 87 King St.
Heyer, J. H., Grocer, Spring St.,
Heynes, J. D., Collector, 13 Prices Alley
Heyward, A. J., Mrs., 63 Calhoun St.
Heyward, Arthur, Planter, Georgia, res. Charlotte St.
Heyward, Charles, Planter, 251 East Bay St.
Heyward, Charles, Planter, Combahee, res. Chapel St.
Heyward, Daniel, Planter, 17 East Battery St.
Heyward, E. B. H., East Bay St.
Heyward, J. B., Planter, 90 Broad St.
Heyward, S., Mrs., 3 Aiken Row
Heyward, T. J., Clerk, 40 East Bay St., res. 63 Calhoun
 St.
Heyward, W. H., Planter, 4 Legare St.
Hicky, E., Mrs., 8 Middle St.
Hiens, H., Grocer, 103 Meeting St.
Higham, Thomas, Commission Merchant, 71 East Bay
 St., res. England
Highams & Co., Commission Merchants, 71 East Bay St.
Hilken, J. H., Grocer, cr. Coming & Spring Sts.
Hill, F. C., Artist, 13 Clifford St.
Hill, John, 19 Mazyck St.
Hill, John, Carpenter, Nassau St.
Hill, John, Fancy Goods, 60 Queen St.
Hill, N. B., Commission Merchant, Atlantic Wharf, res.
 Columbia
Hill, W. M., Bootmaker, 38 Beaufain St.
Hillegiss, C., Mrs., 11 Franklin St.
Hillen, J., Bootmaker, cr. King & Ann Sts.
Hilliam, T., Restaurant, 107 East Bay St., res. 67 Broad
 St.
Hillier, J., Mrs., Private Boarding, 67 Broad St.
Hills, C. E., Clerk, 258 King St.
Hilson, John, Grocer, Meeting St., Ward 5
Hinck, H. M., Publisher "Tueton," 3 Queen St.
Hincken, Jacob, Grocer, 32 Bull St.
Hinckley, C. E., Clerk, 260 King St., res. 236 King St.
Hinnies, William, Clerk, 43 Archdale St.
Hinson, -----, Mrs., Seamstress, 12 Tradd St.
Hippins, P., Mrs., 10 Wentworth St.
Hirschfeld, H., M. D., 4 Chalmers St.
Hislop, S., Mrs., Mantilla Maker, 31 Wall St.

Hislop, W., Clerk, Cotton Press, 31 Wall St.
Hobbs, W., Seedsman & Florist, King St.
Hockaday, W., Livery Stable, 3 Chalmers St.
Hodge, F., Mrs., Hanover St.
Hoff, J. C., Stationer, 10 Broad St.
Hoff, John, Tailor, 190 Meeting St., res. St. Philip St.
Hoffman, H., Grocer, cr. Ashley & Cannon Sts.
Hogan, Ed, Laborer, Jasper's Court
Hogan, M. D., Tavern Keeper, 125 East Bay St., res. 14 State St.
Hogan, -----, Mrs., Milliner, 319 King St.
Hogan, Patrick, Clerk, 125 East Bay St.
Hogan, Richard, Cotton Merchant, 127 East Bay St., res. Radcliffe St.
Hogarth, H., Cooper, Longitude Lane, res. 40 Church St.
Holcombe, E., Clerk, 135 Meeting St., res. Commercial Hotel
Holey, Henry, Fireman, Line St.
Holland, E. C., Wharfinger, Commericial Wharf, res. Ashley St.
Holland, P. G., Dry Goods, cr. Broad & King Sts., res. cr. Friend & Tradd Sts.
Hollens, B., Grocer, Line St.
Holloway, Adeline, 3 Mazyck St.
Holloway, C., Mantuamaker, 58 Calhoun St.
Holloway, Carpenter, 29 Beaufain St.
Holloway, Charles, Carter, 29 Beaufain St.
Holloway, Henry, Cigar Maker, Coming St., Ward 8
Holloway, Mary, 17 College St.
Holloway, Richard, Carpenter, 38 Mazyck St.
Holloway, Samuel, Carter, 67 Calhoun St.
Holmes, A. F., Appraiser, Custom House, 13 East Battery St.
Holmes, Auber, 35 Archdale St.
Holmes, Drayton, Collector, St. Michael's Alley, res. 13 Church St.
Holmes, E. G., Charlotte St.
Holmes, E. H., Collector, St. Michael's Alley, res. 13 East Battery
Holmes, F. M., Sexton, St. Peter's Church, res. 13 Mazyck St.
Holmes, F. S., Professor, Charleston College, res. 58 St. Philip St.
Holmes, H. M., Dr., Planter, Cooper River, res. 2 Council St.
Holmes, Isaac, Clerk, 13 Southern Wharf
Holmes, J. B., Physician, 85 Church St., res. 13 East Battery St.
Holmes, J. H., Commission Merchant, Central Wharf, res. 1 Wall St.
Holmes, J. J., Cashier, Southwestern Railroad Bank, res. 13 Liberty St.
Holmes, J. L., Bookkeeper, Bank of Charleston, res. 5 Pitt St.
Holmes, J. V., Gunsmith, 64 Queen St., res. 32 Coming St.
Holmes, John, Carpenter, 110 Meeting St.
Holmes, Lydia, 21 Rutledge St.
Holmes, M. R., 2 Council St.
Holmes, R. O., Clerk, Vanderhorst's Wharf, res.

Charlotte St.
Holmes, W. E., Clerk, 120 Meeting St., res. Charlotte St.
Holmes, W. H., Charlotte St.
Holmes, W. P., Clerk, 4 Vendue Range, res. cr. Tradd & Council Sts.
Holstan, Elias, Guardman, Spring St.
Holton, M., Mrs., Mantuamaker, 16 Clifford St.
Holton, M., Pastry Cook, 34 Cumberland St.
Honour, J. H., Jr., Penny Postman, cr. Calhoun & Coming St.
Honour, J. Lawrence, Superintendent of Streets, Upper Wards, res. John St.
Honour, John H., President, Charleston Insurance & Trust Co., res. John St.
Honour, Thomas, Bookbinder, Mary St.
Honour, W. E., John St.
Hood, E., Mrs., Toyshop, 116 King St.
Hook, C., Clerk, 19 South Bay St.
Hopkins, Hudson & Co., Factors & Commission Merchants, Central Wharf
Hopkins, J. A., Cooper Adger's Wharf, res. 28 Church St.
Hopkins, L., Factor & Commission Merchant, Central Wharf, res. Augusta, Georgia
Hopley, G. A. & Co., Factor & Commission Merchants, Atlantic Wharf
Hopley, G. A., Factor & Commission Merchant, Atlantic Wharf, res. cr. Legare & Tradd Sts.
Horas, John, Poultry Dealer, King St., Ward 7
Hories, W., Clerk, 38 Church St.
Horin, Michael, Laborer, Bedon's Alley
Horlbeck & Brothers, Brickburners & Layers
Horlbeck Daniel, Clerk, Court of Common Pleas, Court House, res. cr. Calhoun & Meeting Sts.
Horlbeck, E., Bricklayer, 7 Horlbeck Alley
Horlbeck, Elias, Physician, 8 Coming St.
Horlbeck, H., Bricklayer, cr. Calhoun & Meeing St.
Horlbeck, J. F., Grocer, cr. Pinckney & Anson Sts.
Horlbeck, John, Bricklayer, cr. Calhoun & Meeting Sts.
Horlbeck, M., Mrs., 46 BeaufainSt.
Horlbeck, Peter, Physician, 111 Broad St.
Horry, A. E., Tailor, 62 Market St.
Horry, E., Mrs., 39 Meeting St.
Horry, E. S., Planter, Santee River, res. 39 Meeting St.
Horry, J. E., Planter, Santee River, res. 39 Meeting St.
Horry, P. T., Planter, Santee River, res. 39 Meeting St.
Horry, W. B. S., Planter, Santee River, res. 39 Meeting St.
Horsey, F., Clerk, 101 East Bay St., res. 155 East Bay St.
Horsey, -----, Mrs., Private Boarding, 155 East Bay St.
Horsey, T. M. & Co., Hats & Caps, 23 Hayne St.
Horsey, T. M., Hats & Caps, 23 Hayne St., res. 42 Anson St.
Horton, T. A. P., Tin & Hardware, 120 Meeting St., res. 10 Glebe St.
Hosch & Fleming, Candy Manufacturers, 269 King St.
Hosch, William, Candy Manufacturer, 269 King St.
Hosegood, George, Engineer, 89½ East Bay St.
Hotson, Timothy, Carter, St. Philip St., Ward 6
Houle, H., Bootmaker, 13 Queen St.

Houseman, -----, Mrs., Boots & Shoes, 99 East Bay St.
Houston, Robert, Tailor, King St., Ward 5
Houston, W. H., Builder & Contractor, Charlotte St.
Howard, H. M., Naval Officer, Custom House, 259 East Bay St.
Howard, J. L., Clerk, Central Wharf, res. 259 East Bay St.
Howard, Lee, Naval Officer, Custom House, 259 East Bay St.
Howard, M., Drayman, 8 East Bay St.
Howard, S. E., Clerk, Commercial Wharf, 259 East Bay St.
Howard, T. L., Accountant, Fitzsimons' Wharf, res. 259 East Bay St.
Howe, Silas, 29 Archdale St.
Howell, S. S., Dry Goods, Hayne St., res. 9 Hasell St.
Howland & Taft, Commission Merchants, 141 East Bay St.
Howland, S. S., Clerk, 135 Meeting St., res. 9 Hasell St.
Howland, W. E., Clerk, 141 cr. Queen & Franklin Sts.
Howland, William, Dry Goods, 244 King St., res. cr. Lynch & Montague Sts.
Hubbell, T. C., Grist Mill, Calhoun St., Ward 5
Hubert, C. N., Commission Merchant, 71 East Bay St., res. Alexander St.
Huchet, Eugene, Commission Merchant, Adger's Wharf, res. 160 East Bay St.
Huchet, J., Commission Merchant, Market St.
Huchet, Theo, Ship & Commission Merchant, 10 Adger's Wharf, res. 160 East Bay St.
Hudson, J. R., Factor & Commission Merchant, Atlantic Wharf, res. Charleston Hotel
Hudtwalker, T. M., Clerk, Atlantic Wharf, res. East Bay St.
Huff, John, Tailor, St. Philip St., Ward 6
Huff, W. R., Factor & Commission Merchant, Accommodation Wharf, res. Pavilion Hotel
Huff, William, Fireman, Rutledge St., Ward 8
Huffman, Rosa, 3 Bull St.
Huger & Milliken, Dry Goods, 42 East Bay St.
Huger, A. M., Dry Goods, 42 East Bay St., res. 52 Meeting St.
Huger, Alfred, Postmaster, 92 Broad St.
Huger, Benjamin, Planter, St. John's Island, res. Calhoun St., Ward 6
Huger, Benjamin, Tailor, 60 Calhoun St.
Huger, D. E., 24 Meeting St.
Huger, Daniel, 14 South Bay St.
Huger, Daniel, 61 Coming St.
Huger, F., Col., 10 Lamboll St.
Huger, John, 109 Broad St.
Huger, W. H., M. D., Calhoun St., Ward 6
Huggins, Elizabeth, Miss, Private Boarding, 30 Tradd St.
Huggins, John, Ship Carpenter, Coming St., Ward 6
Hughes, E. T., Clerk, Vanderhorst's Wharf, res. Greenhill St.
Hughes, O., Planter, St. James Island, res. 1 Greenhill St.
Hughes, Thomas, Cabinet Maker, 70 & 74 Meeting St.
Hulberg, M. A., Mrs., 1 Society St.
Hulbert, J. C., Clerk, 116 Meeting St., res. 4 Society St.

Hull & Knevals, Drapers & Tailors, 137 Meeting St.
Hull, A. S., Draper & Tailor, 137 Meeting St., res. Charleston Hotel
Hull, S. J., Clerk, 39 Hayne St., res. Pavilion Hotel
Hulsberg, H., Grocer, 64 Tradd St.
Hume, Robert, Planter, Santee, res. 6 Lynch St.
Hume, Thomas M., Broker & Auctioneer, 28 Broad St., res. cr. Thomas & Warren Sts.
Hume, W., Dr., Teacher, Experimental Science, Citadel, res. cr. Mill & Ahsley Sts.
Humme, Henry, Grocer, 102 Tradd St.
Hummel, W., Druggist, cr. King & Mary Sts.
Humphreys, H., Mrs., 8 Smith St.
Humphreys, J., Clerk, 243 King St., res. 8 Smith St.
Humphreys, W., Carpenter, 8 Smith St.
Hunt, B. F. & Son, Attorneys, 13 Broad St., res. cr. Wentworth & Gadsden Sts.
Hunt, B. F., Jr., Attorney, 13 Broad St., res. cr.Wentworth & Gadsden Sts.
Hunt, N., Auctioneer & Commssion Merchant, 20 Vendue Range, res. 33 Anson St.
Hunteman, J. G., Clerk, 29 Hayne St., res. Beaufain St.
Hunter, John, Coming St., Ward 6
Huntington, G. M., Clerk, 143 Meeting St., res. 236 King St.
Huntoon, C. S., Clerk, 149 Meeting St., res. Charleston Hotel
Hurkampt, John, Grocer, 87 Broad St.
Hurst, J. L., Planters Hotel
Husda, William, Tailor, 37 Queen St.
Huson, George, Machinist, 6 Anson St.
Hussey, S. E., Clerk, 1 Hayne St., res. Planters Hotel
Hutchinson, C., Carpenter, 120 King St.
Hutchinson, J. H., Clerk, Commercial Wharf, res. 99½ East Bay St.
Hutchinson, T. L., Meeting St.
Hyams, H., Packer, 145 Meeting St., East Bay St.
Hyams, M., Ship Broker, Brown's Wharf, res. 47 Wentworth St.
Hyams, -----, Mrs., Mantuamaker, 42 King St.
Hyams, Solomon, Umbrella Maker, 16 Calhoun St.
Hyatt, M., Carpenter, Sires St.
Hyatt, McBurney & Co., Dry Goods, 37 Hayne St.
Hyde, G. A., Clothing, 277 King St.
Hyde, S., Hardware, 139 Meeting St., res. 56 Tradd St.
Hyer, -----, Mrs., Sires St.
Hyur, C. W., Musician, 143 Meeting St.
Iliffe, Charles, Shoemaker, 120 King St.
Inglesby, W. H., City Treasurer, 4 Logan St.
Ingliss, William, Barber, 4 Queen St.
Ingraham & Webb, Factors & Commission Merchants, Commercial Wharf
Ingraham, G. H., Factor & Commission Merchant, Commercial Wharf, res. 18 Laurens St.
Inness, C. M., Clerk, 23 Hayne St., res. Charleston Hotel
Irons, W., Carpenter, Spring St.
Irvin, C., Tavern Keeper, 96 Church St.
Isaacs, Alexander, Accountant, 143 Meeting St., res. Charleston Hotel
Iusta, A. W., Iron Worker, 31Queen St.

Izard, H., Mrs., 29 Legare St.
Jackson, A., Mrs., Woolf Street
Jackson, A. P., Mrs., St. Philip St., Ward 6
Jackson, F. C., Clerk, 199 King St., res. 63 Meeting St.
Jackson, G. W., Gasfitter, Woolf St.
Jackson, George, House Furnisher, 275 King St.
Jackson, George, Jr., 275 King St.
Jackson, George, Sail Maker, 52 Queen St.
Jackson, -----, Mrs., Restorer of Old Painings, 63 Meeting St.
Jackson, Thomas, Clerk, 275 King St.
Jacobi & Son, Dry Goods, 221 King St.
Jacobi, Nathan, Dry Goods, 221 King St.
Jacobi, W. J., Dry Goods, 221 King St.
Jacobs, D. H., Mrs., Private Boarding, 82 Queen St.
Jacobs, D., Jeweller, 338½ King St.
Jacobs, F., Rev., Pastor, 2d Presbyterian Church, res. John St.
Jacobs, G. W., Tinsmith, 109 Meeting St., res. King St.
Jacobs, J. C., Clerk, 9 Broad St., res. 11 Smith St.
Jacobs, J. S., Clothier, Market St.
Jacobs, M., Mrs., Spring St.
Jacobs, Meyer, Collecting Clerk, Bank of the State of South Carolina, 11 Smith St.
James Henry, Carpenter, 11 Pinckney St.
James, Robert, Book Publisher, 103 & 105 East Bay St., res. 115 Broad St.
James, William, Pilot, 11 Pinckney St.
Jaques, D. H., Associate Editor, Literary Gazette
Jaques, G. R., Shoe Dealer, Spring St.
Jeaneret, J. C., Accountant, Boyce's Wharf, res. 46 Church St.
Jeffords & Scanlan, Blacksmiths, Marsh Wharf
Jeffords, E. A., Clerk, 98 East Bay St., res. 9 Hasell St.
Jeffords, J. N., Clerk, cr. Market & King Sts., res. cr. Meeting & Market Sts.
Jeffords, James, Blacksmith, Marsh Wharf, res. 19 Wentworth St.
Jeffords, -----, Mrs. Private Bording, cr. Meeting & Market Sts.
Jeffords, R. J., Clerk, 76 East Bay St., res. 9 Hasell St.
Jeffords, Samuel, Clerk, Commercial Wharf, res. 7 Smith's Lane
Jeffords, W. G., Clerk, Adger's Wharf, res. cr. Meeting & Market Sts.
Jenerette, R., Mrs., 5 Philadelphia St.
Jenkins, C. S., Clerk, 211 King St., res. 98 Beaufain St.
Jenkins, J. G., Engineer, 98 Beaufain St.
Jenkins, John, Superintendent, Cotton Press, 91½ East Bay St.
Jenkins, W. F., 106 Church St.
Jennings, A. G., Clothing, 26 Hayne St., res. Charleston Hotel
Jennings, David, Saddlery, 157 Meeting St., res. 6 Montague St.
Jenny, Robert, Saddler, 344 King St.
Jervy, J. C., Import Inspector, Custom House, res. 104 Tradd St.
Jervy, J. P., M. D., 13 George St.
Jervy, Lewis, Bookkeeper, State Bank, res. 13 George St.

Jervy, S. M., 104 Tradd St.
Jervy, T. D., Deputy Collector, Custom House, res. 3 Wall St.
Jervy, William, Attorney, 59 Meeting St., res. 22 George St.
Jessen, H., Grocery Merchant, 139 East Bay St.
Jesup. Z. R., Boots & Shoes, 142 King St.
John, D. E., Clerk, 143 East Bay St., res. Planters Hotel
Johnson & Smith, Tailors, 316½ King St.
Johnson, A. S., Clerk, 279 King St., res. King St., Ward 6
Johnson, Andrew, Clerk, 181 East Bay St., res. 14 New St.
Johnson, B., Umbrella & Wire Safe Maker, 263 & 327 King St.
Johnson, C. H., Clerk, 159 Meeting St., res. King St., Ward 6
Johnson, C., Sea Captain, 89½ East Bay St.
Johnson, D. P., Sea Captain, 14 New St.
Johnson, G. A., Machinist, Anson St.
Johnson, H. D., Clerk, 45 Hayne St., res. King St.
Johnson, H. L., Clerk, 149 Meeting St., res. Charleston Hotel
Johnson, Hagar, Calhoun St., Ward 5
Johnson, Hollis, Boots & Shoes, 240 King St.
Johnson, J. L., Clerk, 149 Meeting St., res. 240 King St.
Johnson, J., Mechanic, Stoll's Alley
Johnson, J. S., Collector, 73 Wentworth St.
Johnson, James, Butcher, Amherst St.
Johnson, James, Tailor, 79 Queen St.
Johnson, John, Butcher, Columbus St.
Johnson, John, Overseer, Line St.
Johnson, Joseph, Druggist, 11 Broad St., res. 107 King St.
Johnson, Joseph, M. D., 107 King St.
Johnson, L., Grocer, 11 Mazyck St.
Johnson, M., Mrs., 19 Montague St.
Johnson, M., Mrs., Midwife, 14 Liberty St.
Johnson, -----, Miss, Teacher, 126 Queen St.
Johnson, N., Mrs., Hampden Court
Johnson, O. E., Accountant, 277 King St., res. King St., Ward 6
Johnson, R., Jr., Spirit Dealer, 98 East Bay St.
Johnson, S., Mrs., 112 Queen St.
Johnson, S., Mrs., 18 Anson St.
Johnson, S., Vanderhorst St.
Johnson, Sarah, Dressmaker, 2 Green St.
Johnson, Sarah, Jasper's Court
Johnson, T. N., Clerk, Central Wharf, res. 107 King St.
Johnson, T. W., Import Inspector, Custom House, res. King St., Ward 6
Johnson, T. W., Johnson Hotel, King St., Ward 6
Johnson, W., Engineer, 35 Montague St.
Johnson, W., Wood Factor, Marshall Wharf, res. 73 Wentworth St.
Johnston, A., Miss, 26 South Bay St.
Johnston, A. S., Dry Goods, 181 East Bay St., res. 193 Meeting St.
Johnston, C., Miss, 26 South Bay St.
Johnston, Crews & Brawley, Dry Goods, 181 East Bay

St.

Johnston, D. C., 71 Queen St.

Johnston, I. M. C., 2d Teller, Bank of Charleston, res. 23 Pitt St.

Joiner, William, Carpenter, Coming St., Ward 8

Jones, A. D., Clerk, 26 East Bay St., res. cr. Broad & Mazyck Sts.

Jones, A. H., Commission Merchant, 60 East Bay St., res. 94 Broad St.

Jones, C. M., Mrs., 11 Rutledge St.

Jones, C., Mrs., Dry Goods, 65 State St.

Jones, E. C., Architect, 46 Broad St., res. 9 Pitt St.

Jones, E. J., Painter & Gilder, 2 Washington St.

Jones, E. J., Ship Carpenter, 96 Anson St.

Jones, E. Miss, 1 Guignard St.

Jones, J. C., Clerk, 256 King St., res. 9 Pitt St.

Jones, J. H., Carpenter, Morris St.

Jones, Jesse, Machinist, 11 Rutledge St.

Jones, John, Carpenter, Coming St., Ward 8

Jones, Paul, 47 George St.

Jones, Paul, Carpenter, Bee St.

Jones, S. M., Clerk, 60 East Bay St., res. 94 Broad St.

Jones, Sarah, Miss, 1 Guignard St.

Jones, Susan, Miss, 1 Guignard St.

Jones, T. S., Deputy Secretary of State, Fire Proof Building, res. King St., Ward 6

Jones, William, Carpenter, 11 Rutledge St.

Jones, William, Steam Boat Captain, 70 King St.

Jordan, G., Baker, 113 Meeting St.

Jordan, Robert, Miller, East Point Mills

Josephs, C. M., Miss, 24 Burns Lane

Josephs, E. C., cr. Calhoun & King Sts.

Josephs, J. J., 6 Green St.

Josephs, J., Mrs., Private Boarding, cr. Calhoun & King Sts.

Josephs, L. H., Clerk, Boyce's Wharf, res. 6 Green St.

Jowitt, John, Printer, 48 Broad St.

Joy, John, Laborer, Hampden Court

Joy, -----, Mrs., 45 Church St.

Judge, C., Blacksmith, 34 Market St.

Jugnot, C., Steam Boat Agent, 122 East Bay St.

Jungbluth, J. H., Tavern Keeper, 7 Market St.

Just, George, Wharf Builder, 34 Hasell St.

Kalaher, Lewis, Laborer, 20 Tradd St.

Kanapaux, C. E., Attorney, Sheriff's Office, res. 131 King St.

Kanapaux, C., Superintendent, Lucas' Mill

Kanapaux, J. D., Tinner, 46 Bull St.

Kanapaux, J. T., Clerk, 14 Hayne St., res. 2 Gadsden St.

Kannahan, Denis, Mason, St. Philip St., Ward 8

Kappleman, M. H., German Books, 119 Meeting St.

Kaufman, A., Bootmaker, 553 Broad St., res. Church St.

Kaufman, A. D., Mrs., Alexander St.

Keckeley, E. C., Dr., Conductor, South Carolina Railroad, res. Meeting St., Ward 5

Keegan, Thomas, Laborer, St. Philip St., Ward 8

Keeling, John, Carpenter, 76 King St.

Keeling, Robert, Carpenter, 76 King St.

Keena, James, Porter, 80 East Bay St., res. 53 Tradd St.

Keenan, J. D., Clerk, 40 East Bay St.

Keenan, William, Engraver, 250 King St., res. 21 St. Philip St.

Keep, J. H., Grocer, 62 Anson St.

Keif, Patrick, Laborer, 13 Burns Lane

Keiffer, John, Leather Dealer, 13 Hayne St. & 27 Market St.

Keils, C., Carpenter, Woolf St.

Keils, C., Carpenter, Woolf St.

Keils, J. S., Grocer, 37 Coming St.

Keith, J. A., cr. Lynch & Montague Sts.

Keith, M. J., Register of Conveyances, Fire Proof Building, res. Aiken Row

Keith, P. T., Pastor, St. Michael's Church, res. 12 Lynch Lane

Keller, C., Coal Yard, 51 Market St., res. Church St.

Kelly, D., Clerk, 214 King St., res. 4 Beaufain St.

Kelly, J. A., Boat Builder, Hard Alley

Kelly, J. G., Clerk, 207 King St., res. Liberty St.

Kelly, James, Printer, 76 Anson St.

Kelly, Michael, Laborer, President St.

Kelly, Michael, Laborer, St. Philip St., Ward 8

Kelly, O., Laborer, St. Philip St., Ward 6

Kelly, Peter, Private Boarding, 3 Linguard St.

Kelly, T., Dry Goods, 214 King St., res. 4 Beaufain St.

Kelly, Thomas, Bootmaker, 43 Broad St.

Kelly, Thomas, Plasterer, 25 Montague St.

Kelly, William, Plasterer, 44 St. Philip St.

Kemme, D. H., Clothing, 39 Broad St., res. 166 King St.

Kemp, R. P., Molder, Hampden Court

Kenard, L., Tanner, Hanover, St.

Kendt, F., Clerk, 189 East Bay St.

Kenefect, John, Clerk, 25 Hayne St., res. 139 King St.

Kennedy, Denis, Butcher, Smith St.

Kennedy, Henry, Carpenter, Line St.

Kennedy, J., Carpenter, Queen St.

Kennedy, J. D., Hardware, 36 Market St.

Kennedy, J. T., Tailor, 4 Coming St.

Kennedy, James, Boarding, 3 Linguard St.

Kennedy, James, Laborer, America St.

Kennedy, John, Private Boarding, St. Philip St., Ward 6

Kennedy, John, Saddler, 302 King St.

Kennedy, M. E., Mrs., 74 Wentworth St.

Kennedy, Michael, Guardman, Linguard St.

Kennedy, P., Boots & Shoes, 79 Market St.

Kennedy, R. A., Clerk, Central Wharf

Kennedy, Thomas, Horse Shoer, 33 Wentworth St.

Kent, Bates & Mitchell, Clothing, 118 Meeting St. & 268 King St.

Kent, E. G., Woolf St.

Kent, Samuel, Guardman, Sires St.

Kent, W. A., Clothing, 118 Meeting St. & 268 King St.

Kenworth, W., Clerk, Poor House

Kerr, S., Miss, King St., Ward 5

Kerr, T. J., Commission Merchant, Atlantic Wharf, res. 1 Society St.

Kerr, T. T., Commission Merchant, Atlantic Wharf

Kerrison, C. & E. L., Dry Goods, cr. King & Market Sts.

Kerrison, Charles, Dry Goods, cr. King & Market Sts., res. 5 New St.

Kerrison, E. L., Dry Goods, cr. King & Market Sts., res.

103 Wentworth St.
Kershaw, A., Mrs., 82 Wentworth St.
Ketchum & Taylor, Dry Goods, 243 King St.
Ketchum, A. H., Clerk, King St., res. 32 Queen St.
Ketchum, Joel, Dry Goods, 243 King St., res. Meeting
St., Ward 5
Kiddell, A., Clerk, 76 East Bay St., res. 23 Friend St.
Kiddell, George, Clerk, 40 East Bay St.
Kiep, J. P., Grocer, 6 Rutledge St.
Killerman, G., Clerk, 23 Market St.
King, A., Dry Goods, 254 King St., res. 88 Market St.
King, C. S., Medical Student, 26 Broad St.
King, F., Dry Goods, 267 King St., res. 58 Wentworth St.
King, G. W., Clerk, 106 Church St.
King, G. W., Proprietor, American Hotel
King, George, Boiler Maker, 24 Washington St.
King, H. C., Attorney, St. Michael's Alley, res. 68 Tradd
St.
King, J. H., Grocer, 123 King St.
King, J. W. & G. W., Proprietors, American Hotel
King, J. W., Proprietor, American Hotel
King, John, Clerk, South Carolina Railroad, res. 42
George St.
King, Mitchel, Attorney, 14 George St.
King, -----, Mrs., Chalmers St.
King, N. S., Wig Maker, 278 King St.
King, S. H., Operator, Telegraph Office, 26 Broad St.
King, W. & F., Dry Goods, 267 King St.
King, W., Dry Goods, 267 King St., res. 58 Wentworth
St.
King, W. L., Clerk, Courier Office, res. Commercial
House
King, W. S., Editor, Courier, 26 Broad St.
Kingdom, Thomas, Engineer, South Carolina Railroad,
res. Rutledge St.,Ward 8
Kingman, Ehab, Penny Post, cr. Calhoun & Coming Sts.
Kingman, G. L., Clerk, 243 cr. King & Market Sts., res.
cr. Calhoun & Coming Sts.
Kingman, J. W., Clerk, cr. King & Market Sts., res. cr.
Calhoun & Coming Sts.
Kingman, John Scavenger, cr. Calhoun & Coming Sts.
Kingman, Robert, Clerk, 163 Meeting St., res. 4
Wentworth St.
Kingman, Samuel, Bookkeeper & Transfer Clerk,
Planters & Mechanics Bank, res. rear of bank
Kinloch, Benjamin, Millwright, 51 Coming St.
Kinloch, Frederick, Librarian, Charleston Library, res.
Mill St.
Kinloch, George, Grain Dealer, Dewees' Wharf, res. 223
East Bay St.
Kinloch, M., Mrs., 4 Aiken Row
Kinloch, R. A., M. D., 223 East Bay St.
Kinloch, R., Millwrights, 15 Bull St.
Kinnay, J., Bootmaker, 144 East Bay St.
Kinnay, Patrick, Blacksmith, President St.
Kinsey, G. F., Accountant, 26 Hayne St., res. cr. King &
Wentworth Sts.
Kinsley, P. E., Crockery Dealer, 120 Church St.
Kinsman, H. W., Upholsterer, 86 Meeting St.
Kirk, John, Hack Driver, 20 Pinckney St.

Kirk, M., Mrs., 8 Magazine St.
Kirk, S. D., Clerk, cr. Beaufain & Lynch Sts., res. 8
Magazine St.
Kirker, James, Wheelwright & Blacksmith, res. King St.,
Ward 5
Kirker, Robert, Wheelwright, 28 Pinckney St., res. 10
Anson St.
Kirkpatrick, J. & J. J., Factors, Atlantic Wharf
Kirkpatrick, J., Factor, Atlantic Wharf, res. 40 East Bay
St.
Kirkpatrick, J. J., Factor, Atlantic Wharf, res. 40 East
Bay St.
Kirkwood, William, Ship Builder, foot of Laurens St.,
res. 17 Laurens St.
Klen, E., Laborer, King St., Ward 6
Klenke, A., Clerk, 65 East Bay St.
Klesick, A., Spirit Dealer, 16 Vendue Range, res. 1
Horlbeck Alley
Klinck & Wickenberg, Grocers, cr. Broad & Church Sts.
Klinck, C. F., Clerk, 369 King St.
Klinck, Henry, Clerk, 2 Middle St.
Klinck, John, Clerk, 29 Anson St.
Klinck, John, Grocer, cr. Broad & Church Sts., res. 84
Church St.
Klintworth, H., Grocer, cr. Washington & Charlotte Sts.
Knapp, C., Mrs., 7 Wentworth St.
Knauf, Henry, Engineer, 23 Wentworth St.
Knauf, T. J., Carpenter, 23 Wentworth St.
Knee, H., Grocer, 38 Church St.
Knee, -----, Mrs., Dry Goods, 38 Church St.
Kneply, S., Import Inspector, Custom House, res. 73
Queen St.
Knight, J. D., Capt., U. S. Navy, Elizabeth St.
Knoblock, John, Clerk, 222 King St., res. 193 King St.
Knoblock, William, Baker, 19 Calhoun St.
Knoke, Albert, Grocer, 18 State St.
Knowles, E., Miss, Milliner & Dressmaker, 202 King St.
Knox, C., Mrs., 14 Green St.
Knox, J. P., Ship Carpenter, 5 Middle St.
Knox, Robert, Wood Factor, Palmetto Wharf, res. 8
Pritchard St.
Kodeweg, F., Watchmaker, 82 Meeting St.
Kohrike, C. F., Grocer, 71 Coming St.
Kollman, N., Grocer, 47 Church St.
Koppman, J., Baker, King St., Ward 8
Korber, H., Grocer, 8 Lynch St.
Koster, J. C., Grocer, Meeting St., Ward 5
Krackie, F., Grocer, cr. Rutledge & Doughty Sts.
Kramer, Jacob, Carpenter, Spring St.
Kramer, L., Mrs., Midwife, King St., Ward 5
Kramer, Philip, Laborer, Coming St., Ward 8
Kramer, W. H., Cabinet Maker, King St., Ward 5
Krate, George, Grocer, 19 Wall St.
Kreeden, F., Grocer, St. Philip St., Ward 8
Krieton, M., Grocer, cr. Columbus & Nassau Sts.
Kruse & Westman, Grocers, 311 King St.
Kruse, A. M., Mrs., 25 Society St.
Kruse, Jacob, Grocer, 311 King St.
Kueffner, F., M. D., 67 Meeting St.
Kuhntmann, H. W., Commission Merchant, Atlantic

Wharf, res. 68 Calhoun St.
Kulinski, J., Watchmaker, 104 Meeting St.
Kumlah, H., Clerk, 104 East Bay St.
Kunhardt, William, Port Warden, 5 Wentworth St.
Kunhardt, William W., Attorney, 51 Broad St., res. 5
Wentworth St.
Kyall, Thomas, Boiler Maker, 20 Anson St.
Kyall, William, Boatman, 20 Anson St.
Labates, C., Mrs., Mantuamaker, 75 Tradd St.
Laboard, A., Mrs., Spring St.
Laboard, J. P., Clerk, East Bay St., res. Spring St.
LaBruse, -----, Mrs., Drake St.
Lacassagire, E., China Dealer, 148 King St.
Lacomb, Susan, 22 Calhoun St.
Lacoste, A. J., Rigger, 77 East Bay St.
Lacoste, T. J., Rigger, 4 Marsh St.
Ladsden, G., 12 West St.
Ladson, J. H. & Co., Factors, 13 Southern Wharf
Ladson, J. H., Factor, 13 Southern Wharf, res. 4 Meeting
St.
Ladson, W. H., Factor, 13 Southern Wharf, 4 Meeting St.
Laendr, Joseph, Clerk, Pavilion Hotel, res. 37 Anson St.
Lafar, D. B., Cooper, cr. Rutledge & Calhoun Sts.
Lafar, John, Molder, Nassau St.
Lafar, M. L. L., Clerk, Gillon St., res. 47 Beaufain St.
Lafar, T. A., Pattern Maker, 47 Beaufain St.
Lafar, W. H., Clerk, 235 King St., res. 47 Beaufain St.
Laffan, J., Watchmaker, 91 Church St.
Laffiteau, S., Accountant, 17 Pinckney St.
Laffitte, E. & Co., Agents, Savannah Steamers,
Fitzsimons' Wharf
Laffitte, E., Agent, Savannah, Steamers Fitzsimons'
Wharf, res. 12 Wentworth St.
Laffitte, J. B., Agent, Savannah Steamers, Fitzsimons'
Wharf, res. Meeting St.
LaGrue, John, Engineer, South Carolina Railroad, Line
St.
Lahman, Daniel, Clerk, 143 King St.
Lakise, Jacob, Cap Maker, 328 King St.
Lalane, P. B., Discount Clerk, Bank of Charleston, res.
118 King St.
Lalaue, J. A., Tobacconist, 46 East Bay St.
Lamb, B., Clerk, 181 East Bay St., res. 191 Meeting St.
Lamb, D. W., M. D., 41 Meeting St., res. 191 Meeting
St.
Lamb, James, 191 Meeting St.
Lamb, James, Jr., 191 Meeting St.
Lambert & Brothers, Carpet Dealers, 219 King St.
Lambert, A., Mrs., St. Philip St., Ward 6
Lambert, Charles, Carpet Dealer, 219 King St., res. 22
Wentworth St.
Lambert, Robert, Carpet Dealer, 219 King St., res. 22
Wentworth St.
Lambla, Joseph, Finisher, Coming St., Ward 6
Lamkin & Hurst, Proprietors, Planters Hotel
Lamkin, J. W., Proprietor, Planters Hotel
Lamont, D., Tailor, Horlbeck Alley
Lamotte, H. J., Printer, 68 Meeting St.
Lamotte, J. A., Printer, 68 Meeting St.
Lampe, F., Grocer & Coal Dealer, 49 Market St.

Lanagan, K., Private Boarding, cr. King & Reid Sts.
Lance, A. J., Broker, 5 State St., res. Broad St.
Lance, D. H., Accountant, Central Wharf, res. Broad St.
Lance, Francis, Broker, 5 State St., res. Broad St.
Lance, H., Rev., Planter, Georgetown, res. Charlotte St.
Lance, L. C., Teacher, High School, King St.
Lance, W. S., Cadet, Citadel, res. Broad St.
Landreth, D. M., Seedstore, 297 King St.
Lane, E. H., Dry Goods, 41 Hayne St., res. Charleston
Hotel
Langdon, E., Tailor, Market St., res. Coming St.
Lange, J. H., Tavern Keeper, 15 Vendue Range
Lanneau & Burckmyer, Grocery Merchants, 14 Hayne St.
Lanneau, B., Accountant, 155 East Bay St., res. 7 Pitt St.
Lanneau, C. H., Clerk, Central Wharf, res. 14 State St.
Lanneau, F., Grocery Merchant, 14 Hayne St., res. 43
Coming St.
Lanneau, John, Clerk, 145 Meeting St., res. 7 Pitt St.
Lanneau, M., Mrs., 22 Anson St.
Lapeine, A. J., Bookbinder, 103 East Bay St.
Lapeine, J. N., Dry Goods, 336 King St.
Lapeine, Sidney, 34 King St.
Larkin, C., Mrs., Private Boarding, 32 Queen St.
Larkin, M., Mrs., 76 Queen St.
Larousseliere, -----, Upholsterer, 161 King St.
Larrandga, V. A., Spanish Consul, 33 Tradd St.
Lassall, J. B., Carpenter, Columbus St.
Lathrop, Joseph, Laborer, Williams Row
Laurens, E. K., 194 East Bay St.
Laurens, Joseph, Furniture Dealer, 52 St. Philip St.
Laurens, Sarah, 1 Wilson St.
Laurent, A., Clerk, 123 Meeting St.
Laury, H. C., Clerk, 25 Vendue Range, res. 63 King St.
Laval, W. J., Clerk, Comptroller General Office, res.
Elizabeth St.
Laval, W., State Treasurer, Fire Proof Building, 1
George St.
Law, M., Bootmaker, 38 Church St.
Lawrence, E., Planter, Coming St., Ward 6
Lawrence, F., Mrs., 23 Lynch St.
Lawrence, S. C., Mrs., 6 Church St.
Lawton, J. C., 24 Montague St.
Lawton, Joseph & Co., Dry Goods, 40 East Bay St.
Lawton, R. P., 24 Montague St.
Lawton, W. M. & Co., Factors, 13 Southern Wharf
Lawton, W. M., Factor, 13 Southern Wharf, res. 17
Rutledge St.
Lawton, William, Planter, 40 South Bay St.
Layman, James, 5 Wall St.
Lazarus, B. D., cr. Smith & Wentworth Sts.
Lazarus, G., Steam Boat Inspector, Custom House
Lazarus, Joshua, President, Gas Works, cr. Laurens &
Wall St.
Leader, M., Mrs., 8 Clifford St.
Leak, W. C., Grocer, King St., Ward 7, res. Columbus St.
Leamont, M., Mrs., 2 Minority St.
Lebby, M. W., Clerk, 123 East Bay St., res. 29
Cumberland St.
Lebby, Robert, Jr., Medical Student, George St., res. 29
Cumberland St.

Lebby, Robert, M. D., 25 Cumberland St., res. 29 Cumberland St.
Lebby, T. F., Printer, 183 King St.
Lebby, W., Engineer & Machinist, foot of Hasell St., res. Wentworth St.
LeBriffe, F., Painter, 17 State St.
Leckie, David, Accountant, South Carolina Shoe Factory, 20 Beaufain St.
Leckie, John, 179 King St.
Leckie, Robert, Umbrella Manufacturer, 133 Meeting St. & 179 King St.
Leclerc, A., Clerk, 7 Motte's Lane
Lee, A. C., Grocer, cr. Market & Archdale Sts.
Lee, A. M., Secretary, Commercial Insurance Company, 4 Broad St., res. Judith St.
Lee, Andrew, Blacksmith, Gadsden's Wharf
Lee, B. F., Teller, State Bank, Alexander St.
Lee, E., Barber, 53 Broad St.
Lee, F. D., Architect, 57 Broad St., res. Alexander St.
Lee, G. C., Grocer, 32 Archdale St.
Lee, J. T., Teacher, High School, 42 Pitt St.
Lee, John, 78 Tradd St.
Lee, John, Pilot, 19 Church St.
Lee, -----, Mrs., 42 Pitt St.
Lee, P. H., Accountant, 1 Hayne St., res. Planters Hotel
Lee, W. T., Carpenter, 4 Hard Alley
Lee, William, Sea Captain, 58 Meeting St.
Leffman, William, Baker, 8 Queen St.
Legare, A., Mrs., 19 Hasell St.
Legare, J. J., Clerk, 16 East Bay St., res. 43 Anson St.
Legare, James, Clerk, 60 East Bay St., res. 2 Greenhill St.
Legare, James, Commercial Wharf, res. cr. Logan & Broad Sts.
Legare, O'Hear & Co., Factors, Commercial Wharf
Legare, S. L., Planter, St. John's Island, res. 103 Tradd St.
Lege, J. G., Clerk, Adger's Wharf, res. King St.
Legg, M., Mrs., 213 East Bay St.
LeGras, G. H., Clerk, Adger's Wharf, res. 206 East Bay St.
Lehre, Thomas, Alexander St.
Leiding, Ann, 14 Coming St.
Leiding, H., Fancy Goods, 141 Meeting St., res. King St.
Leightburn, E. B., Mrs., King St., Ward 6
Leiker, L., Grocer, 1 Tradd St.
Leitch, G. M., Clerk, 133 Meeting St., res. 2 Wall St.
Leitch, R. L., 2 Wall Slt.
Leitch, W. Y., Surveyor, Custom House, cr. Lamboll & Legare Sts.
Leland, J. A., Professor of Mathematics & Astronomy, Citadel Academy
Leman & Aveilhe, Grocery Merchants, 175 East Bay St.
Leman, B. F., Clerk, cr. King & Market Sts., res. Alexander St.
Leman, C. H., Clerk, East Bay St., res. 106 Church St.
Leman, W. W., Dry Goods, cr. King & Market Sts., res. Alexander St.
Lengwick, A., Clerk, 141 Meeting St., res. Victoria Hotel
Lenox, William, cr. Market & Meeting Sts.

Lenthe, H., Clerk, Washington St.
Leonard, E., Clerk, 45 Hayne St., res. Queen St.
Leonard, J., Mrs., 13 Friend St.
Leopold, F., Grocer, cr. Meeting & Columbus Sts.
Leprince, A., Accountant, Vendue Range, res. 131 King St.
Leprince, A. E., Clerk, 15 Vanderhorst's Wharf, res. King St.
Leprince, C. B., Clerk, Fitzsimons' Wharf, res. 131 King St.
Lequex, Benjamin, Jr., Clerk, 97 East Bay St., res. 356 King St.
Lequex, Benjamin, Wood Factor, Gadsden's Wharf, res. 356 King St.
Lequex, S. F., Clerk, 262 King St., res. 356 King St.
Leseman, D., Clerk, 203 East Bay St.
Leseman, F. W., Grocer, cr. Rutledge & Spring Sts.
Leseman, F. W., Tavern Keeper, cr. King & Line Sts.
Lesesne, Daneil, Commission Merchant, Accommodation Wharf, res. Smith St., Ward 6
Lesesne, H. D., Attorney, St. Michael's Alley, res. cr. College & Green Sts.
Lesesne, -----, Miss, 79 Tradd St.
Lesesne, -----, Mrs., 39 Society St.
Lesesne, W. Y., Teacher, Archdale St., res. 79 Tradd St.
Leslie, James, Miller, West Point Mills
Lester, J. C., Clerk, 131 East Bay St.
Levin, M., Clerk, Adger's Wharf, res. 106 Meeting St.
Levin, N., Register Clerk, Custom House, res. 47 Wentworth St.
Levy, C. F., Clerk, 17 Vendue Range, res. Lightwood Alley
Levy, Clarence, Clerk, 26 Vendue Range, res. Lightwood Alley
Levy, E., 30 St. Philip St.
Levy, E., Mrs., Chapel St.
Levy, Elias, Gauger, Vendue Range, res. Lightwood Alley
Levy, L. L., Clerk, 199 King St., res. 174 Meeting St.
Levy, Moses, Clothier, 72 Market St.
Levy, Moses, Police Officer, 3 Tradd St.
Levy, -----, Mrs., Milliner, 72 Church St.
Lewis, A., Mrs., 37 Archdale St.
Lewis, Catherine, Nurse, 3 Bull St.
Lewis, E., Miss, 23 George St.
Lewis, E., Miss, Dressmaker, 99 Market St.
Lewis, H. P., Accountant, Boyce's Wharf, res. 99½ East Bay St.
Lewis, J. M., Bootmaker, 9 Liberty St.
Lewis, John, Carpenter, 26 Tradd St.
Lewis, L., Miss, 21 George St.
Lewis, P., Clerk, 106 Church St.
Lieure, John, Watchmaker, 37 State St.
Limehouse, Robert, 111 Tradd St.
Lindsay, George, Clerk, Accommodation Wharf, res. 8 Guignard St.
Lindsay, H. A., Clerk, 20 East Bay St., res. 8 Guignard St.
Lindsay, J. F., Clerk, 141 East Bay St., res. 155 East Bay St.

Lindsay, J., Painter, cr. Anson & Market Sts.
Lindsay, James, Clerk, Adger's Wharf, res. 8 Guignard St.
Lindsay, M., Mrs., Cannon St.
Lindsay, W., Accountant, 29 Broad St., res. 8 Guignard St.
Linenthal, C., Clerk, 61 Tradd St.
Linestedt, E. B., Grocer, cr. Meeting & Woolf Sts.
Linestedy, Charles, Grocer, 22 New St.
Linestedy, George, Grocer, New St.
Ling, -----, Mrs., 14 Smith St.
Ling, P., Clerk, Charleston Ice House, cr. East Bay St. & Adger's Wharf
Lining, Charles, Port Warden, 24 South Bay St.
Lining, E. B., Bookkeeper, Bank of South Carolina, res. Hampstead St.
Lining, Philip, Laborer, John St.
Lining, Thomas, Clerk, 139 Meeting St., res. Hampstead St.
Linner, Thomas, Laborer, 2 Clifford St.
Lins, H., Grocer, 98 Church St.
Lisman, A., Clerk, 244 King St., res. 4 Beaufain St.
Litter, F., Tailor, Exchange St.
Little, G. & Co., Clothiers, 199 King St., res. 106 Church St.
Little, Gray, Medical Student, res. Carolina Hotel
Livingston, E. B., Mrs., 6 Water St.
Livingston, Jane, 24 Wall St.
Livingston, L., Merchant, 25 Market St.
Lloyd, E. W., Clerk, 138 Tradd St.
Lloyd, Jessee, Hats & Shoes, King St., Ward 8
Lloyd, S. S., Clerk, King St., Ward 7
Lloyd, W. G., Clerk, 7 Broad St., res. 57 Broad St.
Lloyd, William, Carpenter, 138 Tradd St.
Lloyd, William, Stock Broker, 7 Broad St., res. 57 Broad St.
Locke, B. C., Ship Grocery Merchant, 57 East Bay St., res. 12 George St.
Locke, E. H., Grocery Merchant, 66 East Bay St., res. 168 Meeting St.
Locke, F. O., Clerk, South Carolina Railroad, res. 12 George St.
Locke, G. A., Grocery Merchant, 167 East Bay St., res. 3 George St.
Locke, G. B. & Son, Grocery Merchants, 66 East Bay St.
Locke, G. B., Grocery Merchant, 66 East Bay St., res. 12 George St.
Locke, G. R., Clerk, South Carolina Railroad, res. 12 George St.
Locke, W. D., Clerk, Grocery Merchant, 66 East Bay St., res. 12 George St.
Lockwood & Johnston, Machinists, Concord St.
Lockwood, C. D., Mrs., 73 Broad St.
Lockwood, J. A., Clerk, 102 Meeting St., res. Atlantic St.
Lockwood, J. P., Attorney, St. Michael's Alley
Lockwood, J. W., Machinist, Concord St., res. 73 Broad St.
Lockwood, J., Wheelwright, 108 Church St., res. Atlantic St.
Lockwood, P. L., Accountant, Central Wharf, res. 179 King St.
Lockwood, S., Bootmaker, 12 Anson St.
Lockwood, S. L., M. D., 73 Broad St.
Logan & Glen, Clothiers, 261 King St.
Logan, Edward, Butcher, Nassau St.
Logan, H., Mrs., 4 Burns Lane
Logan, J. C., Clothier, 261 King St.
Logan, Martha, Mill St.
Logan, William, Librarian, Charleston Library, res. cr. St. Philip & Warren Sts.
Lonbat, H., Scissors Grinder, Meeting St., Ward 5
Londegran, W., Laborer, Vernon St.
Long, A. K., Gasfitter, 10 Smiths Lane
Long, F. H., Bootmaker, Tradd St.
Long, J., Hatter, 40 Queen St.
Long, M., Mrs., 58 King St.
Long, R. A., Commission Merchant, Dewees' Wharf, res. 14 Mazyck St.
Longman, J. H., Daguerreotypist, 233 King St., res. 204 King St.
Loper, H. G., Paying Teller, South West Railroad Bank, 19 Broad St.
Loper, J. H., Engineer, 19 Broad St.
Loper, J. W., Clerk, 19 Hayne St., res. Planters Hotel
Lopez, David, Sash Door & Blind Factory, Rutledge St., res. 13 Short St.
Lopez, P., Mrs. 41 Coming St.
Lord, J. C., Barber, 91 Market St., res. Vanderhorst St.
Lord, J. F. M., Bricklayer, America St.
Lord, Jacob, Bricklayer, Washington St.
Lord, John, Laborer, Coming St., Ward 8
Lord, Robert, Carpenter, Meeting St., res. Vanderhorst St.
Lord, Samuel, Commission Merchant, 110 East Bay St., res. 18 Society St.
Loryea, A., Clothier, 60 Market St., res. 96 Meeting St.
Loryea, E., Clothier, 64 State St.
Love, A., Miss, Milliner, 157 King St.
Love, Charles, Saddler, cr. Broad & Church Sts., res. 46 Tradd St.
Lovegreen, L. B., Clerk, 253 King St., res. cr. King & Calhoun Sts.
Lovells, Ed, Clerk, Accommodation Wharf, res. Warren St.
Lovells, -----, Misses, Warren St.
Lovet, W., Tavern Keeper, Bedon's Alley
Lowndes, C., Mrs., 30 Montague St.
Lowndes, C. T., East Bay St.
Lowndes, E. B., Mrs., 7 King St.
Lowndes, H. D., Planter, Santee, res. Friend St.
Lowndes, -----, Mrs., Short St.
Lowndes, William, 11 Short St.
Loyal, Charles, Carpenter, Woolf St.
Lubs, P. S. Tobacconist, 263 King St.
Lucas, Benjamin, Bricklayer, 4 Savage St.
Lucas, C. B., M. D., Rutledge St., Ward 6
Lucas, E. S., Planter, Cooper River, res. Rutledge St., Ward 6
Lucas, H. E., Planter, Cooper River, res. Calhoun St., Ward 6

Lucas, J., Commission Merchant, 68 East Bay St., res. Calhoun St., Ward 6
Lucas, J. H., Planter, Rutledge St., Ward 6
Lucas, John, Bricklayer, 4 Savage St.
Lucas, R. H., Engineer, cr. Ashley & Doughty Sts.
Lucas, T. B., Factor & Commission Merchant, Commercial Wharf, res. Calhoun St., Ward 6
Lucas, W. M., Planter, Santee River, res. Rutledge St., Ward 6
Lucas, William, Planter, Santee River, res. Rutledge St., Ward 6
Luchey, J., Mrs., King St., Ward 7
Luhrden, C., Tavern Keeper, 149 East Bay St.
Luhrs, John, Grocer, Marsh St.
Lukins, H., Mrs., Grocer, Radcliffe St.
Lumkins, S., Clerk, cr. King & Market Sts.
Lyall, H. L., Printer, 4 Mazyck St.
Lynass, B., Dry Goods, 212 King St.
Lynch, C. C., Clerk, Atlantic Wharf, res. 66 Queen St.
Lynch, F. C., Tailor, 91 Market St.
Lynch, J. G., Printer, 10 Stolls Alley
Lynch, J., Miss, 34 Archdale St.
Lynch, Patrick, Pastor, 80 Broad St.
Lynch, Thomas, Police Officer, Amherst St.
Lyons, D., Guardman, Linguard St.
Lyons, Denis, Clerk, East Bay St., res. Linguard St.
Lyons, Ellis, Pastor, 48½ Coming St.
Lyons, J. J., Cannon & St. Philip Sts.
Lyons, J. R., Engineer, South Carolina Railroad, res. Reid St.
Lyons, J. V., Clerk, 157 Meeting St., res. Pavilion Hotel
Lyons, M. A., Mrs., Hanover St.
Lyons, Thomas, Clerk, 182 King St.
L'Homdieu, C., Daguerreotypist, 216 King St., res. Victoria Hotel
Macbeth, Charles, Attorney, 41 Broad St., res. cr. Legare & Gibbes Sts.
Macbeth, James, Cotton Broker, Boyce's Wharf, res. 30 South Bay St.
Macbeth, James, Jr., Clerk, Adger's Wharf, res. 30 South Bay St.
Macbeth, Robert, Chief Clerk, Market, res. 5 Smith St.
Macbeth, W., Clerk, 139 Meeting St., res. 30 South Bay St.
Macdonald, A. T., Accountant, 165 East Bay St.
Mack, John, Fancy Goods, 167 Meeting St., res. Charleston Hotel
Mackaboy, M., Gardener, President St.
Mackendow, James, Baker, St. Philip St., Ward 8
Mackey, A. G., M. D., Calhoun St., Ward 5
Mackey, J. G., 314 King St., res. 229 East Bay St.
Mackey, James, Student, 43 St. Philip St.
Mackey, W. A., Sea Captain, 21 Wall St.
Mackie, M., Mrs., 75 Broad St.
Mackie, O. J., Engineer, South Carolina Railroad, res. 75 Broad St.
Mackintosh, Donald, Hardware Dealer, King St., Ward 6
Macriff, B. A., Grocer, Calhoun St.
Magee, Abel, Ship Joiner, Market Wharf, res. 16 Pinckney St.

Magee, Arthur, Captain, 101 Broad St.
Magee, J., Mrs., Mantuamaker, 1 Minority St.
Magee, John, Steam Boat Agent, Vanderhorst's Wharf, res. 101 Broad St.
Maghor, James, Laborer, 32 King St.
Maghor, Patrick, Dry Goods, 112 King St.
Magrath, A. G., Attorney, 29 Broad St., res. St. Philip St., Ward 6
Magrath, Edward, Attorney, 29 Broad St., res. Bee St.
Magrath, John, Factor, Bee St.
Magrath, Michael, Laborer, 17 Queen St.
Maguire, Daniel, Dry Goods, 362 King St.
Maguire, James, Metal Worker, Elizabeth St.
Maguire, M., Clerk, 198 King St., res. 349 King St.
Maguire, Robert, Confectioner, 11 Church St.
Maguire, Thomas, Guardman, Ashley St.
Magwood, C. A., 9 Smith St.
Magwood, Henry, Wheelwright, King St., Ward 5
Magwood, J. H., Brick Burner, St. Philip St., Ward 6
Magwood, Simon, Planter, St. Andrew's Parish, res. Rutledge St., Ward 6
Mahan, Daniel, Laborer, 95 Queen St.
Mahan, Peter, Porter, 80 East Bay St., res. 32 Queen St.
Mahan, Thomas, Laborer, 22 Pinckney St.
Mahan, William, Porter, cr. King & Market Sts., res. 32 Queen St.
Maher, J., Mrs., Calhoun St., Ward 5
Maher, M., Clerk, 79 Market St., res. 44 State St.
Maher, -----, Mrs., Dry Goods, 36 State St.
Mahony, C., Clerk, 13 Broad St., res. 39 King St.
Mahony, James, Accountant, Pinckney St., res. 60 Queen St.
Mahony, John, Hatter, 13 Broad St., res. 39 King St.
Mahony, John, Wheelwright, Calhoun St., Ward 6
Maine, A., Mrs., 17 Wall St.
Maine, A. R., 46 Anson St.
Malancy, H., Packer, 145 Meeting St.
Malcom, M., Accountant, King St., Ward 6
Mallet, F., Baker, 10 Queen St.
Mallory, S., Mrs., Private Boarding, 101 Meeting St.
Malone, Patrick, Laborer, Amherst St.
Malone, T. W., Attorney, 23 Mazyck St.
Malstedt, M., Grocer, cr. St. Philip & Cannon Sts.
Man, John, Bricklayer, 23 Calhoun St.
Manders, William, Laborer, President St.
Mangan, Peter, Blacksmith, Hanover St.
Manigault, A. M., Factor, Vanderhorst's Wharf, res. 14 South Bay St.
Manigault, C. H., Clerk, Atlantic Wharf, res. 6 Gibbes St.
Manigault, Charles, Planter, Cooper River, res. 6 Gibbes St.
Manigault, G., Planter, Georgetown, res. 30 Hasell St.
Manigault, H. H., Planter, Colleton, res. 12 Meeting St.
Manigault, J., Mrs., cr. Meeting & John Sts.
Manigault, W. H., Planter, Colleton, res. 12 Meeting St.
Mansfield, George, Steam Boat Captain, Nassau St.
Manso, A., Fruiterer, 35 Market St.
Many, John, Laborer, Bedon's Alley
Margart, H. N., Blacksmith, 178 Meeting St.
Margart, J. H., Blacksmith, 178 Meeting St.

Margarth, M. M., Line St.
Margriff, Henry, Fisherman, 5 King St.
Marion, A., Miss, Confectioneer, 247 King St.
Marion, John, Confectioner, 289 King St.
Marjenhoff, E. H., Tavern Keeper, 81 East Bay St.
Marquis, James, Wheelwright, Washington St., Ward 5
Marsh, James, Jr., Shipwright, Marsh's Wharf, res. 16 Hasell St.
Marsh, James, Shipwright, 4 Concord St., res. 138 East Bay St.
Marshall & Bogsden, Barbers, 10 Queen St.
Marshall, A. W., Pastor, St. George's Chapel, res. 91 Broad St.
Marshall, Andrew, Shoemaker, 29 Broad St., res. 120 King St.
Marshall, E., Mrs., 21 Smith St.
Marshall, J., Barber, Church St.
Marshall, J. H., Seaman, 15 Franklin St.
Marshall, J. T., Baker, 60 Tradd St.
Marshall, John, Brick Burner, Marshall's Wharf, res. Alexander St.
Marshall, R. N., Clerk, Commercial Wharf, res. 91 Broad St.
Marshall, S. R., Clerk, 54 East Bay St., res. Washington St., Ward 5
Marshall, Samuel, Tailor, 30 Anson St.
Marshall, Susan, 18 Burns Lane
Marshburn, E., Wharfinger, 24 Calhoun St.
Marshman, R., Seaman, Bedon's Alley
Marte, E., Mrs., 70 State St.
Martens, F. W., Tailor, 77 Church St.
Martin & Bryan, Factors & Commission Merchants, Boyce's Wharf
Martin, E., Mrs., 12 Calhoun St.
Martin, H. S., Carpenter, 4 King St.
Martin, Isaac, Boots & Shoes, 85 Market St.
Martin, J. B., Neck Ice House Agent, cr. St. Philip & Vanderhorst Sts.
Martin, J. C., Clerk, 9 Broad St., res. New St.
Martin, J. G., 5 Hayne St., res. 29 Coming St.
Martin, J. M., Clerk, 19 Vendue Range, res. 19 Society St.
Martin, J. S., Bookbinder, Woolf St.
Martin, Jacob, Blacksmith, 46 Wentworth St., res. 29 Coming St.
Martin, James, Factor & Commission Merchant, 47 Anson St.
Martin, John, Grocer, Market Wharf
Martin, P. B., Clerk, 232 King St., res. 29 Coming St.
Martin, Philip, Cannon St.
Martin, Robert, Planter, Charlotte St.
Martin, Sarah, 27 Coming St.
Martin, W. C., Sub-Treasurer, Custom House
Martin, W. E., Attorney, 9 Broad St., res. 5 Orange St.
Martin, W. M., Insurance Agent, 91 Broad St., res. 265 East Bay St.
Martindale & Co., Grocery Merchants, 56 East Bay St.
Martindale, C., O., Grocery Merchant, 56 East Bay St., res. King St.
Mashburn, E. H., Accountant, 89 East Bay St., res.

Montague St.
Mashburn, J. H., Import Inspector, Custom House, res. 24 Calhoun St.
Mashburn, James, Carpenter, 16 Rutledge St.
Mason, C. M., Accountant, 292 King St., res. Merchants Hotel
Masteman, W., Jeweller, King St., res. 9 Horlbeck Alley
Masterdon, P., Fancy Dry Goods, King St., Ward 5
Matherson, J. P., Clerk, Adger's Wharf, res. 19 Laurens St.
Matheson, M. P., Commission Merchant, 114 East Bay St., res. cr. Alexander & Charlotte St.
Matheson, Simons & Co., Commission Merchants, 114 East Bay St.
Matthews & Ropers, Factors, Vanderhorst's Wharf
Matthews, A., Mrs., 77 Queen St.
Matthews, E. W., Factor, Vanderhorst's Wharf, res. 13 Short St.
Matthews, G. A., M. D., 29 East Bay St.
Matthews, G. B., British Consul, Central Wharf, res. Broad St.
Matthews, J. B., Tailor, 34 Calhoun St.
Matthews, J. F., Planter, St. Bartholomew's Parish, res. 29 East Bay St.
Matthews, J. R., Planter, St. Bartholomew's Parish, res. 29 East Bay St.
Matthews, M. A., Miss, 112 Tradd St.
Matthews, P. B., Carpenter, America St.
Matthews, T. D., Bookkeeper, Bank of Charleston, res. 43 Anson St.
Matthews, W. R., Planter, St. Bartholomew's Parish, res. 29 East Bay St.
Matthiessen, F. C., Commission Merchant, cr. Wharf, res. 8 Church St.
Matthiessen, M. T., Clerk, Atlantic Wharf, res. 43 King St.
Matthiessen, William, Clothing, 143 East Bay St., res. 14 Wentworth St.
Maule, C. S., Milliner, 287 King St.
Maum, F., Carpenter, America St.
Mauseau, A., Carpenter, Mary St.
Maxcy, V., Clerk, 40 Broad St., res. 17 South Bay St.
Maxwell, P. J., Clerk, 40 East Bay St., res. 43 East Bay St.
May, C. F., Clerk, Central Wharf, res. 8 Washington St.
May, J. W., Attorney, rear of Court House, res. 62 Queen St.
May, John, Cabinet Maker, 62 Queen St.
May, John, Clerk, Central Wharf, res. 9 Marsh St.
Mayers, S., Dry Goods, 33 King St.
Mayor, O., Leader, German Brass Band, 50 Calhoun St.
Mayrant, -----, Mrs., 20 Laurens St.
Maysey, Thomas, Bootmaker, 55 Broad St.
Mazyck & Sons, Factors, Commercial Wharf
Mazyck, A. H., Collector, 66 Broad St.
Mazyck, Alexander, Planter, Santee, res. 30 Hasell St.
Mazyck, Edward, 30 Hasell St.
Mazyck, H. B., Clerk, Boyce & Co. Wharf, res. Broad St.
Mazyck, N. B., Clerk, Boyce & Co. Wharf, res. 44

Calhoun St.
Mazyck, N. B., Mrs., 44 Calhoun St.
Mazyck, P. P., Planter, Santee, res. 30 Hasell St.
Mazyck, W. S. & J., Factors, Commercial Wharf, res. Charlotte St.
Mazyck, William, Factor, Commercial Wharf, res. cr. Alexander & Chapel Sts.
McAllister, Charles, Dry Goods, 339 King St.
McAndrew, James, Clerk, 17 King St.
McAveeny, Philip, Clerk, 124 Meeting St.
McBride, M., Broker, 1 Chalmers St.
McBride, -----, Miss, Dressmaker, 99 Market St.
McBride, P., Auction & Commission Merchant, 22 Vendue Range
McBride, P., Jr., Clerk, 22 Vendue Range
McBurney, William, Dry Goods, 37 Hayne St., res. 29 George St.
McCaa, W. L., Clerk, Atlantic Wharf, res. Broad St.
McCabe, J. W., Accountant, head of Broad St., res. Merchants Hotel
McCabe, James, Engineer, 15 Pinckney St.
McCabe, James, Laborer, 13 Tradd St.
McCaffer, J., Boots & Shoes, 354 King St.
McCall, Ann, Mrs., 19 Bull St.
McCall, B., Planter, Summerville, res. 100 Tradd St.
McCall, Emmer, Baker, Ashley St.
McCall, J. B., Accountant, 17 Mazyck St.
McCall, M. A., Mrs., 14 Orange St.
McCart, Anthony, Gilder, 225 King St., res. Broad St.
McCarter & Allen, Booksellers & Stationers, 116 Meeting St.
McCarter, C., Laborer, Vernon St.
McCarter, D. L., Clothier, 193 East Bay St.
McCarter, J., Clothier, 193 East Bay St.
McCarter, J. J., Bookseller & Stationer, 116 Meeting St., res. 14 Hasell St.
McCartley, J., Clothing, 142 East Bay St.
McCartney, D., Carpenter, 47 Queen St., res. 41 Queen St.
McCartney, ------, Scavenger, 33 Calhoun St.
McCarty, M., Laborer, 9 Tradd St.
McCauly, Emma, 3 Montague St.
McCays, -----, Misses, 8 Friend St.
McClinton, Robert, Bootmaker, 7 Burns Lane
McClore & Elder, Tanners, John St.
McClore, James, Tanner, John St.
McClure, E. H., Bootmaker, 56 Meeting St., res. 17 Queen St.
McClure, John, 15 Middle St.
McClure, R. C., Clerk, 244 King St., res. Cannon St.
McClure, Thomas, Bootmaker, 17 Queen St.
McClure, W. J., Cannon St.
McClure, William, Clerk, 98 East Bay St., res. Cannon St.
McConky, James, Painter, 54 Broad St.
McConnell, Livery Stables, 102 Church St.
McCormick, J., Private Boarding, 26 Market St.
McCormick, P., Philadelphia St.
McCready, -----, Clerk, Custom House, 81 Broad St.
McCready, Ed, Attorney, 20 Broad St., res. 18 Anson St.

McCully, W. P., Clerk, Post Office
McDermid, D., Engineer & Machinist, foot of Hasell St., res. Marsh St.
McDermid, Robert, Miller, Chisholm's Mill
McDonald, James, Laborer, St. Philip St., Ward 8
McDonald, John, Coming St., Ward 8
McDonald, P. H., Clerk, 143 East Bay St., res. Liberty St.
McDonnell, A. B., Clerk, cr. King & Market Sts., res. 159 King St.
McDonnell, Daniel, Seaman, Bedon's Alley
McDonough, C., Laborer, 64 Queen St.
McDonough, E., Tailor, Meeting St.
McDougall, David, Miller, Chisholm's Mill
McDowall & Co., Dry Goods, 32 East Bay St.
McDowall, Andrew, Dry Goods, 32 East Bay St., res. 8 Meeting St.
McDowell, R. H., Crockery Dealer, 211 King St., res. 21 Bull St.
McElharan, W. C., Horse Shoer, 24 Wentworth St.
McFadden, J. W., Clerk, 153 East Bay St., res. Commercial Hotel
McFaul, J., Clerk, 288 King St., res. 4 Beaufain St.
McFeely, E., Mrs., Line St.
McFetters, M. A., Mrs., Chapel St.
McGary, F. P., Bootmaker, 9 Tradd St.
McGee, C. S., Clerk, Boyce's Wharf, res. St. Philip St., Ward 6
McGibbon, James, Accountant, 248 King St., res. 236 King St.
McGill, J. T., Medical Student, Carolina Hotel
McGillivray, J. G., Accountant, Court House, res. 10 Atlantic St.
McGillivray, W. S., Builder, 10 Atlantic St.
McGillivray, A. C., Accountant, 119 East Bay St., res. 11 Atlantic St.
McGin, James, Lumber Merchant, Rutledge St.
McGowen, John, Porter, 9 Anson St.
McGowen, M. A., Mrs., 2 Savage St.
McGowen, Thomas, Laborer, 9 Anson St.
McGrady, C., Mrs., 14 Anson St.
McGreath, David, 98 Meeting St.
McHeugh, Francis, Attorney, 49 Beaufain St.
McHeugh, M., Mrs., 49 Beaufain St.
McInnis, B., Blacksmith, 30 Chalmers St., res. 54 Queen St.
McIntosh, D. N., Ship Builder, Marshal's Wharf, res. 96 Beaufain St.
McIntosh, W., Carpenter, President St.
McIntosh, W., Clerk, 19 Vendue Range, 96 Beaufain St.
McIntyre, Stewart, Pavilion Hotel, res. 37 Anson St.
McKay, Robert, Molder, 24 Marsh St.
McKee, A., Ship Joiner, Market Wharf, res. 16 Pinckney St.
McKeegan, John, Blacksmith, 180 Meeting St.
McKenize, John, Trader, Sires St.
McKenn, James, Clerk, 26 Archdale St.
McKenzie, A. & P. B., Saddlers, cr. Church & Chalmers Sts.
McKenzie, A., Saddler, cr. Church & Chalmers Sts.

McKenzie, B. F., Dry Goods, 82 East Bay St.
McKenzie, Cadow & Co., Dry Goods, 82 East Bay St.
McKenzie, D., Shoemaker, 29 Broad St.
McKenzie, H. A., Dry Goods, 82 East Bay St., res.
Planters Hotel
McKenzie, J., Cabinet Maker, 77 Church St., res. 83
Church St.
McKenzie, M. M., Mrs., Private Boarding, 23 Society St.
McKenzie, -----, Mrs., Midwife, 83 Church St.
McKenzie, P. B., Saddler, cr. Church & Chalmers St.
McKinley, G., Tailor, 74 Market St., res. St. Philip St.
McKinley, Martha, 42 Coming St.
McKinley, William, Tailor, 54 Coming St.
McKinney, C., First Teller, Bank of Charleston, res. 55
Queen St.
McKinney, Hariet, Wragg Square
McKinney, John, Clerk, 21 Broad St., res. St. Michael's
Alley
McLaren, James, East Point Rice Mills
McLean, Stephen, Carpenter, 79 Queen St.
McLean, William, Farmer, King St., Ward 8
McLeish, Archibald, Blacksmith & Wheelwright, 4
Cumberland St.
McLeish, James, Engineer & Machinist, Gadsden's
Wharf, res. 1 Inspection St.
McLeish, William, Dry Goods, 82 Church St.
McManar, Michael, Laborer, 38 King St.
McManus, John, Drayman, 14 Wall St.
McManus, Thomas, Grocer, 20 South Bay St.
McMaster, M., Dry Goods, 364 King St.
McMillan, J. W., Pressman, Mercury Office, res. 277
East Bay St.
McMillan, John, Private Boarding, 23 Queen St.
McMillan, Thomas, Ship Carpenter, Market St.
McMillan, Thomas, Tailor, 104 Queen St.
McNamar, J., Clerk, 310 King St., res. Liberty St.
McNamar, James, Clerk, 135 East Bay St.
McNamar, Michael, Laborer, Radcliffe St.
McNance, Clerk, 133 Meeting St.
McNeill, H., Mrs., Milkseller, 25 King St.
McNeill, M., Mrs., 2 Savage St.
McNeill, -----, Mrs., 30 Middle St.
McNeill, Robert, Gardener, St. Philip St., Ward 8
McNellage, E., Mrs., 36 Archdale St.
McNellage, -----, Sailmaker, 7 Hasell St.
McNellage, W. H., Clerk, 114 East Bay St., res. 7 Hasell
St.
McNulty, George, Clerk, 358 King St.
McOwen, Patrick, 37 St. Philip St.
McOwen, Patrick, Jr., Clerk, Adger's Wharf, res. 37 St.
Philip St.
McOwen, Seth, Accountant, 256 King St., res. 37 St.
Philip St.
McPeake, J. D., Clerk, 244 King St., res. 279 King St.
McPherson, C., Miss, 137 King St.
McPherson, E., 255 East Bay St.
McQueen, Donald, Clerk, 70 East Bay St., res. Duncan
St.
McSwain, W. A., Pastor, Trinity Church, res. 55
Wentworth St.

McTureons, E. W., Clerk, Atlantic, Wharf, res. Whims
Court
McTureons, Warren, Clerk, 143 East Bay St., res. Whims
Court
McWalder, -----, Coppersmith, 17 Queen St.
McWalder, -----, Stone Cutter, 17 Queen St.
McWalder, -----, Stone Cutter, 17 Queen St.
McWillie, T. W., Clerk, American Hotel
Mealy, John, Treasurer, Lutheran Church, Calhoun St.,
Ward 6
Medler, R., Fruiterer, King St., Ward 5
Meetze, Felix, Proprietor of Drays, Mary St.
Mehrtens, C. F., Grocer, 71 Church St.
Mehrtens, F., Grocer, cr. Coming & Vanderhorst Sts.
Mehrtens, George, Grocer, Washington St.
Mehrtens, H., Grocer, Washington St.
Mehrtens, Henry, Grocer, cr. Elizabeth & Henrietta Sts.
Mehrtens, J. C., Grocer, 7 St. Philip St.
Mehrtens, J., Grocer, cr. Elizabeth & Henrietta Sts., res.
John St.
Mehrtens, L., Clerk, 71 Church St.
Mehrtens, R., Clerk, 32 Vendue Range, res. 28 Queen St.
Mehrtens, William, Sign Painter, Coming & Vanderhorst
Sts.
Meitzler, C., Bootmaker, 100 Meeting St.
Meitzler, J., Bootmaker, 100 Meeting St.
Meitzler, Jacob, Bootmaker, 100 Meeting St.
Meitzler, P., Bootmaker, 100 Meeting St.
Melcher, F., Grocer, King St., Ward 6
Melcher, F., Mrs., Millinery, King St., Ward 6
Melcher, T., Clerk, 63 East Bay St.
Meldan, G. F., Grocer, 64 Meeting St.
Melfe, F., Italian Boarding House, 31 Market St.
Memminger & Jervy, Attorneys, 59 Meeting St.
Memminger, C. G., Attorney, 59 Meeting St., res. cr.
Wentworth & Smith Sts.
Mendal, G., Shopkeeper, 145 King St.
Mendenhall, M. T., Ordinary, Fire Proof Building, res.
81 Meeting St.
Mendt, D. C., Carpenter, 9 Wall St.
Menlove & Lesesne, Commission Merchants,
Accommodation Wharf
Menlove, Edward, Commission Merchant,
Accommodation Wharf, res. New Orleans
Mensing, C., Clerk, 187 Meeting St.
Mensing, E. H., Clerk, 165 King St.
Mensing, H., Clerk, 133 King St.
Mensing, John N., Grocer, 187 Meeeting St., res. Morris
Island
Menzies, William, Clerk, cr. King & Market Sts., res.
Merchants Hotel
Merew, J. W., Planter, St. John's, res. 7½ Burns Lane
Merican, -----, Last Maker, 104 Queen St.
Meridith, J. W., Conductor, South Carolina Railroad, res.
Reid St.
Meridith, Richard, Dry Goods, King St., Ward 6
Merrell, A., Clerk, Meeting St., res. cr. Meeting &
Market Sts.
Messery, L., Accountant, Cannon St.
Mey, F. C., Factor & Commission Merchant,

Accommodation Wharf, res. 8 Washington St.
Meyer & Balman, Grocers, 320 King St.
Meyer, A., Clerk, 320 King St.
Meyer, A., Collector, 21 Society St.
Meyer, A., Mrs., Grocer, 50 St. Philip St.
Meyer, B. H., Spirits Dealer, 51 State St.
Meyer, C., Clerk, cr. Coming & Radcliffe St.
Meyer, C., Grocer, cr. Calhoun & Coming Sts., res. Alexander St.
Meyer, C., Grocer, Hanover St.
Meyer, C. Laney, M. D., Morris St.
Meyer, E. J., Clerk, 29 Vendue Range, res. cr. King & Calhoun Sts.
Meyer, F. C., Grocer, cr. Meeting & Line St.
Meyer, H., Clerk, 20 East Bay St.
Meyer, H., Clerk, 320 King St.
Meyer, Henry, Clerk, Coming St., Ward 6
Meyer, J. D., Clerk, 167 Meeting St., res. Morris St.
Meyer, J. D., Grocer, 320 King St., res. 295 King St.
Meyer, J., Grocer, cr. Calhoun & Coming Sts.
Meyer, J., Tobacconist, 92 Meeting St.
Meyer, James, Bootmaker, 53 State St.
Meyer, John, Clerk, 129 East Bay St.
Meyer, L., Grocer, 6 Archdale St.
Meyer, Martin, Grocer, 129 East Bay St.
Meyer, Morris, Dry Goods, 108 East Bay St.
Meyer, O., Bootmaker, cr. St. Philip & Warren Sts.
Meyer, W., Grocer, 124 Tradd St.
Meyer, William, Baker, 4 Wall St.
Meynardie, B. P., Carpenter, Line St.
Meynardie, C. D., Tinner, Line St.
Meynardie, J. D., Carpenter, Line St.
Michell, A. L., Jeweller, 266 King St., res. 116 Wentworth St.
Michell, E., Mrs., Coming St., Ward 6
Michell, J. A., Surveyor & Architect, Broad St.
Michell, John, Butcher, 24 Middle St.
Michell, John, St. Philip St., Ward 6
Michell, Mydleton, M. D., 74 Queen St.
Michell, R. F., M. D., 74 Queen St.
Michell, W. E., Clerk, Southern Wharf, res. 24 Bull St.
Michell, William, M. D., 74 Queen St.
Micken, Thomas, Painter, 121 King St.
Middleton & Co., Factors, Vanderhorst's Wharf
Middleton, A., Clerk, Accommodation Wharf, res. Calhoun St.
Middleton, C., Engineer, 24 Pinckney St.
Middleton, C. K., M. D., 44 South Bay St.
Middleton, F., Pilot, 16 Tradd St.
Middleton, H. A., Jr., Surrveyor, 44 South Bay St.
Middleton, H. A., Planter, Georgetown, res. 44 South Bay St.
Middleton, J. Izard, Planter, Waccamaw, res. 15 Legare St.
Middleton, Oliver, Planter, 3 New St.
Middleton, R. Izard, Coming St., Ward 6
Middleton, Russell, Planter, Stono, res. St. Philip St., Ward 6
Middleton, Thomas, Factor, Vanderhorst's wharf, res. 6 Meeting St.
Middleton, W., Clerk, East Bay St., res. 24 Pinckney St.
Middleton, W. D., Carpenter, 12 Water St., res. Meeting St.
Middleton, William, Planter, Ashley River, res. 18 Meeting St.
Middleton, Williams, Planter, Combahee, res. 15 Legare St.
Miessner, E., Grocer, 134 Tradd St.
Miler, Daniel, Dry Goods, 143 Meeting St., res. Charleston Hotel
Miles, C. R., Attorney, 20 Broad St., res. 53 Beaufain St.
Miles, E. K., Teacher, 53 Beaufain St.
Miles, F. T., M. D., 53 Beaufain St.
Miles, H. E. Accountant, cr. King & Market Sts., res. 116 Queen St.
Miles, J. W., Professor of Literature, Charleston College, res. 53 Beaufain St.
Miles, -----, Mrs., cr. King & Calhoun Sts.
Miles, S. B., Mrs., 53 Beaufain St.
Miles, S. C., Clerk, 19 Vendue Range, res. 116 Queen St.
Miles, Thomas, Clerk, South Carolina Railroad, cr. King & Calhoun Sts.
Miles, W. P., Professor of Mathematics, Charleston College, res. 53 Beaufain St.
Millar, R. S., Baker, 131 Meeting St.
Millenay, P., Clerk, East Bay St., res. 195 East Bay St.
Miller & Burger, Clothing, 273 King St.
Miller, A. A., Barber, 140 East Bay St., res. Washington St.
Miller, A. E., Job Printer, 5 Broad St., res. 43 Tradd St.
Miller, A. P., Clerk, cr. King & Market Sts., res. Beaufain St.
Miller, Edward, Machinist, King St., Ward 6
Miller, Elizabeth, Cannon St.
Miller, F. C., Clothing, 273 King St., res. Vanderhorst St.
Miller, Frederick, Tailor, 12 Pitt St.
Miller, G., Clerk, 30 Vendue Ranges, res. King St., Ward 6
Miller, J. A., Clerk, 68 East Bay St., res. Warren St.
Miller, J. C., Grain Dealer, Dewees' Wharf, res. Mary St.
Miller, J. C., Pastor, Wentworth St. Methodist Church, res. 65 Coming St.
Miller, J. D., Clerk, Commercial Wharf, res. 22 Friend St.
Miller, J. H., Bootmaker, 32 Tradd St.
Miller, J. W., Carpenter, Vanderhorst St.
Miller, John, Drayman, 26 Laurens St.
Miller, Lewis, Grocer, 11 King St.
Miller, Louis, Bootmaker, 57 Wentworth St.
Miller, Robert, Seaman, 2 Philadelphia St.
Miller, S. S., Job Printer, 50 East Bay St., res. 7 Wall St.
Miller, T. J., Accountant, Warren St.
Miller, T. S., Teacher, John St., res. Hanover St.
Miller, W., Clerk, 198 King St., res. 2 Rutledge St.
Miller, W. H., 50 Queen St.
Miller, W., Porter, Jasper's Court
Miller, W. T. Sailmaker, 19 Franklin St.
Miller, William, Cabinet Maker, 167, 171, 173 King St., res. 99 Queen St.
Miller, William, Teller, Bank of the State of South

Carolina, res. Hudson St.
Miller, Zadock, Sailmaker, 229 East Bay St.
Milles, James, Accountant, Cannon St.
Milles, S. D., Ropemaker, Vanderhorst St.
Milligan, Ed, Blacksmith, cr. Coming & Cannon Sts.
Milligan, Ed, Mrs., Dry Goods, cr. Coming & Cannon Sts.
Milliken, A. T., Accountant, 139 Meeting St., res. 162 Meeting St.
Milliken, E. P., Dry Goods, 42 East Bay St., res. 162 Meeting St.
Milliken, Thomas, Planter, St. George's, res. 162 Meeting St.
Milliken, William, Grocer, 155 East Bay St., res. cr. Society & East Bay Sts.
Mills, Beach & Co., Grain Dealers, cr. East Bay St. & Commercial Wharf
Mills, Clark, Artist, 9 Atlantic St.
Mills, Otis, Grain Dealer, cr. East Bay St. & Commercial Wharf, res. 36 Meeting St.
Mills, S. M., Clerk, 147 Meeting St., res. Meeting St.
Mills, S. S., Grocer, 56 Market St., res. 69 Tradd St.
Milne, A., Planter, St. John's Island, res. 18 Rutledge St.
Milner, J. G., Auctioneer & Commission Merchant, 21 Vendue Range, res. 17 Society St.
Minburg, R., Laborer, America St.
Minildus, D. G., Grocer, St. Philip St., Ward 8
Minis, Robert, Planter, 227 East Bay St.
Minns, M., Mrs., St. Philip St., Ward 8
Minto, J., Clothier, 23 Market St., res. 52 King St.
Miott, Albert, Clerk, Central Wharf, res. Mansion Hotel
Miscally, D. W., Clerk, 7 Marsh St.
Misdorf, Jacob, Sea Captain, 24 Savage St.
Mishaw, John, Bootmaker, 76 Meeting St.
Mishaw, Joshua, 3 College St.
Mishaw, Rebecca, Warren St.
Missroon, Henry, Steam Packet Agent, Adger's Wharf, res. 2 East Bay St.
Mitchell, A. R., Cotton Press, 15 Meeting St.
Mitchell, A., West St.
Mitchell, Ann, Chapel St.
Mitchell, C. M., 270 King St.
Mitchell, C. T. & Co., Commission Merchants, Atlantic Wharf
Mitchell, C. T., Commission Merchant, Atlantic Wharf, res. 15 Meeting St.
Mitchell, D., Clerk, 270 King St.
Mitchell, E., Accountant, 14 State St.
Mitchell, Edward, Planter, Edisto Island, res. 12 Savage St.
Mitchell, F. A., Accountant, 21 Hayne St., res. 98 Wentworth St.
Mitchell, G. A., Clothing, 118 Meeting St., res. Coming St.
Mitchell, H. W., Clerk, Meeting St., res. 98 Wentworth St.
Mitchell, Harriet, 23 Beaufain St.
Mitchell, J. D., Accountant, Vanderhorst's Wharf, res. 98 Wentworth St.
Mitchell, J. E. M., Farmer, St. Andrew's Parish, res.

Cannon St.
Mitchell, J. S., M. D., 91 Meeting St., res. 261 East Bay St.
Mitchell, M. A., Miss, 31 Beaufain St.
Mitchell, M., Mrs., Milliner, 272 King St.
Mitchell, Nelson, Attorney, St. Michael's Alley, res. cr. George & Meeting Sts.
Mitchell, T. C., Cabinet Maker, Queen St.
Mitchell, Thomas, Clerk, Commercial Wharf
Mitchell, William, Clerk, 118 Meeting St.
Mitchell, William, Millwright, 6 Mazyck St.
Mixer, D., Proprietor, Charleston Hotel, res. Meeting St.
Moffet, Alexander, Clerk, 54 East Bay St., res. 198 East Bay St.
Moffet, G. H., Clerk, 54 East Bay St., res. 198 East Bay St.
Moffet, J. R., Commission Merchant, 78 East Bay St., res. 4 Hasell St.
Moise, A., Assistant Cashier, Bank of Charleston, res. 4 Green St.
Moise, Abraham, Attorney, Court House Square, res. 1 College St.
Moise, B. F., Clerk, 29 Hayne St., res. 18 Beaufain St.
Moise, C. H., Accountant, 133 Meeting St., res. 1 College St.
Moise, E. W., Clerk, 30 Vendue Range, res. 1 College St.
Moise, Isaac, Stock Broker, 119 East Bay St., res. 26½ Pitt St.
Moise, R., Mrs., Dry Goods, King St., Ward 6
Moise, T. P., Clerk, Hayne St., res. 18 Beaufain St.
Moison, Arthur, Clerk, 169 Meeting St., res. Spring St.
Moison, U., Machinist, Columbus St.
Molle, H. E., Miss, 8 Savage St.
Molony, J., Grocer, 116 Church St.
Monahan, Richard, Laborer, King St., Ward 6
Moncrieff, George, Cooper, 21 State St.
Monefeldt, W. S., Dentist, 243 King St.
Monpoey, Houvre, Planter, St. Andrew's Parish, res. 40 Bull St.
Montague, C., Mrs., 108 Wentworth St.
Montgomery, A., Watchmaker, 27 George St.
Montgomery, C. W., Clerk, 213 King St., res. 27 George St.
Montgomery, J. W., Watchmaker, 27 George St.
Montgomery, S., Watchmaker, 27 George St.
Mood, E. M., Pump & Block Makers, foot of Hasell St., res. cr. Coming & Duncan Sts.
Mood, J. McC. R., Carpenter, Cannon St.
Mood, J. R., M. D., George St., res. 293 King St.
Mood, John, Silversmith, 293 King St.
Mood, W. G., Dry Goods, 32 East Bay St., res. 75 Wentworth St.
Moodie, A. G., Clerk, Atlantic Wharf
Moody, A. H., Tinsmith, King St.
Moody, G. W., Accountant, Vanderhorst's Wharf, res. East Bay St.
Moody, W. M., St. Charles' Coffee House, 220 King St.
Moore, E., Mrs. 73 Church St.
Moore, F., Mrs., 32 Savage St.
Moore, Franklin, Pattern Maker, 3 Gadsden St.

Moore, G. A., Printer, 188 King St.
Moore, George, Pastor, Beaufort, res. 3 Middle St.
Moore, H. J., 70 King St.
Moore, J., Clerk, East Bay St., res. cr. King & Market Sts.
Moore, J. E., Clerk, Commercial Wharf, res. 32 Savage St.
Moore, J. O. A., Clerk, East Bay St., res. 3 Middle St.
Moore, J. V., Clerk, 157 Meeting St., res. 3 Middle St.
Moore, John, Carpenter, Sires St.
Moore, John, Clerk, Atlantic Wharf, res. 32 Savage St.
Moore, Martin, Drayman, Amherst St.
Moore, -----, Mrs., St. Philip St., Ward 6
Moore, Robert, Engineer, 3 Gadsden St.
Moore, W. B., Dry Goods, 68 Market St.
Moore, William, 32 Savage St.
Moorehead, A., Mrs., Coming St., Ward 6
Moorhead, James, Grocer, 26 Archdale St.
Morall, Alexander, Coach Trimmer, cr. Meeting & Market Sts.
Morallo, J. B. & J., Fruiterer, 129 King St.
Moran, E., Mrs., Henrietta St.
Moran, Edward, M. D., Cannon St.
Moran, F., Porter, 82 East Bay St., res. Queen St.
Moran, J. M., Carpenter, Vernon St.
Mordecai, B., Broker, 9½ State St., res. 49 Wentworth St.
Mordecai, H., Miss, 67 Beaufain St.
Mordecai, M. C., Commission Merchant, 110 East Bay St., res. 43 Meeting St.
Mordecai, T. W., Broker & Auctioneer, 25 Broad St., res. 7 New St.
Moreland, A., 7 South Bay St.
Moreland, E. M., Clerk, Adger's Wharf, res. 7 South Bay St.
Morgan, Benjamin, 16 Middle St.
Morgan, F. E., Mrs., Dry Goods, 11 Middle St.
Morgan, J. B., Sea Captain, 11 Middle St.
Morien, -----, Portrait Painter, 349 King St.
Moroso, A., Fruiterer, 3 Broad St., res. 6 Friend St.
Morrallo, J. B., Fruiterer, 129 King St.
Morrallo, J., Fruiterer, 129 King St.
Morris, A., Mrs., 25 Beaufain St.
Morris, Henry, Discount Clerk, Planters & Mechanics Bank, res. Charlotte St.
Morris, J., Outdoor Clerk, Bank of South Carolina, res. 36 Wentworth St.
Morris, John, Wheelwright, King St., Ward 6, res. 6 Bogard St.
Morrison, James, Laborer, 79 Beaufain St.
Morrison, Robert, Clerk, 133 Meeting St., res. 112 Queen St.
Morrison, Samuel, Clerk, 127 East Bay St.
Morse, A. H., Ship Carpenter, Cannon St.
Morse, M., Mrs., Marion St.
Mortimer, Jackson, Molder, 171 East Bay St.
Mortimer, S. H., Secretary & Treasurer, Charleston Insurance & Trust Co., Drake St.
Mortimer, Thomas, Washington St., Ward 5
Morton, W. R., Hardware Dealer, 133 Meeting St., res.

King St.
Moses, A. J., Clerk, Atlantic Wharf, res. 1 Pinckney St.
Moses, A., Miss, 6 Horlbeck Alley
Moses, E. J., Clerk, 20 East Bay St., res. Meeting St.
Moses, Isaiah, King St., Ward 5
Moses, L. J., Chapel St.
Moses, Levy, Amherst St.
Moses, Samuel, Deputy Sheriff, 47 Wentworth St.
Mosian, John Gunsmith, 50 State St.
Mosimann, -----, Accountant, Standard Office, 183 East Bay St.
Motta, S. A., Mrs., Private Boarding 101 King St.
Motte, Darilla, Mantuamaker, Calhoun St., Ward 5
Motte, Jennette, Pastry Cook, Charlotte St.
Mottet & Huchet, Ship & Commission Merchants, Adger's Wharf
Mottet, E., Ship & Commission Merchant, Adger's Wharf, res. 321 King St.
Moultrie, E., Miss, Dressmaker, 99 Market St.
Moultrie, James, M. D., 14 Montague St.
Moultrie, William, Barber, 106 Meeting St., res. 66 Calhoun St.
Mountrie, Robert, Barber, 2 Anson St.
Mouzon, Charles, 4 St. Philip St.
Mouzon, H. J., Clerk, 116 Meeting St., res. 183 Meeting St.
Mouzon, L. H., Collector, 183 Meeting St.
Mowry, E. C., Attorney, 20 Broad St., res. 175 Meeting St.
Mowry, L. D., Commission Merchant, 74 East Bay St., res. 8 Hasell St.
Mowry, S. & L., Commission Merchants, 74 East Bay St.
Mowry, S., Commission Merchant, 74 East Bay St., res. 175 Meeting St.
Mowry, W. S., Clerk, 74 East Bay St., res. 175 Meeting St.
Muckenfuss, B. S. D., Carpenter, President St.
Muckenfuss, H. & B., Lumber Dealers, Smith St.
Muckenfuss, H., 86 Wentworth St.
Muckenfuss, H. W., Lumber Dealer, Smith St., res. 86 Wentworth St.
Muir, J., Mrs., Private Boarding, 24 Broad St.
Muir, L. W., Mrs., 74 Broad St.
Mullens, D., Pilot, 34 Church St.
Mullens, J., Pilot, 34 Church St.
Mullens, -----, Mrs., 34 Church St.
Muller, C., Dry Goods, 26 Anson St.
Muller, H., Grocer, cr. East Bay & Calhoun Sts.
Muller, H. W., Clerk, 135 King St.
Muller, L., Rev., 277 King St.
Muller, T. D., M. D., 83 Tradd St.
Mullins, H., Pilot, 3 Atlantic St.
Mullins, W., Pilot, 99½ East Bay St.
Mulloy, H. E., Cannon St.
Mulloy, M. L., Plasterer, Cannon St.
Mulry, L., Clerk, 35 Hayne St., res. Queen St.
Mulry, W., Clerk, Meeting St., res. 26 Wentworth St.
Muncreff, A. S., Bricklayer, 71 Queen St.
Munroe, Brewster & Dunkin, Attorneys, 65 Meeting St.
Munroe, George, Clerk, 56 East Bay St., res. 10

Montague St.

Munroe, Robert, Attorney, 65 Meeting St., res. 10 Montague St.

Murden, -----, Misses, Female School, 34 Society St.

Mure, Robert, Commission Merchant, Boyce & Co. Wharf, res. 68 Church St.

Murly, H., Drayman, 12 Middle St.

Murphy, E., Mrs., Midwife, 23 Society St.

Murphy, James, Clerk, Hayne St., res. Mary St.

Murphy, Martin, Porter, 135 Meeting St., res. Vanderhorst St.

Murphy, Patrick, Mary St.

Murphy, Peter, Laborer, 53 Tradd St.

Murphy, Thomas, Bricklayer, 32 Queen St.

Murphy, Thomas, Laborer, 28 State St.

Murray, Charles, 53 King St.

Murray, E., Mrs., 18 South Bay St.

Murray, F., Clothier, 181½ East Bay St.

Murray, James, Plasterer, Calhoun St., Ward 5

Murray, Joseph, Teacher, Collegiate Institute, 7 Friend St.

Murray, M., Mrs., 53 King St.

Murray, T. A., Bootmaker, 144 East Bay St.

Murray, W. C., Commission Merchant, 26 East Bay St., res. cr. South Bay & Church Sts.

Murrell, J. H., Accountant, Courier Office, 20 Savage St.

Murrell, J. J., 23 Middle St.

Murrell, L., Mrs., 3 Wall St.

Mustard, D., Engineer & Machinist, foot of Hasell St., res. cr. Laurens & Marsh St.

Myer, P. F., Clerk, 224 King St., res. Archdale St.

Myers, A., Mrs., 14 Clifford St.

Myers, G., Tailor, 34 Pinckney St.

Myers, H., Miss, 5 Aiken Row

Myers, J. E., Wood Factor, Reid St.

Myers, J. S., Tavern Keeper, 115 Meeting St., res. Archdale St.

Myers, M., Mrs., Ginger Pop Maker, cr. St. Philip & Spring Sts.

Myers, Solomon, 5 Aiken Row

Myette, Edward, Fisherman, 84 King St.

Nabb, John, Sea Captain, 39 George St.

Nabur, M., Mantuamaker, Morris St.

Nachman, A., Dry Goods, King St., Ward 6

Nachman, A., Dry Goods, 100 Anson St.

Nance, F. A., Grocery Merchant, 1 Hayne St., res. Charleston Hotel

Narman, N., Ginger Pop Maker, Meeting St., Ward 7

Narman, Philip, Wood Seller, 22 Montague St.

Naser, F., 16 Coming St.

Nathan, A., Cabinet Maker, 30 St. Philip St.

Nathan, Henry, Seaman, 30 St. Philip St.

Nathan, L., Grocer, King St., Ward 6

Nathan, M. H., Coach Maker, cr. Meeting & Wentworth Sts., res. 30 St. Philip St.

Nathan, Nathan, King St., Ward 6

Nathan, S., Clerk, 4 Gillon St., res. 30 St. Philip St.

Nayel, Vincent, Baker, 97 King St.

Naylor, W., Dry Goods, 40 East Bay St., res. 46 Beaufain St.

Neal, W. M., Carpenter, 29 Queen St.

Neff, B., M. D., 20 Calhoun St.

Nell, Andrew, Engineer, Hampden Court

Nell, Angeline, 13 Mazyck St.

Nelly, -----, Mrs., 349 King St.

Nelme, J. W., Clerk, South Carolina Railroad, res. John St.

Nelson, Christopher, Bar Keeper, Exchange St.

Nelson, Maria, Pitt St., Ward 6

Nelson, Peter, Barber, 169 East Bay St.

Nelson, Purvis, Clerk, 273 King St., res. 269 King St.

Nelson, S. A., Clerk, 43 Hayne St., res. 101 Meeting St.

Nester, John, Molder, 12 East Bay St.

Neuffer & Hendrix, Commission Merchants, res. 124 East Bay St.

Neuffer, G. A., Commission Merchant, 124 East Bay St., res. Commercial Hotel

Neufville, E., Mrs., Shopkeeper, 53 Tradd St.

Neuman, James, Trader, St. Philip St.

Neumayer, Lewis, Clerk, 205 King St.

Neust, George, Clerk, Ferry Boats, 3 Coming St.

Newbold, -----, Mrs., 34 Wentworth St.

Newell, John, Gas Fitter, 4 Montague St.

Newton, J. A., Clerk, East Bay St., res. Coming St., Ward 6

Newton, W. N., Shipwright, Coming St., Ward 6

Newton, William, Captain, Planter, St. George's, res. Cannon St.

Niaause, A. H., Grocer, cr. Calhoun & Smith Sts.

Nichols & Gibbs, Commission Merchants, Boyce & Co. Wharf

Nichols, J. C., Commission Merchant, Boyce & Co. Wharf, res. 59 King St.

Nichols. J. H., Dry Goods, Hayne St., res. Meeting St.

Nicholson, J., Clerk, cr. Broad & Church Sts.

Nickerson, G. W., Printer, Standard Office

Nickerson, S. T., Clerk, Charleston Hotel

Niebuhr, J. P., Druggist, cr. Tradd & Church Sts.

Niebuhr, J. P., Druggist, 89 King St.

Nimitz, A., Grocer, 63 East Bay St.

Nimitz, C., Clerk, 63 East Bay St.

Nipson, T. S., Clerk, 228 King St., res. Queen St.

Nisbet, Douglas, Steam Boat Agent, Boyce & Co. Wharf

Nixon, J. B., Printer & Publisher, 48 Broad St., res. 44 Queen St.

Noble, James, Naval Officer, Ashley St.

Nolan, J. J., Carpenter, 48 Beaufain St.

Nolan, J. J., Mrs., Private Boarding, 48 Beaufain St.

Nolan, John, Carpenter, 10 Anson St.

Norman, A. E., Clerk, 215 King St.

Norman, G. A., St. Philip St., Ward 6

Norris, -----, Distiller, 22 Washington St.

Norris, H. M., Clerk, 157 East Bay St., res. 24 Mazyck St.

Norris, James, City Assessor, East Bay St., res. Lynch St.

Norris, Samuel, Fireman, South Carolina Railroad, res. Coming St.

Norris, W. H., Cooper, Bennet's Mill, res. 20 Washington St.

North, Abram, Drayman, Calhoun St., Ward 5

North, E., M. D., 79 Meeting St.
North, Thomas, Blacksmith, Cannon St.
Northop & Allemong, Attorneys, 17 Broad St.
Northop, C. B., Attorney, 17 Broad St., res. 50 King St.
Northop, L. B., cr. Bee & President Sts.
Northop, L. M., Mrs., cr. Bee & President Sts.
Norton, C., Grocer, Laurens St.
Norton, J., 1st Bookkeeper, Bank of Charleston, res. 115 Queen St.
Norton, J. H., Clerk, 29 Vendue Range, res. 115 Queen St.
Norton, R., Miss, Dress Maker, 214½ King St.
Norton, Richard, Clerk, 288 King St., res. 318 King St.
Nowell, J. L., Planter, Santee, res. Reid St.
Nugent, Michael, Clerk, 65 Anson St.
Oakes, Z. B., Broker & Auctioneer, 7 State St., res. 72 Queen St.
Oakley, R. S., Druggist, 150 King St.
Oakley, W. C., Exchange Office, 26 Broad St.
Oarbis, H., Clerk, 123 King St.
Oates, E. H., Clerk, 134, 236 King St., res. 234 King St.
Oates, George, Music & Bookstore, 234, 236 King St., res. 234 King St.
Oates, H. T., Clerk, 134, 236 King St., res. 234 King St.
Oberhauser, J., Druggist,, 128 Church St.
Oelrick, J. C., Piano & Organ Builder, 70 Queen St.
Oetjen, Henry, Grist Mill, cr. Radcliffe & Coming Sts.
Oettegeu, John, Laborer, King St., Ward 6
Oetten, H., Grain Dealer, 108 Meeting St., res. Coming St.
Ogemall, J. C., Grocer, 370 King St.
Ogier, T. L., M. D., 37 East Bay St., res. 33 East Bay St.
Ogilvie, J. T., Clerk, 15 Broad St., res. Vanderhorst's Wharf
Ogilvie, Mathew, Merchant, 21 Broad St., res. 5 Logan St.
Ohlandt, W., Grocer, 4 Market St.
Ohlrogga, P., Grocer, cr. King & Columbus St.
Oldenbuttle, H. J., Grocer, 53 Market St.
Olier, B., 40 St. Philip St.
Oliver & Aucrum, Tailors, 215 East Bay St.
Oliver, J. H., Gilder, 23 King St.
Oliver, W., Bootmaker, 43 Society St., res. 40 St. Philip St.
Olney, G. W., Commission Merchant, 11 Vendue Range, res. Radcliffe St.
Oltmann, H., Clerk, cr. King & Reid Sts.
Oppenheim & Brother, Commission Merchants, 102 East Bay St.
Oppenheim, H. W., Commission Merchant, cr. King & Hudson Sts.
Oppenheim, J. H., Commission Merchant, 102 East Bay St., res. Meeting St., Ward 5
Oppenheim, S. H., Commission Merchant, 102 East Bay St., res. cr. King & Hudson Sts.
Orchard, Samuel, Wheelwright, Market St.
Orcutti, L., Gilder, 154 King St., res. 104 Queen St.
Orcutti, W., Livery Stables, 9 Mazyck St.
Orwell, George, Linguard St.
Osborn, George, Sea Captain, 38 Archdale St.

Ostendorff, J. H., Clothier, 87 East Bay St.
Osterholtz, J., Grocer, cr. Mill & Ashley Sts.
Otgan, John, Clothier, 95 East Bay St.
Otis, Walker, 2 Church St.
Otten, C., Grocer, 18 Tradd St.
Otten, D. B., Grocer, Elizabeth St.
Otten, H., Grocer, 44 Anson St.
Ottoleugui, J., Broker & Auctioneer, 20 Broad St.
Otyens, -----, Mrs., Baker, 17 Tradd St.
Owens, Alexander, Butcher, Cannon St.
Owens, Hager, Paine Court
Owens, Stephen, Clerk, 70 East Bay St., res. Roper's Court
Owens, W., Gardener, 40 Beaufain St.
Oxlade, T. C., Watchmaker, 61 Broad St., res. 15 Middle St.
O'Brien, Andrew, Bootmaker, 11 Anson St.
O'Brien, Andrew, Clerk, 261 King St., res. 95 Queen St.
O'Brien, Ed, Carpenter, 69 King St.
O'Brien, James, Laborer, Amherst St.
O'Brien, James, Mason, 95 Queen St.
O'Brien, Michael, Laborer, 24 Queen St.
O'Brien, Peter, Clerk, 222 King St., res. 13 College St.
O'Brien, T., Livery Stables, 28 Chalmers St.
O'Callighan, D., Clerk, 116 Church St.
O'Connor, William, Watchmaker, 79 Beaufain St.
O'Dot, Vincent, Confectioner, 81 King St.
O'Driscol, -----, Mrs., Music Teacher, 13 Church St.
O'Garrow, James, Laborer, 83 Queen St.
O'Garrow, T., Clerk, Tradd St., res. 111 Church St.
O'Hara, H., Mrs., 18 Montague St.
O'Hara, William, Clerk, 143 East Bay St., res. 14 Wentworth St.
O'Hear, J. F., Coming St., Ward 6
O'Hear, James, Factor, Commercial Wharf, res. St. Philip St., Ward 6
O'Leary, D., Saddler, Saddler, 89 Church St.
O'Leary, Daniel, Laborer, Bedon's Alley
O'Leary, Daniel, Ship Carpenter, 4 Atlantic St.
O'Maree, John, Second Hand Bookseller, 86 Queen St., res. 76 Queen St.
O'Neale, James, Carpenter, 20 Magazine St.
O'Neale, T. P., Clerk, 122 East Bay St., res. 20 Magazine St.
O'Neale, W. T., Clerk, 17 Chalmers St., res. 20 Magazine St.
O'Neill, E., Mrs., 84 Queen St.
O'Neill, Edmund, cr. Rutledge & Cannon Sts.
O'Neill, Francis, Stone Mason, 15 Franklin St.
O'Neill, H., Mrs., Private Boarding, 41 Queen St.
O'Neill, Hugh, Saddler, 41 Queen St.
O'Neill, J. F., Commission Meerchant, 145 East Bay St., res. Chalmers St.
O'Neill, James, Bootmaker, 98 Meeting St.
O'Neill, Patrick, Laborer, 17 State St.
O'Neill, Patrick, Planter, Cannon St.
O'Neill, Patrick, Rev., St. Patrick's Church, King St., Ward 6
O'Neill, R., Commission Merchant, 135 East Bay St., res. 58 Meeting St.

O'Neill, Thomas, Bootmaker, 98 Meeting St.
O'Neill, William, Laborer, Cannon St.
O'Rielly, J. B., Printer, 4 Mazyck St.
O'Sullivan, J., 181½ East Bay St.
O'Sullivan, John, Laborer, 33 State St.
O'Sullivan, Thomas, Printer, Minority St.
O'Wen, L. D., Clerk, 13 Southern Wharf, res. 102
    Church St.
O'Wen, L., Import Inspector, Custom House
O'Wen, L., M. D., 102 Church St.
Pacetti, A., Marion St.
Paddock, B. C., Clerk, 19 Hayne St., res. Charleston
    Hotel
Padron, Antonius, Cigar Maker, Woolf St.
Page, John, Shopkeeper, 105 King St., res. Reid St.
Pahnkin, C. H., Druggist, 123 Meeting St.
Paine & Lucas, Commission Merchants, 68 East Bay St.
Paine, E. T., Commission Merchant, 68 East Bay St., res.
    Coming St., Ward 6
Paine, Thomas, Captain, U. S. Navy, Vanderhorst St.
Painter, N., M. D., Calhoun St., Ward 5
Palmer, B. W., Clerk, Vanderhorst's Wharf, res.
    Rutledge St., Ward 6
Palmer, J. W., Clerk, Police Office, 7 Hard Alley
Palmer, W. S., Carpenter, 11 Logan St.
Pansin, C., Clerk, under American Hotel
Pape, Y., Grocer, cr. Tradd & Legare Sts.
Papy, J., Saddler, King St.
Parker, A. G., Mrs., Milliner, 200 King St.
Parker, B. J., Clerk, 19 Hayne St., res. 6 George St.
Parker, C., Mrs., King St., Ward 6
Parker, Charles, City Surveyor, Fire Proof Building, cr.
    Lamboll & Legare Sts.
Parker, F. S., Planter, Goose Creek, 10 Legare St.
Parker, M., Mrs., 11 Clifford St.
Parker, -----, Misses, Chapel St.
Parker, R. D., Planter, Washington St., Ward 5
Parker, S. D., Accountant, 6 George St.
Parker, S. J., Mrs., 5 Horlbeck Alley
Parker, Thomas, Clerk, Vanderhorst's Wharf, res. cr.
    Tradd & Logan Sts.
Parker, W. M. J., 26 George St.
Parker, W. S., Carpenter, 60 Meeting St.
Parkeson, John, Bell Hanger, 17 Queen St.
Parkeson, M. S., Mrs., 74 Broad St.
Parks, George & Co., Booksellers & Publishers, 41
    Broad St.
Parks, George, Bookseller & Publisher, 41 Broad St., res.
    cr. Queen & Church Sts.
Parrett, S. G., Mrs., 13 Wall St.
Parsell, W. N., Furniture Dealer, 314 King St., res.
    Merchants Hotel
Parsons, Joseph, Printer, 8 Burns Lane
Parsons, -----, Mrs., 8 Burns Lane
Parsons, T. J., Clerk, 248 King St., res. Friend St.
Passailaigue, J. E., Machinist, St. Philip St., Ward 6
Passailaigue, Lewis, Blacksmith, Spring St.
Passailaigue, -----, Mrs., Rutledge St., ward 8
Patar, James, Sea Captain, Longitude Lane
Patat, A., Mrs., Spring St.

Patat, Charles, Painter, Woolf St.
Patat, Francis, Cabinet Maker, Cannon St.
Patat, Francis, Cabinet Maker, Smith St.
Patat, James, Confectioner, Cannon St.
Patch, N., Carpenter, King St., Ward 6
Paterson & Burns, Blacksmiths & Wheelwrights, cr.
    Meeting & John Sts.
Paterson & Stock, Ship & Commission Merchants,
    Atlantic Wharf
Paterson, B., Commission Merchant,'Atlantic Wharf, res.
    Huntsville, Ala.
Paterson, F. S., Blacksmith & Wheelwright, cr. Meeting
    & John Sts.
Paterson, G. W., Collector, 40 Broad St., res. St. Philip
    St., Ward 6
Paterson, George, Sea Captain, 22 Church St.
Paterson, J. L., Ship & Commission Merchant, Atlantic
    Wharf, res. Queen & Meeting Sts.
Paterson, S. H., Steam Boat Inspector, res. 61 Queen St.
Paterson, W. P., Carpenter, 6 Liberty St.
Paterson, William, Accountant, Atlantic Wharf, res. 85
    Broad St.
Paterson, William, Painter, 110 Meeting St.
Patrick, C., Farmer, King St., Ward 6
Patrick, J. B., Dentist, 231 King St., res. Calhoun St.
Pattani, J., Fruiterer, 19 Market St.
Patton, John, Factor & Commission Merchant,
    Accommodation Wharf, res. Huntsville, Ala.
Patton, W. M., Watchmaker, 235 King St., res. 297 King
    St.
Patton, William, Wharfinger, Union Wharf, res. 16
    Laurens St.
Paul & Brown, Grocers & Spirits Dealers, cr. Broad &
    Church Sts.
Paul, Dunbar, Spirits Dealer, cr. Broad & Church Sts.,
    res. 20 New St.
Paul, John, Clerk, cr. Broad & Church Sts., res. New St.
Pauls, F, Grocer, 15 Franklin St.
Pauls, F., Grocer, 21 Market St.
Pauls, H., Clerk, 44 State St.
Pawly, Rebecca, Calhoun St., Ward 5
Paxton, W. Y., Publisher, Evening News, 54 Wentworth
    St.
Payne, J. S., 19 Friend St.
Payne, -----, Mrs., 18 Hasell St.
Payne, N. K., Bookkeeper, Union Bank, res. 8 Green St.
Payne, R. K., City Surveyor, Court House Square, res.
    Line St.
Pearce, P., Meeting St. Ice House, res. 66 Queen St.
Pearce, Richard, Furniture Dealer, 40 George St.
Pearson, A., Mrs., 22 Smith St.
Pearson, B. E., Carpenter, 215 East Bay St.
Peaucenteler, C., Laborer, Williams Row
Pecare, M., Clerk, 334 King St.
Peirce, Matthews, Clerk, 326 King St.
Pelder, Philip, Bootmaker, 8 Tradd St.
Pelerin, -----, Madame, Milliner & Dressmaker, 294 King
    St.
Pellegrin, P., Plasterer, 42 Market St.
Pelot, J. A., Mercantile Teacher, 167 Meeting St., res. 56

Calhoun St.

Pelot, J. Cooper, Clerk, 244 King St., res. cr. Meeting & Market Sts.

Pelot, J. Crews, Clerk, 244 King St., res. 17 George St.

Pelot, W. L., Clerk, 40 East Bay St., res. 7 Water St.

Pelot, W. M., Teacher, Vanderhorst St.

Pelzer, A. P., M. D., 2 Beaufain St.

Pelzer, F. S., Grocer, King St., Ward 8, res. 8 President St.

Pelzer, G. S., M. D., King St., Ward 6

Pendarois, Jacob, Carpenter, Rutledge St., Ward 8

Penniman, J. L., Clerk, 243 King St., res. 236 King St.

Penseed, Margaret, St. Philip St., Ward 6

Peper, L. M., Grocer, cr. Coming & Cannon Sts.

Pepper, A. M., Mary St.

Pepper, P. M., Clerk, Mary St.

Percival, John, Watchman, Doughty St.

Peronneau, Abram, Laborer, Charlotte St.

Peronneau, H. W., Attorney, 93 Tradd St.

Peronneau, W. H., Attorney, 20 Broad St., res. 5 Gibbes St.

Perry, A., Clerk, 181 East Bay St., res. 193 Meeting St.

Perry, Abraham, Gadsden St.

Perry, Benjamin, Secretary of State, Fireproof Building, res. Summerville, S. C.

Perry, Edward, Clerk, Hayne St., res. 46 Beaufain St.

Perry, Francis, Butcher, St. Philip St., Ward 6

Perry, J., Mrs., 2 St. Philip St.

Perry, R., Mrs., 42 Beaufain St.

Perry, R. W., Clerk, Commercial Wharf, res. cr. Market & Church Sts.

Perry, W. H., Clerk, 229 King St., res. 269 King St.

Perry, William, Private Boarding, 45 Market St.

Peterman, F., Grocer, cr. Church & Atlantic Sts.

Peterman, H., Grocer, Marsh St.

Peterman, M., Grocer, 32 Meeting St.

Peters, George, Seaman, 88 Queen St.

Peters, James, Outdoor Clerk, Southwest Railroad Bank, res. 106 Church St.

Peters, Jane, Miss, 51 Anson St.

Peterson, -----, Mrs., Music Teacher, 8 Middle St.

Petesch, A. H., Car Builder, Line St., res. Elizabeth St.

Petigrew, William, M. D., 64 Broad St.

Petigru & King, Attorneys, St. Michael's Alley

Petigru, D., Attorney, District Court, res. 103 Broad St.

Petigru, J. L., Attorney, St. Michael's Alley, res. 103 Broad St.

Petigru, J. L., Jr., 30 Bull St.

Petigru, J. Louis, Clerk, cr. Vanderhorst's Wharf & East Bay St., res. cr. Market & Church Sts.

Petigru, T., Captain, U. S. Navy, 30 Bull St.

Petit, A. J., Tinner, 62 Market St.

Petit, E. W., Insurance Broker, 4 Broad St., res. 194 King St.

Petit, F., Confectioner, 194 King St.

Petsch, J. D., Transport Agent, South Carolina Railroad, res. Meeting St., Ward 5

Petsch, William, Mechanic, Spring St.

Petzer, F. J., Factor, Adger's Wharf

Peurifoy, A., Dr., Botanic Medicine, Vanderhorst St.

Peysso, M. L., Mrs., 57 Queen St.

Phelps, F. E., Clerk, 84 East Bay St., res. Bee St.

Phelps, M., Mrs., Bee St.

Phillips, C., Clothier, 352 King St.

Phillips, C., Mrs., 14 Pinckney St.

Phillips, E., Mrs., Seamstress, 40 Mazyck St.

Phillips, Edward, Rev., Pastor, St. Thomas & St. Denis Church, res. 44 Beaufain St.

Phillips, George, Bootmaker, 129½ Meeting St., res. cr. Queen & State St.

Phillips, J. E., Attorney, Fire Proof Building, res. Chapel St.

Phillips, John, Attorney, 84 Church St., res. 158 Meeting St.

Phillips, Otis, Grain Dealer, 126 East Bay St., res. 16 New St.

Phillips, St. John, M. D., 44 Beaufain St.

Phimo, Thomas, Clerk, 35 Broad St., res. Broad St.

Phynney, J., Printer, Standard Office

Picault, C., Mrs., Dry Goods, 57 State St.

Pickering, H., 9 West St.

Pickett, John, Pastor, St. James Church, res. Reid St.

Pierson & Jennings, Clothing, 26 Hayne St.

Pierson, E., Clerk, 26 Hayne St., res. Pavilion Hotel

Pierson, J. S., Clothing, 26 Hayne St., res. Charleston Hotel

Pierson, W. J., Clerk, 238 King St., res. King St.

Pinckeny, Hopson, Assistant Teller, State Bank, res. 88 Tradd St.

Pinckney, B. G., Clerk, Adger's Wharf, res. 34 Meeting St.

Pinckney, C. C., Pastor, Grace Church, 15 Rutledge St.

Pinckney, Charles, Import Inspector, Custom House, res. 3 St. Philip St.

Pinckney, H. L., Tax Collector, Fire Proof Building, res. 3 St. Philip St.

Pinckney, H., Mrs., 193 East Bay St.

Pinckney, L., Mrs., 29 Pitt St.

Pinckney, R. Q., Jr., Accountant, Boyce's Wharf, res. 34 Meeting St.

Pinckney, R. Q., Surveyor, 34 Meeting St.

Pinckney, Roger, 28 King St.

Pingle, J. H., Grocer, cr. Calhoun & Elizabeth Sts.

Piot, J. B., Planter, Meeting St., Ward 5

Piot, J. F., Planter, Meeting St., Ward 5

Pitner, A. G., Clerk, 135 Meeting St., res. Charleston Hotel

Plane, Thomas, Clerk, cr. East Bay St. & Adger's Wharf, res. 35 East Bay St.

Plane, W. A., Import Inspector, Custom House, res. 35 East Bay St.

Plaspoldt, H., Laborer, St. Philip St., Ward 8

Plein, H., Grocer, 80 Beaufain St.

Plemeau, J. F., Coppersmith, Meeting St., Ward 5

Plenge, C., Tailor, 94 Meeting St.

Plessman, W., Mattress Maker, cr. King & Reid Sts.

Plogen, P. H., Bootmaker, cr. King & Ann Sts.

Poincigon, A., Cooper, 19 Tradd St.

Poincigon, E., Tinner, 11 Queen St.

Poinsett, P., Barber, 205 East Bay St.

Police, F., 78 Church St.
Pollin, W. B., Tavern Keeper, 20 Queen St.
Ponjaud, A., 25 Hasell St.
Pooser, H., Orderly Sergeant, Guard House, Amherst St.
Pope, J. J., Attorney, 61 Broad St., res. 42 Bull St.
Pope, J. J., Law Student, 2 Glebe St.
Pope, William, Baker, 18 Tradd St.
Popenheim, J. F., Planter, Goose Creek, res. St. Philip St., Ward 6
Poppan, D., Clerk, 11 Mazyck St.
Porcher, C. J., 53 Church St.
Porcher, C., Miss, cr. Smith & Calhoun Sts.
Porcher, F. J., Cotton Broker, Adger's Wharf, res. 7 Water St.
Porcher, F. P., M. D., 28 Wentworth St.
Porcher, F. Y., M. D., 119 Church St.
Porcher, Frederick, Professor, Charleston College, 34 South Bay St.
Porcher, -----, Miss, 34 South Bay St.
Porcher, -----, Mrs., 34 South Bay St.
Porcher, P. J., Broker & Auctioneer, 25 Broad St., res. 28 South Bay St.
Porcher, Peter, Jr., 53 Church St.
Porcher, Peter, M. D., 53 Church St.
Porte, Rebecca, Pastry Cook, 51 Coming St.
Porter, B. F., Attorney, 41 Broad St.
Porter, N. M., Grocer, 222 King St., res. 13 College St.
Porter, W. D., Attorney, 41 Broad St., res. 1 Pitt St.
Porter, William, 13 College St.
Post, R., Pastor, Circular Church, 22 Meeting St.
Potli, M., Mrs., Judith St.
Potter, L. T., Commission Merchant, 147 East Bay St., res. Charleston Hotel
Poughree, L., Picture Seller, Coming St., Ward 6
Powell, J. V., Carpenter, 349 King St.
Powers, Edward, Drayman, 97 Meeting St.
Powers, F., Grocer, cr. State & Market Sts.
Powers, William, Laborer, St. Philip St., Ward 8
Poyas, H. S., Miss, 76 Wentworth St.
Poyas, James, Planter, Santee, 2 Aiken Row
Poyas, -----, Mrs., 124 Tradd St.
Poyas, W. R., Engineer, 76 Wentworth St.
Pratt, C. C., Clerk, 19 Hayne St., res. Charleston Hotel
Pratt, George, Engineer, 120 Wentworth St.
Pregnell, Henry, Carpenter, 16 Rutledge St.
Prellion, Rose, 23 College St.
Prendergast, E., Dry Goods, 131 King St.
Pressley, B. C., Attorney, 41 Broad St., res. 13 Coming St.
Preston, James, Commission Merchant, 100 East Bay St., res. 66 Queen St.
Preston, John S., Planter, Columbia, res. Hudson St.
Preston, Joseph, 12 Hasell St.
Preston, T., Saddler, 2 Chalmers St.
Price, Alfred, Hardware Dealer, 24 Hayne St., res. 59 Meeting St.
Price, E. L., Clerk, Stolls Alley, res. 108 King St.
Price, James, Clerk, Southern Wharf, res. 83 Broad St.
Price, M., Mrs., 10 St. Philip St.
Price, M., Mrs., 59 Coming St.

Price, T., Saddler, 2 Chalmers St.
Price, W. J., Mechanic, 108 King St.
Prince, A. L., Clerk, South Carolina Railroad, res. Woolf St.
Prince, E. C., Clerk, 147 Meeting St., res. Meeting St., Ward 5
Prince, E. J., Clerk, East Bay St., res. 76 Tradd St.
Prince, E., Mrs., Chapel St.
Prince, George, Drugs & Botanic Medicine, 330 King St.
Prince, H., Clothing, 299½ King St., res. King St.
Prince, H. T., Market Wharf
Prince, Henry, Sea Captain, 6 Minority St.
Prince, J. H., Clerk, East Bay St., res. Chapel St.
Prince, S. G., Printer, 211 East Bay St.
Prince, S. H., Clerk, South Carolina Railroad, res. Chapel St.
Prince, S., Mrs., Dry goods, 211 East Bay St.
Prince, S., Mrs., Dry Goods, King St., Ward 6
Prince, Sarah, Miss, 108 King St.
Pringle, B. G., 20 Society St.
Pringle, E. J., Attorney, cr. Broad & Church Sts., res. 9 King St.
Pringle, E., Mrs., 160 Meeting St.
Pringle, J. R., Commission Merchant, Adger's Wharf, res. 9 Legare St.
Pringle, M. A., Commission Merchant, Adger's Wharf, res. Broad St.
Pringle, R. A., Boot & Shoe Dealer, 30 East Bay St., res. 20 Society St.
Pringle, W. A. & E. J., Attorneys, cr. Broad & Church Sts.
Pringle, W. A., Attorney, cr. Broad & Church Sts., res. 18 Meeting St.
Pringle, W. B., Planter, Santee, res. 9 King St.
Printan, Barney, Laborer, 16 Mazyck St.
Prioleau, C. K., Clerk, Central Wharf, res. 4 Gibbes St.
Prioleau, F. C., Col., Clerk, Planters & Mechanics Bank, res. 3 Legare St.
Prioleau, J. Ford, M. D., 96 Meeting St., res. 38 Meeting St.
Prioleau, -----, Mrs., 3 Meeting St.
Prioleau, T. G., M. D., 96 Meeting St., res. 38 Meeting St.
Prioleau, W. H., Clerk, 114 East Bay St., res. 38 Meeting St.
Prior, B. R., Accountant, 43 Hayne St., res. Liberty St.
Prior, John, Clerk, 37 Hayne St., res. 3 Wentworth St.
Prior, S. T., Clerk, 175 Meeting St., res. 26 Burns Lane
Pritchard, C. C., M. D., 150 East Bay St.
Pritchard, Paul, Ship Carpenter, 1 Gibbes St.
Pritchard, W. H., Pyrotechnist, 2 Society St.
Pritchard, William, Clerk, 1 Hayne St., res. 32 Pinckney St.
Proctor, H. G., Clerk, 153 East Bay St., res. 25 Wentworth St.
Proctor, W. E., Clerk, 82 East Bay St., res. 25 Wentworth St.
Proctor, William, Clerk, 141 East Bay St., res. 25 Wentworth St.
Prothro, N. B., Lumber Factor, west end of Broad St.,

res. 256 King St.

Prout, Daniel, Laborer, 7 Burns Lane

Puckerhaber, Jonathan, Grocer, cr. Ashley & Bee Sts.

Purcy, A., Mrs., 27 Mazyck St.

Purse, Benjamin, Cooper, Bee St.

Purse, J. S., Upholsterer, 267 King St.

Purse, R. E. L., Clerk, 37 Market St., res. 34 Anson St.

Purse, R. S., Soda Foundary, 37 Market St., res. 34 Anson St.

Purse, T. F., Accountant, King St., Ward 7, res. Rutledge St., Ward 8

Pye, Henry, Fireman, South Carolina Railroad, Coming St.

Quackenbush, T. L., Grocer, 116 Church St.

Quale, M., Mrs., 337 King St.

Quash, Edward, M. D., 2 College St.

Quash, Francis, Planter, St. Thomas, res. cr. Rutledge & Spring Sts.

Quash, Martha, 40 Pitt St.

Quash, R. H., Mrs., 2 College St.

Quigly, C., Boot & Shoe Dealer, 76 Church St.

Quigly, W. A., Clerk, 39 Hayne St., res. 148 Meeting St.

Quinby, J. H., King St., Ward 5

Quinen, B., Mrs., President St.

Quinn, Daniel, Wheelwright, Vernon St.

Quinn, Michael, Laborer, Vernon St.

Quinn, Michael, Mason, 20 Tradd St.

Quire, Ann, Jaspers Court

Rabb, James, Pump & Block Maker, Market Wharf, res. 32 Pinckney St.

Rabb, John, Engineer, Charleston Factory, Amherst St.

Rabe, Robert, Livery Stables, George St., res. 43 Calhoun St.

Radcliffe, J. T., 7 College St.

Radcliffe, N., Bricklayer, Spring St.

Rahall, Patrick, Tavern Keeper, 124 Meeting St.

Raine, H. J., Clerk, Work House, 41 Beaufain St.

Ralf, C., Clerk, 11 South Bay St.

Rame, C., Baker, 83 East Bay St.

Ramkin, J., Mrs., 85 Tradd St.

Ramsay, C., Miss, Teacher, 62 Broad St.

Ramsay, M., Miss, Teacher, 62 Broad St.

Ramsay, W. G., M. D., 77 Tradd St.

Ramzan, M., Mrs., Meeting St., Ward 5

Rankin, G. F., Clothing, 27 Hayne St., res. Charleston Hotel

Rankin, G., Painter, 119 King St.

Ranorth, E. J., Engineer, South Carolina Railroad, res. Hampden Court

Ranorth, J. H., Engineer, South Carolina Railroad, res. Spring St.

Rantin, William M., Daguerotypist, Radcliffe St.

Rappman, John, Shoemaker, 158 King St.

Raveneau, -----, Teacher, 51 Broad St.

Ravenel & Co., Ship & Commission Merchants, 16 East Bay St.

Ravenel, A. F., Ship & Commission Merchant, 16 East Bay St., 2 East Battery

Ravenel, Daniel, President, Planters & Mechanics Bank, 23 East Battery

Ravenel, Eliza, Mrs., 58 Broad St.

Ravenel, F. G., Ship & Commission Merchant, 16 East Bay St., res. 2 East Battery

Ravenel, Henry, President, Union Bank, 114 Tradd St.

Ravenel, James, Factor & Commission Merchant, 22 East Bay St., res. 19 East Battery

Ravenel, John, 2 East Battery

Ravenel, S. & J., M.D's, 2 East Battery

Ravenel, William, Ship & Commission Merchant, 16 East Bay St., res. 9 East Battery

Raymond, H. H., Attorney, 21 Broad St., res. 2 Water St.

Read, J. Harlston, Planter, Georgetown, 4 Rutledge St.

Read, J. R., Clerk, 237 King St., res. 249 King St.

Reaux, Francis, Clerk, 134 Queen St.

Rebb, Lewis, Contractor & Builder, 27 Bull St.

Recardy, Joseph, Tavern Keeper, 115 East Bay St.

Rechtglaut, H., Tailor, 37 Queen St.

Reddock, A., Carpenter, 81 Queen St.

Redfouz, E. F., Drayman, 62 State St.

Redmond, George, Fruiterer, 110 King St.

Redmond, W. S., Commission Merchant, Commercial Wharf, res. cr. Legare & Tradd Sts.

Reed, J. P., Dry Goods, King St., Ward 6

Reed, -----, Mrs., Seamstress, 120 King St.

Reeder, M. B., Clerk, King St., res. 76 Wentworth St.

Reeder, Oswell, Grocery Merchant, King St., Ward 8

Reedy, J. A., Clerk, cr. East Bay & Market Sts., res. Guignard St.

Reedy, M., Mrs., Private Boarding, 195 East Bay St.

Reeves, M. S., Professor of Music, Warren St.

Reeves, S. L., Jr., Carpenter, 184 Meeting St.

Reeves, Solomon, Carpenter, Reid St.

Reibet, B., Grocer, 82 Anson St.

Reid, Andrew, Accountant, Vanderhorst St.

Reid, G. P., Cashier, Bank of South Carolina, res. 18 New St.

Reid, George, Clerk, Central Wharf, res. 18 New St.

Reid, James, Accountant, Church St., res. Charlotte St.

Reigne, A. P., Clerk, 18 Queen St.

Reilly, Patrick, Amherst St.

Reims, John, Clerk, 345 King St.

Rein, John, Trimming Weaver, Calhoun St., Ward 5

Reincke, George, Tailor, 191 King St.

Reincke, George, Tailor, 348 King St.

Reinhardt, A., Bootmaker, 119 King St.

Reinhardt, -----, Cutler Manufacturer, 121 Meeting St.

Reix, G., Tavern Keeper, 195 East Bay St.

Rekopa, George, Cabinet Maker, 296 King St.

Rendels, Thomas, Private Boarding, 5 Market St.

Rene, B., Carpenter, Coming St., Ward 6

Renneker, J. H., Grocer, 134 King St., head of Queen St.

Rentz, A., Mrs., John St.

Reshland, W., Bootmaker, 95 Meeting St.

Revels, F. C., Barber, cr. Vanderhorst & King Sts.

Rews, William, Laborer, Washington St.

Reynolds & Co., Coach Makers, 85 Meeting St.

Reynolds, A., Mrs., 51 Anson St.

Reynolds, Bishop, 80 Broad St.

Reynolds, G. N., cr. Legare & Lamboll Sts.

Reynolds, G. N., Jr., Coach Maker, 85 Meeting St., res.

28 Hasell St.

Reynolds, R. F., Coach Maker, 85 Meeting St., res. cr. Legare & Lamboll Sts.

Reynolds, William, Proprietor of Drays, cr. Hanover & Reid Sts.

Rhett & Robson, Factors & Commission Merchants, Atlantic Wharf

Rhett & Schorder, Attorneys, St. Michael's Alley

Rhett, B., M. D., 91 Meeting St., res. cr. America & Mary Sts.

Rhett, B. S., Factor & Commission Merchant, Atlantic Wharf, res. Rutledge St., Ward 6

Rhett, C. H., Attorney, 20 Broad St., res. cr. America & Mary Sts.

Rhett, J. S., Attorney, 20 Broad St., res. cr. America & Mary Sts.

Rhett, R., Barnwell Planter, res. Vanderhorst St.

Rhett, Roland, Assistant Clerk, Planters & Mechanics Bank

Rhett, William, Attorney, St. Michael's Alley, res. cr. East Bay & Laurens St.

Rhodes, Sarah, St. Philip St., Ward 8

Rice, C. J., Clerk, 133 Meeting St., res. 9 Lamboll St.

Rice, H. S., Notary Public, 85 East Bay St., res. cr. East Bay St. & Longitude Lane

Rice, J. W., Auctioneer & Commission Merchant, 17 Vendue Range, res. 26 Society St.

Rice, -----, Mrs., Private Boarding, cr. East Bay St. & Longitude Lane

Rice, N., Clerk, 75 East Bay St., res. cr. East Bay St. & Longitude Lane

Rice, William, Judge, City Hall, res. 9 Lamboll St.

Rich, John, Watchmaker, King St., Ward 5

Richards, A., Madame, Milliner, 230 King St.

Richards, E. A., Clerk, 21 Vendue Range, res. 112 Wentworth St.

Richards, F., Draper & Tailor, 32 Broad St., res. 112 Wentworth St.

Richards, G. R., Shipsmith, 130 East Bay St., res. 251 East Bay St.

Richards, Loresa, Amherst St.

Richards, Margaret, Morris St.

Richards, W. C., Editor, Southern Literary Gazette, 249 King St.

Richardson & Brother, Bell Hangers, 89 Meeting St.

Richardson, C. Y., Bell Hanger, 89 Meeting St.

Richardson, F. D., Attorney, 49 Broad St.

Richardson, J. C. E., Bell Hanger, 89 Meeting St.

Richardson, John, Steam Boat Captain, 115 Meeting St.

Richburg, J. C., Clerk, 30 East Bay St., res. Cannon St.

Richon, Lewis, Sail Maker, 15 St. Philip St.

Riddell, J. H., Ladies Shoemaker, 137 King St.

Riddell, J. S., Planter, 8 Lynch St.

Ridgaway, J., Clerk, cr. Meeting & Market Sts., res. Queen St.

Rielly, Alexander, Laborer, 24 Laurens St.

Rielly, Thomas, Factor, Southern Wharf, cr. Meeting & Queen Sts.

Rielly, William, Shoe Dealer, 104 Meeting St.

Riggs, J. S., Harness Maker, 185 Meeting St., res. St.

Philip St., Ward 6

Riggs, J. S., Jr., Broker & Auctioneer, 4 State St.

Righton, J. M., Import Inspector, Custom House, res. 8 Bull St.

Riker, Robert, Engineer, South Carolina Railroad, Spring St.

Riley, J. J., Painter, 32 Queen St.

Riley, William, State Assessor, Fire Proof Building, res. 13 Church St.

Ring, C., Auctioneer & Commission Merchant, 297 King St., res. 30 Savage St.

Ring, D. A., 30 Savage St.

Ring, G. E., Auctioneer & Commission Merchant, 291 King St., res. 9 Bull St.

Rinker, C. F., M. D., 104 King St.

Riols, B., 48 Wentworth St.

Ripley, N. F., Lamp & Oil Deliverer, 262 King St., res. cr. St. Philip & Beaufain Sts.

Rising, W. C., Bookkeeper, Charleston Hotel

Rivea, H. P., Cabinet Makers & Undertaker, 125 King St.

Rivers, David S., Wharfinger, Atlantic Wharf, res. 99½ East Bay St.

Rivers, J. E., Attorney 49 Broad St., res. 36 Wentworth St.

Rivers, W. H., Printer, 14 Beaufain St.

Rivers, W. J., Teacher, 22 Coming St., res. 182 Meeting St.

Roach, B. M., Clerk, 126 East Bay St., res. 11 Society St.

Roach, E., Mrs., 11 Society St.

Roach, Ed, Tailor, 10 Smith St.

Roach, Ed, Wharfinger, Atlantic Wharf, res. 11 Society St.

Roach, Henry, Carpenter, Cannon St.

Roach, J. B., Clerk, 24 Vendue Range, res. 20 Montague St.

Roach, Maurice, Laborer, 178 Meeting St.

Roach, -----, Mrs., 20 Montague St.

Roach, N., Planter, Smith St., Ward 6

Roach, William, Clerk, cr. East Bay St. & Adger's Wharf, res. 11 Society St.

Roassis, J., Cigar Maker, 66 State St.

Robb, James, Grocer & Spirits Dealer, 198 King St., res. 2 Rutledge St.

Robb, James, Jr., Grocer & Spirits Dealer, 198 King St., res. 2 Rutledge St.

Robb, W., Clerk, East Point Mills, res. 2 Rutledge St.

Robbins, A., Fruiterer, 9 Market St., res. 70 Market St.

Rober, John, Clerk, Market Wharf

Roberts, A. J., Printer, 23 Tradd St.

Roberts, A. M., Clerk, Southern Wharf, res. 1 Burns Lane

Roberts, Isaac, 10 Rutledge St.

Roberts, J. F., Accountant, State St., res. 122 Wentworth St.

Roberts, J. F., Clerk, 13 Chalmers St., res. 122 Wentworth St.

Roberts, J. S., Boot & Shoe Dealer, 233 King St., res. 254 King St.

Roberts, Samuel, Blacksmith, 44 Coming St.

Roberts, Stephen, Clerk, 233 King St., res. 8 Vernon St.

95

Roberts, W. A., Bootmaker, 95 King St.
Robertson & Blacklock, Factors, cr. Vanderhorst's Wharf & East Bay St.
Robertson, Alexander, Factor, cr. Vanderhorst's Wharf & East Bay St.
Robertson, F. M., Inspector of Drugs, Custom House, res. Maiden Lane
Robertson, F. M., M. D., Charleston Hotel, res. 1 Maiden Lane
Robertson, George, Cotton Broker, Central Wharf, cr. South Bay & Meeting Sts.
Robertson, George, Molder, 18 Wall St.
Robertson, George, Music Teacher, 25 Mazyck St.
Robertson, James, Commission Merchant, Vanderhorst's Wharf, res. 37 Church St.
Robertson, James, Proprietor of Drays, Calhoun St., Ward 5
Robertson, L. F., Attorney, 46 Broad St., res. 43 East Bay St.
Robertson, Maria, Pitt St., Ward 6
Robertson, William, Mechanic, 16 Calhoun St.
Robinson & Caldwell, Factors & Commission Merchants, Atlantic Wharf
Robinson, Alexander, Clerk, 11 Central Wharf, res. 7 Broad St.
Robinson, Ann, Mrs., 41 King St.
Robinson, David, Fireman, cr. Columbus & Nassau Sts.
Robinson, E. D., Clerk, 153 East Bay St., res. 155 East Bay St.
Robinson, J. J., Pilot, 41 King St.
Robinson, J. K., Factor & Commission Merchant, Atlantic Wharf, res. Judith St.
Robinson, John, Clerk, 116 East Bay St., res. Judith St.
Robinson, John, Fireman, cr. Columbus & Nassau Sts.
Robinson, R., King St., Ward 5
Robinson, S. A., Outdoor Clerk, Bank of Charleston, res. King St., Ward 5
Robinson, S. J., Mrs., Teacher, 90 Anson St.
Robinson, S. T., Cashier, Planters & Mechanics Bank, res. Judith St.
Robinson, W. J., Clerk, South Carolina Railroad, res. Radcliffe St.
Robion, -----, Mrs., Dry Goods, 42 Queen St.
Robson, J. N., Factor & Commission Merchant, Atlantic Wharf, res. cr. Meeting & Wentworth Sts.
Robson, S. A., Mrs., 36 Wentworth St.
Roddy, M., Mrs., 23 St. Philip St.
Roddy, Martin, Laborer, 10 Washington St.
Rodgers, James, Carpenter, Warren St.
Rodgers, T. L., Superintendant, Bennett's Mills
Rodrigues, B. A., Dr., Dentist, 95 Meeting St.
Roesster, F., Locksmith, 18 St. Philip St.
Roeth, M., Mrs., 12 Liberty St.
Rogers, A., Tailor, 13 Horlbeck Alley
Rogers, C., King St., Ward 6
Rogers, E. H. & Co., Factors, Adger's Wharf
Rogers, E. H. & Co., Grocers, King St., Ward 8
Rogers, E. H., Factor, Adger's Wharf, res. King St., Ward 8
Rogers, E., Miss, Mantuamaker, 12 Clifford St.

Rogers, J. R., Clerk, City Council, res. Savage St.
Rogers, M. E., Mrs., 6 Orange St.
Rogers, Murray, Medical Student, res. Carolina Hotel
Rogers, S. B., Jeweller, 156 King St.
Rogers, S. W., Clerk, King St., Ward 8
Rogers, T. J., 13 Archdale St.
Rogers, T. L., Clerk, Adger's Wharf, res. 43 Archdale St.
Rogers, T. W., Clothier, 242 King St.
Rogers, William, Clerk, Courier Office, res. 41 Tradd St.
Roggy, C., 13 Water St.
Rohlfing, H., Bootmaker, 129½ Meeting St., res. 140 King St.
Romaine, A. C., Mason, America St.
Roman, W., Druggist, King St., Ward 6
Rondad, P., Bootmaker, 94 Meeting St.
Roos, David, Clothing, 68 State St.
Roosevelt, H. L., Hardware Dealer, 139 Meeting St., res. Charleston Hotel
Roosevelt, Hyde & Clark, Hardware Dealers, 139 Meeting St.
Roper, B. D., Attorney, St. Michael's Alley, res. 11 Meeting St.
Roper, Benjamin, 25 Legare St.
Roper, -----, Mrs., 30 Society St.
Roper, Richard, Factor, Vanderhorst's Wharf, res. 27 Legare St.
Rose, A. G., President, Bank of Charleston, res. 9 Rutledge St.
Rose, A., Miss, Rutledge St., Ward 6
Rose, Arthur, Dr., Planter, cr. Rutledge & Mill Sts.
Rose, E., Mrs., Ann St.
Rose, James, President, South West Railroad Bank, res. 74 Broad St.
Rose, John, Laborer, Columbus St.
Rosenkranz, A., Clerk, 163 East Bay St.
Ross, Ann, Mrs., 265 East Bay St.
Ross, E. C., Mrs., Tailoress, 24 Pinckney St.
Ross, James, Blacksmith, 28 Vernon St.
Ross, James, Port Warden, 17 Exchange St.
Ross, John, Engineer, Hanover St.
Ross, William, Blacksmith, Motte's Lane
Roullain, A., Coach Maker, 102 Meeting St., res. 5 Glebe St.
Roumillat, A., Confectioner, 63 Broad St.
Roumillat, J., Clerk, 141 Meeting St., res. cr. East Bay & Anson Sts.
Rouse, W. M., Watch Maker, 2 Queen St.
Roux, F., Clerk, 70 East Bay St., res. Queen St.
Royal, L., Tailor, Horlbeck Alley
Roye, N. A., Tinner, 7 Queen St.
Ruddock, T. D., Music Teacher, 23 Pinckney St.
Ruffin, Henry, Laborer, King St., Ward 8
Ruffio, Charles, Clerk, 271 King St., Ward 6
Rumkin, J. S., Tavern Keeper, 28 Queen St.
Rumly, James, Laborer, 20 Tradd St.
Rummillatti, J., Clerk, Meeting St., res. 171 East Bay St.
Rumphel, G. H., Clerk, 159 Meeting St.
Runner, C., Grocer, cr. Meeting & Reid Sts.
Russ, Benjamin, Ship Carpenter, 16 Washington St.
Russ, John, Ship Carpenter, 16 Washington St.

Russ, Richard, Brick Layer, 16 Washington St.
Russell, Albert, Carpenter, 8 Orange St.
Russell, Charles, Clerk, 103 East Bay St., res. Middle St.
Russell, Fortin, Tailor, 10 Pitt St.
Russell, J. B., Clerk, 29 Hayne St., res. cr. Broad & King Sts.
Russell, J. B., Wheelwright, Hanover St.
Russell, John, Bookseller, 256 King St., res. 9 Pitt St.
Russell, M., Mrs., cr. King & Broad Sts.
Russell, Peter, Laborer, St. Philip St., Ward 6
Russell, Richard, Mason, America St.
Ruth, James, Laborer, Savage St.
Rutherford, -----, Mrs., Private Boarding, Broad St.
Rutjes, A. J., Confectioner, 174 King St.
Rutland, J. W., Printer, East Bay St.
Rutledge, E. C., 101 Tradd St.
Rutledge, H. P., Mrs., 101 Tradd St.
Rutledge, H. R., Assistant Cashier to Deputy Collector, Custom House, Vanderhorst & Smith
Rutledge, J. R., Bookkeeper, South West Railroad, res. cr. Vanderhorst & Smith Sts.
Rutledge, John, Planter, St. George, res. cr. Vanderhorst & Smith Sts.
Rutledge, S., Mrs., 193 East Bay St.
Ryan, H. J., Printer, 32 Tradd St.
Ryan, H., Mrs., 21 Middle St.
Ryan, J., Coach Driver, 97 Market St.
Ryan, J. S., Stock & Exchange Broker, 36 Broad St.
Ryan, John, Jr., Clerk, Boyce & Co. Wharf, res. 64 King St.
Ryan, John, Sr., Appraiser of Goods, Custom House
Ryan, Julia, Mrs., St. Philip St., Ward 6
Ryan, Matthews, Carpenter, President St.
Ryan, O. M., 11 Archdale St.
Ryan, Peter, Livestock Dealer, King St., Ward 7
Ryan, T. C., Clerk, 141 Meeting St., res. 42 Church St.
Ryan, T. E., Clerk, 85 Meeting St., res. 11 Archdale St.
Ryan, Thomas & Son, Brokers & Auctioneers, 12 State St., res. 11 Archdale St.
Ryan, W. B., Broker & Auctioneer, 12 State St., res. 11 Archdale St.
Ryan, W. H., Engineer, Pinckney St., res. 89 Church St.
Ryan, W. K., Factor & Commission Merchant, Boyce & Co. Wharf, res. 64 King St.
Ryan, W., Private Boarding, 89 Church St.
Sabitou, Robert, Seaman, Ashley St.
Sachtelben, A., Teacher, 51 Wentworth St.
Sage, William, Clerk, 145 Meeting St., res. 30 Pinckney St.
Sahlaman, C., Grist Mill, Calhoun St., Ward 6
Sahlaman, H., Grocer, 2 Middle St.
Salas, R., Clerk, Central Wharf, res. Queen & Church Sts.
Salinas, A. J., Broker & Auctioneer, 1 State St., res. Franklin St.
Saltan, Thomas R., Ship Carpenter, Mary St.
Saltus, T. W., Clerk, Central Wharf, res. 25 Mazyck St.
Salvo, G., Painter, 166 King St.
Salvo, James, Clerk, 110 East Bay St., res. 88 King St.
Salvo, -----, Mrs., Dry Goods, 88 King St.

Salvo, V. M., Grocer, King St., Ward 8
Sams, D. D., M. D., Queen St., res. 106 Church St.
Samson, A. J., 98 Tradd St.
Samson, J., Deputy Assessor, 98 Tradd St.
Samson, S., Glass Stainer, 186 King St.
Samuel, M., Tailor, 340 King St.
Sarbs, A., Clerk, cr. King & Columbus Sts.
Saspotas, F. C., Millwright, Nassau St.
Saspotas, J. A., Butcher, Nassau St.
Sass & Rives, Cabinet Makers & Undertakers, 125 King St.
Sass, G. W., Cabinet Maker & Undertaker, 125 King St.
Sass, J. K., 3rd Teller, Bank of Charleston, 34 Society St.
Sassard, John, Steamboat Captain, 16 Vernon St.
Satliffe, John, Wheelwright, King St., Ward 5
Satterwhite, G. W., Clerk, cr. King & Market Sts., res. 279 King St.
Saunders, A. W. O., Accountant, 5 Hayne St., res. Commercial Hotel
Saunders, J. T., Mason, 49 George St.
Saunders, John, Brick Burner, Alexander St.
Saunders, Joseph, Bricklayer, Pitt St., Ward 6
Saunders, S., Barber, Church St., res. Chalmers St.
Saunders, S., Bricklayer, Pitt St., Ward 6
Saunders, Thomas, Bricklayer, Calhoun St.
Saunders, Thomas, Factor, Bell's Wharf, res. Alexander St.
Saunders, W. T., Carpenter, Ashley St.
Savage, S., Miss, 34 Savage St.
Savage, Sylva, 7 Montague St.
Savage, Thomas, Fisherman, Coming St., Ward 6
Sawrie, J. T., Clerk, 1 Hayne St., res. King St.
Sayers, Thomas, Private Boarding, 12 Market St.
Sayles, A. A., Engineer, 15 Franklin St.
Saylor, L. C., Mrs., 15 Meeting St.
Sayre, J. A., Clerk, 29 Hayne St., res. 23 East Bay St.
Scaife, C. T., Commission Merchant, Atlantic Wharf, res. Chester District
Scaife, Hill & Co., Commission Merchants, Atlantic Wharf
Scanlan, C. A., Shipsmith, 37 King St.
Scanlan, C., Shipsmith, 37 King St.
Scanlan, S. E., Blacksmith, Marsh St., res. 14 Wentworth St.
Scarling, H., Tailor, 92 Meeting St., res. 41 Queen St.
Schachte, John, Tavern Keeper, cr. King & Vanderhorst Sts.
Schachte, William, Clerk, cr. King & Vanderhorst Sts.
Schanner, Simeon, Laborer, St. Philip St., Ward 8
Scharfull, H., Clerk, King St., Ward 7
Scharlock, Alex, Police Officer, cr. Meeting & Queen Sts.
Schem, S., Mrs., Shopkeeper, 27 Tradd St.
Schew, B., Dry Goods, 101 King St., res. 58 Broad St
Schewfisie, A., Carpenter, 166 King St.
Schieb, M., Tailor, 92 Meeting St.
Schirmu, J. F., Cooper, Commercial Wharf, res. King St.
Schirmu, W. H., Cooper, Commercial Wharf, res. 46 Queen St.
Schlechtren, -----, Mrs., Private Boarding, 29 State St.

Schleyer, C., Grocer, cr. Rutledge & Line Sts.

Schleyer, Henry, Carpenter, Motte's lane

Schlimmermeyer, John, Clerk, 15 Vendue Range

Schlinmeringer, C., Clerk, 101 Church St.

Schmetzer, C., Butcher, Ashley St.

Schmidt & Lebby, M. D., 25 Cumberland St.

Schmidt, D. W., Clerk, 1 Hayne St., res. 27 Cumberland St.

Schmidt, E., Mrs., 15 Montague St.

Schmidt, J. M., Clerk, Central Wharf, res. 43 East Bay St.

Schmidt, J. W., M. D., 25 Cumberland St., res. 27 Cumberland St.

Schmidt, W., Conductor, South Carolina Railroad, res. 17 Liberty St.

Schnierle, John, Major, 21 Pitt St.

School, Philip, Engineer, South Carolina Railroad, res. St. Philip St., Ward 8

Schouboe, F., Police Officer, Society St.

Schreiner, -----, Grocery Merchant, Gillon St., res. 231 East Bay St.

Schriaars, D, Clerk, 3 South Bay St.

Schriaars, D., Clerk, 11 King St.

Schroanvvervell, John, Laborer, Woolf St.

Schroder, C., Grocer, 12 Rutledge St.

Schroder, F., Cabinet Maker, 6 Archdale St.

Schroder, F., Fruiterer, 62 Meeting St.

Schroder, H., Grocer, 85 Queen St.

Schroder, H. W., Attorney, St. Michael's Alley, res. 24 George St.

Schroder, John, Grocer, 7 Cumberland St.

Schroder, John, Sailmaker, 184 Meeting St.

Schroder, W. H., Assistant, Bennett's Mills, res. 184 Meeting St.

Schrogens, John, Fireman, Woolf St.

Schulken, F., Grocer, 9 Pinckney St.

Schulken, H., Grocer, 9 Pinckney St.

Schultz, H., Clerk, 95 East Bay St.

Schultz, J. H., Clerk, Saw Mills, res. 102 Beaufain St.

Schulye, J. W., Clerk, King St., Ward 5

Schwalke, A., Clerk, King St., Ward 5

Schweitze, O., Watchmaker, 190 King St.

Schweitzer, O., Jeweller, 335 King St.

Schwerin, J., Clothier, 319 King St.

Schwertz, H., Clerk, 57 Market St.

Scigwald, Henry, Engineer, Concord St.

Scinlin, James, Laborer, 24 State St.

Scott & Beveaux, Factors, Vanderhorst's Wharf

Scott, B. F., Factor, Vanderhorst's Wharf, res. 18 Coming St.

Scott, E. C., Accountant, Mercury Office, 44 Society St.

Scott, H., Clerk, 181 East Bay St., res. Meeting St.

Scott, J. J., Clerk, Vanderhorst's Wharf, res. 18 Coming St.

Scott, N. B., Mrs., 44 Society St.

Scott, T., Millwright, 68 Anson St.

Scraig, A., Sea Captain 104 Wentworth St.

Screvens, R. E., Factor, 62 East Bay St., res. Meeting St.

Scruggs, Drake & Co., Commission Merchants, Atlantic Wharf

Scruggs, J. W., Commission Merchant, Atlantic Wharf, res. Huntsville, Ala.

Seabrook, E. M., Attorney, 61 Meeting St.

Seabrook, William, Planter, James Island, res. 121 Broad St.

Sebring, Ed, President, State Bank, res. Calhoun St., Ward 6

Seckendorf, Isaac, Dry Goods, 184 King St.

Seely, A., Clerk, 23 Hayne St., res. 236 King St.

Segelty, J. F., Fruiterer, King St., Ward 6

Sehmetzer, Louis, Engineer, Coming St., Ward 8

Seighler, -----, Clerk, 348 King St.

Seignious, Charles, 366 King St.

Seignious, F. P., Turner, Meeting St.

Seirs, Peter, Clerk, East Bay St., res. Spring St.

Seixas, D. C., Commission Merchant, Atlantic Wharf, res. 204 East Bay St.

Seixas, J. M., Commission Merchant, Atlantic Wharf, res. 204 East Bay St.

Senor, J. Y., Barber, King St., Ward 8

Sergeant, George, Boots & Shoes, 89 Market St.

Service, S., Mrs., 11 Friend St.

Seydel, A., Clerk, cr. Broad & Church Sts., res. Anson St.

Seyle, Charles, 204½ King St.

Seyle, John, Carpenter, 14 Bull St.

Seyle, P. W., Clerk, Johnson's Hotel, res. King St.

Seyle, Samuel, Poor House, res. Mazyck St.

Seymour, A. A., Dressmaker, 101 Queen St.

Seymour, J. T., 69 Coming St.

Seymour, R. W., Attorney, Meeting St., res. 13 Franklin St.

Seymour, S., Milliner, 101 Queen St.

Seymour, W. W., Tavern, 101 Queen St.

Shackelford & Graeser, Factors & Commission Merchants, Central Wharf

Shackelford, E., Mrs., 9 College St.

Shackelford, Ed, Engineer, 9 College St.

Shackelford, F. R., Factor and Commission Merchant, Central Wharf, res. 10 Hasell St.

Shackelford, J. M., Commission Merchant, 151 East Bay St., res. 43 Church St.

Shaffer, F. J., Attorney, 20 Broad St., res. cr. Calhoun & Pitt Sts.

Shaffer, F., Planter, Georgetown, res. cr. Calhoun & Pitt Sts.

Shalloe, Michael, Clerk, 274 King St., res. 269 King St.

Shana, A., Mrs., Shopkeeper, 103 King St.

Shaper, E., Clerk, 47 King St.

Sharlow, John, Blacksmith, Line St.

Shaw, Charles, Conductor, South Carolina Railroad, res. Columbus St.

Shaw, James, House Furnishing Store, 176 King St.

Shayer, Peter, Laborer, St. Philip St., Ward 8

Shea, George, Tailor, 9 Tradd St.

Shecut, L. A., Clerk, Central Wharf, res. 27 Pitt St.

Shecut, William, Conductor, South Carolina Railroad, res. King St., Ward 6

Shelton, H., Mrs., 274 King St.

Shepherd, -----, Clerk 99¾ East Bay St., res. Coming St.

Shepherd, William, Clerk, 120 Meeting St., res.
  Merchant's Hotel
Sheppard, J. J., Saddler, 34 Coming St.
Sheppard, T. C., Wharfinger, Boyce's Wharf, res. 11
  Wentworth St.
Sheppard, W. A., Saddler, 40 Coming St.
Sherfesee, William, Clerk, 208 King St., res. 166½ King
  St.
Sheridan, Michael, Slater, 6 Smith St.
Sheridan, P. M., Bootmaker, 74 King St.
Sheridan, Patrick, Laborer, Calhoun St., Ward 5
Sherry, John, Laborer, King St., Ward 8
Shields, C., Painter, 112 Queen St.
Shiffer, H. W., India Rubber Store, 270 King St., res.
  Charleston Hotel
Shingler, H. P., 20 George St.
Shingler, J. S., Planter, Goose Creek, res. 20 George St.
Shingler, T. J., Clerk, 20 George St.
Shirer, C. P., Butcher, Ashley St.
Shirer, G. S., cr. King & Woolf Sts.
Shirer, H., Mrs., Sires St.
Shirer, J. B., Machinist, res. cr. King & Woolf Sts.
Shirer, J. E., Accountant, Adger's Wharf, res. cr. King &
  Woolf Sts.
Shirer, Michael, Clerk, Atlantic Wharf, res. cr. King &
  Woolf Sts.
Shirlet, E., Mrs., Calhoun St., Ward 5
Shirmer, J. F., 124 King St.
Shokes, George, Captain, Calhoun St., Ward 5
Shokes, Henry, Pump & Blockmaker, Hampden Court
Shokes, J. C., Engineer, Hampden Court
Sholke, G. H., Clerk, 82 Church, res. 2 Liberty St.
Shoote, -----, Mrs., Sires St.
Short, James, Accountant, King St., Ward 7
Shrewsbury, George, Butcher, St. Philip St., Ward 8
Shuckman, Lewis, Francy Goods, 205 King St.
Shuler, E., Mrs., Seamstress, cr. Nassau & Line Sts.
Shulz, H. H., Mrs., 6 Aiken Row
Siams, George, Carpenter, King St., Ward 8
Siddons, Joseph, Confectioner, Queen St.
Siddons, L. L., Jeweller, 266 King St., res. Merchants
  Hotel
Siegling, Henry, Clerk, 227 King St.
Siegling, John, Jr., Attorney, Court House Square, res.
  227 King St.
Siegling, John, Music Store, 227 King St.
Siegmundt, C. H., Clerk, 139 East Bay St.
Sievels, J. A., Clerk, 370 King St.
Siffy, Henry, 18 Friend St.
Sigwald, C. B., Clerk, 43 Hayne St., res. 49 East Bay St.
Sigwald, H. W., Engineer, Hampden Court
Sigwald, Henry, Engineer, 10 Burns Lane
Sigward, M., Mrs., 10 Burns Lane
Sigward, Thomas, Carpenter, 10 Burns Lane
Silcox, D. H., Cabinet Maker, 224 King St., res. 22
  Magazine St.
Silcox, James, Clerk, 224 King St., res. 22 Magazine St.
Silliman, E., Mrs., 21 Cumberland St.
Silliman, H. K., Clerk, 135 Meeting St., res. 21
  Cumberland St.

Simmins, J. A., Accountant, Central Wharf, res. 270
  King St.
Simmons, J. Ward, Pastor, St. Stephen's Church, res.
  Montague St.
Simmons, M., Miss, Longitude Lane
Simons & Sons, Factors, Vanderhorst's Wharf
Simons, C. L., Mrs., Smith St., Ward 6
Simons, C. W., Farmer, Mary St.
Simons, F. W. P., Sea Captain, 144 Queen St.
Simons, Harris, Factor & Secretary, Santee Canal,
  Adger's Wharf, res. Thomas St.
Simons, J. C., Paint & Oil Dealer, 226 King St., res. 11
  Bull St.
Simons, J. H., Factor, Vanderhorst's Wharf, res.
  Rutledge St., Ward 6
Simons, James, Attorney, 77 Broad St.
Simons, Lewis, Planter, 26 Montague St.
Simons, N., Clerk, 226 King St.
Simons, R. L., Commission Merchant, 114 East Bay St.,
  res. 20 Rutledge St.
Simons, R. S., Machinist, 50 Bull St.
Simons, R. W., Printer, 7 Atlantic St.
Simons, Rose, Spring St.
Simons, S., Commission Merchant, 114 East Bay St., res.
  26 Montague St.
Simons, T. Y., Jr., Attorney, rear of Court House, res. 49
  Tradd St.
Simons, T. Y., M. D., 49 Tradd St.
Simons, Thomas G., Factor, Vanderhorst's Wharf, res.
  50 Bull St.
Simons, Thomas G., Jr., Factor, Vanderhorst's Wharf,
  res. 50 Bull St.
Simons, W. F., Painter, 49 Queen St.
Simonton, C. H., Attorney, 65 Meeting St., res. 267 East
  Bay St.
Simonton, James, 267 East Bay St.
Simpson, -----, Misses, Teachers, 59 Wentworth St.
Sims & Nance, Grocery Merchants, 1 Hayne St.
Sims, J. T., Grocery Merchant, 1 Hayne St., res. cr.
  Meeting & Society Sts.
Sims, William Gilmore, Author, Smith St., Ward 6
Sinclair, M., Mrs., 193 Meeting St.
Singletery, J. J., Line St.
Singleton, Thomas, 4 Aiken Row
Sinkler, John, Planter, St. John's, res. 7 Lamboll St.
Sire, Francis, Marion St.
Sires, Joseph, Carpenter, Radcliffe St.
Skrine, T. C., Associate Editor, Southern Standard
Skrine, W. A., Druggist, King St., Ward 6, res. 207 King
  St.
Slack, John, Porter, 157 Meeting St.
Slarech, John, Sea Captain, 9 Queen St.
Slawson, H., Jr., Accountant, 8 Archdale St.
Sloan, E. B. B., Clerk, 37 Hayne St., res. Commercial
  Hotel
Sloman, E., Mrs., 33 Bull St.
Sloman, J. W., Blacksmith, 37 King St.
Sloman, John, 29 Wentworth St.
Sloman, -----, Misses, Music Teachers, 29 Wentworth St.
Sloper, A., Foreman, South Carolina Shoe Factory, cr.

King & John Sts.

Sluter, M., Mrs., 37 George St.

Slyter, Henry Carpenter, 5 Motte's Lane

Small, J. S., Clerk, cr. King & Market Sts., res. 7 Liberty St.

Small, Jacob, Baker, 193 King St.

Small, Robert, Clerk, 137 Meeting St., res. 7 Liberty St.

Small, Robert, Private Boarding, 7 Liberty St.

Small, Stephen, Painter, 38 Pitt St.

Small, Thomas, Carpenter, Coming St., Ward 8

Small, W. C., Clerk, 143 Meeting St., res. Calhoun St.

Smallwood, B., Upholsterer, 3 March St.

Smidt, D., Carpenter, Spring St.

Smith & Longman, Daguerreotypists, 233 King St.

Smith & Whilden, Ship Chandlers, 60½ East Bay St.

Smith, A. C., Cashier, Union Bank, res. 125 East Bay St.

Smith, A., Grocer, Marsh St.

Smith, A., Mrs., Washington St., Ward 5

Smith, A. P., Soda Water Bottler, 97 Meeting St.

Smith, B. F., Ship Chandler, 60½ East Bay St., res. cr. John & Meeting Sts.

Smith, B., Mrs., Fruiterer, King St., Ward 6

Smith, Benjamin, Assistant, Turpentine Factory, foot of Calhoun St., res. cr. Meeting & John Sts.

Smith, Benjamin, cr. Meeting & John Sts.

Smith, C. M., Cash Book Keeper, Union Bank, res. 10 Wentworth St.

Smith, C., Mrs., Coming St., Ward 6

Smith, Catherine, 16 Smith St.

Smith, Charles, Car Loader, Sires St.

Smith, E. L., Mrs., 10 Wentworth St.

Smith, E., Miss, 71 Broad St.

Smith, E., Mrs., St. Philip St., Ward 6

Smith, E., Pilot, 57 East Bay St.

Smith, Ed, Clerk, Boyce's Wharf, res. 8 Atlantic St.

Smith, Emily, 26 Smith St.

Smith, H., Mrs., 1 New St.

Smith, H. S., Clerk, 35 Hayne St., res. 87 Wentworth St.

Smith, H. S., Daguerreotypist, 233 King St., res. 236 King St.

Smith, Hampden, Engineer, South Carolina Railroad, res. Rutledge St.

Smith, J. A., Clerk, 35 Hayne St., res. 87 Wentworth St.

Smith, J. A., Miss, Private Boarding, 69 Broad St.

Smith, J. E., Carpenter, 44 Bull St.

Smith, J. E., Jr., Clerk, cr. East Bay St. & Adger's Wharf, res. 87 Wentworth St.

Smith, J. E., Teller, Union Bank, res. 87 Wentworth St.

Smith, J. J. G., Clerk, 1 Society St.

Smith, J. L., Accountant, Boyce's Wharf, res. Meeting St.

Smith, J. R., Engineer, Calhoun St.

Smith, James, Inspector of Weights & Measures, Market, res. 32 Society St.

Smith, James, Mechanic, Calhoun St., Ward 5

Smith, Jane, 45 St. Philip St.

Smith, John, Clerk, St. Philip's Church, res. 10 Magazine St.

Smith, John, Furniture, 152 King St.

Smith, John, Pilot, 72 Church St.

Smith, John, Porter, 147 Meeting St., res. King St.

Smith, John, Tavern Keeper, cr. Meeting & Market Sts.

Smith, Joseph, Ship Carpenter, Henrietta St.

Smith, Joshua, Engineer, 136 Meeting St.

Smith, Julius C., 10 Wentworth St.

Smith, L., Miss, Judith St.

Smith, M., Mrs., Milliner, 132 King St.

Smith, -----, Mrs., 34 South Bay St.

Smith, N. W., Clerk, 139 Meeting St., res. Water St.

Smith, O., Clerk, Hayne St., res. 45 Wentworth St.

Smith, P. F., Teacher, 54 Wentworth St.

Smith, Pringle, Planter, Savannah River, res. 18 Meeting St.

Smith, R. A., Miss, Milliner, 196 King St.

Smith, R. C., Assistant, Turpentine Factory, foot of Calhoun St., res. cr. Meeting & John Sts.

Smith, S., Carpenter, 11 Chalmers St.

Smith, S., Miss, Judith St.

Smith, Sidney, Clerk, Accommodation Wharf

Smith, T. A., 10 Wentworth St.

Smith, T. D., Clerk, Atlantic Wharf, res. Meeting St.

Smith, T. P., Dry Goods, 40 East Bay St., res. 82 Beaufain St.

Smith, U. G., Clerk, cr. Calhoun & King Sts., res. Cannon St.

Smith, U., Mrs., Dressmaker, 12 Archdale St.

Smith, W. B. & Co., Commission Merchants, 60 East Bay St.

Smith, W. B., Commission Merchant, 60 East Bay St., res. 95 Broad St.

Smith, W. B., Engineer, Calhoun St., Ward 5

Smith, W. C., Clerk, 14 Hayne St., res. Charlotte St.

Smith, W. E., Clerk, Atlantic Wharf, res. East Bay St.

Smith, W. H., Clerk, 259 King St., res. 72 Church St.

Smith, W. H., Turpentine Factory, foot of Calhoun St., res. cr. Meeting & John Sts.

Smith, W. Henry, Clerk, 35 Broad St., res. 21 Franklin St.

Smith, W. J., Coastwise Inspector, Custom House, Smith's Wharf

Smith, W. R., Planter, Ashley River, res. 2 Gibbes St.

Smith, Walter D., Attorney, 31 Broad St., res. 297 King St.

Smitt, H. A., Clerk, cr. King & Market Sts., res. 279 King St.

Smythe, Eneas, Clerk, 157 Meeting St., res. Queen St.

Smythe, Thomas, Pastor, 2d Presbyterian Church, Spring St.

Smyzer, Henry, Ship Joiner, Pritchard St.

Snider, William, Clerk, 288 King St., res. 318 King St.

Snizer, Henry, Bootmaker, 13 Queen St.

Snowden, W. E., Factor & Commission Merchant, 6 South Wharf, res. 202 East Bay St.

Sollie, Francis, Clerk, Vendue Range, res. 6 Bull St.

Sollie, Henry, Agent, Mount Pleasant Ferry Co., res. 6 Bull St.

Sollie, Henry, Jr., Clerk, Adger's Wharf, res. cr. Pitt & Bull Sts.

Sollie, -----, Mrs., 65 Church St.

Solomons & Polock, Dry Goods, 281 King St.

Solomons, E. J., 42 Calhoun St.
Solomons, J. R., Dr., Dentist, 95 Meeting St.
Solomons, Thomas, Painter, 5 Minority St.
Sommer, E., Dry Goods, 334 King St.
Sopteen, M., Baker, King St., Ward 5
Soyer, Alfred, Confectioneer, 285 King St.
Spakle, E., Porter, 118 Meeting St., res. Society St.
Sparnick, H., Export Inspector, Custom House, res. 19
    Queen St.
Spear, J. E., Jeweller & Watchmaker, 235 King St.
Spear, W. W., Pastor, Grace Church, 12 Bull St.
Spegel, C., Laborer, Spring St.
Speght, F., Bootmaker, 69 Wentworth St.
Speissegger, E., Grocer, cr. America & Amherst Sts.
Speissegger, T. C., Grocer, 17 Pinckney St.
Speissegger, T. W., Tobacconist, Columbus St.
Speissegger, W., Accountant, 17 Pinckney St.
Spell, John, Guardman, Rutledge St., Ward 8
Spelman, A., Grocer, 45 Market St.
Spencer, A., Mrs., Private Boarding, 279 King St.
Spencer, Allen, Engineer, South Carolina Railroad, res.
    279 King St.
Spencer, D., 26½ Smith St.
Spencer, G. W., Clerk, 250 King St., res. 271 King St.
Spencer, M., Mrs., Private Boarding, 271 King St.
Spencer, Seth, Broker & Auctioneer, State & 271
    Chalmers Sts.
Spenkin, M., Grocer, 25 Savage T.
Spicer, A., Miss, 12 Cumberland St.
Spiegel, W., Watchmaker, King St., Ward 6
Sprague, H. B., Clerk, 4 Hayne St., res. 277 East Bay St.
Sprague, J. W., Grain Dealer, 4 Hayne St., res. 277 East
    Bay St.
Spratt, L. W., Attorney, Court House Square, res. 38
    Wentworth St.
Spreckles, C., Grocer, 29 Anson St.
Sprigg & Brady, Wood Factors, Smith's Wharf
Sprigg, Ross, Wood Factor, Smith's Wharf, res.
    Hampstead St.
Springs, R., Clerk, 1 Hayne St., res. Charleston Hotel
St. Amand, M. W., Clerk, 179 East Bay St., res. 27
    Friend St.
Stadecker, Isaac, Dry Gods, 184 King St.
Staffard, J. F., Tinner, 5 State St.
Stafford, H. R., Carpenter, Line St.
Stafford, J., Carpenter, Columbus St.
Stall, Frederick, Ashley St.
Stall, William, Finisher, Hampden Court
Stanfield, A., Baker, 42 Queen St., res. Meeting St.
Stanhouse, Thomas, Drayman, Ann St.
Stanton, John, Porter, 219 King St.
Stapleton, C., Carpenter, Line St.
Starr, W. P., Clerk, Victoria Hotel
Steckley, John, Tavern Keeper, cr. St. Philip & Line Sts.
Steedman, James, Clerk, 250 King St., res. Vanderhorst
    St.
Steedman, Louisa, 12 Mazyck St.
Steedman, Sarah, 32 Calhoun St.
Steedman, T., Import Inspector, Custom House, res. cr.
    Coming & Cannon Sts.

Steedman, W. B., Accountant, 31 Hayne St., res.
    Vanderhorst St.
Steele, E. C., M. D., 64 Market St., res. 28 Bull St.
Steele, J. H., Clerk, 231 King St., res. 39 Coming St.
Steele, James, Billiard Table Keeper, cr. Elizabeth &
    Mary Sts.
Steele, W. N., Clerk, 266 King St., res. 39 Coming St.
Steele, Walter, Hatter, 231 King St., res. 3 Beaufain St.
Steen, Thomas, Proprietor, Merchants Hotel
Steiger, D., Grocer, Calhoun St., Ward 5
Steinke, F., Baker, 115 Church St.
Steinmeyer, J. F., Carpenter, Calhoun St.
Steinmeyer, J. H., Steam Saw Mills, Gadsden St., res.
    100 Beaufain St.
Steinmeyer, John, Laborer, 13 Smith St.
Stelling, E. H., Grocer, 29 King St.
Stelljes, P., Grocer, King St., Ward 6
Stemmermann, H., Grocer, 18 Bull St.
Stemmermann, A., Clerk, 18 Bull St.
Stephens, E. B., Newspaper & Periodical Agent, 5 Broad
    St., res. 300 King St.
Stephens, -----, Mrs., Dressmaker, 300 King St.
Sterling, -----, Grocer, 15 Market St., res. King St.
Stevens & Betts, Hardware, 80 East Bay St.
Stevens, Amelia, 5 Montague St.
Stevens, J. R., Clerk, 189 King St., res. 57 King St.
Stevens, James H., Teller, Planters & Mechanics Bank,
    res. Smith St., Ward 6
Stevens, Joel, Hardware, 80 East Bay St., res. 51 Tradd
    St.
Stevens, John, Cigar Maker, King St., Ward 6
Stevens, Judith, 67 Calhoun St.
Stevens, R., Mrs., 89 Wentworth St.
Stevens, William, 42 Tradd St.
Stevenson, W., Clerk, 25 Hayne St., res. King St.
Stewart, -----, 95 Church St.
Stewart, J., Mrs., 5 Greenhill St.
Stewart, James., Upholsterer, 161 King St.
Stewart, -----, Packer, 147 Meeting St., res. State St.
Stewart, R. L., Cashier, Bank of South Carolina, res. 3
    Smith St
Stewart, S., Drayman, St. Philip St., Ward 6.
Stewart, W. J., Printer, 28 Wall St.
Stillman, A. R., Clerk, cr. King & Market Sts., res. 2
    Mazyck St.
Stillman, -----, Deputy Boarding Officer, Custom House,
    res. 8 Horlbeck Alley
Stineback, A., Clerk, 145 Meeting St., res. 236 King St.
Stinemetz, M., Mrs., Jones Hotel, 65 Broad St.
Stock, J. Y, Ship & Commission Merchant, Atlantic
    Wharf, res. 11 Montague St.
Stock, N. B., Clerk, Atlantic Wharf, res. 11 Montague St.
Stocker, H., Clerk, 43 Wall St
Stocker, H. R., Grocer, cr. Market & Anson Sts.
Stocker, J. D., Clerk, 86 East Bay St., res. 59 Church St.
Stocker, J. J., Clerk, Central Wharf, res. 59 Church St.
Stocker, J. M., Wharfinger, Palmetto Wharf, res. 59
    Laurens St.
Stocking, D. S., Grain Dealer, Commercial Wharf, res.
    12 South Bay St.

Stockman, L., Mrs., Dry Goods, King St., Ward 6
Stoddard, E. B. & Co., Boot & Shoe Dealers, 165 Meeting St.
Stoddard, E. B., Boot & Shoe Dealer, 165 Meeting St., res. Charleston Hotel
Stoddard, H., Boot & Shoe Dealer, 45 Hayne St., res. Charleston Hotel
Stoddard, S. B., Clerk, 45 Hayne St., res. Charleston Hotel
Stohr, B., Clerk, 66 Market St.
Stokes, E. R., Bookbinder, 59 Broad St.
Stoll, C., Mrs., Ann St.
Stoll, H. C., Clerk, 304 King St., res. Ann St.
Stoll, J. C., Clerk, 304 King St., res. Ann St.
Stone, M., Miss, Mill St.
Stone, R. G., Crockery Dealer, 147 Meeting St., res. Coming St., Ward 6
Stoney, C. F., Dr., Druggist, 245 King St., res. 26 Hasell St.
Stoney, E., Mrs., 26 Hasell St.
Stoney, S. D., Clerk, Atlantic Wharf, res. 26 Hasell St.
Stoney, Theodore, Factor, Commercial Wharf, res. 36 Meeting St.
Stoppelleim, L. C., Carpenter, 29 Montague St.
Stoy, J. W., Bookseller, 258 King St.
Strainger, B., Gilder, 225 King St., res. Liberty St.
Stralford, T. G., Carpenter, 118 Wentworth St.
Stratton, W., Baker, 76 Market St.
Straus, James, Seaman, Ashley St.
Straus, M., Mrs., 68 Queen St.
Strawinski, F. T., Dancing School, 3 Broad St.
Streckfuss, J. F., Grocer, cr. Morris & St. Philip Sts.
Street, H. T. & Brother, Grocery Merchants, 64 East Bay St.
Street, H. T., Grocery Merchant, 64 East Bay St., res. 6 Society St.
Street, S. A., Grocery Merchant, 64 East Bay St., res. 3 Society St.
Street, Thaddeus, Commission Merchant, Boyce's Wharf, res. Hampstead St.
Strobel, B. M., Ship Grocer, 147 East Bay St., res. 249 East Bay St.
Strobel, D., Fireman, Sires St.
Strobel, D. H., Clerk, Adger's Wharf, cr. Liberty & St. Philip Sts.
Strobel, M. D., Teller, Bank of South Carolina, 3¾ Smith St.
Strobel, -----, Mrs., cr. Liberty & St. Philip St.
Strobel, R. H., cr. Rutledge & Bee Sts.
Strohecker, C. C., Clerk, 35 Hayne St., res. 9 Beaufain St.
Strohecker & Ewbank, Hardware, 155 Meeting St.
Strohecker, H. F., Hardware, 155 Meeting St.
Strohecker, H., Mrs., 81 Beaufain St.
Strohecker, J. P., Clerk, 155 Meeting St., res. 9 Beaufain St.
Strohecker, -----, Mrs., 9 Beaufain St.
Stromer, H. J., Mantuamaker, 11 West St.
Strong, C., Grocer, cr. Coming & Warren Sts.
Strong, George, Carpenter, Hampden Court

Stropps, George, Carpenter, 14 Beaufain St.
Strosse, George, Leather Dealer, King St., Ward 6
Stuart, Harper & Co., Commission Merchants, Atlantic Wharf, res. 5 Meeting St.
Stuart, J. P., Commission Merchant, Atlantic Wharf, res. 5 Meeting St.
Stuart, J. W., Attorney, St. Michael's Alley, res. Vanderhorst St.
Stuart, Samuel, Carpenter, 16 Rutledge St.
Stuffell, Henry, Carpenter, 10 Liberty St.
Stunkens, H., Tailor, 104 Queen St.
Sturges, J. T., Accountant, 29 Hayne St., res. Calhoun St.
Sturges, -----, Mrs., 26 South Bay St.
Suares & Co., Cabinet Markers, 284 King St.
Suares, B., Tailor, 13 Middle St.
Suares, J. E., Cabinet Maker, 284 King St., res. 293 King St.
Sullivan, H. W., Factor & Commission Merchant, Atlantic Wharf, res. cr. Church & Battery Sts.
Sullivan, M., Drayman, Linguard St.
Sullivan, M. T., Mrs., 72 Anson St.
Sullivan, Thomas, Shopkeeper, 22 State St.
Sullivan, Timothy, Pastor, 80 Broad St.
Summers, T. O., Rev., Editor, 15 Hasell St.
Sureau, F., Bootmaker, 9 St. Philip St.
Sussdorf & Leiding, Fancy Goods, 141 Meeting St.
Sussdorf, G., Fancy Goods, 141 Meeting St.
Sutcliffe, D., Mrs., Line St.
Sutters, T., Captain, Assistant Harbor Master, 89 East Bay St., res. 2 Friend St.
Sutton, A., Accountant, Central Wharf, res. Mansion House
Swain, R. W., Clerk, 253 King St., res. cr. King & Wentworth Sts.
Sweegan, E. F., Clerk, 120 East Bay St., res. 61 State St.
Sweegan, M., Grocer, 61 State St.
Sweeney, B., Private Boarding, 14 Market St.
Sweeney, James, Ship Carpenter, 76 Anson St.
Swicken, Thomas, Clerk, 244 King St.
Swinton, E. A., Carpenter, Meeting St., Ward 7
Swinton, M. C., Mrs., Meeting St., Ward 7
Swinton, Rebecca, Mantuamaker, 57 Anson St.
Swinton, W. H., Lumber Factor, west end of Montague St., res. 28 Montague St.
Syfan, Charles, Engineer, South Carolina Railroad, res. Spring St.
Sylvester, C., Clerk, 86 Meeting St.
Syme, T. P., Clerk, cr. King & Market Sts., res. Beaufain St.
Symmes, Thomas, Guardman, Hanover St.
Symmes, W. L., Accountant, Hanover St.
Symons, John, Rigger, 44 Tradd St.
Taber, T. G., Clerk, East Bay St. & Adger's Wharf, res. cr. Coming & Radcliffe Sts.
Taber, W. R., Teller, State Bank of South Carolina, res. cr. Coming & Radcliffe Sts.
Tackman, W., Clerk, cr. Church & Tradd Sts.
Tackman, William, Clerk, cr. Church & Tradd Sts.
Taft, A. R., Commission Merchant, 141 East Bay St., res.

29 Laurens St.
Taft, David, Clerk, 141 Meeting St., res. King St.
Tager, H., Grocer, 32 Pitt St.
Tagliorani, A., Fruiterer, 75 Market St., res. Linguard St.
Tamplet, C. D., Clerk, 39 Hayne St., res. 11 Hasell St.
Tannlunson, A., Upholsterer, 160 King St.
Tarr, F., Grocer, 146 East Bay St.
Tarr, J. B., Grocer, 146 East Bay St.
Tatan, C., Clerk, cr. King & Markets Sts., res. Tradd St.
Taveau, A. L., Attorney, 20 Broad St., res. 20 Rutledge St.
Tavel, R. A., Boarding Officer, Mercury & Courier, res. Pritchard St.
Taylor, A., Mrs., 6 King St.
Taylor, Charlotte, Coming St., Ward 6
Taylor, George, Seaman, 3 Motte's Lane
Taylor, H. R., Miss, 30 Tradd St.
Taylor, Isaac, Tailor, 41 Society St., res. 30 Society St.
Taylor, Isabella, Nassau St.
Taylor, J. H. & Co., Auctioneers & Commission Merchants, 17 Vendue Range
Taylor, J. H., Auctioneer & Commission Merchant, 17 Vendue Range, res. 26 Society St.
Taylor, J. M., Fancy Goods & Military Dealer, 225 King St.
Taylor, James, Painter, 209 East Bay St.
Taylor, Joseph, Conductor, South Carolina Railroad, res. 43 St. Philip St.
Taylor, M., Laborer, Mary St.
Taylor, M., Mrs., Spring St.
Taylor, M. S., Mrs., 6 Lamboll St.
Taylor, -----, Mrs., 117 Queen St.
Taylor, O., Dry Goods, 243 King St., res. 249 King St.
Taylor, T. B., Accountant, 243 King St., res. 297 King St.
Taylor, T. R., Boot & Shoe Dealer, 241 King St.
Taylor, Thomas, Clerk, 179 King St.
Taylor, W. M., Factor, 13 Southern Wharf, res. 58 Meeting St.
Teadsdale, E., Mrs., 8 Liberty St.
Teague, J. N., Clerk, 14 Hayne St., res. King St., Ward 7
Teap, M., Miss, Milliner, 166 King St.
Teasdale, R., Import Inspector, Custom House, res. Wragg's Square
Teber, W. R., Attorney, St. Michael's Alley, res. Coming St.
Tenbert, -----, Clerk, 104 East Bay St.
Tenhet, Isabella, Mrs., 7 Minority St.
Tennent, J. S., Bookkeeper, Planters & Mechanics Bank, res. 60 Anson St.
Tennent, William, Brick Burner, Cooper River, res. 60 Anson St.
Tennett, J. B., Hardware Dealer, 35 Hayne St., res. South Bay St.
Tenny, D. G., Lace Dealer, 237 King St., res. 236 King St.
Teppe, A., Clerk, 343 King St., res. St. Philip St., Ward 6
Teppe, F., Clerk, 338 King St., res. St. Philip St., Ward 6
Teppe, W., Constable, res. St. Philip St., Ward 6
Terry, J., Tavern Keeper, 28 Market St.

Terry, Silas, Carpenter, 60 Meeting St.
Terry, William, Joiner, Longitude Lane
Tessier, E. L., Inspector, Commercial Insurance Company
Tessier, E., Sea Captain, 48½ Coming St.
Thackam, F., Carpenter, Spring St.
Thackam, F., Clerk, Sires St.
Thames, J. E., Clerk, 248 King St., res. 48 Calhoun St.
Tharin, E. C., Auctioneer & Commission Merchant, 24 Vendue Range, res. America St.
Thayer, E., Fancy Goods, 149 Meeting St., res. Charleston Hotel
Thayer, Eben, Teacher, Free School, 20 Mazyck St.
Thayer, T. H., Exchange Broker, 18 Broad St., res. 76 Broad St.
Thayer, T. H., Jr., Clerk, Post Office, res. 43 East Bay St.
Thayer, T. W., Accountant, 37 Hayne St., res. 236 King St.
Thayer, William, Accountant, Boyce & Co. Wharf, res. 61 Beaufain St.
Thee, J. H., Amherst St.
Thees, Henry, Clerk, cr. East Bay & Elliott Sts., res. 18 Tradd St.
Therears, Carew, 10 Coming St.
Therling, F., Bootmaker, 325 King St.
Thiele, E., Tailor, 17 Queen St.
Thierman & Pringle, Commission Merchants, Adger's Wharf
Thierman, Herman, Commission Merchant, Adger's Wharf, res. Broad St.
Thomas, J. M., Carpenter, Woolf St.
Thomas, S., Accountant, 165 Meeting St., res. 9 Wentworth St.
Thomas, S. J., Collector, 48 Broad St.
Thomas, William, Clerk, Merchants Hotel
Thomas, William, Stone Cutter, 76 Tradd St.
Thomee, John, Tailor, King St., Ward 6, res. Cannon St.
Thomlinson, R., Saddler, 157 Meeting St., res. 16 Liberty St.
Thompson, E. H., Accountant, 141 Meeting St., res. Church St.
Thompson, F., Saddler, cr. Broad & Church Sts., res. Church St.
Thompson, George, Bricklayer & Contractor, 10 Glebe St.
Thompson, H., Mrs., 1 Bull St.
Thompson, Henry, Clerk, Bedons Alley
Thompson, J. M., Clerk, 253 King St., res. cr. King & Wentworth Sts.
Thompson, J. P., Printer, 113 Broad St.
Thompson, James, Spindle Worker, Line St.
Thompson, John, Seed Store, 264 King St.
Thompson, N., Painter, 126 King St.
Thompson, T., Bootmaker, 87 Church St.
Thompson, Theo, Sea Captain 89½ East Bay St.
Thompson, Thomas, Bootmaker, 144 East Bay St.
Thompson, Thomas, Finisher, King St., Ward 8
Thompson, William, Mason, 18 Wentworth St.
Thompson. W. B., 44 Tradd St.
Thornly, George, Engineer, 28 Mazyck St.

Threadcraffe, Joseph, 1 Savage St.
Thrower, C., Mrs., 27 Beaufain St.
Thurston, E. N., Accountant, cr. Vanderhorst's Wharf & East Bay St., res. 45 Anson St.
Tibbets, A., Mrs., 48 George St.
Tiedeman, J. F., Clerk, 18 Tradd St.
Tiedeman, O., Grocer, cr. Calhoun & Washington Sts.
Tiedeman, William, Clerk, Coming St., Ward 6
Tierney, J., Coach Driver, 102 Church St.
Tierney, James, Laborer, 1 Philadelphia St.
Tietyen, J. H., Cannon St.
Tilton, E. M., Engineer, 24 Pinckney St.
Tilton, N. O., Engineer, 24 Pinckney St.
Tilton, R., Mrs., Private Boarding, 24 Pinckney St.
Tilton, W. C., Clerk, cr. Cumberland & Meeting Sts., res. 24 Pinckney St.
Timmashank, J., Grocer, 178 East Bay St.
Timmerman, H., Watchmaker, 31 Tradd St.
Timmons, F. R., M. D., 4 Smith's Lane
Timmons, G. C., 51 Broad St.
Timmons, J. R., 4 Smith's Lane
Timmons, W. L., Hardware Dealer, 153 East Bay St., res. 13 Wentworth St.
Tinbrook, Emily, Miss, Berresford St.
Tincken, Henry Tailor, 18 Tradd St.
Tincken, John, Grist Mill, America St.
Tinin, Martin, Laborer, St. Philip St., Ward 6
Tinkman, -----, Miss, 32 Wentworth St.
Tinsly, Samuel, Seaman, Reid St.
Tinsly, Thomas, Molder, Reid St.
Tisman, C., Mary St.
Tityen, Henry, Clerk, cr. King & Mary Sts.
Tobias, A. & Sons, Commission Merchants, 86 East Bay St.
Tobias, A., Commission Merchant, 86 East Bay St., res. 96 Wentworth St.
Tobias, A. L., Secretary, South Carolina Insurance Company, 109 East Bay St., res. 26 Church Tobias, C. H., Attorney, 26 Hayne St., res. 26 Church St.
Tobias, Isaac, 26 Church St.
Tobias, J. L., Commission Merchant, 86 East Bay St., res. 96 Wentworth St.
Tobias, T. J., Commission Merchant, 86 East Bay St., res. 96 Wentworth St.
Tobias, V. J., Attorney, Broad St., res. 26 Church St.
Tobin, J., Clerk, 78 Church St., res. 195 East Bay St.
Tobin, Richard, Clerk, 29 Church St., res. 195 East Bay St.
Tobin, Richard, Farmer, Amherst St.
Tomas, W., Seaman, Bedons Alley
Tomates, E., Painter, 49 Queen St.
Tomlinson, F. F., Clerk, 133 Meeting St.
Tomlinson, J., Clerk, 41 Hayne St.
Tonchone, Julia, Calhoun St., Ward 6
Tonhey, Maurice, Bootmaker, 17 Queen St.
Toomer, A., Mrs., 57 Calhoun St.
Toomer, H., Miss, Judith St.
Toomer, H. P., Bricklayer, 57 Calhoun St.
Toomer, H. V., M. D., Chapel St.
Toomer, Lawrence, Planter, Ashepoo, res. Thomas St.

Toomer, Robert, Painter, 80 Wentworth St.
Torlay, E., Mrs., 27 Beaufain St.
Torlay, Joseph, Planter, Meeting St., Ward 5
Torn, J. G., Spinner, America St.
Torre, P. D., Attorney, 48 Broad St., res. 117 Broad St.
Torrent, John, Rigger, 10 Prichard St.
Torrey, A., Miss, 8 New St.
Torrington, M., Mrs., 23 Tradd St.
Toussiger, E., Mrs., 20 Water St.
Townsends, Crane & Co., Dry Goods, 1 Hayne St.
Toy, Joseph, Drayman, Amherst St.
Tracey, Maurice, Printer, 30 Tradd St.
Trapier, M. E., Miss, 6 Logan St.
Trapier, Paul, Rev., Pastor, Calvary Church, res. 37 Meeting St.
Trapman, L. & Co., Commission Merchants, 20 East Bay St.
Trapman, L., Commission Merchant, 20 East Bay St.
Trenholm, C. L., Commission Merchant, Fitzsimons' Wharf, res. 18 Smith St.
Trenholm, E. L., Commission Merchant, Central Wharf, res. Liverpool
Trenholm, G. A., Commission Merchant, Central Wharf, Rutledge St., Ward 6
Trescot, C. F., Sea Captain, Archdale St.
Trescot, Henry, Cashier, State Bank, res. 4 Anson St.
Triest, Maier, Clerk, Southern Wharf, res. Market St.
Trist, J., Clothier, 87 Market St.
Trobblefield, John, Carpenter, Spring St.
Trott, A. W., Clerk, 131 Meeting St., res. 79 King St.
Trott, C. Y., Mrs., 35 Tradd St.
Trott, E. M., Mrs., 71 King St.
Trott, T. C., Clerk, Mercury Office, King St.
Trou, A. W., Jeweller & Engraver, 187 King St.
Trout & DeLange, Commission Merchants, 112 East Bay St.
Trout, T. B. Commission Merchant, 112 East Bay St.
Trout, Thomas, Commission Merchants, 112 East Bay St., res. cr. Pitt & Wentworth St.
Trout, W., 76 Beaufain St.
Troy, Thomas, Watchman, President St.
Trumbo, C. C., Bricklayer, 55 Tradd St.
Tucker, John, Planter, Cooper St.
Tucker, R. H., Commission & Ship Merchant, Boyce's Wharf
Tuesdale, F., Mrs., 20 Bull St.
Tully, Thomas, Calhoun St., Ward 5
Tupp, C., Clerk, 180 King St.
Tupper, F., Clerk, 52 Tradd St.
Tupper, James, Master in Equity, 52 Broad St.
Tupper, S. Y., Commission Merchant, Brown's Wharf, res. 60 Church St.
Tupper, T. & Son, Commission Merchants, Brown's Wharf
Tupper, T., Commission Brown's Wharf, res. 52 Tradd St.
Tupper, T., Jr., Accountant, Brown's Wharf, res. 52 Tradd St.
Turly, M. A., Mrs., 15 Franklin St.
Turnbull, A., Mrs., 15 Calhoun St.

Turnbull, Andrew, 14 Meeting St.
Turnbull, R., Mrs., 1 Logan St.
Turnbull, W. O., Clerk, 279 King St., res. Hasell St.
Turner, Richard, Tallow Chandler, Woolf St.
Turner, S., Mrs., 27 Archdale St.
Turns, Peter, Shoemaker, St. Philip St., Ward 6
Tutley, William, Carpenter, 16 Rutledge St.
Tweed, -----, Mrs., Teacher, Charlotte St.
Tweedy, W. H., Clerk, 1 Hayne St., res. King St.
Twohill, Daniel, Police Officer, cr. Anson & Hasell Sts.
Tylee, C. A., Clerk, 103 East Bay St., res. 34 Chalmers
St.
Tylee, J. W. L., Clerk, 103 East Bay St., res. 34
Chalmers St.
Tylee, N., Jr., Clerk, foot of Hasell St., res. 34 Chalmers
St.
Tylee, N., Ship Chandler & Wire Manufacturer, 123 East
Bay St., res. 34 Chalmers St.
Tyrrell, J. M., Clerk, 80 East Bay St., res. 155 East Bay
St.
Ufferhardt & Campson, Dry Goods, 140 King St.
Ufferhardt, William, Dry Goods, 140 King St.
Uivhlen, D., Grocer, cr. Tradd & Church Sts.
Ulmo, P. H., Master, Work House, 24 Pitt St.
Utes, John, Printer, 115 King St.
Vaerfelder, S., Bootmaker, 73 Meeting St.
Valentine, S., 42 Society St.
Vanderhorst, Elias, Planter, Ashepoo, res. Chapel St.
Vanderhorst, Martha, Pastry Cook, 117 King St.
Vanderzee, H., Dry Goods, 41 Hayne St., res. Charleston
Hotel
VanDyck, John, Clerk, 39 Hayne St.
VanNess, Joel S., Clerk, 80 East Bay St., res. 51 Tradd
St.
Vannogle, J. A., Clerk, 149 Meeting St.
Vannoy, J. H., Clerk, 118 Meeting St., res. 356 King St.
Vanwinkle, Hardware, 308 King St., res. 63 Coming St.
Varner, Charles, 28 Mazyck St.
Venning, D. B., Student, 16 Society St.
Venning, H. M., Lumber Factor, Gadsden's Wharf, res.
16 Society St.
Venning, J. L., Clerk, 6 Savage St.
Venning, J. M., Factor & Commission Merchant,
Gadsden's Wharf, res. Charlotte St.
Venning, W. C., Clerk, Gadsden's Wharf, res. Charlotte
St.
Vente, Eugene, M. D., 15 Beaufain St.
Vente, -----, Vice Consul, 30 Broad St.
Verea, Robert, 20 Water St.
Veree, John, Carpenter, 6 Pitt St.
Vernon, Henry, Carpenter, cr. Cannon & Ashley Sts.
Vernon, M., Mrs., Cannon & Ashley Sts.
Veronee, G. H., Tinsmith, cr. State & Linguard Sts.
Veronee, Samuel, Proprietor of Drays, Meeting St., Ward
7
Veronee, T. W., Clerk, Adger's Wharf, res. Meeting St.,
Ward 7
Veronee, W. B., Tinsmith, cr. State & Linguard Sts.
Veronee, W., Tinsmith, cr. State & Linguard Sts.
Vial, Joseph, Fruiterer, 102 King St.

Vidall, Lewis, Jr., Clerk, 3 Minority St.
Vidall, Lewis, Sea Captain, 3 Minority St.
Villepigue, P. A., Clerk, Accommodation Wharf, res. 4
College St.
Villepigue, P. T., Factor & Commission Merchant,
Accommodation Wharf, res. 4 College St.
Vincent, Hugh, Ship Chandler, 75 East Bay St.
Vincent, J. C., Clerk, 1 Hayne St., res. East Bay St.
Vincent, J. W., Clerk, 69 East Bay Co.
Vincent, W. J., Clerk, 24 Hayne St.
Vocelle, A., Gunsmith, 50 State St.
Vogartank, G., Gadsden St.
Voight, Charles, Bootmaker, 83 King St.
Volarse, L., Upholsterer, 161 King St.
Volger, Bernard, Cigar Manufacturer, 345 King St.
Von Dohlen & Farnum, Grocery Merchants, 189 East
Bay St.
Von Dohlen, A., Grocer, 46 State St., res. 88 Anson St.
Von Dohlen, C., Grocery Merchant, 189 East Bay St.,
res. Pavilion Hotel
Von Glahn, B., Clerk, 230 King St.
Von Glahn, C., Grocer, cr. Coming & Radcliffe Sts.
Von Glahn, H., Grocer, Columbus St.
Von Glahn, M., Grocer, 1 Coming St.
Von Kolnitz, H., Guardman, cr. St. Philip & Cannon Sts.
Von Santen, F., Clerk, 208 King St.
Voorhies, M., Mrs., 8 Orange St.
Vop Ronne, John, Clerk, 134 King St.
Vose, Carson, Planter, Goose Creek, res. Rutledge St.,
Ward 6
Waggener, F., Clerk, 37 Market St.
Wagner, E., Planter, Christ Church Parish, res. 1 Wall St.
Wagner, Edward, Pastor, Holy Communion, Coming St.,
Ward 6
Wagner, G., Mrs., Coming St., Ward 6
Wagner, G. O., Private Boarding, 159 King St.
Wagner, K. R., Clerk, 19 Vendue Range, res. Coming
St., Ward 6
Wagner, S. J., Storekeeper, Custom House, res. 114
Queen St.
Wagner, T. D., Commission Merchant, Central Wharf,
res. 1 Wall St.
Walcutt, J., Clerk, 129 Church St., res. King St.
Waldron, G. Z. & Co., Clothing, 27 Hayne St.
Waldron, G. Z., Clothing, 27 Hayne St., res. Charleston
Hotel
Walker & Duffus, Cotton Press, Dewees' Wharf
Walker & James, Book Publishers, 103 & 105 East Bay
St.
Walker, & Seabrook, Attorneys, 61 Meeting St.
Walker, Ann, Mrs., 15 Wall St.
Walker, D. A., Marble Cutter, 4 Anson St.
Walker, E. J., Clerk, 194 East Bay St., res. Pitt St.
Walker, G. W., Grocery Merchant, 56 East Bay St., res.
Rutledge St., Ward 6
Walker, George, Architect, 32 Broad St., res. 13 Logan
St.
Walker, H. D., Carpenter, 2 Wilson St., res. 18 Magazine
St.
Walker, H. P., Attorney, 32 Broad St., res. 4 Tradd St.

Walker, J. C., Clerk, 101 East Bay St., res. 155 East Bay St.

Walker, J., Commission Merchant, 28 Vendue Range, res. King St.

Walker, J. F., Accountant, Boyce's Wharf, res. Rutledge St., Ward 6

Walker, J. M., Attorney, 32 Broad St., 4 Council St.

Walker, John, Blacksmith, Market St., res. 100 King St.

Walker, John, Butcher, Coming St.

Walker, Joseph, Stationer, 101 East Bay St., res. 5 Hasell St.

Walker, R. T., Factor & Commission Merchant, Boyce's Wharf, res. 259 East Bay St.

Walker, Sarah, 14 St. Philip St.

Walker, W. H., Cotton Press, Dewees' Wharf, res. 4 Council St.

Walker, W. S. & Brother, Marble Cutters, 4 Anson St.

Walker, W. S., Marble Cutter, 4 Anson St.

Walker, William, Engineer, South Carolina Railroad, res. Nassau St.

Walkinshedd, William, Saddler, 4 Magazine St.

Wall, E. P., Tailor, 28 St. Philip St.

Wallace, H., Grocer, 67 Tradd St.

Wallace, London, Painter, 10 St. Philip St.

Wallace, R. A., Baker, cr. King & Tradd Sts.

Wallace, Thomas, Dry Goods, 288 King St., res. 318 King St.

Wallen, M., Clerk, Hayne St., res. Market St.

Wallers, J. H., Tavern Keeper, Meeting St., Ward 7

Wallis, E., Bootmaker, 41 State St.

Walseman & Reincke, Tailors, 191 King St.

Walseman, William, Tailor, 191 King St.

Walsh, Patrick, Clerk, 35 Hayne St., res. Market St.

Walters & Walker, Factors & Commission Merchants, Boyce's Wharf

Walters, E., Mrs., 94 Wentworth St.

Walters, E. W., Factor & Commission Merchant, Boyce's Wharf, res. Woolf & Meeting Sts.

Walters, G. H., Factor & Commission Merchant, Boyce's Wharf, res. Woolf & Meeting Sts.

Walters, W., Clerk, King St., res. 106 Church St.

Walton, J. M., Boot & Shoe Dealer, 137 Meeting St., res. 79 Wentworth St.

Wanicker, H., Carpenter, Woolf St.

Ward, H. A., 24 George St.

Ward, J. J., Clerk, 215 King St.

Ward, John, Wharfinger, Adger's Wharf, res. 25 Pitt St.

Ward, M. M., Mrs., 19 Geroge St.

Ward, M. S., Miss, 24 Smith St.

Ward, S. A., Miss, 24 Smith St.

Wardell, S., Mrs., Vanderhorst St.

Wardlaw, W. A., Factor & Commission Merchant, Atlantic Wharf, res. Charleston Hotel

Warem, John, Sail Maker, 11 Tradd St.

Waring, H. S., M. D., 57 Meeting St.

Waring, J. B., Planter, St. John's Parish, res. Charlotte St.

Waring, M. A., Planter, St. Paul's Parish, res. St. Philip St.

Waring, P. H., Medical Student, 10 Gadsden's Wharf

Waring, P. H., Planter, St. Paul's Parish, 10 Gadsden's Wharf

Waring, T. R., Cashier, Bank of the State of South Carolina, res. Cannon St.

Waring, T. S., Medical Student, 10 Gadsden's Wharf

Waring, Theo, Mason, 5 Gadsden's Wharf

Warn, A., 5 West St.

Warnes, Thomas, Spring St.

Warnkerr, J., Accountant, 139 East Bay St.

Warpken, H. G., Bootmaker, Sires St.

Warren B. W., Clerk, 29 Hayne St., res. 10 Calhoun St.

Warren, C., Seaman, 86 Meeting St.

Warton, George, Brick Layer, America St.

Washington, Maria, Radcliffe St.

Wasting, Lydia, Henrietta St.

Waterbury, W. C., Police Officer, cr. Cumberland & Meeting Sts.

Waterman, C., Clerk, 87 King St.

Waterman, C., Grocer, 63 Market St.

Waterman, John, Grocer, cr. Meeting & Mary Sts.

Waters, A. B., Druggist, 17 Calhoun St.

Waters, W. F., Clerk, 37 Broad St., res. 6 Pinckney St.

Waters, William, Clerk, Market St., res. 6 Pinckney St.

Waties, J. P., Import Inspector, Custom House

Waties, T. D., Clerk, Central Wharf, cr. Vanderhorst & Pitt Sts.

Watkins, C. W., Overseer, Sires St.

Watson, Alex, Private Boarding, 19 Tradd St.

Watson, Thomas, Sea Captain, 5 Atlantic St.

Wattles, J. M., Glass Stainer, 186 King St.

Watts, -----, Mrs. & Miss Smith, Milliners, 196 King St.

Wayne, D. G., Carpenter, St. Philip St., Ward 6

Wear, John, Cordwainer, 45 Meeting St.

Weaver, A., Fruiterer, 346 King St.

Webb & Rice, Shipping Masters, 85 East Bay St.

Webb, D. C., Clerk, 40 East Bay St.

Webb, Michael, Shipping Master, 85 East Bay St., res. 8 Water St.

Webb, T. L., Factor & Commission Merchant, Commercial Wharf, res. Cannon St.

Webb, W., Gamer, 40 King St.

Webb, W. L., Clerk, Comercial Wharf, res. cr. Cannon & Rutledge Sts.

Webb, W. R., Mechanic, 132 East Bay St., res. 14 Middle St.

Webb, Warren R., Clerk, 155 East Bay St., res. Commercial Hotel

Weber, C., Clerk, Adger's Wharf, res. East Bay St.

Weber, F., Bootmaker, cr. King & Ann Sts.

Weber, George, Tavern Keeper, Mary St.

Weber, J., Ship Joiner, Washington & Laurens Sts.

Weber, John, Bootmaker, 119 King St.

Weber, P., Tavern Keeper, 33 Queen St.

Wedejerner, F., Carter, 32 Bull St.

Wedow, Jacob, Guardman, St. Philip St., Ward 8

Weed, Alfred, Engineer, South Carolina Railroad, res. Coming St., Ward 6

Weed, J. B., Clerk, 164 Meeting St., res. 249 King St.

Weelholz, J. P., Clothing, 133 East Bay St.

Weens, N., Laborer, Morris St.

Wehlert, J. C., Grocer, cr. Coming & Duncan Sts.

Wehman, F., Grocer, 135 King St.
Weinberg, B., Dry Goods, Market St.
Weiskopf, L., Painter, 30 Beaufain St.
Welch, John, Jr., Carpenter, Mary St.
Welch, John, Mary St.
Welch, M. C., Clerk, 147 Meeting St., Hampden Court
Welch, Michael, Laborer, 8 Philadelphia St.
Welch, R. M., Gentleman's Furnishing Store, cr. Meeting & Market Sts., res. Charleston Hotel
Welch, S. B., Bookbinder, 101 Meeting St., res. 9 Smith's Lane
Welch, W. H., Bookbinder, 101 Meeting St., res. 1 St. Philip St.
Welch, William, Finisher, Mary St.
Welden, John, Laborer, Warren St.
Welelkin, John, Laborer, Coming St., Ward 8
Weller, C., Saddler, Church St.
Wellin, Ed, Carpenter, Beaufain St.
Wellin, Samuel, Beaufain St.
Wells, Hagar, Alexander St.
Wells, Robert, Carpenter, 186 Meeting St.
Wells, W. B., Clerk, cr. King & Market Sts., res. 204 King St.
Welsman, J. T., Commission Merchant, 165 East Bay St., res. 16 Church St.
Welsman, James, Ship & Commission Merchant, Boyce's Wharf, res. 2 Church St.
Wemann, F., Clerk, 18 Queen St., res. King St.
Wendelken, H., Grocer, cr. Hanover & Columbus St.
Wendelken, M. H., Grocer, 8 Wall St.
Wenning, W. L., Planter, Alexander St.
Werneka, C., Overseer, Spring St.
Werner, C., Iron Foundry, cr. Cumberland & State Sts., res. 43 State St.
Werner, H., Grocer, 42 Queen St.
Werson, L., Sculptor, King St., Ward 8
West, C. H. & Son, Ship Chandlers, 77 East Bay St.
West, C. H., Jr., Ship & Commission Merchant, Boyce's Wharf, res. 3 Church St.
West, C. H., Ship Chandler, 77 East Bay St., res. 3 Church St.
West, E. A., Ship Chandler, 77 East Bay St., res. 3 Church St.
West, E. C., Mrs., Proprietor, Victoria Hotel
West, Preston, Livery Stables, 85 Meeting St., res. 97 Queen St.
Westendorff, C. P. L., Anson St.
Westendorff, C. W., Sea Captain, 8 Anson St.
Westendorff, J. S., Clerk, Meeting St., res. 8 Anson St.
Westman, G., Grocer, 311 King St.
Weston, A., Millwright, Calhoun St.
Weston, F., Planter, Pee Dee, res. Drake St.
Weston, J., Tailor, 100 Queen St., res. 1 Green St.
Weston, S. & J., Tailors, 100 Queen St.
Weston, S., Tailor, 100 Queen St.
Westurland, C. F., Sea Captain, 6 Savage St.
Wetherhahn, M., Clothing, 19 Market St.
Wetherhahn, P., Clerk, 208 King St., res. 19 Market St.
Wever, A. A., Tavern Keeper, 51 Broad St.
Weyman, A. C., Mrs., 63 Beaufain St.

Whaley, B. F., Attorney, 20 Broad St., res. 9 George St.
Whaley, W., Attorney, 20 Broad St., res. 19 Rutledge St.
Wharton & Petsch, Car Builders, Line St.
Wharton, Thomas, Car Builder, Line & Woolf Sts.
Whelen, A., Mrs., 15 Clifford St.
Whilden, B. F., Clerk, Vanderhorst's Wharf, res. cr. Meeting & Queen Sts.
Whilden, James, Ship Chandler, 60½ East Bay St., res. 16 Magazine St.
Whilden, -----, Mrs., Private Boarding, cr. Meeting & Queen St.
Whilden, Robert, Engineer, 7 Archdale St.
Whilden, W., Clerk, 56 East Bay St., res. Washington St.
Whilden, W. G., Clerk, 250 King St., res. Beaufain St.
Whilden, W. H., Clerk, 338 King St., res. 7 Archdale St.
Whitaker, E., 3 St. Michael's Alley
Whitaker, M., Mrs., St. Philip St., Ward 6
White, A. J., Broker & Auctioneer, 27 Broad St., res. cr. Tradd & Meeting Sts.
White, B. O. A., M. D., 24 Legare St.
White, C. G., M. D., 19 State St.
White, C. O., Commission Merchant, 92 East Bay St.
White, Charles, Steamboat Captain, 58 Queen St.
White, E. B., Architect, Civil Engineer & Surveyor, 122 East Bay St., res. 42 Meeting St.
White, George, Planter, Christ Church Parish, res. 271 East Bay St.
White, I. D., Clerk, Central Wharf, res. 26 Savage St.
White, J. B., Coastwise Inspector, Custom House, res. 21 Legare St.
White, J. H., Factor, Atlantic Wharf, res. Mansion House
White, James, Tavern Keeper, 280 King St., res. 13 Rutledge St.
White, John, Confectioner, 356 King St.
White, John, Marble Yard, 117 Queen St.
White, Joseph, Jr., Confectioner, 356 King St.
White, Joseph, Sr., Confectioner, 356 King St.
White, Maria, 21 College St.
White, P., Mrs., Shopkeeper, 16 Friend St.
White, Robert, Furniture Dealer, 342 King St.
White, Sims, 26 Savage St.
White, Susan, 12 Mazyck St.
White, W. F., Confectioner, 356 King St.
White, W. J., Assistant, Bennett's Rice Mill, res. 3 Wentworth St.
White, W. M., Clerk, 120 East Bay St., res. Liberty St.
White, W. R., Clerk, 243 King St., res. Wentworth St.
White, W. W., Clerk, Southern Wharf, res. 26 Savage St.
Whitemore, C., Soap & Candle Manufacturer, Radcliffe St.
Whitemore, -----, Mrs., Private Boarding, 58 Meeting St.
Whiting, E. M., Turner, Calhoun St., Ward 5
Whiting, W., Carpenter, 116 Church St.
Whitney, C. G., Broker & Auctioneer, 3 State St., res. 5 Franklin St.
Whitney, F. H., Soap & Candle Manufacturer, cr. Meeting & Reid Sts.
Whitney, J., Clerk, 26 Hayne St., res. 58 Meeting St.
Whitney, O. L., Clerk, 301 King St., res. 10 Smith's Lane
Whitney, T. A., Broker & Commission Agent, Franklin

St.
Whittier, S., Accountant, 151 Meeting St.
Wickenburg, F. R., grocer, cr. Broad & Church Sts.
Wiech, Henry, Printer, Calhoun St.
Wienges, C., Clerk, Exchange St., res. 12 Water St.
Wienges, E., Fireman, cr. Columbus & Nassau Sts.
Wienges, G. W., Bookseller, opposite Post Office, res. John St.
Wienges, George, Guardman, Columbus St.
Wienges, J. J., Cotton Dresser, Columbus St.
Wienges, Jacob, 17 Montague St.
Wieters, F., Clerk, 63 Market St.
Wightington, P., Rags Store, 34 Mazyck St.
Wightman, J. H., Painter, 85 Tradd St.
Wightman, J. T., 96 Meeting St.
Wightman, -----, Mrs., 32 Chalmers St.
Wightman, William, Editor, Southern Christian Advocate, Meeting St., Ward 5
Wilbur, T. A., Clerk, 21 Vendue Range, res. 115 Wentworth St.
Wilbur, W. G., Gamer, Charleston Hotel
Wilbur, W. W., Auctioneer & Commission Merchant, 301 King St., res. 115 Wentworth St.
Wild, B., Boiler Maker, 2 Inspection St.
Wilder, J. M., Clerk, 277 King St.
Wilder, T. D., Clerk, 153 East Bay St., res. 20 Savage St.
Wiley, A. S., M. D., Meeting St., res. 269 King St.
Wiley, Banks & Co., Dry Goods, 41 Hayne St.
Wiley, James, Crockery, 375 King St.
Wiley, M., Mrs., 14 Atlantic St.
Wiley, Samuel, Grocer, 361 King St.
Wiley, W. J., Clerk, 361 King St., res. 16 Green St.
Wilkening, J. H., Grocer, 57 Market St.
Wilkens, G. M., Student, 11 Lamboll St.
Wilkens, M. L., Student, 11 Lamboll St.
Wilkens, -----, Mrs., 11 Lamboll St.
Wilkie, G. W., Import Inspector, Custom House, res. 14 Horlbeck Alley
Wilkie, J. G., Clerk, 27 Broad St., res. 14 Horlbeck Alley
Wilkie, O., Clerk, 25 Vendue Range, res. 8 Liberty St.
Wilkie, W. B., Mrs., 8 Liberty St.
Wilkinson, E., Trader, Coming St., Ward 6
Wilkinson, Francis, Buthcer, Coming St., Ward 6
Wilkinson, J. W., Attorney, 7 Broad St., res. 16 East Bay St.
Wilkinson, P. O., Fireman, Coming St., Ward 8
Wilks, C. H., Factor, Vanderhorst's Wharf, res. 13 Meeting St.
Wilks, J. M., Bootmaker, 55 Broad St.
Wilks, John, Planter, St. Andrew's Parish, res. 13 Meeting St.
Wille, S., Fancy Goods, 208 King St.
William, Paris, Barber, 11 Society St.
Williams & Butler, Commission Merchants, 84 East Bay St.
Williams, C., Mrs., 19 Beaufain St.
Williams, D., Mrs., 52 Beaufain St.
Williams, Daniel, Clerk, 33 Market St.
Williams, E. H., Clerk, Central Wharf
Williams, G. P., Seedman & Florist, 331 King St.

Williams, H. H. & Co., Hat & Cap Dealers, 159 Meeting St.
Williams, H. H., Hat & Cap Dealer, 159 Meeting St., res. 1 Liberty St.
Williams, Henry, Clerk, 20 Vendue Range, res. 52 Beaufain St.
Williams, Henry, Proprietor of Drays, King St., Ward 6
Williams, J., Mrs., cr. Ashley & Spring Sts.
Williams, J., Mrs., Spring St.
Williams, J., Steward, 66 Meeting St.
Williams, J. W., Clerk, 28 Vendue Range, res. 52 Beaufain St.
Williams, John, Commission Merchant, 84 East Bay St., res. Baltimore
Williams, Mary, Smith St., Ward 6
Williams, Samuel K., Printer, King St., Ward 6
Williams, W. B., Factor, Central Wharf, res. 275 East Bay St.
Williams, W. S., Clerk, 1 Hayne St., res. 32 Pinckney St.
Williamson, -----, Captain, Smith St., Ward 6
Williamson, John, Broker & Auctioneer, Coming St., Ward 6
Williamson, -----, Mrs., Rutledge St., Ward 6
Williman, A. B., M. D., 70 Church St.
Williman, C., Accountant, 71 East Bay St., res. 70 Tradd St.
Williman, J., Attorney, St. Michael's Alley, res. 43 East Bay St.
Williman, Jacob, Clerk, Court House, res. East Bay St.
Williman, -----, Mrs., Calhoun St., Ward 6
Willington, A. S. & Co., Proprietor, Courier
Willington, A. S., Editor, Courier, res. New St.
Willis, B. G., Clerk, 265 King St., res. 269 King St.
Willis, Henry, Broker & Auctioneer, 50 Broad St., res. Queen St.
Willis, John G., Boot & Shoe Dealer, 182 King St.
Wills, J. W., Clerk, 21 Hayne St.
Wilmans & Price, Hardware Dealers, 24 Hayne St.
Wilmans, A. F., Hardware Dealer, 24 Hayne St., res. 6 Hasell St.
Wilson, A. B., Planter, St. George's, res. St. Philip St., Ward 6
Wilson, Abram, Planter, St. Paul's Parish, res. 21 Montague St.
Wilson, Angus, Teacher, 90 Wentworth St.
Wilson, E., Mrs., 90 Wentworth St.
Wilson, E., Mrs., Dress Maker, 46 Society St.
Wilson, F. S., Mrs., Thomas St.
Wilson, George, Bootmaker, 31 Wentworth St.
Wilson, George, Bootmaker, 7 Burns Lane
Wilson, Hugh, Planter, cr. Rutledge & Spring Sts.
Wilson, J. B., Clerk, Post Office, 10 New St.
Wilson, J. E., Clerk, Central Wharf, res. Montague St.
Wilson, J. M., Boot & Shoe Dealer, 43 Hayne St., res. 6 New St.
Wilson, J., Mrs., Dry Goods, King St., Ward 6
Wilson, John, Cabinet Maker, King St., Ward 6
Wilson, John, King St., Ward 6
Wilson, Joseph, Student, 90 Wentworth St.
Wilson, M. E., Mrs., 15 Church St.

Wilson, M., Mrs., 113 Queen St.
Wilson, -----, Mrs., 17 Hasell St.
Wilson, R. W., Attorney, Thomas St.
Wilson, Samuel, M. D., 10 New St.
Wilson, St. Julian, Thomas St.
Wilson, Thomas, Ship Carpenter, 10 Tradd St.
Wilson, W. A., Watchmaker, 95 East Bay St., res. East Bay St.
Wilson, W. M., Mail Agent, 10 New St.
Wilson, William, 21 Montague St.
Wiltberger, J. R., Druggist, 245 King St., res. 23 Laurens St.
Winberg, J., Mrs., Fancy Goods, 276 King St.
Winberg, John, Wharfinger, Atlantic Wharf, res. 276 King St.
Wincy, John, Engineer, 84 Beaufain St.
Windelkin, C., Grocer, cr. King & Line Sts.
Wineman, F., Druggist, 29 Hayne St., res. 4 Society St.
Winestock, M., Fancy Goods, 295 King St., res. 306 King St.
Wing, Robert, Locksmith & Bell Hanger, 121 King St.
Winkleman, D., Clerk, 83 Beaufain St.
Winkleman, O., Clerk, cr. King & Line Sts.
Winningham, H., Carpenter, Columbus St.
Winred, John, Carpenter, 2 Cliffords Alley
Winslow, E., Agent, Wilmington Boats, foot of Laurens St., res. 43 Beaufain St.
Winthrop, H., M. D., 32 Society St., res. 95 Tradd St.
Winthrop, J. A., Factor, Adger's Wharf, res. 99 Tradd St.
Winyard, John, Planter, America St.
Wise, A., Painter, 130 King St.
Wise, E., Clerk, Adger's Wharf, res. East Bay St.
Wise, Isreal, Carpenter, Coming St., Ward 6
Witchel, C., Grocer, King St., Ward 6
Witchen, F., Laborer, Sires St.
Witherby, Joel, Boot & Shoe Dealer, cr. King & Market Sts., res. Merchants Hotel
Withers, M., Mrs., St. Philip St., Ward 6
Withers, -----, Mrs., 15 Savage St.
Withers, William, Butcher, St. Philip St., Ward 6
Witschens, C., Grocer, 27 College St.
Witsell, John, Accountant, 135 Meeting St., res. cr. Queen & Meeting Sts.
Witte, P. F., Bootmaker, 20 Tradd St.
Witter, A., Printer, 6 Friend St.
Wittschen, F., Clerk, 115 Church St.
Wittschen, H., Baker, 115 Church St.
Wohlers, -----, Grocer, 30 Coming St.
Wohlken, H., Clerk, 49 Market St.
Wohlken, L., Fruiterer, 49 Market St., res. 31 Market St.
Wolff, J. M., Clothier, 332 King St.
Wolff, William, Bootmaker, 28 Anson St.
Woltman, H., Clerk, 29 Bull St.
Wood, Daniel, Hanover St.
Wood, E. J. C., 233 King St.
Wood, G. W. E., Clerk, 21 Hayne St.
Wood, George, Grocer, 81 Market St., res. Cumberland St.
Wood, L. S., Accountant, 1 Hayne St., res. 236 King St.
Wood, S., Mrs., 233 King St.

Wood, William, Finisher, 7 Motte's Lane
Wooddrup, John, Clerk, 29 Hayne St., res. 100 Tradd St.
Wooddy, James, Seaman, America St.
Wooddy, Thomas, Blacksmith, Meeting St., Ward 5
Woodman, C., Sea Captain, Spring St.
Woodruff, Josephus, Printer, 39 Archdale St.
Woodruff, T., Bookbinder, 47 King St.
Woodside, John, Tavern Keeper, 191 East Bay St.
Woodside, S. A., Clerk, 191 East Bay St.
Woodside, William, Clerk, 147 Meeting St., res. 191 East Bay St.
Woodward, E. S., Mrs., 20 Mazyck St.
Woodward, John, Engineer, 105 Meeting St.
Woodward, T., Superintendent, Bennett's Mill, res. 8 Washington St.
Woodworth, E., Mrs., Spring St.
Worrill, J. W., Clerk, 165 Meeting St., res.Victoria Hotel
Woss, John, Sea Captain, Coming St., Ward 6
Wotherspoon & Porcher, Cotton Brokers, Adger's Wharf
Wotherspoon, Robert, Cotton Broker, Adger's Wharf, res. 80 Tradd St.
Wotten, Henry, Bricklayer, Calhoun St., Ward 6
Wragg, Henry, Carpenter, Spring St.
Wragg, T. L., Ship & Commission Merchant, Adger's Wharf, res. 72 Broad St.
Wragg, W. T., M. D., 64 Wentworth St.
Wrede, J., Clerk, 108 East Bay St.
Wright, A., Miss, 3½ Archdale St.
Wright, C. T., Dry Goods, 122 King St.
Wright, Celia, Coming St., Ward 6
Wright, H., Mrs., Fancy Goods, 178 King St.
Wright, J. D., Painter, 38 Tradd St.
Wright, R. S., Mechanic, Mary St.
Wright, Samuel, Butcher, 7 Burns Lane
Wright, T. B., Clerk, 71 East Bay St., res. Mary St.
Wulbern, C., Clerk, 55 East Bay St.
Wulbern, H., Grocer, 54 State St.
Wurfell, H., Fruiterer, 86 Church St.
Wurthman, H., Grocer, Spring St.
Wyly, A. C., Clerk, 37 Hayne St., res. Victoria Hotel
Yanson, -----, Mrs., 124 Tradd St.
Yates, E. L., Clerk, 89 East Bay St., res. cr. East Bay & Broad Sts.
Yates, F. S., Bookkeeper, Bank of South Carolina, res. cr. East Bay & Broad Sts.
Yates, F. W., Clerk, Vanderhorst's Wharf, res. Commercial Hotel
Yates, J. D., Sheriff, 9 Church St.
Yates, J., Jr., Boarding Officer, Custom House, cr. Water & Church Sts.
Yates, J. L., Clerk, 151 East Bay St., res. Church St.
Yates, John, Engineer, South Carolina Railroad, res. Nassau St.
Yates, W. B., Pastor, Mariners Church, 25 East Bay St.
Yates, William, Dr., Planter, 6 Church St.
Yattro, G. W., Watchmaker, 266 King St., res. 286 King St.
Yeadon & Macbeth, Attorneys, 41 Broad St.
Yeadon, Richard, Attorney, 41 Broad St., res. 56 Wentworth St.

Yeadon, W., Mrs., Radcliffe St.
You, D. C., 8 Archdale St.
You, M. A., Mrs., 8 Archdale St.
Young, Henry, Clerk, 201 King St.
Young, J., Clerk, 44 Broad St., res. 33 Church St.
Young, Martha, 48 Coming St.
Young, -----, Mrs., 12 New St.
Young, P. H., Clerk, Boyce's Wharf, res. 155 East Bay
St.
Young, Thomas, Pastor, St. Michael's Church, 27
Meeting St.
Young, W., Clerk, 44 Broad St., res. 33 Church St.
Zachariah, -----, Mrs., Corset Store, 147 King St.
Zealy, Joseph, Discount Clerk, Union Bank, 25 Bull St.
Zeigenbein, W., Tailor, 18 Calhoun St.
Zeigler, M. W., Coach Maker, 24 Wentworth St.
Zell, W., Clerk, 6 Market St.
Zerbs, H. Grocer, cr. Ducan & Pitt Sts.
Zerenow, John, Inspector, Gas Works, 26 Wentworth St.
Zergmann, E., Tobacconist, 64 Market St., res. King St.
Zimmerman, W. A., Clerk, cr. King & Market Sts., res.
Ann St.
Zogbaum, F. & Co., Music Store, 201 King St.
Zogbaum, F., Music Store, 201 King St., res. cr. King &
Beaufain Sts.
Zollicoffer, G., Clerk, cr. Meeting & Market Sts.
Zylstra, J. P., Ship Grocer, 59 East Bay St., res. 51 King
St.

The 1855 Directory

David M. Gazlay, who lists himself as a general commission agent, published *The Charleston City Directory and General Business Directory for 1855: Containing the Names of the Inhabitants, Their Occupations, Places of Business and Dwelling Houses: A Business Directory, A List of the Streets, Lanes, Alleys, the City Offices, Public Institutions, Banks, &c.* (Charleston: David M. Gazlay, 1855). In the Preface he states that he is "aware that in it exists many mistakes and imperfections, which are principally confined to the Upper Wards." He says, "I met with a great many obstacles. . . the most prominent of which was the defect in regard to the houses not being numbered, and in many cases if numbered, not properly done, in the Upper Wards." He promised he would issue thereafter a directory " annually, corrected and revised." Other cities, he indicated had annual directories -- "why need Charleston be so far behind the age?" This, however, is the only one he published. It has 5,368 entries. The volume has a number of interesting advertisements, some with drawings.

Abbot, Ann, Mrs., Vanderhorst St.

Abbott, Thomas H., Student, 4 Linguard St.

Abrahams & Burns, Blacksmiths, cr. John & Meeting Sts.

Abrahams, A. H., Auctioner and Commission Merchant, 22 Vendue Range, res. 38 Queen St.

Abrahams, Alfred, Colored, Fruit, East Bay St., res. 27 Hasell St.

Abrahams, T. H., Carpenter, res. 38 State St.

Adams & Co., Express Office, 20 Broad St.

Adams & Frost, Commission Merchants, Adger's North Wharf

Adams, C. D. C., Clerk, 3 Broad St., res. 38 State St.

Adams, Estel, Factor, Adger's Wharf, res. cr. Smith & Montague Sts.

Adams, Hugh, Wheelwright, cr. Meeting & Spring Sts., res. Coming St.

Adams, Thomas, Painter, Radcliffe St., res. Radcliffe St.

Adams, W. F., Stoves & Grates, 18 Broad St.

Addison, Edward, Car Builder, Meeting St., res. St. Philip St.

Addison, George, Watchmaker, King St., res. King St.

Addison, Henry L., Clerk, 27 Hayne St., res. 26 Beaufain St.

Addison, Joseph, Shipwright, East Bay St., res. 200 East Bay St.

Adger, James & Co., Commission Merchants, Adger's North Wharf

Adger, James, Commission Merchant, Adger North Wharf, res. King St.

Adger, James E., Hardware, 54 East Bay St., res. 200 East Bay St.

Adger, James, Jr., Commission Merchant, Adger's North Wharf, res. King St.

Adger, Joesph A., Hardware, 200 East Bay St., res. East Bay St.

Adger, Robert, Commission Merchant, Adger's North Wharf, res. King St.

Adger, William, Mrs., res. 2 Legare St.

Adicks, J., Shoemaker, 16 Beaufain St.

Affanassieffe, D., Paints & Oils, Coming St., res. President St.

Agnew, James, Wheelwright, res. Woolf St.

Ahrens, Charles D., Grocer, 165 King St., res. 165 King St.

Ahrens, J., Wheelwright, 25 Friend St., res. 25 Friend St.

Ahrens, John, Grocer, 53 East Bay St., res. 53 East Bay St.

Aiken, Joseph D., Lawyer, 20 Broad St., res. cr. Charlotte & Alexander Sts.

Aiken, William, Planter, res. cr. Elizabeth & Judith Sts.

Aimar, Charles P., Clerk, 244 King St., res. Anson St.

Aimar, G. W., Druggist, cr. King & Vanderhorst Sts.

Aimar, Thomas, Clerk, South Carolina Institute, res. 30 Archdale St.

Alarat, S., Pilot, Schooner Marion, res. 7 Stoll's Alley

Albergotti, Thomas W., Baker, King St., res. King St.

Albergotti, Washington, Clerk, East Bay St., res. 7 Horlbeck Alley

Albers, Frederick, Grocer, cr. St. Philip St. & McBride's Lane

Albers, H. & G., Flour Mill, Calhoun St.

Albers, Henry, Churabasco Steam Grist Mill

Albers, John, Churabasco, Steam Grist Mill

Albright, N., Grocer, cr. Queen & Friend Sts.

Aldrich, Thomas, Physician, Chapel St., res. Chapel St.

Alexander, George, Teacher, res. Bull & Lynch Sts.

Alexander, Hannah, Mrs., res. Short St.

Alexander, Henry D., Collection Clerk, Union Bank, res. South St.

Alexander, J. D., Exchange Clerk, Bank of the State

Alexander, R. M., Clerk, 25 Vendue Range, res. Queen St.

Alexander, Samuel, Labor Master, 38 East Bay St., res. cr. Bull & Lynch Sts.

Alexander, Thomas, Commission Merchant, South Atlantic Wharf, res. 1 Short St.

Alexander, Thomas, Factor, South Atlantic Wharf, res. Short St.

Allander, Ann P., Mrs., res. Spring St.

Allars, Christopher, Grocer, Calhoun St.

Allemong, A. A., Lawyer, 17 Broad St., res. 61 Meeting St.

Allen, Alexander, Carpenter, res. Rutledge St.

Allen, Grace, res. 26 Marsh St.

Allen, Isabella, Mrs., Milliner, res. Rutledge St.

Allen, J. M., Commission Merchant, 7 Hayne St., res. Columbia S.C.

Allen, Peter, Carpenter, res. Rutledge St.

Allen, -----, Printer, Mercury Office, res. Queen St.

Allen, Rachel, Colored, Washerwoman, res. Calhoun St.

Allen, Thomas P., res. 17 Middle St.

Allen, W. H., Dentist, res. 72 Wentworth St.

Allers, C., Grocer, Calhoun St., res. Calhoun St.

Alley, J. B. P., Cabinent Maker, 62 Queen St., res. 17 Franklin St.

Allison, George, Shoemaker, Queen St., near Meeting St.

Allison, William, Wheelwright, res. Nassau St.
Allston, Catharine, Colored, Seamstress, res. Princess St.
Allston, Robert, Clerk, 143 Meeting St., res. Cannon St.
Allston, Samuel, Mason, res. Coming St.
Allston, William, Planter, res. Ashley St.
Alston, Benjamin, Mrs., res. 9 East Bay St.
Alston, Charles, Planter, res. 15 East Bay St.
Alton, Eliza, Mrs., res. 141½ Queen St.
Ambler & Selman, Hats & Caps, 161 Meeting St.
Ambler, David A., Hats & Caps, 161 Meeting St., res. Charleston Hotel
Amiel, John W., Superintendent of Rice Mills, res. Ashley St.
Amme, C., Baker, res. King St., 7th Ward
Amme, D. A., Grocer, cr. Meeting & Market Sts., res. St. Philip St.
Anchor, G. V., Commission Merchant, 3 Adger's South Wharf, res. cr. Beaufain & St. Philip Sts.
Anderson, Andrew F., Hardware, 137 Meeting St., res. Wentworth St.
Anderson, Edward J., Lawyer, 84 Church St., res. South Carolina Hall
Anderson, J. A., Clerk 149 Meeting St., res. Charleston Hotel
Anderson, John, Dentist, 235 King St., res. 235 King St.
Anderson, Robert, Clothing, 16 Hayne St., res. 16 Hayne St.
Andrews, Ann, Mrs., res. 1 Horlbeck Alley
Andrews, Augustus O., Col., Commission Merchant, 165 East Bay St., res. 27 Hasell St.
Andrews, Fredrick, Student, res. 1 Horlbeck Alley
Andrews, Fritz, Laborer, South Carolina Railroad, res. St. Philip St.
Andrews, Louisa, Mrs., res. 70 Anson St.
Andrews, S. T., Clerk, 143 East Bay St., res. Church St.
Andrews, Warren, Student, res. 1 Horlbeck Alley
Anerum, John, Tailor, 209 East Bay St., res. Henrietta St.
Angel, M., Mrs., res. Tradd St., opposite Greenhill St.
Anger, Joseph, Cooper, Stoll's Alley, res. 225 East Bay St.
Angerman, Fredrick, Carpenter, Cannon St., res. Cannon St.
Anody, Amelia, Mrs., res. 8 Rutledge St.
Anthony, Adeline, Fruit, res. Calhoun St.
Apler, D., Grocer, cr. Reid & Meeting Sts.
Apler, Frederick, Miller, Calhoun St., res. cr. Chapman & Elizabeth Sts.
Appiriares, Christolph, Fruit, 211 East Bay St., res. 211 East Bay St.
Appleton, James, Locksmith, 79 King St., res. 79 King St.
Armstrong, Alexander D., Clerk, 25 Hayne St., res. 30 Wentworth St.
Armstrong, Archibald, Bookkeeper, 33 Hayne St.
Armstrong, D. F., Clerk, 155 East Bay St., res. 30 Wentworth St.
Armstrong, J. R., Commission Merchant, 4 East Bay St., res. Mansion House
Armstrong, James, Forwarding & Commission Merchant, 42 Market St., res. 42 Market St.

Armstrong, Louisa, Mrs., res. 17 Middle St.
Armstrong William, Bookkeeper, Bennett's Mills, res. 30 Wentworth St.
Arnau, Michael, Blacksmith, res. Calhoun St.
Arnau, William, Blacksmith, res. Calhoun St.
Arner, John J., Clerk, King St., res. 102 Church St.
Arnold, George H., Auctioneer, 17 Vendue Range, res. Rutledge St.
Arnold, John, Stone Cutter, res. 11 Tradd St.
Arnold, Lousia, Mrs., res. 17 Bull St.
Arnold, Richard, Blacksmith, res. Chapel St.
Arnold, T., Printer, East Bay St., res. 2 Mazyck St.
Arnold, William H., Painter, 96 Meeting St., res. 96 Meeting St.
Ashe, Anne, Mrs., res. Ashley St.
Ashe, Henry, Hatter, 145 King St., res. 145 King St.
Ashe, Joanna, Colored, res. St. Philip St.
Ashhurst, John, Bookkeeper, 29 Hayne St., res. cr. Market & Church Sts.
Ashim, Simon, Clothing, 310 King St., res. 310 King St.
Ashley, Alice, Mrs., res. 8 Berresford St.
Ashley, G. W., Painter, 17 State St., res. 151 East Bay St.
Ashley, H., Mrs., Boarding House, 43 East Bay St.
Ashley, J. H. & G. W., Painters, 17 State St.
Ashley, J. H., Painter, 17 State St., res. 151 East Bay St.
Astle, George, Speculator, res. 84 King St.
Atkins, Sampson, Capt., Steamer Nina, res. East Bay St.
Atkinson, C. & Co., Commission Merchants, 14 Central Wharf
Atkinson, Christopher, Commission Merchant, 14 Central Wharf, res. Mansion House
Atkinson, George A., Clerk, 232 King St., res. 228 King St.
Aubury, George, Fruit, 337 King St., res. 337 King St.
Auld, M., Miss, Teacher, 17 Broad St., res. 24 Society St.
Austin, Peter W., Hats & Caps, 25 Hayne St., res. Charleston Hotel
Austin, Phillip, Clerk, Church St., res. 31 King St.
Austin, Robert, Negro Trader, State St., res. Line St.
Aveilhe, Phillip A., Commission Merchant, Accommodation Wharf, 7 George St.
Averill, Caleb N., Commission Merchant, 2 Hayne St., res. Calhoun St.
Avery, C. N., Commission Merchant, 7 Hayne St., res. Calhoun St.
Avery, Lucius, Bookkeeper, 157 Meeting St., res. Queen St.
Axon, Charles H., Lawyer, Court House Square, res. Smith St.
Axon, H. T., Clerk, South Carolina Railroad, res. 117 Meeting St.
Axon, J. Waring, Clerk, 33 Hayne St., res. 17 Meeting St.
Axon, William J., Factor, North Commercial Wharf, res. 17 Meeting St.
Ayers, Daniel, Laborer, 4 Linguard St., res. 4 Linguard St.
Babcock Frederick, Clerk, 259 King St., res. 18 Montague St.

Babcock Thomas C., Clerk, 259 King St., res. 18 Montague St.

Babcock William R., Books, etc., 259 King St., res. 18 Montague St.

Bachman, John D., Clergyman, res. Rutledge St.

Bachman, William, Lawyer, St. Michael's Alley, res. Rutledge St.

Backis, Francis, Watchmaker, 82 Queen St., res. 82 Queen St.

Backus, Frederick, Dry Goods, 190 King St., res. 190 King St.

Bacon, Charles J. S., Clerk, 211 King St., res. Commercial Hotel

Bacot, D. D., Bookkeeper at Wardlaw, Walker & Burnsides, res. 43 East Bay St.

Bacot, R. D., Clerk, 26 East Bay St., res. 61 Coming St.

Bacot, R. Wainwright, Factor, Southern Wharf, res. cr. Tradd & Meeting Sts.

Baeer, Eliza, Mrs., Boarding House, res. 63 Church St.

Baggett, Patrick, Laborer, res. Calhoun St.

Bahntge, Henry, Grocer, cr. Meeting & Woolf Sts., res. Meeting St.

Bahntge, Henry, Grocer, cr. Church & Elliot Sts., res. Calhoun St.

Bahr, L. M., Shipping Master, 87 East Bay St.

Bailey & Douglas, Grocers, 198 King St.

Bailey, John A., Grocer, 198 King St., res. 198 King St.

Bailey, R. S., Physician, res. Hudson St.

Bailey, S. M., Clerk, 8 East Bay St., res. 12 South Bay St.

Bailey, Samuel, Rigger, 6 Guignard St., res. 8 Bedons Alley

Bailie & Lambert, Carpet Warehouse, 219 King St.

Bailie, George A., Bookkeeper, 219 King St., res. 6 Coming St.

Bailie, James G., Carpets, 219 King St., res. 6 Coming St.

Bakeman, Adolph, res. Coming St.

Baker, Ann, Mrs., res. Tradd St.

Baker, B. E., Clerk, 40 East Bay St., res. 8 Lamboll St.

Baker, C. E., Clerk at H. F. Baker Co., res. 21 Queen St.

Baker, E. B., Clerk, 159 Meeting St., res. 38 Beaufain St.

Baker, Ellen, Mrs., Tailoress, res. Pitt St.

Baker, Frederick, Carpenter, res. Gadsen St.

Baker, H. Hyme, Clerk, 181 East Bay St., res. 8 Lamboll St.

Baker, Henry, Carpenter, res. 21 Queen St.

Baker, Henry F. & Co., Forwarding & Commission Merchants, Central Wharf

Baker, Henry F., Commission Merchant, Central Wharf, res. 21 Queen St.

Baker, Issac, Engineer, South Carolina Railroad, res. Morris St.

Baker, James A., Clerk, H. F. Baker & Co., res. 21 Queen St.

Baker, James, Clerk, 159 Meeting St., res. 38 Beaufain St.

Baker, R. S., Pastor, St. Mary's Church, 62 Wentworth St.

Baker, William, Laborer, 14 Philadelphia St.

Baldwin, Stephen G., 235 King St., res. 260 King St.

Balk, Henry, Clerk, 190 King St., res. 187 Meeting St.

Ball, H. S., Clerk, North Commercial Wharf, res. 25 Lynch St.

Ball, Isaac, Mrs., res. cr. Vernon & East Bay Sts.

Ball, John, Mrs., res. cr. Vernon & East Bay St.

Ballard, John, Clerk, 306 King St., res. 297 King St.

Ballard, Joseph, Bookkeeper, 54 Broad St., res. 75 King St.

Bampfield, Joseph, Colored, Wheelwright, res. Heyward's Court

Bancroft, Betts & Marshall, Dry Goods, cr. Market & King Sts.

Bancroft, Edward, Clerk, 94 East Bay St., res. 18 Coming St.

Bancroft, Edward W., Dry Goods, 211 King St., res. Charleston Hotel

Bancroft, James, Commission Merchant, 94 East Bay St., res. 15 Coming St.

Bancroft, James, Jr., Grocer, 94 East Bay St., res. 22 Society St.

Bancroft, W. G., Dry Goods, 235 King St., res. 10 Wentworth St.

Banks, Chase, Mrs., res. 9 Short St.

Banks, Hugh R., Dry Goods, 41 Hayne St., res. 75 Wentworth St.

Banks, Lane & Co., Dry Goods, 41 Hayne St.

Banter, C., Grocer, McLeish's Wharf, res. Washington St.

Baraeau, Gabriel, Colored, Tailor, Church St., res. Mazyck St.

Barboga, Jose A., Cigars & Tobacco, 87 Church St., res. 87 Church St.

Barbot & Seyle, Architects, 57 Broad St.,

Barbot, A. O., Engineer, 57 Broad St., res. cr. Tradd & Meeting Sts.

Barbot, C. D., Secretary & Treasurer, Fireman's Insurance Co., res. cr. Tradd & Meeting Sts.

Barbot, L. J., Architect, 57 Broad St., res. cr. Tradd & Meeting Sts.

Barclay, E. S., Clerk, 37 Hayne St., res. American Hotel

Bardwell, Joseph, Pastor, French Protestant Church, res. Vanderhorst St.

Barfield, Benjamin H., Clerk, Union Bank, res. 40 St. Philip St.

Bargeman, Borchard, Grocer, cr. Cannon & Ashley St.

Bargeman, Henry, Grocer, cr. Cannon & Ashley Sts

Barker, -----, Mrs., res. 26 George St.

Barker, R., Mrs., res. Chapel St.

Barker, S. G., Planter. res. cr. Wentworth & Glebe Sts.

Barker, T. G., Lawyer, 34 Broad St., res. cr. Wentworth & Glebe Sts.

Barksdale, S., Mrs, res. 16 Savage St.

Barlake, Hermann, Planter, res. Spring St.

Barless, William H., Paying Teller, Southwest Railroad Bank, res. Broad St.

Barnes, George W., Clerk, 235 King St., res. Wentworth & King Sts.

Barnes, John, Drayman, res. Columbus St.

Barnett, J., Clothing, 16 Hayne St., res. Newark, New

Jersey

Barnett, John, Clothing, 268 King St., res. Pavilion Hotel

Barnett, Sarah, Colored, res. Radcliffe St.

Barnett, U., Tailor, State St., res. Duncan St.

Barney, Jacob, Fruit, 53 Church St., res. 53 Church St.

Barnwell, Benjamin S., Bookkeeper, Accomodation Wharf

Barnwell, Edward, Factor, 3 Southern Wharf, res. 35 Meeting St.

Barnwell, Edward, Jr., Factor, 3 Southern Wharf, res. 35 Meeting St.

Barnwell, James S., Factor cr. East Bay & Hasell Sts., res. Quinn St.

Barr, John, Liquor, cr. Market & State Sts., res. 24 George St.

Barr, L. N., Shipping Merchant, East Bay St., res. Cannon St.

Barr, Robert, Clerk, East Bay St., res. 183 Meeting St.

Barreau, Francis, Carpenter, Duncan St., res. Duncan St.

Barreau, John E., Colored, Carpenter, res. Mazyck St.

Barrett, Jacob, Planter, Georgia, res. Drake St.

Barrett, William A., Auctioneer, 19 Vendue Range, res. opposite the Mall

Barrigan, William, Grocer, cr. Church & Chalmers Sts.

Barring, Daniel, Colored, Tailor, res. Broad St.

Barring, James, Laborer, res. 4 Linguard St.

Barron, Emma, Colored, Mantuamaker, res. St. Philip St.

Bart, C., Fruit, res. King St.

Bartlett, Franklin C., Boots & Shoes, 283 King St., res. Coming St.

Bartlett, Hiram, Boots & Shoes, 283 King St., res. Coming St.

Bartlett, William, Capt., res. America St.

Bartoll, B., Porter House, 2 Vendue Range, res. 2 Vendue Range

Barton, A., Clerk, 89 Beaufain St., res. 89 Beaufain St.

Barton, A. G., Carpenter, res. St. Philip St.

Barton, Francis, Clothing, 68 State St., res. 68 State St.

Barton, Joseph, Physician, 225 King St., res. Waverly House

Baruc, Bernard S., Fancy Goods, 208 King St., res. 208 King St.

Bascom, Ashley R., Upholsterer, 166 King St., res. 166 King St.

Bascom, Sophia, Colored, Mantaumaker, res. Coming St.

Bass, Margarget, Mrs., res. Coming St.

Bassett, Orrin, Printer, 119 East Bay St., res. 38 Coming St

Bassett, T. J., Boiler Maker, res. Columbus St.

Bateman, John D., Porter, 41 Hayne St., res. Duncan St.

Bates & Mitchell, Clothing, 118 Meeting St.

Bates Edmund, Engineer, res. 8 Stoll's Alley

Bates, Edwin, Clothing, 118 Meeting, res. 118 Meeting St.

Bates, J. Russell, Clerk, 211 King St, res. American Hotel

Bates, Mary, Miss, res. 14 Church St.

Batman, Charles, Clerk, South Carolina Railroad, res. Duncan St.

Baum, E. & H., Clothing, 324 King St.

Baum, Elkin, Clothing, 324 King St., res. 115 King St.

Baum, Heman, Clothing, 324 King St., res. 315 King St.

Baum J. P. & Son, Leather Dealers, 286 King St.

Baum, John A., Leather, 286 King St., res. 286 King St.

Baum, John S., Leather, 286 King St., res. 286 King St.

Baurmeister, G. C., Commission Merchant, Exchange Wharf, res. King St.

Baussang, Sophia, Mrs., Fruit, 78 King St., res. 78 King St.

Bayer, H., Clerk, 25 Broad St., res. 99 East Bay St.

Beach, Elais M., Grain Merchant, 8 East Bay St., res. Meeting St.

Beach, Pratt & King, Fancy Dry Goods, 19 Hayne St.

Beach, W. H., Fancy Goods, 19 Hayne St., res. New York

Beamer, Rebecca, Colored, Mantuamaker, res. St. Philip St.

Beanmer, Sarah, Colored, Mantuamaker, res. St. Philip St.

Beard & Kolando, Coopers, Exchange St.

Beattie, James, Butcher, Line St.

Beaufort, Andrew, Bootmaker, Queen St.

Becase, Charles, Colored, Porter, cr. Meeting & Hasell Sts., res. 12 Middle St.

Becase, Mary Ann, Colored, Mantuamaker, 12 Middle St.

Beckman, Charles, Bookkeeper, South Carolina Railroad, res. Radcliffe St.

Beckman, Christian, Planter, res. St. Philip St.

Beckman, Jacob, Machinist, Hasell St.

Beckman, James A., Teacher, res. 18 Archdale St.

Beckman, John C., Grain Merchant, 61 Market St., res. St. Philip St.

Beckman, W. W., Clerk, 179 East Bay St., res. Morris St.

Beckman, William, Merchant, East Bay St.

Bee & Tylee, Ship Chandlers, 123 East Bay St.

Bee, Benjamin, Finisher, South Carolina Railroad, res. Rutledge St.

Bee, J. P., Wharfinger, Southern Wharf, res. 108 Tradd St.

Bee, J. S., Teller, Bank of the State, res. America St.

Bee, James M., Collector & Notary for State Bank, res. Beaufain St.

Bee, James R., Ship Chandler, 123 East Bay St., res. 8 Beaufain St.

Bee, John B., Outdoor Clerk, State Bank, res. 8 Beaufain St.

Bee, John J., Carpenter, res. Cannon St.

Bee, Mary V., Mrs., 183 Meeting St.

Bee, Richard, Finisher, South Carolina Railroad, res. Rutledge St.

Bee, Robert R., Cooper, Adger's Wharf, res. cr. South Bay & Legare Sts.

Bee, Samuel, Clerk, res. America St.

Bee, T. S., Clerk, 76, East Bay St., res. Smith St.

Bee, William C. & Co., Factors & Commission Merchants, 18 Vanderhorst's Wharf

Bee, William C., Factor, 18 Vanderhorst's Wharf, res. 108 Tradd St.

Bee, William, Finisher, South Carolina Railroad, res.

Rutledge St.

Beehan, Thomas, Gardener, res. Spring St.

Beekman, G. E., Landlord, King St.

Beesley, Absalom, Laborer, res. Woolf St.

Behr, H., Clerk, cr. Beaufain & Coming Sts.

Behrens, F. W., Tailor, 80 Market St.

Belcher, Louisa, Mrs., res. 20 Friend St.

Belitzer, Issac, Clothing, 318 King St., res. 318 King St.

Bell, David, Accountant, res. Radcliffe St.

Bell, Edwin Q., Bookkeeper, 11 Market St., res. Radcliffe St.

Bell, John L., Cooper, Exchange, res. 57 King St.

Bell, Samuel, Blacksmith, res. America St.

Bell, Sarah, Mrs., Midwife, res. Cannon St.

Bell, Sarah, Mrs., res. 47 Tradd St.

Bell, Thomas, Cooper, res. Cannon St.

Bell, William, Mrs., res. 38 Society St.

Bellinger, John, Physician, 11 College St.

Belon, Thomas S., Planter, res. cr. King & Cannon Sts.

Belser, William M., Clerk, res. Short St.

Benedict, Ferdinand, Coach Maker, cr. Meeting & Wentworth Sts., res. 273 King St.

Benga, Peter, Liquors, res. King St.

Benie, Charles J., Clerk, 265 King St., res. 65 King St.

Benjamin, David, Clerk, 300 King St., res. 265 King St.

Benjamin, Solomon A., Clothing, King St., under American Hotel

Benjamin, William H., Carpenter, 141 Queen St.

Bennett, Catherine, Colored, Seamstress, res. Coming St.

Bennett, Christopher G., Printer, 117 East Bay St., res. St. Philip St.

Bennett, Elias, Physician, res. 24 Rutledge St.

Bennett, George, Rigger, 6 Guignard St., res. 2 Pinckney St.

Bennett, I. S. K., Teller, Planters & Merchants Bank

Bennett, John B., Printer, 111 East Bay St., res. St. Philip St.

Bennett, S., Bootmaker, 102 Queen St., res. 15 Wall St.

Bennett, Samuel, Lumber Measurer, res. 98 Beaufain St.

Bennett, W. J., Miller, foot of Wentworth St., res. 28 Montague St.

Bennett, William J., Auctioneer & Commission Merchant, Exchange St.

Bensch, Charles, Tavern Keeper, 143 King St.

Benstine, Nathan, Iron & Rags, 23 Tradd St., res. 23 Tradd St.

Bentford, Mary S., Colored, Dressmaker, Spring St.

Benton, Robert, Mrs., res. cr. Smith & Vanderhorst Sts.

Bentscher, Charles, Clerk, 210 King St., res. 265 King St.

Bercoats, Joseph, Factor, East Bay St., res. 16 Coming St.

Beree, Robert, res. 23 Water St.

Berger, S. J., Clothing, Hayne St., res. 69 Beaufain St.

Bergman, A., Baker, cr. King & Line Sts.

Bernard, C. H., Mrs., Millinery, 336 King St., res. 336 King St.

Bernard, Caroles, Mariner, res. Meeting St.

Bernard, Caroline, Mrs., Dress Maker, 73 King St.

Bernard, D. T., Tailor, 133 Meeting St., res. Mills House

Bernard, Levy, Tailor, res. 96 Wentworth St.

Bernheim, G. D., Pastor, Zion Evangelical Luthern Church

Berry, Alexander J., Clerk, 215 King St., res. 47 Calhoun St.

Berry, Charles H., Clerk, 165 Meeting St., res. Charleston Hotel

Berry, John, Colored, Carpenter, res. Bogard St.

Berry, Thomas H., Clerk, 143 East Bay St., res. 47 Calhoun St.

Berry, William, Carpenter, res. Bogard St.

Betman, John, Engineer, South Carolina Railroad, res. Rutledge St.

Betsell, John M., Coach Maker, res. cr. Beaufain & Rutledge Sts.

Bettisen, Elizabeth, Mrs., res. 14 Magazine St.

Betts, F. B., Saddlery, cr. Meeting & Hasell Sts., res. New York

Betts, James B., Dry Goods, 211 King St., res. Montague St.

Betts, William H., Hardware, 80 East Bay St., res. Mills House

Bevason, J. G., Clerk, 13 Beaufain St., res. 40 Archdale St.

Bibb, Wilson, Factor, South Atlantic Wharf, res. Huntsville, Ala.

Bicaise, Benjamin, Gun & Locksmith, 26 State St., res. 26 State St.

Bickley & Glover, Factors, foot of Beaufain St.

Bickley, John C., Grocer, 70 East Bay St., res. Vanderhorst St.

Bickley, John, Factor, foot of Beaufain St., res. Vanderhorst St.

Bilton, George, Tailor, res. 8 Whim's Court

Bing, John, Tailor, Market St., res. 3 Cannon St.

Bing, Margaret, Mrs., Tailoress, res. 3 Cannon St.

Bing, Sarah, Colored, Mantuamaker, res. Coming St.

Bingham, Samuel H., Telegraph Operator, 3 State St., res. City Hotel

Bingley, Selina, Mrs., res. 253 East Bay St.

Bird, Charlton, H., Military Goods, 225 King St., res. 16 Coming St.

Bird, John S. & Co., Military Goods, 225 King St.

Bird, John S., Military Goods, 225 King St., res. 16 Coming St.

Bird, Sarah, Mrs., res. 52 Church St.

Bird, Sinclair, Ship Carpenter, 23 South Bay St., res. 100 Wentworth St.

Bird, William, Shipyard, 23 South Bay St., res. 100 Wentworth St.

Birley, William, Grocer, 29 King St., res. 39 King St.

Birnie & Ogilvie, Hardware, 21 Broad St.

Birnie, William, Clerk, 1 Hayne St., res. Smith St.

Birnie, William, Hardware, 21 Broad St., res. Smith St.

Bischoff, A., Grocer, 153 East Bay St., res. cr. Meeting & Ann Sts.

Bischoff, H., Grocer, 55 East Bay St., res. 59 East Bay St.

Biscoff, J., Clerk, 55 East Bay St., res. 55 East Bay St.

Bissell, John B., Clerk, 147 Meeting St., res. Mary St.

Bissell, Miller, Dentist, 218 King St., res. 218 King St.

Bissell, Titus L., Hardware, 155 Meeting St., res. Mary St.

Bissell, Titus L., Jr., Clerk 155 Meeting St., res. Mary St.

Black, A.W., Shipping Master, 91 East Bay St., res. Savage St.

Black, Alexander F., Shipping Office, East Bay St., res. Calhoun St.

Black, Francis C., Commission Merchant, 11 Exchange St., res. 45 Church St.

Black, Francis C., Jr., Shipping Office, East Bay St., res. Calhoun St.

Black, George W., Mason, res. 29 Spring St.

Black, Joseph A., Clerk, 268 King St., res. 249 King St.

Black, S. C., Clerk, 11 Exchange St., res. 45 Church St.

Black, Thomas, Mason, res. 29 Society St.

Black, William, Mattress Maker, Anson St.

Blackburne, Joe, Clerk at C. Atkinson Co.

Blacklock, John F., Commission Merchant, 18 East Bay St., res. 2 Bull St.

Blackman, James, Freight Agent, South Carolina Railroad, res. 22 Beaufain St.

Blackman, Joseph, Druggist, 17 Broad St., res. 22 Beaufain St.

Blackman, William, Tailor, Coming St.

Blain, Allard, Planter, Santee Island, res. Broad St.

Blain, L. T., Mrs., Teacher, 120 Queen St., res. 120 Queen St.

Blair, Thomas M., Clerk, 253 King St.

Blaise, C. L., Grocer, 61 Tradd St., res. 61 Tradd St.

Blake, Daniel B., Planter, Combahee, res. Charlotte St.

Blake, Edward, Clerk, Bank of South Carolina, res. 10 Water St.

Blake, Ezekiel, Coppersmith, res. Anson St.

Blake, John J., Carpenter, Radcliffe St.

Blake, Julius, Clerk, 76 East Bay St., res. 10 Water St.

Blake, Peter, Drayman, res. Henrietta St.

Blakeley, J. M., Commission Merchant, Central Wharf, res. 158 East Bay St.

Blanch, John, Confectionary, cr. America & Amherst Sts.

Blanchard, Edward, Carpenter, Radcliffe St.

Blanchard, S., Carpenter, Marion St.

Blancy, Adeline, Mrs., Mantuamaker, res. Vanderhorst St.

Blank, Josiah, Jeweller, 143 King St., res. 143 King St.

Blank, Mary, Mrs., Dressmaker, res. Pitt St.

Blank, Sarah, Colored, Grocery, St. Philip St.

Blank, William, Colored, Carpenter, 6 Middle St., res. 6 Middle St.

Blank, William, Sailor, Pitt St.

Blaze, J. H., Grocer, cr. State & Linguard Sts.

Bligh, Bridget, Mrs., Shoe Store, King St.

Bliss, Thomas W., Tinsmith, 184 King St., res. 184 King St.

Blohne, Johanna, Grocer, cr. State & Queen Sts.

Blondeau, Stephen, res. 42 Queen St.

Blow, M. R., Clerk, 76 East Bay St., res. cr. Church & Queen Sts.

Bluett, John J., Constable, res. 8 Orange St.

Blum, F. C. & Son, Lumber Merchants, foot of Wentworth St.

Blum, Frederick C., Lumber, foot of Wentworth St.

Blum, J. A., Teacher, res. Mary St.

Blum, J. C., Commission Merchant, res. 6 Beaufain St.

Blum, Robert, Lumber, foot of Wentworth St.

Blyden, Christopher, Bookkeeper, 143 Meeting St.

Blythe, John, Clerk, 235 King St., res. cr. East Bay & Laurens Sts.

Boag, E. M., Mrs., res. Liberty St.

Boag, James, Bookkeeper, 88 East Bay St., res. Montague St.

Boes, H., Baker, King St

Boesch, John J., Dyer, 80 King St., res. 80 King St.

Boesch, John U., Coopersmith, cr. East Bay & Anson Sts.

Boesch, Nicholas, Dyer, 80 King St., res. 80 King St.

Boignard, Henry, Cooper, Longitude Ln., res. 40 Church St.

Boisden & Canneville, Barbers, 10 Queen St.

Boisden, Edward, Barber, 10 Queen St., res. 10 Queen St.

Bokotti, William, Shoemaker, Queen St.

Bolchoz, Theodore, Molder, res. Hampden Mall

Bole, -----, Mr., Carpenter, 3 Pritchard St., res. 3 Pritchard St.

Boles, A., Superintendent of Cemetery, res. 65 Calhoun St.

Bollmann, B., Liquors, 16 Vendue Range, res. City Hall

Bollmann, H., Clerk, 16 Vendue Range

Bolte, John D., Grocer, 7 Calhoun St., res. 7 Calhoun St.

Bomar, A., res. Commercial House

Bomar, J. E., Clerk at Hall & Co., res. Commercial House

Bonneau, E. M., Miss, res. Smith St.

Bonneau, F. M., Clerk, 1 Southern Wharf, res. cr. of King & Tradd Sts.

Bonneau, G. A., Bookkeeper, 30 Broad St., res. Franklin St.

Bonneau, J., Mrs., res. 44½ Coming St.

Bonnell, John, Jr., Iron Merchant, Boyce & Co. Wharf, res. 57 Broad St.

Bonnell, John, Merchant, res. 52 Broad St.

Bonnell, Thomas, Bookkeeper, res. 6 Atlantic St.

Bonner, John, Cabinet Maker, 104 Queen St., res. 104 Queen St.

Boone, William, Plasterer, res. Bee St.

Borgard, Alfred G., Tinsmith, 298 King St., res. 298 King St.

Boring, William H., Cigars & Tobacco, 297 King St., res. 297 King St.

Borneman, Frederick W., Engraver, 231 King St., res. 250 King St.

Borner, G. F., Clerk, 108 East Bay St., res. 108 East Bay St.

Bornon, C., Grocer, cr. Beaufain & Mazyck Sts.

Borr, John, Laborer, res. St. Philip St.

Bosch, J. F., Grocer, cr. Beaufain & Lynch Sts.

Bosselmann, Dederick, Clerk, 82 Anson St., res. 82 Anson St.

Bosselmann, Henry, Grocer, 82 Anson St., res. 82 Anson St.
Bostick, Edward, Lawyer, 21 Broad St., res. 11 Short St.
Boulkin, Henry, Drayman, res. Spring St.
Bounetheau, E. N., Magistrate, res. 101 King St.
Bounetheau, H. B., Artist, cr. Broad & King Sts., res. 196 East Bay St.
Bourie, Henry, Shoemaker, Beaufain St., res. 11 Calhoun St.
Bourie, Mary L., Tailoress, res. 10 Calhoun St.
Boux, F. L., Bookkeeper, 173 East Bay St.
Bowen, John, Butcher, res. Spring St.
Bowen, Margaret, Mrs., res. 25 East Bay St.
Bowen, O. A., Dry Goods, 122 Meeting St., res. Charleston Hotel
Bowers, Edward, Gunsmith, res. Cannon St.
Bowers, John E., 6th Lieutenant, City Guard, res. Victoria Hotel
Bowie, J. S. & L. & Co., Dry Goods, Wholesale, 122 Meeting St.
Bowie, James S., Dry Goods, 122 Meeting St., res. 22 Hasell St.
Bowie, John A., Clerk, 122 Meeting St., res. 22 Hasell St.
Bowie, Langdon, Dry Goods, 122 Meeting St., res. Charleston Hotel
Bowie, Robert, Clerk, 122 Meeting St., res. Pavilion Hotel
Bowman, George, Bookkeeper, 30 Broad St., res. 3 Franklin St.
Bowman, Thomas B., Miller, Robb's Mill, res. 8 Wharf St.
Box, Kitson, Teacher, 66 Broad St., res. 18 Laurens St.
Boyce, John, Drayman, res. Ann St.
Boyle, Michael, Laborer, 2 Pinckney St.
Boyle, William, Blacksmith, Meeting St., res. Tradd St.
Boyles, C. C., Bookkeeper, 235 King St.
Boylston, J. Reid, Dry Goods, cr. Hayne & Meeting Sts.
Brad, James H., Clerk, 235 King St., res. 10 Wentworth St.
Bradford & Sanders, Commission Merchant, Accomodation Wharf
Bradford, J. B., Commission Merchant, Accomodation Wharf, res. Huntsville, Ala.
Bradford, William, Ship Carpenter, res. 16 Vernon
Bradley, Elisha, Ship Carpenter, res. 29 Church St.
Bradley, Joseph, Factor, South Atlantic Wharf, res. Huntsville, Ala.
Brady, D., Plasterer, res. Woolf St.
Brady, Edward, Grocer, 13 Tradd St., res. 13 Tradd St.
Brady, Hugh, Dry Goods, 218 King St., res. Victoria Hotel
Brady, James, Bricklayer, res. Woolf St.
Brady, Patrick, Dry Goods, 76 King St., res. 76 King St.
Brady, Patrick, Wood Factor, Smith's Wharf, res. 3 Wilson St.
Brady, Phillip, Constable, res. Line St.
Brag, Dedrick, Merchant, Hayne St., res. Radcliffe St.
Braggeman, Henry, Shoemaker, res. Meeting St.
Brahe, A. H., Leather, 13 Hayne St., res. New York

Brahe, A. H. & Co., Leather Dealers, 13 Hayne St.
Brahe, C. D., Leather, 13 Hayne St., res. Radcliffe St.
Brailsford, John M., Physician, Stoll's Alley, res. Anson St.
Brailsford, Robert McL., Physician, res. Chapel St.
Brailsford, W. R., Commission Merchant, Exchange St., res. 1 Orange St.
Brailsford, W., Wharfinger, res. 1 Orange St.
Bramer, A. J., Grocer, cr. America & Drake Sts.
Branan, Owen, Laborer, res. Meeting St.
Branch, J. L., Engineer, 91 East Bay St., res. Broad St.
Brand, John, Fruit, 62 Church St., res. Tradd St.
Brandt, Charles W., Ship Carpenter, res. 2 Washington St.
Brandt, Henry F., Confectioner, 299 King St., res. 299 King St.
Brandt, James F., Ship Carpenter, res. 3 Wharf St.
Brandt, Pierre, Clerk, cr. Market & King Sts.
Brandt, Thomas, Watchman, res. 94 Anson St.
Brantford, Charles, Coach Maker, res. King St.
Brase, Peter, Deputy Sheriff, res. Spring St.
Brawley, J. H., Dry Goods, 181 King St., res. Mills House
Brawley, J. M., Dry Goods, 181 East Bay St., res. Charleston Hotel
Brawley, James, Clerk, 220 King St.
Bredenberg, C. F., Grocer, cr. Calhoun & St. Philip Sts.
Bredenberg, John H., Grocer, cr. Broad & King Sts.
Bredenburg, J. J., Clerk, cr. Calhoun & St. Philip Sts.
Bredhaimer, William, Laborer, res. Meeting St.
Breese, William C., Cashier, Farmers & Exchange Bank, res. Maiden Lane
Bremer, Christopher, Blacksmith, State St.
Bremer, John, Clerk, 29 King St., res. 29 King St.
Brennan, Patrick, Laborer, res. 41 Wentworth St.
Brennan, Thomas, Drayman, res. 13 Marsh St.
Brentmyer, August, Clerk, res. Inspection St.
Brewer, John H., Printer 29 Pinckney St.
Brewer, Martha, Mrs., res. 175 King St.
Brewer, William, Laborer, res. St. Philip St.
Brewster, C. R., Lawyer, 65 Meeting St., res. Vanderhorst St.
Brewster, Christopher, Tailor, res. Cannon St.
Brewster, Walter S., Bookkeeper, 211 King St., res. Vanderhorst St.
Brickman, Henry, Engineer, South Carolina Railroad, res. Line St.
Brickwedel, James H., Ale & Port Maker, res. Lodge Alley
Bridell, Theodore F., Clerk, cr. Meeting & Market Sts.
Brideman, Henry, Mariner, res. State St.
Briggs, D., Painter, 94 Queen St.
Brinkard, William, Bricklayer, res. 18 Mazyck St.
Brisbin, Thomas, Stevadore, res. 13 Pinckney St.
Brissinden, H. J., Teacher, res. 99 Wentworth St.
Bristoll, Aristoa, Tailor, Meeting St., res. 12 Horlbeck Alley
Bristoll, James A., Clerk, 228 King St., res. 228 King St.
Bristoll, John D., Clerk, 232 King St., res. 228 King St.
Bristoll, Timothy M., Boots & Shoes, 232 King St., res.

232 King St.
Bristoll William B., Boots & Shoes, 228 King St., res. 228 King St.
Britton, John F., Printer, 119 East Bay St., res. 3 Whim's Court
Britton, Richard A., Printer, res. 9 Inspection St.
Broadfoot, John, Boot & Shoemaker, 43 Broad St.
Brock, Sandy, Molder, South Carolina Railroad, res. Cannon St.
Brodie, John, Lumber Factor, Broad St., res. 15 Queen St
Brodie, R. H., Planter, res. 45 Coming St.
Brodie, Robert, Lumber Factor, Broad St., res. Wentworth St.
Brodie, Thomas H., 21 Calhoun St. res. 21 Calhoun St.
Brookbank, William, Gas Fitter, 152 King St., res. 152 King St.
Brooker, Edward, Clerk, 211 King St., res. Merchants Hotel
Brooks & Schoen, Milliners & Dress Makers, 147 King St.
Brooks, Sarah, Mrs., Milliner, 147 King St., res. 147 King St.
Brosnehan, Daniel, Tavern, 18 Market St., res. 18 Market St.
Bross B., Police Officer, City Hall
Broughton, Alexander, Collector, res. New St.
Broughton, Martha, Mrs., res. Ann St.
Broughton, Philip, Mrs., res. 37 Society St.
Broughton, William W., Clerk, 235 King St., res. cr. Wentworth & King Sts.
Brower, William, Gilder, res. Henrietta St.
Brown & Hyams, Commission Merchants, Brown's Wharf
Brown & Porter, Lawyers, 32 Broad St.
Brown & Stone, China & Glassware, 147 Meeting St.
Brown, Alexander H., Lawyer, 32 Broad St., res. 105 Tradd St.
Brown, Alexander McD., Bookkeeper, 200 East Bay St., res. 8 Glebe St.
Brown, Allan, Clerk, 234 King St., res. 234 King St.
Brown, Andrew S., Clerk, 232 King St., res. Hasell St.
Brown, Anna C., Mrs., res. 39 Society St.
Brown, Benjamin H., China & Glassware, 147 Meeting St., res. 154 Meeting St.
Brown, C. P., Printer, 119 East Bay St., res. Carolina Hotel
Brown, E. G., Clerk, 19 Hayne St., res. Charleston Hotel
Brown, E. T., Clerk, 31 Hayne St., res. 29 Anson St.
Brown, Elizabeth, Colored, Mantuamaker, res. Coming St.
Brown, Gabriel B., Clerk, 246 King St., res. 2 Society St.
Brown, George, Grocer, 47 Broad St., res. 47 Broad St.
Brown, George H., Clerk, 147 Meeting St., res. Mary St.
Brown, George S., Clerk, 211 King St., res. 17 Pitt St.
Brown, George W., Commission Merchant, Brown's Wharf, res. 8 Montague St.
Brown, Geroge, Coach Trimmer, 142 Meeting St., res. 35 Society St.
Brown, Hannah, res. 2 Philadelphia St.
Brown, Issac, Clerk, 257 King St., res. 22 Meeting St.

Brown, J. P., Clerk, 145 Meeting St., res. 8 Montague St.
Brown, James, Clerk, Market St., res. Beaufain St.
Brown, James W., Teller, People's Bank, res. 2 George St.
Brown, James, Wharfinger, Boyce & Co. Wharf, res. 84 Meeting St.
Brown, John, Confectioner, 27 Tradd St., res. 27 Tradd St.
Brown, John, Laborer, res. Amherst St.
Brown, Julia, Mrs., res. 56 Beaufain St.
Brown, M. A., Mrs., res. Gadsen St.
Brown, M., Mrs., res. 23 Coming St.
Brown, Mary, Mrs., res. 39 Society St.
Brown, Peter, Colored, Barber, Elliot St., res. 3 Price's Alley
Brown, Peter W., Tinner, res. America St.
Brown, Pinckney, Teacher, Archdale St., res. 49 Anson St.
Brown, Robert & Co., Factors, 3 Southern Wharf
Brown, Robert, Clerk, 8 East Bay St., res. 41 Tradd St.
Brown, Robert E., Factor, 3 Southern Wharf, res. 43 Church St.
Brown, Robert, Factor, 3 Southern Wharf, res. 43 Church St.
Brown, Scott K., Stair Builder, res. 24 Coming St.
Brown, Thomas, Colored, Barber, 49 Broad St., res. Stoll's Alley
Brown, William S., Dentist, 294 King St., res. 294 King St.
Browne, John D., res. Calhoun St.
Browne, Robert C., Grain Merchant, 8 East Bay St., res. 41 Tradd St.
Brownell, M. F., Mrs., res. 95 Church St.
Brownfield, J. W., Clerk, State Bank, res. 26 Magazine St.
Browning & Leman, Dry Goods, 211 King St., cr. Market St.
Browning Andrew F., Dry Goods, 211 King St., res. Limehouse St.
Browning, Charlton H., Clerk, 211 King St.
Browning, John H., Clerk, 253 King St.
Brundes, William, Grocer, cr. Coming & George Sts.
Brung, John, Grocer, 18 Pinckney St., res. 18 Pinckney St.
Bruns, Henry, Teacher, res. cr. Wentworth & Pitt Sts.
Brunson, Wesley, Clerk, cr. King & George Sts.
Bryan, George S., Lawyer, 26 Broad St., res. 27 Church St.
Bryan, John, Appraiser, Custom House, res. President St.
Bryan, John, Laborer, res. Woolf St.
Bryan, Jonathan J., Bookkeeper, cr. Meeting & Pinckney Sts., res. 1 Hasell St.
Bryan, Michael, Clothing, King St., res. King St.
Bryan, Michael, Finisher, res. Meeting St.
Buchanan, Dinah, Colored, Midwife, 54 Anson St.
Buchanan, Hugh, Porter, 80 East Bay St., res. Cedar Court
Buchiet, Phillip, Baker, cr. Line & Meeting Sts.
Buck, Lewis, Grocer, cr. Coming & Spring Sts.
Buckheister, Andrew, Bookbinder, 101 East Bay St.

Bucking, John H., Painter, Coming St.

Bucklet, James, Tailor, 80 Meeting St., res. 80 Meeting St.

Budd, T. G., Commission Merchant, 76 East Bay St., res. 21 Anson St.

Budd, T. S. & T. G., Commission Merchants, 76 East Bay St.

Budd, T. S., Commission Merchant, 76 East Bay St., res. 21 Anson St.

Budds, J. D., Reporter, Standard Office

Buelow, Thomas, res. cr. Cannon & King Sts.

Buerro, A., Fruit & Cigars, 56 Market St., res. 56 Market St.

Buerro, Emanuel, Fruit, 101 King St., res. 101 King St.

Buhra, D., Laborer, res. cr. America & Blake Sts.

Buist, Charles B., 5th Lt. of the Guard, res. Victoria Hotel

Buist, George, Lawyer, Courthouse Square, res. 3 Rutledge St.

Buist, Henry, Lawyer, Courthouse Square, res. 3 Pitt St.

Bull, Edmund, Coppersmith, 138 East Bay St., res. 138 East Bay St.

Bull, Elias, Factor, East Bay St., res. Lynch & Bull Sts.

Bull, Swinton, Clerk, East Bay St., res. cr. Lynch & Bull Sts.

Bullock, Robert, Wheelwright, 4 Cumberland St., res. State St.

Bulwinkle, D., Grocer, Coming & Bull Sts., res. Coming & Bull Sts.

Bulwinkle, D., Grocer, cr. Meeting St. & Lightwood Alley, res. Queen St.

Bulwinkle, D., Grocer, cr. Queen & Mazyck Sts.

Bulwinkle, Debrick, Grocer, cr. Woolf & America Sts.

Bulwinkle, H., Grocer, 2 Archdale St.

Bulwinkle, Henry, Grocer, cr. Charlotte & Henrietta Sts.

Bulwinkle, Martin, Grocer, cr. Elizabeth & Ann Sts.

Bunch, Adger, Carpenter, res. Coming St.

Bunch, Dennis, Butcher, res. 98 Queen St.

Bunch, Robert, British Consul, res. 58 Tradd St.

Bunger, Charles R., Cigars & Tobacco, 263 King St., res. 263 King St.

Burch, John R., Tavern, cr. Reid & Hanover Sts.

Burch, Richard T., Clerk, cr. Reid & Hanover Sts.

Burckmyer & Moffett, Commission Merchants, 78 East Bay St.

Burckmyer, Cornelius L., res. 26 Society St.

Burckmyer, J. A., Commission Merchant, 98 East Bay St., res. 106 Tradd St.

Burckmyer, J. C., Commission Merchant, 78 East Bay St., res. Society St.

Burckmyer, John, Commission Merchant, Accomodation Wharf, res. 106 Tradd St.

Burckmyer, Sarah, Colored, Mantuamaker, res. Calhoun St.

Burdell, Edward, Bookkeeper, Hayne St., res. Chapel St.

Burdell, Francis C., Bookkeeper, 25 Hayne St.

Burdell, R., Mrs., res. Chapel St.

Burdell, Sarah, Colored, Washerwoman, res. Cannon St.

Burdell, Thomas J., Clerk, 306 King St., res. 13 Franklin St.

Burdell, Thomas S., Bookkeeper, Hayne St., res. Chapel St.

Burden, K., Jr., Clerk, 151 East Bay St., res. New St.

Burden, Kinsie, Clerk, 133 Meeting St., res. Tradd & Logan Sts.

Burden, William B., Clerk, 133 Meeting St., res. Logan St.

Burdick, Phillip T., Clerk, 253 King St., res. cr. Wentworth & King Sts.

Burge, W. Troup, Clerk, 211 King St., res. Charleston Hotel

Burger, S. J., Bookkeeper, 16 Hayne, res. 63 Beaufain St.

Burke, A. J., Job Printer, 40 Broad St., res. 23 Tradd St.

Burke, Dennis, Carpenter, res. 1 Philadelphia St.

Burke, Edward, Carpenter, res. Line St.

Burke, Ellen, Mrs., res. 1 Philadelphia St.

Burke, J. W., Clerk, 118 Meeting St., res. State St.

Burke, James, Dry Goods, 186 King St., res. 186 King St.

Burke, James, Dry Goods, 136 King St., res. 136 King St.

Burke, John, Clerk, 165 Meeting St.

Burke, John, Clerk, cr. Meeting & Hasell Sts., res. 40 St. Philip St.

Burke, John, Pilot, res. 7 Church St.

Burke, Joseph, Rags, etc., res. Calhoun St.

Burke, M. W., Porter, 143 Meeting St., res. 80 Market St.

Burke, O., Dry Goods, 5 St. Philip St., res. 5 St. Philip St.

Burke, Samuel, Boat Builder, foot of Market St., res. 33 Wall St.

Burke, William, Pilot, res. 7 Church St.

Burkett, H. D., Clerk., 149 Meeting St., res. 3 Society St.

Burleigh, William H., Dry Goods, 41 King St., res. 41 King St.

Burnham, Eliza, Mrs., res. Laurens St.

Burnham, Robert W., Dry Goods, 343 King St., res. 343 King St.

Burns, David M., Baker, cr. Tradd & Meeting Sts., res. cr. Tradd & Meeting Sts.

Burns, Edward, Blacksmith, cr. Meeting & John Sts., res. Coming St.

Burns, Edward, Laborer, res. State St.

Burns, Garrett, Tavern, 18 Queen St., res. 18 Queen St.

Burns, Henry, Seaman, res. Cannon St.

Burns, James, Shoemaker, 62 State St., res. 62 State St.

Burns, John, Conductor, South Carolina Railroad, res. St. Philip St.

Burns, John, Factor, Kerr's Wharf, res. 56 King St.

Burns, John, Merchant, 127 East Bay St., res. 52 Church St.

Burns, John, Mrs., Private Boarding, 32 Queen St.

Burns, Julia, Grocer, cr. Laurel & Bogard Sts.

Burns, Micheal, Blacksmith, res. Woolf St.

Burns, O. J., Clerk, 165 Meeting St., res. Merchants Hotel

Burns, Robert S., Clerk, 211 King St., res. cr. Wentworth & Pitt Sts.

Burns, Rose, Mrs., Cakes, etc., res. King St.

Burns, T. A., Wharfinger, Vanderhorst's Wharf, res. cr. Coming & Wentworth Sts.

Burnside, A., Factor, South Atlantic Wharf, res. Augusta, Ga.

Burnside, H., res. 27 Bull St.

Burnside, James, Boots & Shoes, 137 King St., res. 137 King St.

Burrell & Patch, Door & Sash Manufacturers, Rutledge St.

Burrows, Charles, Carpenter, res. 20 Church St.

Burrows, Frederick, Pilot, res. 20 Church St.

Burrows, Henry, Pilot, res. 20 Church St.

Burrows, James, Carpenter, res. 20 Church St.

Burrows, Samuel, Pilot, Schooner Palmetto, res. 31 Meeting St.

Bursch, Charles, Cabinet Maker, 143 King St., res. 143 King St.

Busby, G. W., Bricklayer, res. St. Philip St.

Busby, John, Tailor, cr. East Bay & Queen Sts., res. 3 Whim's Court

Busch, John, Clerk, cr. Laurel & Bogard Sts.

Busch, Steven, Grocer, cr. Laurel & Bogard Sts.

Buse, John F., Grocer, cr. Ashley & Palmetto Sts.

Bush, Levi, Clothing, 339 King St., res. 339 King St.

Bushel, James G., Carpenter, 26 Queen St., res. Logan St.

Bushing, Henry, Fruit, res. St. Philip St.

Butler, Andrew, Marble Polisher, Anson St., res. 14 Market St.

Butler, Charles, res. 123 Wentworth St.

Butler, Mary, Mrs., res. Elizabeth St.

Butler, Richard M., Commission Merchant, 165 East Bay St., res. 17 Wentworth St.

Butler, Thomas, Laborer, res. Columbus St.

Butoul, A., Mrs., Confectionery & Fruit, res. King St., 8th ward

Butterfield, H. L., Proprietor, Pavilion Hotel, cr. Meeting & Hasell Sts.

Butts, Frederick J., Mariner, res. Woolf St.

Butts, John A., Printer, 111 East Bay St., res. 99 East Bay St.

Byron, James, Colored, Wheelwright, res. Calhoun St.

Byron, John, Colored, Wheelwright, res. Calhoun St.

Byron, Joseph, Colored, Wheelwright, res. Calhoun St.

Cadow, William, Dry Goods, 171 East Bay St., res. Charleston Hotel

Cahaw, Joseph, Harness Maker, Meeting St., res. Calhoun St.

Cahill, Martin, Laborer, res. Cannon St.

Cahill, William, Tavern, John St., res. John St.

Cain, Dennis, Tavern, 50 State St., res. 50 State St.

Cain, James, Physician, res. 20 Wentworth St.

Calahan, James, Laborer, res. Anson St.

Calahan, Mary, Mrs., Milk Dairy, 5 Linguard St.

Calahan, Thomas, res. Mary St.

Calder, Alexander, Auctioneer & Commission Merchant, 26 Vendue Range, res. 6 Beaufain St.

Calder, George, Clerk, 246 King St., res. 246 King St.

Calder, James, Cabinet Maker, res. 6 Beaufain St.

Calder, James, Jr., Bookkeeper, 173 East Bay St., res. 246 King St.

Calder, James M., Factor, Boyce's North Wharf

Calder, William, Dry Goods, 246 & 248 King St., res. 246 King St.

Caldwell & Brother, Upholsterers & Paper Hangers, 220 King St.

Caldwell, A. P., Commission Merchant, 27 Vendue Range, res. 74 Meeting St.

Caldwell, A. W., Ship Broker, 38 East Bay St., res. 63 Wentworth St.

Caldwell, Blakely & Co., Commission Merchants, Central Wharf

Caldwell, E. A., Clerk, 14 Central Wharf, res. Warren St.

Caldwell, J. W., Ship Broker, 38 East Bay St., res. 63 Wentworth St.

Caldwell, James M., Commission Merchant, North Atlantic Wharf, res. Judith St.

Caldwell, James, Upholsterer, 220 King St., res. cr. South Bay & King Sts.

Caldwell, John, Jr., Upholsterer, 220 King St., res. Merchants Hotel

Caldwell, R. & A. P., Commission Merchants, 27 Vendue Range

Caldwell, Richard, Commission Merchant, 2 Vendue Range, res. 65 Wentworth St.

Caldwell, Robert, Commission Merchant, Central Wharf, res. New York

Caldwell, W. S., Discount Clerk, Bank of South Carolina

Calvitt, John M., Blacksmith, Meeting St., res. Woolf St.

Cambridge, Charles C., Bookkeeper, cr. State & Chalmers Sts., res. 8 Calhoun St.

Cambridge, Joseph, Colored, Carpenter, res. Duncan St.

Cameron, Eliza, Mrs., res. Bull St.

Cameron, John, Plumber, 31 Broad St., res. Calhoun St.

Caminade, H., Mrs., Private Boarding, 21 Pinckney St.

Caminade, Henry, Machinist, Engineer, South Carolina Railroad, res. 44 Queen St.

Caminade, Henry, Mechanic, res. 21 Pinckney St.

Campbell, C. E., Tailor, 39 Broad St., res. Queen St.

Campbell, J. B., Lawyer, 40 Broad St., res. 84 Beaufain St.

Campbell, James M., Physician, Office 89 Broad St., res. 89 Broad St.

Campbell, James T., Clerk, 21 Vendue Range, res. 89 Broad St.

Campbell, John B., Pastor, St. Philip's Church, res. cr. Franklin & Shote Sts.

Campbell, John, Carpenter, res. 46 Bull St.

Campbell, Laurence F., Barber, King St., Upper Wards

Campbell, Mary T., Mrs., res. Meeting St., Upper Wards

Campbell, Owen, Bricklayer, res. 89 Broad St.

Campbell, W. M., Commission Merchant, 171 East Bay St., res. 155 East Bay St.

Campsen & Ellerhorst, Grain Merchants, 6 Market St.

Campsen, Henry, Dry Goods, 140 King St., res. 159 King St.

Campsen, Henty C., Boot & Shoemaker, 329 King St., res. 329 King St.

Campsen, J. F., Grocer, cr. Meeting & Queen Sts., res. cr. Meeting & Queen Sts.

Campsen, John, Grain Merchant, 6 Market St., res. cr. East Bay & Anson Sts.

Canady, A., Dry Goods, 181 East Bay St., res. Charleston Hotel

Canale, A., Fruiter, 11 Market St., res. 11 Market St.

Candler, Edward, Nautical Store, 69 East Bay St.

Canning, Charles, Printer, Christian Advocate Office, res. 24 Atlantic St.

Cannon, Catherine A., Mrs., res. St. Philip St., 8th Ward

Cannon, George, Clerk, 211 King St., res. 74 Wentworth St.

Cannon, Jeremiah, Sea Captian, res. St. Philip St.

Canter, R. M., Mrs., res. 18 Savage St.

Cantrell, Elizabeth, Mrs., res. 11 Marsh St.

Cantwell, Drayton, Clerk, 151 Meeting St., res. Washington St.

Cantwell, L., Clerk, 143 East Bay St., res. Church St.

Cantwell, P., Clerk, 42 Broad St., res. 72 Queen St.

Cantwick, Thomas, Laborer, res. St. Philip St.

Capers & Heyward, Auctioneers, Vanderhorst's Wharf

Capers, Thomas F., Auctioneer, Vanderhorst's Wharf, res. 12 Legare St.

Cappel, A. J., Baker, 113 Meeting St., res. 113 Meeting St.

Carberry, James, Merchant, East Bay St., res. Elizabeth St.

Carberry John, Bookkeeper, Kerr's Wharf, res. Elizabeth St., 8th Ward

Carcens, Adolf, Clerk, res. Line & Rutledge Sts.

Cardo, Joseph, Tavern, Colombus St.

Cardozo, Emeline, Colored, Seamstress, res. Duncan St.

Cardozo, Isaac, Weigher, Custom House, res. 204 East Bay St.

Cardozo, J. N., Assistant Editor, Evening News, res. 249 King St.

Carew, John E., Planter, Goose Creek, res. Blake & America Sts.

Carew, William G., Wharfinger, Adger's Wharf, res. 1 Orange St.

Carey, Catherine, Mrs., res. 1 Bedons Alley

Carey, E. M., Druggist, 35 Broad St., res. 35 Broad St.

Carey, George, Bookkeeper, 311 King St., res. Queen St.

Carey, James, Custom House, res. 204 East Bay St.

Carey, John, Laborer, res. 11 Anson St.

Carle, James, Blacksmith, Liberty St., res. Radcliffe St.

Carlisle, W. B., Editor, 11 East Bay St., res. Pavilion Hotel

Carmalt & Briggs, Paints & Oils, 97 East Bay St.

Carmalt, J. W., Paints, Oils, etc., 97 East Bay St., res. Whim's Court

Carmidy, John, Laborer, res. President St.

Carmidy, John, Porter, 141 East Bay St., res. 4 Ashley St.

Carney, Peter, Porter, 200 East Bay St.

Carnighan, John, Pilot, Schooner Charleston, res. 71 Tradd St.

Carpenter, William, Plasterer, res. Queen St.

Carr, C. D. & Co., Merchant Tailors, 30 Broad St.

Carr, Charles D., Merchant Tailor, 30 Broad St., res. 21 Meeting St.

Carr, Henry W., Merchant Tailor, 30 Broad St., res. 21 Meeting St.

Carr, John, Printer, 119 East Bay St., res. Mount Pleasant

Carr, Joseph P., Lawyer, 38 Broad St., res. 21 Meeting St.

Carriere, M. E., Physician, res. Radcliffe St.

Carriere, W. G., Wharfinger, Adger's Wharf, res. 1 Orange

Carrington, William & Co., Jewellers, 256 King St.

Carrington, William, Jeweller, 256 King St., res. 77 Wentworth St.

Carroll, Alexander, Assistant Editor, Courier, res. Pavilion Hotel

Carroll, B. R., Teacher, King St., 5th Ward

Carroll, C. R., Planter, Barnwell, South Carolina, res. Pitt St.

Carroll, James, Boots & Shoes, 65 Anson St., res. 65 Anson St.

Carroll, Patrick, Blacksmith, res. 16 Mazyck St.

Carroll, Thomas, Boots & Shoes, 174 East Bay St., res. 174 East Bay St.

Carroll, Thomas, Porter, 139 Meeting St., res. Calhoun St.

Carson & Son, Factors & Commission Merchants, 7 Boyce's Wharf

Carson, Elisha, Factor, 7 Boyce's Wharf, res. Rutledge St.

Carson, Elizabeth, Mrs., res. Ann St.

Carson, James M., Factor, 7 Boyce's Wharf, res. Rutledge St.

Carson, William M., Factor, 7 Boyce's Wharf, res. Rutledge St.

Carsten, C., Saddler, 45 Broad St., res. 167 East Bay St.

Carsten, E. H., Police Officer, res. 24 Montague St.

Cart, F. G., Bookkeeper, 165 East Bay St., res. Calhoun St.

Cart, G., res. 26 Bull St.

Carter, Alex, Books & Stationery, 163 Meeting St., res. Charleston Hotel

Carter, E., Mrs., Flour & Feed Store, 48 Queen St., res. 48 Queen St.

Carter, John G., Clerk, 122 Meeting St., res. American Hotel

Carter, Laura, Colored, Mantuamaker, Calhoun St.

Cartledge, John G., Clerk, Bookkeeper, 145 Meeting St., res. Charleston Hotel

Carver, John, Sea Captain, res. 85 Tradd St.

Casen, Edward, Carpenter, res. Drake & Blake Sts.

Casey, Henry, City Inspector, res. 13 Franklin St.

Casey, Thomas, Blacksmith, res. Calhoun St.

Cassen, Washington, Tinsmith, 2 Queen St., res. 2 Queen St.

Cassiday, Charles R., res. Amherst St.

Cassiday, Charles, Superintendent of Drays, Woolf St., near Meeting St.

Cassiday, Edward, House Carpenter, res. 8 Horlbeck Alley

Casswell, William, res. Henrietta St.

Casten, George, Tavern, cr. Elizabeth & Henrietta Sts.

Castion, John C., Colored, Tobacconist, St. Philip St., res. Duncan St.

Castion, Mary, Colored, Mantuamaker, Duncan St.

Castion, Thomas, Dry Goods, cr. Tradd St. & Bedons Alley

Castle, Louisa, Colored, Mantuamaker, res. Coming St.

Cater, T. M., Auctioneer, 24 Vendue Range, res. President St.

Cattle, Robert, Drayman, res. Ashley St.

Caulfield, James, Clerk, 171 King St., res. King St.

Caulier, George, Physician, 152 Meeting St., res. Meeting St.

Caulker, George, Fisherman, res. 12 Vernon St.

Causse, Robert, Dry Goods, 304 King St., res. Radcliffe St.

Cavanaugh, George, Bartender, 107 East Bay St., res. City Hotel

Cavarro, Elizabeth, Mrs., res. Mary St.

Cay, J. Alfred, Commission Merchant, Union Wharf, res. cr. Meeting & George Sts.

Chafee & Clarke, Liquor Merchants, 179 East Bay St.

Chafee, C. H., Liquors, 163 East Bay St., res. cr. Hasell & East Bay Sts.

Chafee, O. G., Liquor Merchant, 179 East Bay St., res. cr. John & Meeting Sts.

Chaffee, Sarah A., Mrs., res. cr. Hasell & East Bay Sts.

Chaffee, St. Armand & Croft, Liquor & Tobacco, 179 East Bay St.

Chalk, John G., Superintentent, Northeastern Railroad, res. Morris St.

Chamberlain, Charles V., Dry Goods, 143 Meeting St., res. 34 St. Philip St.

Chamberlain, Joseph, Bookkeeper, 258 King St., res. 73 Tradd St.

Chamberlain, Miller & Co., Dry Goods, 143 Meeting St.

Chambers, J. S., Factor, South Atlantic Wharf, res. 2 Hudson St.

Chambers, J. W., Bookkeeper, Chambers, Jeffords, & Co., res. 2 Hudson St.

Chambers, James, Factor, Exchange, res. 2 Hudson St.

Chambers, James, Merchant, Broad St., res. 28 Market St.

Chambers, Jeffords & Co., Factors & Commission Merchants, South Atlantic Wharf

Champlin, A. J., Mason, res. Trapmann St.

Champlin, William E., Mason, res. Trapmann St.

Chapin, Leonard, Coachmaker, 142 Meeting St., res. 40 Wentworth St.

Chaplin, William, Clerk, 356 King St.

Chapman & Wienges, Commission Merchants, Exchange St.

Chapman, Edward, Bookkeeper, res. 1 Pinckney St.

Chapman, James, Commission Merchant, Exchange St., res. 4 Water St.

Chapman, Perry, Pilot, res. 1 Atlantic St.

Chapman, R. B., Commission Merchant, Exchange, res. 4 Water St.

Chapman, Richard, Blacksmith, 37 Calhoun St., res. 37 Calhoun St.

Chapman, Samuel, Pilot, res. 33 Tradd St.

Chapman Thomas, res. St. Philip St.

Chapman, William H., Clerk, 173 East Bay St., res. King St.

Chappeaux, Mary, Mrs., res. 94 Church St.

Chappeaux, Phelix, res. 94 Church St.

Chappeaux, Thomas T., Clerk, 6 Broad St., res. 94 Church St.

Charlon, James, Speculator, res. Line St.

Charlon, John, Blacksmith, Workshop of the South Carolina Railroad

Charlon, Peter, Engineer, South Carolina Railroad, res. St. Philip St.

Charrar, John E., Grocer, East Bay St., res. Rutledge St.

Chase, James P., Wharfinger, Union Wharf, res. 111 Church St.

Chase, Phillip A., Clerk, 232 King St., res. 96 Queen St.

Chase, Phillip S., Clerk, 142 King St., res. 96 Queen St.

Chavez & Miller, Grocers, 106 East Bay St.

Chavez, R. G., Grocer, 106 East Bay St., res. 76 Green St.

Chazal, John P., Physician, res. Anson St.

Cheesborough, Eliza, Miss, res. 18 Church St.

Cheesborough, John, Assistant Cashier, Bank of Charleston, res. 16 Laurens St.

Cheney, E., Clerk, 57 East Bay St., res. 99 East Bay St.

Cheney, F., Mrs., Private Boarding House, 99 East Bay St.

Cherrill, Edward, Millinery Goods, 188 King St., res. 188 King St.

Cherry, John, Laborer, res. Line St.

Chew, Thomas R., Blacksmith, 3 Market St., res. 3 Market St.

Childs, Jane, Mrs., res. Vanderhorst St.

Chion, Thomas C., Tailor, res. Cannon St.

Chisholm, John J., Physician, 20 Wentworth St., res. 20 Wentworth St.

Chisholm, Caroline, Colored, Mantuamaker, 101 King St., res. 101 King St.

Chisolm, Casper A., Chisolm's Mill, res. Rutledge St.

Chisolm, Diana, Colored, Dressmaker, 101 King St., res. 101 King St.

Chisolm, Elizabeth, Colored, Mantuamaker, res. 18 Washington St.

Chisolm, H. L., Forwarding & Commission Merchant, South Atlantic Wharf, res. 13 Hasell St.

Chisolm, John M., Mrs., res. 45 Anson St.

Chisolm, Octavius, Auctioneer, 33 Broad St., res. cr. Church & Water Sts.

Chisolm, Robert F., Chisolm's Mills, res. Rutledge St.

Chisolm, Robert G., Chisolm's Mills, res. Rutledge St.

Chisolm. P. H., Mrs., res. cr. Meeting St. & Wragg Square

Chitter, Joseph, Carpenter, 7 Princess St., res. 7 Princess St.

Choate, Thomas, Collector, res. 104 Tradd St.

Choisel, Count X. De., French Consul, 30 Broad St., res. 30 Broad St.

Chrietzberg, J. R., Carpenter, 265 East Bay St., res. King St.

Chrietzberg, R. S., Carpenter, 60 Wentworth St., res. 60 Wentworth St.

Chrietzburg, Thomas, Carpenter, res. 21 Beaufain St.

Christ, John, Boot & Shoemaker, 105 Church St., res. 105 Church St.

Christian, Peter, Ferryboat Captain, Market Wharf, res. 84 Anson St.

Christiansen, Jasper, Grocer, 180 King St., res. 180 King St.

Christie, David L., Sash & Blindmaker, res. St. Philip St.

Christopher, George, Miller, foot of Calhoun St., res. Calhoun St.

Chroder, C. F., Cabinet Maker, res. 10 Liberty St.

Chupein, L.Y., Confectioner, 105 East Bay St., res. 105 East Bay St.

Chupein, Theodore F., Dentist, 223 East Bay St., res. 105 East Bay St.

Church, Charles A. D., Printer, 111 East Bay St., res. 30 Queen St.

Church, Joseph F., Plumber, 31 Broad St., res. 28 Calhoun St.

Church, S. A., Saddlery, cr. Meeting & Hasell Sts.

Cigney, John J., Teacher, res. St. Philip St.

Cilstrove, John P., res. 86 King St.

Clacius, C., Bookkeeper, 92 East Bay St.

Clancy, John, Engineer, South Carolina Railroad, res. Warren St.

Clancy, William, Clerk, Post Office, res. Warren St.

Clarke, Charles, Druggist, 33 Market St., res. 6 Anson St.

Clarke, D. Otis, Liquors, 163 East Bay St., res. 163 East Bay St.

Clarke, Francis, Proprietor, Union Coffee House, Cumberland St.

Clarke, Henry B., Clerk, 149 Meeting St., res. 22 Bull St.

Clarke, Henry, Lumber Merchant, 89 Beaufain St., res. 100 Beaufain St.

Clarke, Hyde, & Co., Hardware, 139 Meeting St.

Clarke, John, Turner, Gadsden St., res. Gadsden St.

Clarke, Richard, Port Warden, res. 11 Church St.

Clarke, Robert A., Hardware, 139 Meeting St., res. 11 George St.

Clarke, Thomas A. G., Clerk, 213 King St., res. Commercial House

Clarke, William, Tavern, 20 Queen St., res. 20 Queen St.

Clarkson & Mey, Factors & Commission Merchants, Central Wharf

Clarkson, Robert H., Factor, Central Wharf, res. Smith St. & Montague St.

Clary, Patrick, Laborer, res. 182 East Bay St.

Claussen Brothers, Bakers, 183 East Bay St.

Claussen, David B., Bookkeeper, 147 Meeting St., res. Pavilion Hotel

Claussen, F.W., Baker, 183 East Bay St., res. 183 East Bay St.

Claussen, J. C. H., Baker, 183 East Bay St., res. 183 East Bay St.

Claussen John C., Sexton, German Luthern Church, res. Spring St.

Clayton, V. L. A., Printer, 3 Broad St., res. Queen St.

Clayton, William C., Printer, 3 Broad St., res. Queen St.

Clayton, William, Carpenter, Queen St., res. 17 South Bay St.

Cleapor, Charles W., Clerk, 110 East Bay St., res. 136 East Bay St.

Cleapor, Mary, Mrs., res. 136 East Bay St.

Cleapor, P. L., Clerk, 110 East Bay St., res. 136 East Bay St.

Cleary, Patrick, Laborer, res. Woolf St., near America St.

Cleland, Joseph, Clerk, 34 Broad St.

Clement, J. Pinckney, Superintendent of Streets, res. Amherst St.

Cleveland, William L., Physician, 217 King St.

Clifford, A. R., Carpenter, 17½ State St., res. 8 Laurens St.

Cline, Emmet, Laborer, res. America St.

Clinton, E. J. D., Physician, 8 Market St., res. 8 Market St.

Clinton, Margaret, Miss, res. 6 West St.

Clipper, Henry, Ship Carpenter, res. Vernon St.

Clipper, James, Carpenter, res. Coming St.

Cliver, Christopher, Laborer, res. Warren St.

Close, Langford P. H., res. Spring St.

Clyde & Beckman, Tavern, King St., Upper Ward

Clyde, H., Tavern, King St., res. Mary St.

Clyde, Thomas E., Grocer, res. 188 Meeting St.

Coates, William, Ship Cotton Press, res. 8 Bull St.

Cobb, E. W., Boots & Shoes, 141 Meeting St., res. Tradd St.

Cobert, Henry, Bookkeeper, East Bay St., res. 61 Beaufain St.

Cobert, Thomas, Bookkeeper, East Bay St., res. 61 Beaufain St.

Cobia, Francis, Col., res. cr. Reid & Meeting Sts.

Cobia, Henry & Co., Auctioneers & Commission Merchants, 26 Vendue Range

Cobia, Henry, Auctioneer, 26 Vendue Range, res. 88 Wentworth St.

Cobia, William, Carpenter, res. Woolf St., near King St.

Coburn, Peter R., Superintendent, 1st Division South Carolina Railroad, res. Spring St.

Coby, Edward, Carpenter, res. Line St.

Cochran, Adelaide, Mrs., res. Ann St.

Cochran, John C., Cashier, Southwest Railroad Bank, res. Drake St.

Cochran, Louisa, Colored, Mantuamaker, res. St. Philip St.

Cochran, Patrick, Laborer, res. Bogard St.

Cochran, Stephen, Carpenter, res. Coming St.

Cochran, Thomas, Cabinet Maker, res. Calhoun St.

Cochran, W. S., Receiving Teller, Southwest Railroad Bank, res. Warren St.

Coffee, Thomas, Laborer, res. 7 Tradd St.

Coffin & Pringle, Factors & Commission Merchants, 7 Adger's North Wharf

Coffin, George M., Factor, 7 Adger's North Wharf, res. 86 Broad St.

Cogdell, C. S., Assistant Clerk, Bank of the State of South Carolina

Cogswell, Harvey, Clerk, 131 Meeting St., res. 4 St. Philip St.

Cohen & Jacobi, Clothing, 341 King St.

Cohen, Aaron, Clothing, 261 King St., res. New York

Cohen, David E., res. Chapel St.

Cohen, G., Clerk, 19 Hayne St., res. Church St.
Cohen, H., Mrs., Fruit, 71 Market St., res. 71 Market St.
Cohen, Hartung, res. Warren St.
Cohen, Isaac S., Auctioneer, East Bay St., res. 15 Society St.
Cohen, J. S., Auctioneer, 29 Vendue Range, res. 15 Society St.
Cohen, Jacob, Broker & Auctioneer, 29 Broad St., res. 12 Friend St.
Cohen, Jacob H., Clothing, 125 East Bay St., res. 46 Meeting St.
Cohen, John J., Factor, Accommodation Wharf, res. 20 Coming St.
Cohen, Leopold, Clerk, 261 King St., res. 46 Meeting St.
Cohen, Lewis, Clothing, 341 King St., res. King St.
Cohen, Marx E., Planter, res. Ashley St.
Cohen, Melvin M., Student, 77 Broad St., res. 4 Society St.
Cohen, N. A., Clothing, 261 King St., res. 48 Meeting St.
Cohen, P. M. & Co., Druggist, 29 Hayne St.
Cohen, Phillip M., Druggist, 29 Hayne St., res. 4 Society St.
Cohen, Phillip, res. 8 Wentworth St.
Cohrs, C. H., Dry Goods, 171 East Bay St., res. Charleston Hotel
Colbert, John, Bookkeeper, Adger's Wharf, res. Line St.
Colbert, John, Painter, res. Queen St.
Colburn & Holland, Dry Goods, cr. King & Broad Sts.
Colburn, Benjamin P., Planter, res. cr. Elizabeth & Charlotte Sts.
Culburn, J. H., Clerk, 244 King St., res. Wall St.
Colburn, James S., Dry Goods, cr. King & Broad Sts., res. cr. King & Broad Sts.
Colcock, Charles J., Commission Merchant, North Atlantic Wharf, res. cr. Tradd & Limehouse Sts.
Colcock, John, Factor, North Commercial Wharf, res. 2 Orange St.
Colcock, Richard H., Clerk, Legare & Colcock, res. 2 Orange St.
Colcock, Thomas, Clerk, East Bay St., res. 2 Orange St.
Colcock, W. F., Collector, res. cr. Short & Mazyck Sts.
Cole, Albert, Baker, res. King St.
Cole, George F., Piano & Music, 175 King St., res. 175 King St.
Cole, Sophia, Mrs., Dry Goods, King St., Upper Wards
Cole, William R., Printer, res. 99 East Bay St.
Coleman, Dederick, Grocer, cr. Coming & Warren Sts.
Coleman, James, Laborer, South Carolina Railroad, res. Morris St.
Coleman, William, Laborer, res. Marsh St.
Collins, James M., Teacher, 86 Anson St., res. 86 Anson St.
Collins, Michael, Carpenter, res. cr. Mary & Nassau Sts.
Collins, Richard, Dry Goods, 124 Church St., res. 124 Church St.
Collins, Sarah, Mrs., res. 42 King St.
Collins, Timothy, Drayman, res. cr. America & Woolf Sts.
Collough, Patrick, Laborer, res. 9 Marsh St.
Colman, G. & J., Dry Goods, 217 King St.

Colman, George, Dry Goods, 217 King St., res. 228 King St.
Colman, Joseph, Dry Goods, 217 King St., res. 228 King St.
Colson, Charles, Dry Goods, 27 Middle St., res. 27 Middle St.
Combs & Co., Express, cr. Market & Meeting Sts.
Combs, S. T., Express, cr. Market & Meeting Sts., res. Augusta, Ga.
Commins, John, Boots & Shoes, 274 King St., res. 274 King St.
Commins, M., Fancy Goods, 278 King St., res. 278 King St.
Comstock, D. B., Bookkeeper, 122 Meeting St., res. cr. Tradd & Friend Sts.
Conaway, Ferdinand, Carpenter, 67 Anson St., res. 67 Anson St.
Condict, J. E., Clerk, 157 Meeting St.
Condict, Stephen H., Saddlery, 157 Meeting St., res. Newark, N. J.
Condy, Thomas D., U. S. Marshal, res. Rutledge St.
Conklin, Mary, Mrs., res. Nassau St.
Conley, Barney, Boarding House, 21 Tradd St.
Conley, Benjamin, Boots & Shoes, 21 Hayne St., res. Augusta, Ga.
Connell, Michael, Laborer, res. Woolf St., near King St.
Conner, Alexander, Boiler Maker, Hasell St., res. 22 Washington St.
Conner, Charles, Molder, res. 22 Washington St.
Conner, Daniel, Blacksmith, Meeting St., res. Tradd St.
Conner, George, Bookkeeper, 161 Meeting St., res. Broad St.
Conner, George, Hats & Caps, Calhoun St.
Conner, Henry W., Banker, 13 Broad St., res. 9 Meeting St.
Conner, Henry W., Jr., Clerk, 13 Broad St., res. 9 Meeting St.
Conner, James, Lawyer, 13 Broad St., res. 9 Meeting St.
Conner, Michael, Laborer, 178 East Bay St., res. 10 Philadelphia St.
Conner, William J., Jeweler, 250 King St., res. Wentworth St.
Conneville, Jacob, Colored, Barber, 10 Queen St., res. 10 Queen St.
Connoly, John, Blacksmith, 28 Pinckney St., res. 9 Vernon St.
Constantine, Alexander, Tavern, cr. Church & Tradd Sts.
Conway, Samuel, Bricklayer, res. 83 Queen St.
Coogan, P. G., Bar Room, 157 East Bay St., res. 157 East Bay St.
Cook, George S., Daguerrean Artist, 235 King St., res. 260 King St.
Cook, James E., Clerk, 302 King St., res. 302 King St.
Cook, John A., Grocer, cr. Mary & King Sts., res. cr. Mary & King Sts.
Cook, William, 308 King St., res. 308 King St.
Cook, William, Cigars & Tobacco, 92 Meeting St., res. Market St.
Cooper & Rivers, Lawyers, 49 Broad St.
Cooper, George W., Lawyer, 49 Broad St., res. Queen St.

Cooper, William, Cooper, res. Morris St.
Copes, James A., Proprietor, Cotton Press, cr. Chalmers & Church Sts.
Corbet, James, Clerk, 322 King St., res. 322 King St.
Corbet, James N., Dry Goods, 322 King St., res. 322 King St.
Corcoran, C. B., Teacher, High School, res. 27 Legare St.
Corcoran, Ellen, Mrs., res. Doughty St.
Corcoran, Hannah, res. President St.
Corcoran, James, Drayman, res. Heyward's Court
Corcoran, John, Conductor, South Carolina Railroad, res. Meeting St.
Corcoran, John M., Bookkeeper, 147 East Bay St., res. 65 Beaufain St.
Corcoran, Patrick, Laborer, res. Woolf St., near King St.
Corcoran, Timothy D., Conductor, South Carolina Railroad, res. Mary St.
Cordes, Dedrick, Grocer, cr. Charlotte & Washington Sts.
Cordes, George, Grocer, 56 Anson St., res. 56 Anson St.
Cordes, Theodore, Liquors, 55 Market St., res. 55 Market St.
Cordray, Edmund, Ship Carpenter, 1 Pinckney St., res. 2 Hard Alley
Cordray, Lewis E., Ship Carpenter, 1 Pritchard St., res. 2 Hard Alley
Corkle, Edward C., Printer, 111 East Bay St.
Cormier, William, Boiler Maker, res. Meeting St.
Cornwall, Ezra H., Agent for Adam's Patent Gas Burner, Hatch's Hall, Hasell St.
Cornwall, Ezra H., Clerk, 243 King St., res. 3 Hatch's Hall, Hasell St.
Corrie, Samuel, Clerk, cr. Hayne & Meeting Sts., res. Charleston Hotel
Corrigan, James, Dry Goods, 83 Church St., res. 83 Church St.
Corrigan, P. M., Boots & Shoes, 78 Church St., res. 78 Church St.
Cosgrove, James, Soda Water Manufactory, 37 Market St.
Costa, V., Mrs., Dry Goods, 10 King St., res. 10 King St.
Cotchett, C. M., Cotton Broker, Boyce's North Wharf
Cotchett, George, Clerk, Southern Commercial Wharf, res. Beaufain St.
Courier, C., Mrs., res. 7 Tradd St.
Courtenay, C., res. Mary St., near King St.
Courtenay, Edward S., Boarding Officer, Custom House, res. East Bay St.
Courtenay, S. G. & Co., Books & Stationery, 3 Broad St.
Courtenay, S. Gilman, Books, etc., 3 Broad St., res. 3 Green St.
Courtenay, William A., Books, etc., 3 Broad St., res. cr. East Bay & Hasell Sts.
Courtney, Tennent & Co., Hardware, 35 Hayne St.
Courtney, William C., Hardware, 35 Hayne St., res. Meeting St.
Coutrier, J. R. E., Teller, Bank of Charleston, res. 249 East Bay St.
Covert, Henry C., Gas Fixtures, 201 King St., res. 61 Beaufain St.
Covert, Thomas N., Bookkeeper, 118 Meeting St., res. 61 Beaufain St.
Cowperthwaite, Edwin R., Furniture, 267 King St., res. 76 Beaufain St.
Coyne, Thomas, Laborer, res. 182 East Bay St.
Crabtree, Addison D., Carpenter, 161 King St., res. 116 King St.
Crabtree, Seth H., Carpenter, 161 King St., res. 116 King St.
Crafts, William J., Clerk, 111 East Bay St., res. Queen St.
Cragan, James, Laborer, res. President St.
Cramer, George W., Engineer, 19 Pinckney St.
Crancer, Bulah, Mrs., res. Spring St.
Cranch, Charles W., Lawyer, res. South St.
Crane, Boylston & Co., Dry Goods, cr. Hayne & Meeting Sts.
Crane, John G., Dry Goods, cr. Hayne & Meeting Sts., res. Charleston Hotel
Crane, Lemuel, Clerk, 165 Meeting St., res. Pavilion Hotel
Crawford, Daniel, Factor, Boyce's Wharf, res. Planter's Hotel
Crawford, Mary, Mrs., res. 50 Meeting St.
Creevey, William, Clerk, 211 King St., res. King St.
Creighton, J. McPherson, Clerk, State Bank, res. Rutledge St.
Creighton, James, Miller, Chisolm's Rice Mills, res. Rutledge St.
Creigmiles, P. M., Dry Goods, 131 Meeting St., res. Tennessee
Crews, A. J., Dry Goods, 181 East Bay St., res. 17 George St.
Crews, E. B., Auctioneer, 24 Vendue Range, res. Mount Pleasant
Crews, Isaac M., Conductor, South Carolina Railroad, res. America St., near Woolf St.
Crimal, Emma, Colored, Washerwoman, res. 11 Inspection St.
Crocker, Edmund G., Coachmaker, cr. Meeting & Wentworth Sts.
Croft, S. E., Mrs., Boarding House, 204 King St.
Croft, Thomas H., Liquors, etc., 179 East Bay St., res. 44 Wentworth St.
Cromley, Catherine, Mrs., Boarding House, 30 Queen St., res. 30 Queen St.
Cromley, Daniel, Bootmaker, res. 30 Queen St.
Cromwell, E. O., Miss, res. 44 Church St.
Cromwell, S. T., Professor of Music, Cromwell's Terrace
Crosby, William, Carpenter, res. Line St.
Crose, James, Miller, 61 Market St., res. Ann St.
Cross, Hamson, Bricklayer, res. Franklin St.
Cross, Joseph, Pastor, Trinity Church, res. 15 Hasell St.
Cross, Martin W., Bricklayer, res. cr. Church & Atlantic Sts.
Cross, William, Bookkeeper, 38 Queen St., res. 11 Middle St.
Cross, William, Merchant, East Bay St., res. 25 Beaufain St.

Cruikshank, Samuel, Tanner, res. Hanover St.
Cudworth, Edmund M., Bookkeeper, 35 Hayne St., res. Cannon St.
Cudworth, John, Inspector Custom House, res. Henrietta St.
Cullinane, Patrick, Dry Goods, 356 King St., res. 356 King St.
Culpepper, Samuel, Mrs., res. 230 East Bay St.
Cummings, James, Conductor, South Carolina Railroad, res. Bogard St.
Cummings, John A., Clerk, 257 King St., res. 257 King St.
Cunningham, A., Carpenter, res. 4 Beaufain St.
Cunningham, Anne, Mrs., res. Henrietta St.
Cunningham, John, Lawyer, 119 East Bay St., res. Pitt St.
Cunningham, Richard, res. Henrietta St.
Curdy, William, Grocer, 52 King St., res. 52 King St.
Curley, Hugh, Laborer, res. 8 Hasell St.
Curley, Jeremiah, Drayman, res. Washington St.
Curran, James C., Bar Room, 161 King St., res. Victoria Hotel
Currell, William, Clerk, Custom House, res. 8 Liberty St.
Curtis, James, Carpenter, res. Spring St.
Curtis, Mary, Mrs., Tailoress, res. 13 Inspection St.
Curtis, William, Paints & Oils, 137 East Bay St., res. 137 East Bay St.
Cuthbert, J. H., Pastor, res. 41 Montague St.
Cuyler, Ezra P., Clerk, 257 King St., res. Hasell St.
Cuyler, Stephen G., Bookkeeper, 257 King St., res. Hasell St.
Daggett, Sheppard, Carpenter, 11 Horlbeck Alley, res. America St.
Dail, Elias, Carpenter, 1 Queen St., res. 3 Middle St.
Dalfin, William, Laborer, res. Cromwell's Terrace
Dallas, William, Shoemaker, 56 Meeting St., res. 33 Broad St.
Daly, Edward, Boots & Shoes, 306 King St., res. 306 King St.
Daly, John & Co., Boots & Shoes, 326 King St.
Daly, John, Boots & Shoes, 326 King St., res. 326 King St.
Daly, John, House Painter, res. 92 King St.
Daly, Michael, Laborer, res. 14 Laurens St.
Daly, Thomas, Laborer, res. Spring St.
Daly, William, Clerk of the Poor House, res. 95 Queen St.
Damon, Q. A., Bookkeeper, 18 Broad St., res. Laurens St.
Dana, John M., Clerk, 261 King St., res. Society St.
Dana, William C., Pastor, Central Presbyterian Church, res. 19 Laurens St.
Dangerfield, Richard, Carpenter, res. Warren St.
Daniels, Thomas, Pilot, res. 8 Stoll's Alley
Dappray, J. E., Dentist, Society St., res. King St., 8th Ward
Darant, J. L., Bookkeeper, Ingraham & Webb's, res. 106 Tradd St.
Darby, Frederick, Coppersmith, 325 King St., res. 325 King St.
Darby, John T., Clerk, 199 East Bay St., res. Radcliffe St.

Darby, Martin, Porter, 211 King St., res. Pitt St.
Darcy, Peter, Porter, 200 East Bay St., res. 40 State St.
Darcy, Thomas, Grocer, Vernon St., res. Vernon St.
Darley, John, House Painter, 40 Queen St.
Darr, Horace L., Printer, 111 East Bay St., res. 230 King St.
Darrell, Nicholas, res. cr. St. Philip & George Sts.
Dart, William, Colored, Painter, Coming St., res. Coming St.
Daur, F., Teacher of Flute, 72 Church St., res. 72 Church St.
Davega, Isaac, Lawyer, Law Place, res. cr. Wentworth & Pitt Sts.
Davenport, George, Pilot, res. 69 East Bay St.
Davey, Robert, Livery Stable, res. 14 Beaufain St.
David & Latham, Fruiterers, 69 Market St.
David, Edward, Fruiterer, 69 Market St., res. 110 King St.
David, M., & Co., Jewellers, 335 King St.
David, Marquis, Jeweller, 335 King St., res. 335 King St.
David, R. Lewis, Clothing, 332 King St., res. 265 King St.
Davidson, B. B., Clerk, East Bay St., res. 66 Church St.
Davidson, Thomas, res. 61 Calhoun St.
Davidson, W. S., Bookkeeper, Carson & Sons, res. Boundary St.
Davidson, William, Commission Merchant, East Bay St., res. 66 Church St.
Davies, John S., Bookkeeper, Farmers & Exchange Bank, res. 260 King St.
Davis, D., Shoemaker, 38½ Church St., res. 38½ Church St.
Davis, George W., Pilot, res. 69 East Bay St.
Davis, Isaac B., Bookkeeper, Bradford & Sanders
Davis, Jane, Mrs., Proprietress, Mansion House, Broad St.
Davis, John, Clerk, 40 East Bay St., res. 27 Mazyck St.
Davis, Joseph, Clerk, 35 Hayne St., res. Charleston Hotel
Davis, Mary A., Mrs., res. 92 King St.
Davis, Ross C., Pilot, res. 51 East Bay St.
Davis, Sarah, Miss, res. 8 George St.
Davis, Warren A., Clerk, 211 King St., res. cr. Society & Meeting Sts.
Davis, William, Agent, American Tract Society, res. Coming St.
Davis, William R., Cotton Shipper, res. 3 Glebe St.
Davis, Z., Bookkeeper, Adams & Frost's, res. 3 Glebe St.
Dawson & Blackman, Druggists, 17 Broad St.
Dawson, C. M., Miss, res. 38 Bull St.
Dawson, Charles P., res. 11 New St.
Dawson, Franklin, Grocer, 96 East Bay St., res. cr. Smith & Beaufain Sts.
Dawson, J. & F., Grocers, 96 East Bay St.
Dawson, J. E., Physician, res. 11 New St.
Dawson, J., Grocer, 96 East Bay St., res. 84 Beaufain St.
Dawson, J. L., Dr., City Register, res. 48 Tradd St.
Dawson, James, Drayman, res. 8 Linguard St.
Dawson, James H., Clerk, South Carolina Railroad, res. 6 Green St.

Dawson, Joseph, Druggist, 17 Broad St., res. Limehouse St.

Dawson, T. O. & Co., Lumber Factors, Potter's Wharf

Dawson, W. H., Bookkeeper, 72 East Bay St., res. 9 Lynch St.

Dawson, W. H., Jr., Clerk, 80 East Bay St., res. 9 Lynch St.

Dawson, William, Clerk, 96 East Bay St., res. 9 Lynch St.

Dawson, William, Mrs., res. 3 Meeting St.

Day, A. M., Bookkeeper, 97 East Bay St., res. Meeting St.

Day, David F., Clerk, 133 Meeting St., res. 260 King St.

Day, Fisher, Mrs., Boarding House, 260 King St.

Day, John, Clerk, res. 8 Liberty St.

Day, Sarah, Colored, Washer Woman, res. 21 Middle St.

Day, W. H., Bookkeeper, 102 Meeting St., res. 1 Montague St.

Deas, John, Clerk, cr. Meeting & Hayne Sts.

Deas, Thomas H., Planter, res. 3 Glebe St.

Deazel, Charles, Planter, res. Pitt St.

Debos, William, Engineer, res. Hanover St.

Dedden, H. L., Teacher, res. 14 Cumberland St.

Degnan, Charles, Ship Carpenter, Gadsden's Wharf

DeGohren, J., Bookkeeper, 75 East Bay St., res. 75 East Bay St.

Dehon, Theodore, Physician, res. 37 Meeting St.

Delaigle, Lewis, Factor, Accommodation Wharf

Delaine, Isabel, Mrs., res. 84 Wentworth St.

Deland, A. B., Physician, 257 King St.

Deland, Charles, Dry Goods, 257 King St., res. 257 King St.

Delarge, J., Tailor, 74 Market St., res. Coming St.

Delarge, Mary, Colored, Mantuamaker, 36 Spring St.

Deleon, H. H., Clerk, Farmers & Exchange Bank, res. College St.

Delgado, J., Clerk, 110 East Bay St., res. 247 King St.

Demar, Samuel T., Tailor, Calhoun St.

Demmerick, C., Shoemaker, 126 Meeting St.

Demmerick, T., Shoemaker, 126 Meeting St.

Deneaux, Thomas E., Upholsterer, 176 Meeting St.

Dennis, D., Mrs., res. 9 Magazine St.

Denoon, David Henry, Printer, Courier Office

Depass, S. C., Bookkeeper, Holmes & Stoney's

Depass, William L., Clerk, 253 King St.

Dereef, Edward, Colored, Wood Factor, Washington St., res. 21 Calhoun St.

Dereef, J. M. F., Colored, Wood Factor, Brown's Wharf

Dereef, R. E., Colored, Wood Factor, Dereef's Wharf

Dereef, R. E., Jr., Colored, Wood Factor, Dereef's Wharf

DeRojas, Francisco, Portrait Painter, 93 King St.

DeSaussure & Son, Lawyers, 23 Broad St.

DeSaussure, Charles A., Insurance Agent, 36 East Bay St., res. 26 Meeting St.

DeSaussure, Henry A., Lawyer, 23 Broad St., res. 33 Meeting St.

DeSaussure, Henry W., Physician, res. 77 Meeting St.

DeSaussure, John B., Factor, Adger's North Wharf, res. 33 Meeting St.

DeSaussure, Lewis D., Broker & Auctioneer, 23 Broad St., res. 33 Meeting St.

DeSaussure, Wilmot G., Lawyer, 23 Broad St., res. 31 East Bay St.

Desell, B. M., Clerk, 80 East Bay St., res. Pitt St.

DeTreville & Brewster, Lawyers, Meeting St., near Broad St.

DeTreville, E., Lawyer, 20 Broad St., res. Coming St.

DeTreville, Richard, Lawyer, Meeting St., near Broad St.

Deveaux, John P., Factor, 16 Vanderhorst's Wharf, res. St. Philip St.

Devereaux, Charles, Cooper, 71 Anson St., res. 71 Anson St.

Devine, Charles, Laborer, res. 41 Anson St.

Devineau, E., Nurseryman, res. 304 King St.

Dewees, John, Planter, res. 44 Bull St.

Dewees, Thomas H., Rice Merchant, 72 East Bay St., res. Alexander St.

Dewees, William, Rice Merchant 72 East Bay St., res. Alexander St.

Dewing, Hiram, Fancy Goods, 149 Meeting St., res. 3 Society St.

Dewing, Leonard C., Fancy Goods, 149 Meeting St., res. New York

Dewitt, Gabriel, Clerk, 211 King St., res. 24 Beaufain St.

Diamond, John, Laborer, res. 176 East Bay St.

Diaz, Jose, Cigars & Tobacco, 76 Market St., res. 76 Market St.

Dibble, H. M., Mrs., Boarding House, 249 King St.

Dibble, P. Virgil, Hatter, 37 Broad St., res. 37 Broad St.

Dibble, Samuel, Clerk, 12 East Bay St., res. 249 King St.

Dickinson, Eliza, Mrs., res. Logan St.

Dickson, Samuel H., Physician, res. cr. Hudson & Meeting Sts.

Diersson, William, Dry Goods, etc., cr. Coming & Morris Sts.

Dill, Joseph T., Factor, 13 Southern Wharf, res. Legare St.

Dill, Josiah H., Clerk, 243 King St., res. Tradd St.

Dillon, Michael, Conductor, South Carolina Railroad, res. St. Philip St.

Dillon, Richard, Books, 103 King St., res. 103 King St.

Dingle, G. W., Lawyer, 40 Broad St.

Dining, William, res. 300 King St.

Disher, Robert W., Planter, res. Nassau St.

Disher, William L., Butcher, res. St. Philip St.

Divine, John, Bookkeeper, res. 106 Tradd St.

Divine, Michael, Tavern, 90 Meeting St.

Divver, John B., Clerk, 211 King St., res. Commercial House

Divver, Joseph M., Clerk, 211 King St., res. Commercial House

Doar, Marcus, Blacksmith, South Carolina Railroad, res. St. Philip St.

Doar, Thomas W., Clerk, 211 King St.

Doig, George, Engineer, res. 3 Vernon St.

Doly, A., Sign Painter, 45 Queen St.

Donnell, B. W., Broker, 40 Queen St.

Donnelly, John, res. 132 Meeting St.

Donohoe, J., Carpenter, res. 143 Queen St.

Dorbaum & Menke, Tailors, cr. Church & Queen Sts.

Dorbaum, Conrad, Tailor, cr. Church & Queen Sts.
Dorn, Andrew, Carpenter, 52 Queen St., res. Gibbes St.
Dorr, Stephen, Planter, res. Bull St.
Dorres, H. W., Baker, 369 King St., res. 369 King St.
Dorrill, Augustus, Lumber Merchant, cr. Beaufain & Lynch Sts.
Dorsey, Patrick, Shoemaker, 43 Broad St., res. Queen St.
Doscher, J., Grocer, 105 Broad St., res. 105 Broad St.
Dothage, John, Grocer, cr. Calhoun & Anson Sts.
Doucin, Phillip M., Wharfinger, Potter's Wharf
Dougherty, John, Wood Factor, res. 19 South Bay St.
Doughty, Charles W., Bookkeeper, res. 10 Middle St.
Douglass, B. & Co., Mercantile Agency, 54 Broad St.
Douglass, B., Mercantile Agency, res. New York City
Douglass, Campbell, Grocer, 198 King St., res. Broad St.
Douglass, John, Clerk, res. cr. America & Broad Sts.
Douglass, Robert, Livery Stable, Pinckney St.
Douglass, William, Painter, 166 King St., res. 36 Beaufain St.
Dowd, Martin, Wine Bottler, 32 Anson St., res. 32 Anson St.
Dowell, Samuel L., Bookkeeper at Chambers, Jeffords & Co.
Dowie, George, Bookkeeper, 153 Meeting St.
Dowie, Robert B., Bookkeeper, 179 East Bay St., res. 204 King St.
Dowley, Michael, Porter, 33 Hayne St., res. 4 Beaufain St.
Downey, Robert, res. 68 Church St.
Downing, F. T., Wharfinger, res. 48 Anson St.
Doyle, Hugh, Shoemaker, 43 Broad St., res. 89 Church St.
Doyle, James, Porter, 35 Hayne St., res. 38 Market St.
Doyle, John, Carpenter, cr. King St. & Whim's Court
Doyle, P., Painter, res. 78 Wentworth St.
Doyle, Thomas, Coach Trimmer, res. 19 St. Philip St.
Drago, Anthony, Fruiterer, 73 Market St., res. 135 King St.
Drago, Bianca, Mrs., Dry Goods, 135 King St., res. 135 King St.
Drake, Charles C., Lace Goods & Embroideries, 233 King St.
Drayton, Alfred R., Clerk, Southwestern Railroad Bank, res. 15 George St.
Drayton, Mary Ann, Mrs., res. Coming St., Ward 6
Drayton, Sarah, Colored, Dressmaker, res. 57 Anson St.
Drayton, Thomas H., Planter, res. Coming St., Ward 6
Drew, Edward, Watchman, Robb's Mill, res. 1 Wharf St.
Drier, C., Grocer, 31 Church St., res. cr. Spring & St. Philip Sts.
Droger, F., Grocer, cr. Wentworth & Lynch Sts.
Drummond, John, Boots & Shoes, 55 Broad St., res. 55 Broad St.
Dublin, Henry, Clothing, King St., Upper Ward
Duboise, John, Planter, res. 16 Vernon St.
Ducker, Christian G., Bar Keeper, 41 Wentworth St.
Duff, Thomas, Laborer, South Carolina Railroad
Duffin, Samuel, Carpenter, res. 44 Bull St.
Duffitt, Dennis, Clerk, South Carolina Railroad, res. 4 Cannon St.

Duffus, Alexander W., Clerk, 137 Meeting St., res. 13 Lynch St.
Duffus, James A., Clerk, City Council, res. Morris St.
Duffy, Hugh, Drayman, res. cr. Broad & Rutledge Sts.
Duffy, Michael, Clerk, 43 Hayne St., res. Charleston Hotel
Duffy, William, Boot & Shoemaker, Anson St.
Dufort, A., Gunsmith, King St., Ward 8
Dufort, E., Machinist, Meeting St., Ward 7
Dufort, J., Tinsmith, Line St., Ward 8
Dugal, James, Laborer, res. 20 Calhoun St.
Dugan, Arthur, Clerk, 6 Vendue Range
Dugan, Patrick, Mason, res. 19 State St.
Dukes, Charlton, Clerk, East Bay St., res. Charlotte St.
Dukes, H. A., Tinware, King St., Upper Ward
Dukes, J. H., Lawyer, 61 Broad St.
Dukes, John R., Factor, South Atlantic Wharf, res. 25 Laurens St.
Dukes, T. C. H., Factor, South Atlantic Wharf, res. Charlotte St.
Dukes, W. C. & Sons, Factors, South Atlantic Wharf
Dukes, W. C., Factor, South Atlantic Wharf, res. 25 Laurens St.
Dukes, W. C., Lawyer, 61 Broad St.
Dulin, J. M., Clerk at Rice Dulin's, res. 189 Meeting St.
Dulin, Rice, Factor, Central Wharf, res. 189 Meeting St.
Duly, John, Laborer, res. Woolf St.
Dunaman, Charles, Pattern Maker, res. Hanover St.
Duncan, John, Boiler Maker, foot of Hasell St.
Duncan, Langdon C., Druggist, 215 King St.
Dunga, Henry, Omnibus Driver, res. 20 Queen St.
Dunham, C. T. & Co., Boots & Shoes, 141 Meeting St.
Dunham, Cornelius T., Boots & Shoes, 141 Meeting St., res. 80 Tradd St.
Dunkin, Alfred H., Lawyer, 65 Meeting St., res. Coming St.
Dunkin, B. F., Judge, Court of Equity, res. foot of Warren St.
Dunlap, James, res. 3 Lynch St.
Dunn, James, Grocer, 22 Calhoun St., res. 22 Calhoun St.
Dunn, Thomas, Drayman, res. 37 Calhoun St.
Dunohoe, John, Laborer, Bennett's Saw Mill
Dupont, Francis, Upholsterer, 203 King St., res. 203 King St.
Duprat, Mary, Colored, Cake Shop, 111 King St.
Dupree, John L., Engineer, res. 78 Tradd St.
Dupree, Josiah, Carpenter, res. Line St.
Dupree, Julia, Mrs., Female Seminary, 196 East Bay St.
Duquereron, Francis, Clerk, res. 96 Tradd St.
Duquereron, Leopold, Clerk, Post Office, res. 96 Tradd St.
Durr, Joseph, Laborer, res. 12 Pinckney St.
Dursse, Augustus, Finisher, 101 East Bay St., res. Smith St.
Duryea, R. S., Lawyer, 84 Church St., res. 110 Meeting St.
Duval, Eugene A., Tinsmith, 298 King St., res. 298 King St.
Duval, John B., Tinsmith, 298 King St., res. 298 King St.
Duval, Lawrence A., Tinsmith, 298 King St., res. 298

King St.

Duval, Milford G., Watch Maker, 298 King St.

Dwyer, Patrick, Wheelwright, 28 Pinckney St., res. 9 Vernon St.

Dwyra, John, Porter, 40 East Bay St.

Dye, John H., Deputy Sheriff, res. 2 Price's Alley

Eady, Alexander, Carpenter, res. cr. Blake & America Sts.

Eady, Nathaniel, Colored, Ship Carpenter, Marsh Dock Yard

Earle, Benjamin F., Carpenter, res. 30 Calhoun St.

Earle, James P., Bricklayer, res. 30 Calhoun St.

Eason, C. D., Mrs., res. 2 Glebe St.

Eason, George W., Clerk, 26 Vendue Range, res. 2 Glebe St.

Easterby, George, Clerk, 173 East Bay St., res. Mill St.

Easterby, Stuart D., Clerk, Atlantic Wharf, res. Mill St.

Easton, J. M. & Brother, Iron Founders, cr. Columbus & Nassau Sts.

Easton, James M., Iron Founder, res. Drake St.

Easton, Robert H., Bricklayer, res. 35 Coming St.

Easton, Thomas, Iron Founder, res. America St.

Easton, William, Bricklayer, res. 35 Coming St.

Eberhard, Brick, Bootmaker, 28 Anson St., res. 28 Anson St.

Edgar, William M., Clerk, 173 East Bay St.

Edgerton & Richards, Merchant Tailors, 32 & 34 Broad St.

Edgerton, E. W., Tailor, 32 Broad St., res. 3 Orange St.

Edgerton, James E., Student, res. 3 Orange St.

Edgerton, S. F., Tailor, 32 Broad St., res. 3 Orange St.

Edmondston, Charles, Factor, South Atlantic Wharf, res. 8 Legare St.

Edmondston, Charles, Wharfinger, res. 20 Savage St.

Edmondston, Henry, Clerk, 211 King St., res. 8 Legare St.

Edmondston, L. A., Factor, South Atlantic Wharf, res. 8 Legare St.

Edwards, Charles L., Clerk, Bank of South Carolina, res. cr. New & Broad Sts.

Edwards, Evan, Assistant Post Master, res. 7 Logan St.

Edwards, Frank N., Clerk at Rice Dulin's, res. 7 Logan St.

Edwards, James F., Commission Merchant, 62 East Bay St., res. 26 Wall St.

Edwards, John J., Clerk, Central Wharf, res. cr. New & Broad Sts.

Edwards, John J., Commission Merchant, Central Wharf, res. cr. New & Broad Sts.

Edwards, John, Tailor, Vanderhorst St.

Edwards, Joseph, Carpenter, res. Anson St.

Edwards, R. C., Telegraph Operator, 3 State St.

Edwards, W. S., Clerk, Bank of Charleston, res. 5 Gibbes St.

Egan, John, Dry Goods, 61 King St., res. 61 King St.

Egleston, G. W., Lawyer, 20 Broad St., res. Warren St.

Egleston, George, Clerk, 9 Hayne St., res. 9 Hayne St.

Egleston, James L., Discount Clerk, State Bank, res. 72 Anson St.

Egleston, Thomas R., Clothing, 6 Queen St., res. cr.

Anson & Market Sts.

Eheny, Edwin W., Ship Blacksmith, cr. Pritchard & Concord Sts.

Eilands, A. W., Printer, 117 East Bay St., res. 99 East Bay St.

Elfe, Albert, Jr., Clerk, 198 King St., res. 19 Lynch St.

Elfe, Anna, Miss, res. 74 Wentworth St.

Elfe, George, Planter, Cooper River, res. Washington St.

Elfe, Maria, Miss, res. 9 Society St.

Elfe, Robert, Carpenter, res. 19 Lynch St.

Elfe, Robert, Clerk, Charleston Hotel, res. 14 Archdale St.

Elfe, William, res. 9 Society St.

Elford, Frederick P., Wharfinger, res. 17 Coming St.

Elford, John, Cotton Presser, cr. Elizabeth & Charlotte Sts.

Ell, James B., Clerk, 142 King St., res. 142 King St.

Ell, L., Clothing, 72 Market St., res. 72 Market St.

Ellerhorst, H. W., Feed Store, 6 Market St., res. 6 Market St.

Elliott, Benjamin, Stevedore, res. Bogard St.

Elliott, Emeline, Colored, Seamstress, res. 8 Minority St.

Elliott, J. H., Pastor, res. 24 Broad St.

Elliott, R., Physician, res. cr. Queen & Trapmann Sts.

Elliott, Thomas O., Lawyer, 61 Broad St.

Elliott, William, Teacher, Charleston College, res. 17 Church St.

Ellis, H. H., Saddlery, cr. Meeting & Hasell Sts.

Ellish, M. A., Fruit Store, 163 King St., res. 163 King St.

Elms & Johnson, Commission Merchants, 62 East Bay St.

Elms & Johnson, Factors, South Atlantic Wharf

Elms, W. W., Factor, 62 East Bay St., res. Charlotte, N.C.

Elsworth, Isaac R., Molder, Hasell St., res. Anson St.

Elsworth, John T., Gauger, Custom House, res. 10 Laurens St.

Emory, Jonathan R., South Carolina Railroad, res. 45 Calhoun St.

England, Alexander, Engineer, res. 44 Meeting St.

England, Edward, Bricklayer, res. 59 Beaufain St.

England, William, Bookkeeper, res. 59 Beaufain St.

Englert, William, Tavern, 43 Market St.

English, James, Shipwright, res. 15 South Bay St.

Enright, Charles, Driver, 9 Hayne St.

Enslow, J. A., Commission Merchant, 110 East Bay St., res. 108 East Bay St.

Enslow, Joseph L., res. 128 Tradd St.

Enston, Alfred, Furniture, res. Horlbeck Alley

Enston, E. D., Drayman, res. 101 Wentworth St.

Enston, William C. & Co., Furniture, 169, 171 & 173 King St.

Enston, William C., Furniture, res. 118 Queen St.

Epstein, David, Jewelry, 335 King St., res. 335 King St.

Erichson, James L., Paints & Oils, cr. State & Queen Sts.

Erichson, K., Carpenter, res. cr. King & Woolf Sts.

Esdorn, Albert, Grocer, res. 27 Bull St.

Esdorn, H. F., Grocer, cr. Council & Tradd Sts.

Esdra, Eugene, Librarian, Mercantile Library Association

Essen, E. H., Fruit, 341 King St., res. 341 King St.

Estell, William, Printer, 119 East Bay St., res. 5 Lynch St.

Evans, Benjamin F., Stationer, 101 East Bay St., res. Cannon St.

Evans, E. F., Mrs., Boarding House, 190 King St.

Evans, Eliza, Mrs., res. Washington St.

Evans, J. W., Clerk, 147 East Bay St., res. Franklin St.

Evans, James B., Hardware, 27 Hayne St., res. 20 King St.

Evans, Joseph, Carpenter, res. Bogard St.

Evans, Robert, Turner, res. 14 Archdale St.

Everhart, Henry, Boots & Shoes, 119 King St.

Everts, Charles, Cigars, etc., 6 Queen St.

Ewan, William H., Jewelry, 127 King St., res. 127 King St.

Ewing, Robert, Mrs., Boarding House, 277 King St.

Fackler, C. M., Factor, North Atlantic Wharf, res. Huntsville, Ala.

Fackler, Colcock & Co., Factors, North Atlantic Wharf

Fackler, J. J., Factor, North Atlantic Wharf

Fagan, Thomas, Laborer, res. 12 Laurens St.

Fagan, Thomas R., Coach Painter, res. cr. Market & Church Sts.

Fairchild, Daniel, Factor, res. 113 Wentworth St.

Fairley, Arthur H., Clerk, 229 King St., res. 190 King St.

Fairley, Franklin, Clerk, King St., res. 190 King St.

Falk, Abraham, Clothing, 265 King St., res. 265 King St.

Falk, George, Clothing, 265 King St., res. New York City

Falk, Isaac L. & Co., Clothing, 265 King St.

Falk, Isaac L., Clothing, 265 King St., res. New York City

Falk, Zachariah, Clothing, 210 King St., res. 265 King St.

Fancounette, Charles, French Vice-Consul, 30 Broad St., res. 1 Montague St.

Faneson, Thomas, Laborer, res. 14 Anson St.

Fanning, Frederick D., Hats & Caps, 31 Hayne St., res. New York

Fanning, Frederick, Jr., Clerk, 37 Hayne St.

Faren, James, Fancy Store, 26 Tradd St., res. 26 Tradd St.

Farena, M., Clerk, 76 Market St., res. 74 Market St.

Farenback, S., Laborer, South Carolina Railroad, res. Line St.

Farhin, Michael, Carpenter, res. Calhoun St.

Farley, Maria A., Mrs., Milliner, 146 King St., res. 146 King St.

Farnum, Oliver, Grocer, 189 East Bay St., res. Cannon St.

Farr, Ann, Colored, Seamstress, res. 19 Middle St.

Farrall, John, Clerk, res. 35 George St.

Farrar & Brothers, Grocers, 173 East Bay St.

Farrar, C. D., Grocer, 173 East Bay St., res. 28 Society St.

Farrar, J. C., Grocer, 173 East Bay St., res. 28 Society St.

Farrar, S. S., Grocer, 173 East Bay St., res. 160 Meeting St.

Fash, A. R., Blacksmith, Meeting St., res. Concord St.

Feil, Henry, Clerk, 190 King St., res. 190 King St.

Feldu, Mary Mrs., Clothing, cr. Alexander & Chapel Sts.

Feldu, Robert, Clerk, King St., res. St. Philip St.

Felipe, J. Q., Cigars & Tobacco, 68 Market St., res. 68 Market St.

Fell, E. M., Mrs., res. 213 King St.

Fennell, Henry, Molder, cr. Line & Meeting Sts.

Fenwick, C., Cotton Presser, 18 Vendue Range

Ferguson, A. J., Blacksmith, res. 44 Meeting St.

Ferguson, Alexander, Machinist, res. 44 Meeting St.

Ferguson, Daniel, Blacksmith, res. 44 Meeting St.

Ferguson, Emeline, Mrs., res. 35 George St.

Ferguson, Susan, Mrs., res. 24 Market St.

Ferguson, William C., Clerk, 39 Hayne St., res. Victoria Hotel

Ferguson, William, Engineer, res. cr. Reid & Nassau Sts.

Ferrall, J. J., Bookkeeper, 19 Hayne St.

Ferrand, William, Clerk, 189 East Bay St., res. Church St.

Ferrell, Timothy, Bar Keeper, 142 East Bay St.

Ferrette, John F., Fruiterer, 41 Market St., res. 41 Market St.

Fetzger, C. F., Leather, 71 Market St., res. 71 Market St.

Fickling, William B., Lawyer, 63 Broad St., res. 7 Short St.

Fiegel, Julius, Hats & Caps, 164 King St., res. 164 King St.

Fielas, Michael, Carpenter, Meeting St.

Fields, Nathaniel, Proprietor, Ice House, cr. Church & Market Sts.

Fifer, Paul, Cigar Maker, King St., res. Radcliffe St.

Figeroux, Benjamin, Millinery Goods, 206 King St., res. 206 King St.

Fllette, A., Mrs., Dry Goods, 133 King St., res. 133 King St.

Filette, Theodore, Clerk, 29 Hayne St., res. 133 King St.

Finegan, John, Tailor, res. 15 Franklin St.

Fink, Hamer, Blacksmith, Spring St.

Finkin, Albert, Grocer, cr. Elizabeth & John Sts.

Finley, E., Mrs., Dr., res. 4 King St.

Finley, Hamilton, Clerk, East Bay St., res. 4 King St.

Finley, James H., Clerk, 34 East Bay St., res. King St.

Finley, James, Mrs., Millinery, 367 King St.

Finley, James, Porter, 80 East Bay St., res. 369 King St.

Finley, W. P., Teacher, Charleston College, res. cr. Montague & Pitt Sts.

Finn, Michael, Carpenter, res. Calhoun St.

Fisher, F., Bootmaker, 6 Tradd St., res. 6 Tradd St.

Fisher, John, Machinist, res. Hanover St.

Fisher, Samuel, Millinery, 252 King St., res. 252 King St.

Fisher, Samuel W., Assistant Treasurer, Savings Bank, res. 21 Friend St.

Fisher, William, Blacksmith, res. Hanover St.

Fitch, Cornelius, Clerk, 243 King St., res. 249 King St.

Fitch, William, Physician, 78 Meeting St., res. 4 Smith St.

Fitzgibbon, Michael, Finisher, res. Woolf St.

Fitzgibbon, P. S., Hats & Caps, 104 Meeting St., res. 104 Meeting St.

Fitzpatrick, John, Bar Keeper, Brock's Exchange

Fitzpatrick, Timothy, Clerk, 165 Meeting St., res. Linguard St.

Fitzsimons, Bernard, Saddler, 266 King St., res. Doughty

St.
Fitzsimons, E., Mrs., res. 26 Hasell St.
Fitzsimons, Gaillard, Physician, 26 Hasell St.
Fitzsimons, Robert T., Saddler, 266 King St., res. Doughty St.
Flach, George W., Jeweller, 191 King St., res. 191 King St.
Flach, James, Porter, 211 King St.
Flagg, Charles E. B., Lawyer, 59 Meeting St., res. 15 Archdale St.
Flagg, George, Artist, res. New St.
Flaherty, John, Porter, 155 Meeting St.
Flaherty, Patrick, Drayman, res. 12 Laurens St.
Flanigan, Hugh, Shoemaker, 312 King St., res. 344 King St.
Flanigan, Richard, Boots & Shoes, 312 King St., res. 312 King St.
Flatter, Joseph, Caulker, res. 28 Vernon St.
Fleming, D. F. & Co., Boots & Shoes, 43 Hayne St.
Fleming, David F., Boots & Shoes, 43 Hayne St., res. Charleston Hotel
Fleming, John, Bricklayer, res. Mary St.
Fleming, Robert, Confectionery, 269 King St., res. 269 King St.
Florney, William, Carpenter, res. Line St.
Floyd, L., Miss, res. 101 Market St.
Flynn, A. R., Tavern, 12 Queen St.
Flynn, James, Porter, East Bay St., res. 58 Church St.
Flynn, John, Porter, 211 King St.
Flynn, John, Porter, Mills House, res. 132 King St.
Flynn, John T., Tailor, 30 Broad St., res. New St.
Flynn, Michael, Tavern, Woolf St.
Flynn, Thomas, Bookkeeper, 131 Meeting St., res. Beaufain St.
Flynt, John T., Clerk at Wardlaw, Walker & Burnside
Fogartie & Deland, Dry Goods, 257 King St.
Fogartie, Arthur, Dry Goods, 257 King St., res. Wall St.
Foley, Bartholomew, Boots, etc., 85 Market St., res. 85 Market St.
Foley, James, Clothing, 84 East Bay St., res. Market St.
Foley, Maria, Miss, res. 126 Queen St.
Folger, Edward J., China Store, cr. Alexander & Chapel Sts.
Folker, Octavius, Agent, South Carolina Railroad, res. Vanderhorst St.
Follin & Fourgeaud, Grocers, cr. Meeting & Market Sts.
Follin, Gustavus, Grocer, res. Wentworth St.
Foote, Eliza, Mrs., res. 47 Beaufain St.
Forbes, Robert, Tinsmith, 5 Tradd St., res. 5 Tradd St.
Force, B. W. & J. P. & Co., Boots & Shoes, 21 Hayne St.
Force, B. W., Boots, etc., 21 Hayne St., res. Augusta, Ga.
Force, J. P., Boots, etc., 21 Hayne St., res. 11 Hasell St.
Ford, B., Boots & Shoes, 99 East Bay St., res. Ashley St.
Ford, Frederick A., Lawyer, 41 Broad St., res. Grove St.
Ford, J. Drayton, Stock Broker, 7 Broad St.
Ford, J. O., Clerk, 157 Meeting St.
Fordham, Richard, Planter, res. cr. Washington & Charlotte Sts.
Fordham, William R., Barber, Meeting St.

Forgartie, Edward, Bricklayer, res. 28 Calhoun St.
Forgarty, Daniel, Coach Driver, Charleston Hotel, 2 Clifford St.
Forgarty, L., Mrs., res. 21 George St.
Forgeaud, Eugene, Grocer, cr. Meeting & Market Sts., res. 18 Wentworth St.
Forgeaud, Mary, Mrs., res. 18 Wentworth St.
Forran, John J., Clerk, 181 East Bay St., res. 3 Hasell St.
Forrest, Elizabeth S., Mrs., res. 91 Wentworth St.
Forrest, John, Pastor, 1st Presbyterian Church, res. 8 King St.
Forrester, James, Machinist, Hasell St., res. Vernon St.
Forsyth, Robert J., Clerk, 371 King St., res. 371 King St.
Forsyth, William C., Dry Goods, 371 King St., res. 371 King St.
Foster, Charles, Clerk, 37 Hayne St.
Foster, Elizabeth, Mrs., res. 3 Vernon St.
Foster, William B., Discount Clerk, Bank of the State, res. 14 Broad St.
Fowler, Andrew D., Clerk, 244 King St.
Fowler, Franklin, Clerk, 139 Meeting St.
Fowler, Jessie P., Mrs., Dry Goods, Rutledge St.
Fox, R., Plasterer, res. Cromwell's Terrace
Fox, Sarah, Seamstress, res. 76 Anson St.
Fox, William, Laborer, res. 22 Tradd St.
Frain, Thomas, Grocer, cr. Church & Chalmers Sts.
Francis, George M., Saddler, 344 King St., res. 344 King St.
Francis, John L., Colored, Barber, 316 King St., res. 316 King St.
Frank, Charles, Blacksmith, res. 140 King St.
Franklin, Linguard, res. cr. King & Ann Sts.
Fraser & Thompson, Factors, 5 Adger's North Wharf
Fraser, Charles C., res. 33 King St.
Fraser, F. E., Factor, 5 Adger's North Wharf, res. 97 Tradd St.
Fraser, G., Miss, res. 91 Tradd St.
Fraser, Henry, Boiler Maker, res. 2 Washington St.
Fraser, John & Co., Factors & Commission Merchants, Central Wharf
Fraser, John, Factor, Central Wharf, res. 3 Short St.
Fraser, William, Clerk, South Carolina Railroad, res. Hampden Court
Frazer, Charles P., Bathing Saloon, 67 Meeting St., res. 67 Meeting St.
Frazer, John M., Bookkeeper, 67 Meeting St., res. 67 Meeting St.
Fredsburg, J. M., Shipping Merchant, Commercial Wharf
Freer, James, Clerk, Southern Wharf, res. Hanover St.
Friend, George, Boiler Maker, res. Concord St.
Fripp, John F., Planter, res. 112 Wentworth St.
Froelick, Nicholas, Conductor, South Carolina Railroad, res. Nassau St.
Froneberger, Caleb, Boots & Shoes, 166 Meeting St., res. 190 King St.
Frost, E. H., Commission Merchant, Adger's North Wharf, res. cr. Tradd & Logan Sts.
Frost, Edward, Lawyer, res. 110 Tradd St.
Frost, Elias O., res. 110 Tradd St.
Frost, Henry R., Physician, 70 Broad St.

Frost, Richard, Clerk, res. 110 Tradd St.
Frost, Thomas, Lawyer, St. Michael's Alley, res. 110
Tradd St.
Fryer, William De B., Bookkeeper, 250 King St., res.
Pavillion Hotel
Fulkerson, Isaac, Clerk, 5 Hayne St.
Fuller, Thomas A., Bookkeeper, res. 52 Calhoun St.
Fullings, Anderson & Co., Clothing, 16 Hayne St.
Fullings, Edward, Clothing, 16 Hayne St., res. Newark,
N. J.
Furber, J. M., Clerk, 143 Meeting St.
Furlong, Michael, Porter, 141 Meeting St.
Furman, C. M., President, Bank of the State of South
Carolina
Furman, Charles, Student, res. 8 Liberty St.
Gadsden, Alexander, Clerk, 62 East Bay St., res.
Hampden Court
Gadsden, B. C., Planter, Goose Creek, res. Broad St.
Gadsden, C. E., Mrs., res. cr. Charlotte & Alexander Sts.
Gadsden, Christopher, Pastor, St. Philip's Church, res. 30
Hasell St.
Gadsden, Fisher, Clerk, res. Hampden Court
Gadsden, James & Co., Commission Merchants, 62 East
Bay St.
Gadsden, James, Commission Merchant, 62 East Bay St.,
res. Meeting St.
Gadsden, James, Minister to Mexico, res. cr. Ann &
Meeting Sts.
Gadsden, Thomas, Clerk, 62 East Bay St., res. 30 Hasell
St.
Gadsden, Thomas N., Auctioneer & Broker, cr. State &
Chalmers Sts., 36 South Bay St.
Gadsden, W. S., Broker & Auctioneer, 36 Broad St., res.
Hampstead St.
Gage, A., Proprietor, Neck Ice House, res. Vanderhorst
St.
Gailbraith, Robert M., Ship Carpenter, res. Alexander St.
Gaillard & Snowden, Factors, 6 Southern Wharf
Gaillard, Edward, Clerk, 19 Hayne St., res. Bull St.
Gaillard, P. C., Factor, 6 Southern Wharf, res. Smith's
Lane
Gaillard, P. C., Physician, 60 Broad St., res. 60 Broad St.
Gaillard, William, Bricklayer, res. 36 Bull St.
Gale, R. White, salesman, 40 Wentworth St.
Galliot, Alexis, Cigars & Tobacco, 155 East Bay St., res.
155 East Bay St.
Galloway, Mary, Miss, Milliner, 181 King St., res. 181
King St.
Gambatti, Alexander, Dry Goods, 88 King St., res. 88
King St.
Gamble, Samuel, Shoemaker, res. Reid St.
Gambo, Joseph, Teacher, res. 126 Meeting St.
Gannon, Michael, Stone Cutter, res. 42 State St.
Gannon, Roger, Dry Goods, 130 Church St.
Ganther, Thomas, Teacher, Citadel Academy
Gantt, James L., Factor, Accommodation Wharf, res. 28
Pitt St.
Gantt, R. S., Bookkeeper, 171 East Bay St., res.
Wentworth St.
Gantt, Thomas J., Register in Equity, Court of Appeals,

Court House
Gardelle & DeLaigle, Factors & Commission Merchant,
Accommodation Wharf
Gardelle, A., Factor & Commission Merchant,
Accommodation Wharf
Gardin, Benjamin, Druggist, 162 King St., res. 162 King
St.
Gardner, Andrew Y., Clerk, 250 King St., res. 6 Glebe
St.
Gardner, James M., Watchmaker, 250 King St., res. 6
Glebe St.
Gardner, Mary, Colored, Seamstress, res. 15 Cumberland
St.
Gardner, Mary, Colored, Washerwoman, res. 2 Guignard
St.
Garney, George, Bricklayer, res. 20 Washington St.
Garrity, Thomas, Hardware, 14 Cumberland St., res. 42
Society St.
Garrity, Thomas, Porter, 139 Meeting St., res. 32 Queen
St.
Gary, Grandison, Deputy Sheriff, res. Cannon St.
Gatewood, W. C., Cotton Press, Union Wharf, res. 17
Legare St.
Gayer, E. F., res. 3 Pitt St.
Gayer, William J., Coach Maker, 142 Meeting St., res. 3
Pitt St.
Gazlay, David M., General Commission Agent, Office
225 King St.
Gazmar, John, Laborer, res. 3 Philadelphia St.
Geddings, Eli, Physician, 16 George St., res. 16 George
St.
Geddings, J. F. M., Physician, 16 George St., res. 16
George St.
Geer, John S., res. Meeting St., near Ann St.
Gehrs, John H., Grocer, 169 East Bay St., res. 169 East
Bay St.
Gellestet, J., Tailor, 39 Broad St.
George, John, Clerk, 40 East Bay St.
George, Reuben, Engineer, res. Coming St.
Gerdts, C. H., Grocer, cr. Beaufain & Archdale Sts.
Gerdts, Henry, Grocer, 203 East Bay St., res. 203 East
Bay St.
Gerdts, Jacob, Grocer, cr. Ashley & Doughty Sts.
Gerkin, D., Clerk, 20 Hasell St., res. 20 Hasell St.
Gerkin, Henry, Grocer, 20 Hasell St., res. 20 Hasell St.
German, Augustus, Confectionary, King St. near Mary
St.
Gerraghty, Barney, Grocer, 5 South Bay St., res. 5 South
Bay St.
Gerraghty, Christopher, Grocer, 22 South Bay St., res. 22
South Bay St.
Gerraghty, Ellen, Mrs., Confectionary, Elizabeth St.
Gerraghty, Thomas, Packer, res. Elizabeth St.
Gervais, Paul T., Pastor, res. 23 Legare St.
Gervais, Theodore, res. cr. Montague & Lynch Sts.
Getting, C., Tailor, 39 Broad St.
Getty, C. W., Marine Inspector, 4 Broad St., res. Meeting
St.
Getty, Campbell, Clerk, Meeting St., near Ann St.
Gibbes & Battersby, Factors & Commission Merchants,

Adger's South Wharf

Gibbes, A. S., Bookkeeper, Gibbes & Battersby, res. cr. Lamboll & Legare Sts.

Gibbes, B., res. Coming St.

Gibbes, Frederick C., Clerk, Post Office, res. Montague St.

Gibbes, Henry P., Physician, 51 King St., res. 61 Tradd St.

Gibbes, J. B., Clerk, 133 Meeting St., res. 61 Tradd St.

Gibbes, J. R., Bookkeeper, Meeting St., res. 45 Tradd St.

Gibbes, James P., Clerk, 122 Meeting St., res. Hasell St.

Gibbes, James S., Factor, Adger's Wharf, res. 5 Short St.

Gibbes, James, Wheelwright, res. Elizabeth St.

Gibbes, John B., Clerk at Gibbes & Battersby, res. 83 Broad St.

Gibbes, John, Factor, Boyce & Co. Wharf, res. 83 Broad St.

Gibbes, Joseph, Planter, res. cr. Legare & Lamboll Sts.

Gibbes, Lewis, Professor, Charleston College, res. 3 Wentworth St.

Gibbes, Sarah B., Mrs., res. 66 Tradd St.

Gibbes, William G., Clerk, Bank of South Carolina, res. 261 King St.

Gibbes, William H., Bookkeeper, 26 Broad St., res. 54 Tradd St.

Gibbon, G., res. 9 New St.

Gibson, A. E., Clerk at J. & J. D. Kirkpatrick's, res. Alexander St.

Gibson, Alexander, res. cr. Montague & Pitt Sts.

Gibson, C., Mrs., res. 15 Franklin St.

Gibson, David C., City Assessor, City Hall, res. 173 Meeting St.

Gibson, Henry, res. St. Philip St.

Gibson, William, res. Hampden Court

Gidion, John J., Clerk, 338 King St., res. 338 King St.

Gidion, P. R., Mrs., Dry Goods, 338 King St., res. 338 King St.

Gilbert, E. M., Coach Maker, 40 Wentworth St., res. 47 Beaufain St.

Gilbert, S. & E. M., Coach Makers, 35 & 40 Wentworth St.

Gilbert, S., Coach Maker, 40 Wentworth St., res. 47 Beaufain St.

Gilbert, Seth H., Printer, 3 Broad St., res. 190 King St.

Gilbreth, N. M., Paints & Oils, 83 Market St.

Gilchrist, John M., Broker & Auctioneer, 11 State St.

Gilchrist, Robert B., U. S. Judge, Chalmers St., res. 245 East Bay St.

Gilchrist, Robert C., Lawyer, Chalmers St., res. 245 East Bay St.

Giles, Robert, res. 2 Gibbes St.

Gilfillan, William G., Bookkeeper, 261 King St., res. Victoria Hotel

Gill, John, Carpenter, res. Coming St.

Gillespie, J. T., Clerk, 16 Hayne St., res. 16 Hayne St.

Gilliland, George W., Clerk, 33 Hayne St., res. 48 Market St.

Gilliland, Howell & Co., Dry Goods, 33 Hayne St.

Gilliland, James, Dry Goods, 33 Hayne St., res. 225 King St.

Gilliland, Mary, Mrs., res. 24 Hasell St.

Gilliland, Peter, Factor, East Bay St., res. 5 Smith's Lane

Gilliland, William H., Dry Goods, 33 Hayne St., res. 24 Hasell St.

Gillispie, A. O., Clerk, 246 King St.

Gillispie, Alfred L., Dry Goods, 37 Hayne St., res. Charleston Hotel

Gillon, Alexander, Waiter, 41 Wentworth St., res. 41 Wentworth St.

Gilman, C., Mrs., res. Columbus St.

Gilman, Samuel, Pastor, Unitarian Church, res. 7 Orange St.

Gilmear, Augustus, Bookkeeper, East Bay St., res. Cannon St.

Gilpin, Francis S., Bookkeeper, 23 Hayne St., res. 260 King St.

Gindrat & Duncan, Druggists, 215 King St.

Gindrat, Abraham, Druggist, 215 King St., res. 215 King St.

Ginon, Michael, Stone Cutter, res. 42 State St.

Girardeau, Mary, Mrs., res. Meeting St.

Girardeau, W. H., Clerk, 13 Southern Wharf, res. cr. Queen & Church Sts.

Gitsinger, Benjamin R., Printer, 3 Broad St., res. 22 Cumberland St.

Given, George, res. cr. Beaufain & Wilson Sts.

Gladden, George, Pilot, res. 22 Church St.

Gladden, T., Mrs., res. Mazyck St.

Glahn, B. Von, Dry Goods, 230 King St., res. 230 King St.

Glahn, Cason Von, Grocer, cr. Radcliffe & Coming Sts.

Glenn, D. L., Dauguerrian Artist, 221 King St., res. Beaufain St.

Glenn, Ellen C., Mrs., res. cr. Reid & Meeting Sts.

Glenn, Martha, Mrs., Shop Keeper, 10 Archdale St.

Glover, Adam B., Bookkeeper, 94 East Bay St., res. Alexander St.

Glover, Sanders L., Wood Factor, cr. Beaufain & Rutledge Sts.

Godett, Ann, Miss, res. 4 Liberty St.

Godfrey, Ellen, Mrs., Clothing, 43 State St., res. 43 State St.

Golding, James, Watchman, Potter's Mills

Goldsmith, Maurice, Deputy U. S. Marshal, res. 98 Tradd St.

Goldsmith, Moses, Speculator, res. Nassau St.

Goldstein, Abraham, Clothing, 346 King St., res. 346 King St.

Goldstein, Isadore, Clothing, 346 King St., res. 346 King St.

Goldstein, J. & A., Clothing, 346 King St.

Goldstein, Jacob, Jeweller, 157 King St., res. 157 King St.

Gonzalez, B., res. 4 George St.

Goodrich, George C., Clerk, 29 Hayne St., res. King St.

Goodrich, Nathaniel E., Butcher, cr. Rutledge & Line Sts.

Goodwin, George M., Liquor Merchant, 114 East Bay St., res. 7 Society St.

Gordon, Alexander, Collection Clerk, Bank of South

Carolina, res. Glebe St.

Gordon, Charles, Carpenter, South Carolina Railroad, res. St. Philip St.

Gordon, Charles P., Bookkeeper, Atlantic Wharf, res. St. Philip St.

Gordon, Isaac, Finisher, South Carolina Railroad, res. St. Philip St.

Gordon, James, Plumber, 94 Meeting St., res. 94 Meeting St.

Gordon, Joseph, Finisher, South Carolina Railroad, res. St. Philip St.

Gordon, W. S., Clothing, 16 Hayne St., res. 16 Hayne St.

Gossage, Charles, Clerk, 257 King St., res. cr. King & Wentworth Sts.

Gotjen, John, Grocer, 65 East Bay St., res. 65 East Bay St.

Gourdin, Theodore S., City Sheriff, City Hall, res. Alexander St.

Gourdin, William Alston, Commission Merchant, 56 East Bay St., res. Limehouse St.

Goutvegner, Peter, Cutler, 43 Queen St., res. 43 Queen St.

Gowan, Alexander H., Watch Maker, Meeting St., res. 8 South Bay St.

Gowan, P. & Son, Watch Makers, cr. Meeting & Chalmers Sts.

Gowan, P., Watch Maker, Meeting St., res. 8 South Bay St.

Graddick, Charles C., Butcher, 11 Market St., res. 26 Calhoun St.

Grady, James R., Bookkeeper, 211 King St., res. King St.

Grady, James, Tailor, 144 King St., res. 144 King St.

Graham, John, Clerk, 211 King St.

Grant, Ives, Tailoress, res. 53 Calhoun St.

Grant, Thomas, Machinist, South Carolina Railroad, res. Coming St.

Graser, C. A., Clerk at John Fraser & Co., res. American Hotel

Graser, John, Shoemaker, 37 Queen St., res. 37 Queen St.

Graveley, Cowlan, Hardware, 44 East Bay St., res. 28 Broad St.

Graveley, John & Co., Hardware, 44 East Bay St.

Graveley, John, Hardware, 44 East Bay St., res. 28 Broad St.

Gravell, George, Carpenter, King St., near Reid St.

Graver, John H., Grocer, cr. King & Reid Sts.

Graves, Charles, Bricklayer, res. 33 Society St.

Graves, Charles, Mrs., res. Coming St.

Graves, Daniel, Physician, res. 4 Friend St.

Graves, R. L., Clerk, 143 Meeting St., res. Mills House

Gray, Alexander, Collector, res. 20 Coming St.

Gray, James F., Teacher, 68 Calhoun St., res. 68 Calhoun St.

Gray, James W., Lawyer, cr. Chalmers & Meeting Sts., res. 88 Beaufain St.

Gray, John B., Clerk, City Hall, res. 52 Anson St.

Gray, Mary E., Mrs., Teacher, 24 Society St., res. 24 Society St.

Gray, Walter, Engineer, res. 50 Church St.

Grayson, Henry, Boarding Officer, Custom House, res. East Bay St.

Grayson, William J., Planter, Wando River, res. East Bay St.

Gready, Andrew P., Collector, res. Mill St.

Gready, James R., Bookkeeper, 211 King St.

Greaton, John, Inspector, Charleston Insurance Co., 8 Broad St., res. Tradd St.

Greaver, John, Shoemaker, 120 King St., res. 120 King St.

Green, Caroline, Mrs., res. Mary St., near Meeting St.

Green, Charles, Carpenter, 11 Inspection St.

Green, James F., Factor, 4 East Bay St., res. Charlotte St.

Green, James F., Jr., Clerk at J. E. Adger's, res. Charlotte St.

Green, James F., Son & Co., Factors & Commission Merchants, 4 East Bay St.

Green, Owen, Tailor, 93 Queen St., res. 93 Queen St.

Green, Patrick, Tailor, 16 Calhoun St., res. 16 Calhoun St.

Green, R. M., Factor, 4 East Bay St., res. Charlotte St.

Green, Thomas, Physician, Washington St., Ward 5

Green, William, Mariner, res. 14 Orange St.

Greenland, John, Wood Factor, William's Wharf, res. 28 Archdale St.

Greenland, Melvin, Physician, cr. Laurens & Wall Sts.

Greer, J. M., Book Store, 207 King St., res. Smith St.

Greer, William, Tavern, 280 King St., res. Wentworth St.

Gregg, Ann, Mrs., Dress Maker, res. Vanderhorst St.

Gregg, John, Shoemaker, 170 Meeting St., res. Heyward's Court

Gregg, William, Clerk, 211 King St., res. Calhoun St., Ward 6

Gregory, F. M., Tailor, 143 East Bay St., res. 143 East Bay St.

Grice & Covert, Gas Fixtures, 201 King St.

Grice, George D., Gas Fixtures, 201 King St., res. St. Philip St.

Grickson, John, Clerk, res. Vanderhorst St.

Gridiron, William, Factor, res. 1 Limehouse St.

Grierson, John W., Druggist, 221 King St., res. 270 King St.

Grierson, William H., Clerk, 268 King St., res. 96 Wentworth St.

Grimball, John B., Planter, res. 38 Meeting St.

Grimes, James, Blacksmith, Tradd St.

Grimes, Lawrence, Blacksmith, 28 Pinckney St., res. 9 Hasell St.

Grinkie, Edward, Surveyor, res. 13 Savage St.

Grinkie, John, Physician, 48 St. Philip St.

Groning, Caspar A., Bookkeeper, 37 Hayne St.

Groning, L., Cotton Presser, Anson St., res. 86 Beaufain St.

Groves, E., Mrs., Boarding House, 1 Queen St.

Gruber, George H., Clerk, 222 King St., res. cr. Reid & Green Sts.

Gruber, George W., Tavern, cr. King & Line Sts.

Gruber, William, Plasterer, 83 Market St., res. foot of Wentworth St.

Gruendal, Augustus, Blacksmith, 31 Queen St., res. 31

Queen St.

Guenveur, E. M., Mrs., Dry Goods, 348 King St., res. 348 King St.

Guenveur, John U., Crockery, 118 King St., res. 118 King St.

Guerry, T. M., Clerk, 54 Broad St.

Guerry, G., Deputy Sheriff, res. Islington Court

Guerry, Peter C., Clerk, 211 King St., res. 99 East Bay St.

Gun, Phillip, Carpenter, res. 88 Beaufain St.

Gunther, Charles, Bookkeeper, 74 East Bay St., res. Rutledge St.

Gurney, A. B., Superintendent, Billiard Saloon, res. City Hotel

Guy, James, Carpenter, res. 7 Clifford St.

Guy, Joseph, Carpenter, 227 East Bay St., res. 227 East Bay St.

Guy, T. B. & Son, Commission Merchants, 5 Hayne St.

Guy, T. B., Commission Merchant, 5 Hayne St., res. 106 East Bay St.

Guymanner, A., Bookkeeper, 147 East Bay St.

Gwinn, Elizabeth, Mrs., Milk Seller, res. 11 Inspection St.

Gwinner, H. W., Printer, 111 East Bay St., res. 99 East Bay St.

Gyles, John A., Lawyer, 54 Broad St., res. 81 Broad St.

Haas, John, Blacksmith, res. 26 Friend St.

Habenicht, G. F., Grocer, 38 Elliott, res. 38 Elliott St.

Hacker, F. B., Clerk at W. C. Dukes, res. Meeting St.

Hacker, George S., Car Builder, South Carolina Railroad, res. King St., Ward 7

Hackett, Patrick, Laborer, res. 5 Stoll's Alley

Haferty, Thomas, Clerk, 19 Hayne St., res. Beaufain St.

Hagan, G. R., Furniture, 80 Church St., res. 80 Church St.

Hague, Edward, Cotton Marker, East Bay St., res. Warren St.

Hahn, H. M., Grocer, 4 Market St., res. 4 Market St.

Hahn, John C., Bookkeeper, 31 Cumberland St., res. 31 Cumberland St.

Haig, Alexander R., Planter, St. Andrew's Parish, res. Ashley St.

Haig, George, Planter, St. Andrew's Parish, res. Rutledge St.

Haig, H. M., Physician, 20 Meeting St., res. 20 Meeting St.

Haig, M., Clerk at Thomas G. Simons & Sons, res. Rutledge St.

Halenback, John F., Grocer, cr. Anson & Pinckney Sts.

Hall & Co., Commission Merchants, Central Wharf

Hall, C. G., Wharfinger, Central Wharf, res. 363 East Bay St.

Hall, H. M., Bookkeeper at Hall & Co., res. Planters Hotel

Hall, H. T., Commission Merchant, Central Wharf, res. Planters Hotel

Hall, James, Rigger, 29 Pinckney St., res. Columbus St.

Hall, W. P., Commission Merchant, Central Wharf, res. Planters Hotel

Hall, William, Physician, 363 East Bay St., res. 363 East Bay St.

Halter, William, Carpenter, res. 125 Church St.

Ham, William, Engineer, 93 Church St., res. 93 Church St.

Hamilton, George, Carpenter, cr. Queen & Philadelphia Sts.

Hamilton, John A., Clerk, 222 King St., res. Beaufain St.

Hamilton, William W., Bookkeeper, 80 East Bay St., res. Meeting St.

Hamlin, Edward, Printer, Mercury Office, res. 5 Vernon St.

Hamlin, George, Blacksmith, Church St., res. 113 Wentworth St.

Hamlin, James, Wood Factor, res. 113 Wentworth St.

Hamlin, Samuel, res. Nassau St.

Hamlin, William, Printer, 40 Broad St., res. 40 Broad St.

Hammond, A. L., Physician, res. America St.

Hammond, S., Framemaker, res. cr. Beaufain & Coming Sts.

Hanabergh, Alfred, Clothing, 223 King St., res. New York

Hanahan, James, Ship Carpenter, res. 48 King St.

Hanahan, John C., Cooper, Longitude Lane, res. 136 Tradd St.

Hanahan, R. S. H., General Agent, St. Michael's Alley

Hancke, John H., res. 30 Laurens St.

Hanckel, Allen S., Clerk, 40 East Bay St., res. 62 Calhoun St.

Hanckel, C., Pastor, St. Paul's Church, res. 62 Calhoun St.

Hanckel, Charles F., Secretary & Treasurer, Savannah & Charleston Railroad Company

Hanckel, John, Bookkeeper, Bank of the State of South Carolina, res. Coming St.

Hanegan, Calvin, Clerk, 21 Hayne St., res. Mills House

Happoldt, A. M., Bookkeeper, 133 Meeting St., res. Hatch's Hall

Happoldt, Albert, Butcher, res. Cannon St.

Happoldt, Edward, Physician, 9 John St., res. 9 John St.

Happoldt, George B., Coach Trimmer, 40 Wentworth St., res. 16 Wall St.

Happoldt, John M., Gunsmith, 45 State St., res. 45 State St.

Happoldt, John P., Molder, South Carolina Railroad, res. Cannon St.

Harbers, Charles H., Grocer, cr. America & Meeting Sts.

Harbers, D. H., Grocer, cr. Wentworth & Coming Sts.

Harbers, H. A., Bookkeeper, 141 Meeting St., res. Meeting St.

Harberson, John, Dry Goods, 350 King St., res. 350 King St.

Harbeson, John S., Dry Goods, 136 King St., res. 350 King St.

Harbson, Joseph, Clerk, 350 King St., res. 350 King St.

Harby, Abraham, Clerk, 23 Broad St., res. Planters Hotel

Hare, Robert W., Mrs., res. 6 Society St.

Harkamp, John, Grocer, cr. King & Broad Sts

Harleston, Edward, Measurer, Custom House, res. Rutledge St.

Harleston, John, Captain, City Guard, res. 57 Meeting St.

Harleston, John, Clerk, 169 East Bay St., res. Rutledge St.
Harleston, John, Jr., Clerk, 114 East Bay St., res. Rutledge St.
Harleston, Summers, Planter, res. Cannon St.
Harleston, T. C., Bookkeeper, Bank of Charleston, res. 18 Hasell St.
Harlon, Michael, Laborer, South Carolina Railroad, res. Morris St.
Harlon, Sophia, Mrs., res. 22 Washington St.
Harmond, S. L., Clerk, 11 Broad St., res. American Hotel
Harms, A., Grocer, 1 Market St., res. 1 Market St.
Harms, Charles, Steam Grist Mill, cr. Cannon & Coming Sts.
Harper & Calvo, Printers, Chalmers St., opposite City Square
Harper, F. M., Printer, Chalmers St., opposite City Square
Harper, J., Wood Factor, William's Wharf, res. 10 Inspection St.
Harper, James M., Clerk, 17 Hayne St., res. Broad St.
Harrall, Hugh, Druggist, King St., res. 4 Glebe St.
Harrall, James, Druggist, 23 Hayne St., res. New York City
Harrall, Nichols & Co., Saddlery Warehouse, cr. Meeting & Hasell Sts.
Harrall, William, Saddlery, cr. Meeting & Hasell Sts., res. 4 Glebe St.
Harrenburg, Henry, Clerk, 61 Tradd St., res. 61 Tradd St.
Harrington, Thomas, res. 7 Archdale St.
Harrington, Timothy, Carpenter, 8 Pritchard St., res. Marsh St.
Harrington, William H., Druggist, 153 Meeting St.
Harris, Charles, Clerk, 207 East Bay St., res. 207 East Bay St.
Harris, Charles F., Clerk, 139 Meeting St., res. 139 Meeting St.
Harris, H., Bookbinder, 59 Broad St., res. Smith St.
Harris, H., Grocer, cr. Archdale & Berresford Sts.
Harris, Isaac, Fruiterer, 39 Market St., res. 39 Market St.
Harrison, A. T., Clerk, 179 East Bay St., res. Pavilion Hotel
Harrison, J. B., Shoemaker, 33 Beaufain St.
Harrison, James F., Tailor, res. St. Philip St.
Harrison, John, Paints & Oils, 72 Meeting St., res. 46 Queen St.
Harrison, Joseph W., Artists Materials, 72 Meeting St., res. 46 Queen St.
Harrod, Patrick, Conductor, South Carolina Railroad, res. Woolf St.
Hart, Hyman N., Hardware, cr. Market & King Sts., res. Calhoun St.
Hart, Jacob J., Clerk, 261 King St., res. cr. Wentworth & Meeting Sts.
Hart, S. N. & H. N., Hardware, cr. Market & King Sts.
Hart, Samuel N., Jr., Hardware, cr. Market & King Sts., res. Meeting St.
Hart, Samuel N., Sr., Books & Stationery, 300 King St.
Harten, J. V., Grocer, cr. Mary & Nassau Sts.
Hartigan, John, Laborer, res. 28 Vernon St.

Hartman, John, Coachmaker, res. 9 Archdale St.
Hartman, William, Grocer, cr. Cannon & St. Philip Sts.
Hartwell, Thomas, Blacksmith, res. President St.
Hartz, John H., Grocer, 192 Meeting St., res. 192 Meeting St.
Harvey, George, Agent, East Bay St., res. 55 King St.
Harvey, James, Wheelwright, 4 Cumberland St., res. 114 Church St.
Harvey, John, Exchange Broker, 33 Broad St., res. 78 Queen St.
Harvey, John, Laborer, res. 74 Anson St.
Haskell, W. E., Planter, St. Paul's Parish, res. Ashley St.
Haslette, James, Commission Merchant, 8 Vendue Range, res. Coming St.
Hassell, P. G., Clerk, North Commercial Wharf, res. 18 Laurens St.
Hasselltine & Walton, Boots & Shoes, 137 Meeting St.
Hasseltine, Albert, Boots & Shoes, 137 Meeting St., res. Charleston Hotel
Hasselltine, Daniel, Blacksmith, foot of Hasell St.
Hasselltine, William, Dry Goods, 37 Hayne St., res. Mills House
Hastedt, H., Grocer, cr. King & Woolf Sts.
Hastie, Calhoun & Co., Saddlery & Coach Trimmings, 39 Hayne St.
Hastie, William S., Saddlery, 39 Hayne St., res. Mills House
Hastings, George, Tavern, 22 Queen St.
Hastings, Patrick, Conductor, South Carolina Railroad, res. America St.
Hatch, Charlotte, Mrs., res. 12 Stoll's Alley
Hatch, Henry, Ship Carpenter, res. 109 Church St.
Hatch, L. M. & Co., Commission Merchants, 120 Meeting St.
Hatch, L. M., Commission Merchant, 120 Meeting St., res. 8 Society St.
Hatch, William, Ship Carpenter, res. 109 Church St.
Haviland, Harrell & Co., Druggists, 23 Hayne & 250 King St.
Haviland, James C., Druggist, 23 Hayne St., res. New York City
Hawley, Richmond, Hats & Caps, 240 King St., res. 240 King St.
Hayden & Whilden, Jewellers & Watchmakers, 250 King St.
Hayden, A. H., Jeweller, 250 King St., res. cr. College & Green Sts.
Hayden, H. Sidney, Jeweller, 250 King St., res. Mills House
Hayforce, Ann, Mrs., Fruiteress, cr. King & Woolf Sts.
Hayforce, Gardiner, Carpenter, cr. King & Woolf Sts.
Haygood, Eugene C., Bricklayer, res. 21 Liberty St.
Haygood, Franklin R., Clerk, 145 Meeting St., res. 21 Society St.
Haygood, John W., Piano Tuner & Repairer, res. 21 Society St.
Hayne & Miles, Lawyers, 22 Broad St.
Hayne & Yates, Commission Merchants, 151 East Bay St.
Hayne, A. P., Col., res. Legare St.

Hayne, Arthur P., Physician, 26 King St.
Hayne, Isaac W., Lawyer, 22 Broad St., res. 6 Logan St.
Hayne, James M., Carpenter, res. Meeting St.
Hayne, Mary H., Miss, res. 25 Meeting St.
Hayne, Paul H., Editor, 119 East Bay St., res. Alexander St.
Hayne, Susan, Mrs., res. Ashley St.
Hayne, William A., Lawyer, res. 26 King St.
Hayne, William E., Commission Merchant, 151 East Bay St., res. 1 Church St.
Haynsworth, Charles D., Dry Goods, 243 King St., res. 260 King St.
Hays, Henry, Sailmaker, res. Hanover St.
Hays, Leroy W., Clerk, 41 Hayne St., res. Charleston Hotel
Hays, Michael, Laborer, res. Woolf St.
Hays, Richard, Watchmaker, res. Reid St.
Hays, Stephen, Fireman, res. Woolf St.
Hays, Thomas H., Printer, 3 Queen St., res. Washington St.
Hazard, William, Shoemaker, Vanderhorst St.
Hazelhurst, George, Bookkeeper, Torre's Mill
Headly, S., Mrs., res. 38 Archdale St.
Healy, Mary Ann, Mrs., Dressmaker, 95 King St.
Heath, Eliza, Mrs., res. Spring St.
Heath, Samuel, Engineer, res. Spring St.
Heathcoat, James, Encoustic Tiler, res. 34 Alexander St.
Hedderly, George, Grocer, cr. Bull & Rutledge Sts.
Hedderly, James P., Brass Founder, Union Wharf, res. 10 Magazine St.
Heeseman, John, Clerk, 133 Meeting St.
Heffron, Dennis, Wheelwright, res. Calhoun St.
Heffron, J. & T. S., Saddle & Harnessmakers, King St., near Calhoun St.
Heffron, John, Saddler, res. King St., near Calhoun St.
Heffron, T. S., Saddler, res. King St., near Calhoun St.
Heidt, Mary, Mrs., Confectionary, 289 King St., res. 289 King St.
Heidt, Valentine, Basketmaker, 289 King St., res. 289 King St.
Heine, Weinrich, Tailor, 133 King St., res. 133 King St.
Heins, Debright, Grocer, cr. Church & Cumberland Sts.
Heins, Henry, Grocer, 103 Meeting St., res. 103 Meeting St.
Heins, James, Porter, res. 13 Price's Alley
Heins, John, Cabinetmaker, 73 King St., res. 73 King St.
Heins, John, Grocery, 1 King St., res. 1 King St.
Helling, Charles, Boot & Shoemaker, 5 Queen St., res. 5 Queen St.
Henderson, Charles, res. Drake St.
Henderson, James M. A., Printer, Standard Office, res. 102 Church St.
Hendricks, Henry W., Molder, South Carolina Railroad, res. Cannon St.
Hendricks, J. M. & Co., Soda Water Manufactory, 37 Market St.
Hendricks, J. M., Soda Water, 37 Market St., res. 37 Market St.
Hendricks, Laurence C., Collection Clerk, Southwest Railroad Bank

Hendrix, James R., Bookkeeper, American Hotel
Hendrix, Richard, Conductor, South Carolina Railroad, res. America St.
Hendrix, Richard E., Commission Merchant, 148 East Bay St., res. 249 King St.
Henercy, William S. & Co., Iron & Brass Founders, Meeting St., Upper Wards
Henercy, William S., Iron & Brass Founder, Meeting St., res. America St.
Henessy, Patrick, Porter, 219 King St., res. King St.
Henessy, Thomas, Junk Store, 38 & 56 King St., res. 38 King St.
Henke, H., Tailor, 39 Broad St.
Henken, Henry, Grocer, King St., Ward 6
Henry, C. W., Commission Merchant, 20 Vanderhorst's Wharf, res. 13 Meeting St.
Henry, Edward, Clerk, 143 Meeting St., res. Pavilion Hotel
Henry, Edward L., Bookkeeper, 244 King St., res. 3 Liberty St.
Henry, J., Mrs., res. 3 Liberty St.
Henry, John T., Bricklayer, res. 14 Wentworth St.
Henry, William, Engineer, South Carolina Railroad, res. America St.
Herbert, Michael, Clothing, 67 State St., res. 67 State St.
Herbert, Thomas, Tavern, 64 State St.
Herckenwrath, Leon, Commission Merchant, Adger's Wharf, res. Holland St.
Herckenwrath, Wragg & Co., Commission Merchants, Adger's Wharf
Herde, Charles, Bookkeeper, Hopkins, Hudson & Co., res. 250 King St.
Heriot & Holmes, Commission Merchants, 4 Vendue Range
Heriot & Petit, Average Adjusters & Forwarding Merchants, 36 East Bay St.
Heriot, B. D., Navy Agent, cr. East Bay & Exchange Sts., res. 73 Beaufain St.
Heriot, Benjamin G., Insurance Agent, cr. East Bay & Exchange St., res. 86 Beaufain St.
Heriot, Daniel, Conductor, South Carolina Railroad, res. Bogard St.
Heriot, Daniel, Mrs., Young Ladies' Seminary, Radcliffe St.
Heriot, Edwin, Inspector, Custom House, res. 73 Beaufain St.
Heriot, G. A., Commission Merchant, 4 Vendue Range, res. Limehouse St.
Heriot, John R., Clerk, Gas Works, res. Limehouse St.
Heriot, Robert, Engineer, South Carolina Railroad, res. 23 Montague St.
Heriot, W. B., President, Commercial Insurance Company, 4 Broad St., res. 3 King St.
Heriot, W. C., Bookkeeper, 70 East Bay St., res. 123 Wentworth St.
Heriot, William J., Clerk, Gas Works, res. Limehouse St.
Herman, Henry A., Grocer, Spring St.
Hernandez, J. J. & Co., Dry Goods, 213 King St.
Hernandez, James J., Dry Goods, 213 King St., res. Cannon St.

Hernandez, John, Engineer, South Carolina Railroad, res. Cannon St.

Herron, John, Commission Merchant, South Atlantic Wharf, res. Mill St.

Herron, William R., Clerk, Custom House, res. 47 St. Philip St.

Herron, William R., Ship Carpenter, 122 East Bay St., res. 47 St. Philip St.

Hertz, Frederick E., Bookkeeper, 151 Meeting St., res. 67 King St.

Hertz, Isaac E., Commission Merchant, 110 East Bay St., res. 43 King St.

Hertz, Thaddeus E., Medical Student, res. 67 King St.

Hesh, Christian, Clothing, 58 State St., res. Bee St.

Hewitt, O., Clerk, 141 Meeting St., res. Cannon St.

Hews, Elias, Engineer, res. 10 Anson St.

Heyer, J. H., Grocer, Spring St.

Heyward, Daniel, Planter, res. 17 East Bay St.

Heyward, George C., Factor, 16 Vanderhorst's Wharf, res. 28 King St.

Heyward, J. B., Planter, Combahee, res. 90 Broad St.

Heyward, T. S., Auctioneer, 16 Vanderhorst's Wharf, res. Legare St.

Heyward, Thomas, Custom House, res. 8 Liberty St.

Heyward, William H., Planter, Combahee, res. 4 Legare St.

Hibbers, C. M., Grocer, cr. Wentworth & St. Philip Sts.

Hickey, Charles, Frame Maker, 154 King St., res. 154 King St.

Hicks, Henry, Drayman, res. Spring St.

Higenbuttle, Martin, Grocer, 152 East Bay St., res. 152 East Bay St.

Higgins, John, Drayman, res. President St.

Higgins, John, Drayman, res. 122 Church St.

Higgins, Michael, Clerk, 186 King St., res. Market St.

Highland, Patrick, Drayman, res. cr. Broad & Rutledge Sts.

Highway, R., Mrs., Boarding House, 180 East Bay St.

Hill, Alexander S., Coach Maker, 23 Hasell St., res. 23 Hasell St.

Hill, Francis C., Artist, res. 13 Clifford St.

Hill, James, Machinist, res. Columbus St.

Hill, John, Carpenter, res. Columbus St.

Hillburn, Eliza, Cake Shop, res. Cannon St.

Hillegas, Caroline, Mrs., res. 5 Franklin St.

Hillen, Jacob, Boot & Shoemaker, cr. King & Anson Sts.

Hillier, John, Porter, res. 78 Queen St.

Hillier, Thomas, Proprietor, City Hotel, cr. Broad & East Bay Sts.

Hillman, H., Tailor, 99 East Bay St., res. Tradd St.

Hilson, John, Grocer, Meeting St., Ward 5

Hinson, William, Ship Carpenter, res. Calhoun St.

Hippers, Phoebe, res. 10 Wentworth St.

Hobbs, William, Seedsman, 271 King St., res. 271 King St.

Hodson, Elizabeth, Tailoress, res. 3 Calhoun St.

Hoff, John C., res. 10 Orange St.

Hoffman, G., Tailor, 24 State St., res. 24 State St.

Hoffman, Henry, Grocer, President St.

Hoffman, William, Shoemaker, res. Hanover St.

Hogan, Richard, Factor, Kerr's Wharf, res. Radcliffe St.

Holcombe, Elias, Clerk, 211 King St., res. American Hotel

Holland, Edward C., Wharfinger, Commercial Wharf, res. Ashley St.

Holland, Parker J., Dry Goods, cr. King & Broad Sts., res. cr. Tradd & Friend Sts.

Holland, Willian, Sailmaker, East Bay St., res. Radcliffe St.

Hollarn, Patrick, Laborer, res. McBride's lane

Hollings, Benjamin N., Grocer, cr. Rutledge & Line Sts.

Hollingshead, William, Printer, res. 10 Bull St.

Holloway, James, Carpenter, 25 Middle St., res. 25 Middle St.

Holloway, Samuel, Drayman, res. 66 Calhoun St.

Holmes & Stoney, Commission Merchants, Boyce's North Wharf

Holmes, C. R., Clerk 135 Meeting St.

Holmes, Edward, Drayman, res. Charlotte St.

Holmes, Emma J., Colored, Nurse, res. 17 Cumberland St.

Holmes, Francis S., Professor, Charleston College, res. 60 St. Philip St.

Holmes, Isaac, Clerk, 27 Hayne St.

Holmes, J. H., Commission Merchant, Boyce's Wharf, res. cr. Rutledge & Radcliffe Sts.

Holmes, J. V., Collector, res. 32 Coming St.

Holmes, James C., Clerk, 246 King St.

Holmes, James, res. 13 East Battery St.

Holmes, James, Teacher, res. 2 Greenhill

Holmes, John L., res. 5 Pitt St.

Holmes, Mary E., Mrs., res. 16 Water St.

Holmes, Robert, Clerk, Vanderhorst's Wharf, res. Charlotte St.

Holmes, Thomas, Clerk, res. Charlotte St.

Holmes, W. P., Commission Merchant, 4 Vendue Range, res. cr. Tradd & Council Sts.

Holmes, William E., Clerk, 120 Meeting St., res. Charlotte St.

Holwell, T. W., Clerk at James Wilman's, res. 110 Meeting.

Honour, J. H., Sr., President, Charleston Insurance Company, 8 Broad St. res. 14 John St.

Honour, J. L., Bookkeeper, 8 Broad St., res. Radcliffe St.

Honour, John, Penny Post, res. Charlotte St.

Honour, T. A., Clerk, 26 Hayne St.

Honour, Theodore, Clerk, res. 34 Alexander St.

Honour, Thomas, Mrs., res. Morris St.

Honour, William, Clerk, Post Office, res. Wragg Square

Hood, Eliza, Mrs., Fancy Goods, 116 King St., res. 116 King St.

Hood, Henry, Clerk, 141 Meeting, res. 116 King St.

Hooke, R. M., Factor, Brown's Wharf, res. Chattanooga, Tenn.

Hopkins, Hudson & Co. Commission Merchants, Accommodation Wharf

Hopkins, J. Ward, Bookkeeper at C. T. Mitchell & Co., res. 28 Tradd St.

Hopkins, James, res. 20 Church St.

Hopkins, L., Commission Merchant, Accommodation

Wharf, res. Augusta, Ga.

Horber J., Mathematical Instrument Maker, 64 Market St., res. 64 Market St.

Horlbeck, Daniel, Clerk, Court of Common Pleas, res. cr. Calhoun & Meeting Sts.

Horlbeck, E., Physician, cr. Wentworth & Coming Sts.

Horlbeck, Edward, Bricklayer, res. Washington St., near Calhoun St.

Horlbeck, Henry, Bricklayer, cr. Calhoun & Meeting Sts.

Horlbeck, John, Wood & Brick Factor, Calhoun St.

Horlbeck, Peter, res. 111 Broad St.

Horlbeck, William, Physician, cr. Wentworth & Coming Sts.

Horsey, John R., Clerk, 211 King St., res. 155 East Bay St.

Horsey, S., Mrs., Boarding House, 155 East Bay St.

Horsey, T. M. & Co. Hats & Caps, 25 Hayne St.

Horsey, Thomas M., Hats & Caps, 25 Hayne St., res. Bee St.

Horton, John A., Saddlery, 157 Meeting St., res. Newark, N. J.

Horton T. A. P., Tin & Hardware, 120 Meeting St., res. 10 Glebe St.

Hosch & Flemming, Confectioners, 269 King St.

Hosch, William, Confectioner, 269 King St., res. 269 King St.

Howard, C. P., Mrs. res. cr. Washington St. & Potter's Wharf

Howard, Henry M., Naval Officer, Custom House, res. Washington St.

Howard, Irby, Clerk at Hopkins, Hudson & Co., res. 190 King St.

Howard, Jane, Colored, Seamstress, 221 East Bay St.

Howard, Joseph L., Clerk at John Frazer & Co., res. Washington St.

Howard, Lee, Assistant Naval Officer, Custom House, res. Washington St.

Howard, Robert, Colored, Wood Factor, Gadsden's Wharf, res. 80 Anson St.

Howard, Stephen L., Factor, South Commercial Wharf, res. 259 East Bay St.

Howard, Thomas, Commission Merchant, Frazer's Wharf, res. Washington St.

Howe, Silas, res. cr. Vernon & Concord Sts.

Howell, S. S., Jr., Clerk, 219 King St. res. 9 Hasell St.

Howell, Sidney S., Dry Goods, 33 Hayne St., res. 9 Hasell St.

Howland & Taft, Commission Merchants, 141 East Bay St.

Howland, B. J., Commission Merchant, 141 East Bay St., res. New York City

Hubbell Thaddeus C., Broker & Auctioneer, 33 Broad St., res. Calhoun St.

Hubert, C. N., Commission Merchant, 71 East Bay St., res. cr. Alexander & Charlotte Sts.

Huchet, Eugene, Commission Merchant, Adger's North Wharf, res. 82 Market St.

Huchet, Theodore, Factor, Adger's Wharf, res. 60 Beaufain St.

Hudson, John R., Commission Merchant,

Accommodation Wharf, res. Charleston Hotel

Hudson, Peter, Engineer, South Carolina Railroad, res. King St.

Hudson, S. D., Printer, 29 Pinckney St., res. Columbus St.

Hudson, Thomas, Guardman, res. King St.

Huger & Milliken, Dry Goods, 42 East Bay St.

Huger, Alfred, Post Master, res. cr. Broad & Mazyck Sts.

Huger, Arthur M., Dry Goods, 42 East Bay St., res. 52 Meeting St.

Huger, C. K., Dry Goods, 12 & 14 East Bay St.

Huger, Cleland, res. foot of Warren St.

Huger, Daniel E., res. 24 Meeting St.

Huger, Daniel, res. 61 Coming St.

Huger, Elizabeth, Mrs., res. 2 Logan St.

Huger, F., Col., res. 2 Logan St.

Huger, T. P., President, North Eastern Railroad, res. 91 East Bay St.

Huger, W. H., Physician, Calhoun St., Ward 6

Huger, William, Physician, 79 Church St., res. 79 Church St.

Hughes, Edward T., Clerk, Planters & Mechanics Bank, res. Limehouse St.

Hughes, O. E., Planter, St. Andrew's Parish, res. Limehouse St.

Hughes, Thomas, Furniture, 68 Meeting St., res. 68 Meeting /st,

Hughes, William, Shoemaker, Cannon St.

Hulan, M. A., Confectionary, 327 King St., res. 327 King St.

Hulesburg, Henry, Grocer, cr. Wentworth & Anson Sts.

Hull, A. S. & Co., Merchant Tailors, 133 Meeting St.

Hull, A. S., Tailor, 133 Meeting St., res. Charleston Hotel

Hull, Samuel James, Bookkeeper, 39 Hayne St., res. 6 Society St.

Hume, -----, Misses, res. 200 East Bay St.

Hume, Thomas M., Broker & Auctioneer, 28 Broad St., res. cr. Thomas & Warren Sts.

Hume, William, Teacher, Citadel Academy, res. cr. Ashley & Mill Sts.

Hummell, William, Druggist, cr. King & Mary Sts.

Hunt, David, Auctioneer & Commission Merchant, 20 Vendue Range, res. 33 Anson St.

Hunt, James E., Clerk, 20 Vendue Range, res. 33 Anson St.

Hunt, N., Auctioneer & Commission Merchant, 20 Vendue Range, res. 33 Anson St.

Hunter, Amanda, Seamstress, State St., near Broad St.

Hunter, Robert, res. Charlotte St.

Huntington, George M., Clerk, 143 Meeting St., res. Merchants Hotel

Huntoon, Charles S., Fancy Goods, 149 Meeting St., res. Mills House

Hurst, James L., Propietor, Merchants Hotel

Hussell, Christian G., Shoemaker, 209 East Bay St., res. 209 East Bay St.

Hutchins, Thompson, Clerk 253 King St., res. 249 King St.

Hutchinson, Edward, res. Queen St., near Franklin St.

Hutchinson, Joseph, res. Queen St., near Franklin St.

Hutchinson, Mary, res. Anson St.

Hutchinson, Thomas Legare, Mayor, City Hall, res. 64 Church St.

Huth, L., Saddler, 60 State St.

Hutson, T. J., Deputy City Sheriff, res. King St.

Hyams, Hamilton, Rice Merchant, 79 East Bay St., res. 79 East Bay St.

Hyams, M., Commission Merchant, Brown's Wharf, res. 47 Wentworth St.

Hyams, M. D. & Sons, Rice Merchants, 79 East Bay St.

Hyams, M. D., Rice Merchant, 79 East Bay St., res. 79 East Bay St.

Hyams, Pinckney, Rice Merchant, 79 East Bay St., res. 79 East Bay St.

Hyams, Solomon, Clerk, cr. Calhoun & East Bay Sts.

Hyatt, Edward, Dry Goods, 37 Hayne St., res. New York City

Hyatt, McBirney & Co. Dry Goods, 37 Hayne St.

Hyde, George A., Clothing, 279 King St., res. New York City

Hyde, Simeon, Hardware, 139 Meeting St., res. 56 Tradd St.

Hyer, James, Gas Fitter, Montague St., 1 door from Coming St.

Hyer, William, Finisher, foot of Hasell St.

Hymer, William, Drayman, res. cr. America & Mary Sts.

Hymes, H., Clothing, King St., Upper Ward

Ingleburt, George, Laborer, South Carolina Railroad, res. Coming St.

Inglesby, W. H., City Treasurer, City Hall, res. 4 Logan St.

Ingless, Gay, Colored, Barber, 49 Queen St.

Ingless, William, Colored, Barber 49 Queen St.

Ingraham & Webb, Factors & Commission Merchants, North Commercial Wharf

Ingraham, Duncan N., Capt., U. S. Navy, res. Legare St., near Lamboll St.

Ingraham, George H., Commission Merchant, North Commercial Wharf, res. 18 Laurens St.

Ingraham, George H., Jr., Ship Merchant, Vanderhorst's Wharf, res. 18 Laurens St.

Ingraham, W. P., Planter, res. cr. Wentworth & Smith Sts.

Inness, Charles M., Clerk, 25 Hayne St., res. 8 Queen St.

Inness, James, Laborer, res. 8 Queen St.

Isaacs, Alexander, Dry Goods, 143 Meeting St., res. Charleston Hotel

Isenberg & Brother, Clothing, King St., Upper Ward

Isenburg, Benjamin, Clothing, King St., Upper Ward

Isenburg, Joseph, Clothing, King St., Upper Ward

Issertel, Richard, Clerk, 190 King St., res. 92 King St.

Izard, C. P., Mrs., res. 29 Legare St.

Izard, Walter, Officer, Northeast Railroad, res. 63 Calhoun St.

Jackson, Charles F. & Co., Clothing, 199 King St.

Jackson, Charles F. Clothing, 199 King St., res. 63 Meeting St.

Jackson, E., Clerk, res. 63 Meeting St.

Jackson, E. H., Livery Stable, Pinckney St., res.

Charleston Hotel

Jackson, George, Tinware, 275 King St., res. 275 King St.

Jackson, J., Mrs. res. 63 Meeting St.

Jackson, Rose, Nurse, 221 East Bay St.

Jackson, William, Engineer, South Carolina Railroad, res. Cannon St.

Jacobi, Cornelius, Butcher, res. Cannon St.

Jacobi, Morris, Clothing, 341 King, res. 341 King St.

Jacobs, B. H., Mrs., Boarding House, res. 82 Queen St.

Jacobs, F. C., Clerk, 28 Vendue Range, res. cr. Smith & Bull Sts.

Jacobs, Ferdinand, Rev., Principal, Female Seminary, cr. Vanderhorst & King Sts.

Jacobs, George, Tinsmith, 184 King St., res. 184 King St.

Jacobs, J. S., Junk Store, 77 Market St., res. 77 Market St.

Jacobs, Solomon, Pastor, res. 21 St. Philip St.

Jager, H., Mrs., Midwife, res. cr. Bull & Pitt Sts.

Jager, Hans, Grocer, cr. Bull & Pitt Sts.

Jager, John, Grocery, King St. near Spring St.

Jailand, William H., Engineer, res. William's Row

James, Henry, Carpenter, Marsh St., res. Marsh St.

James, James W., Florist, res. Doughty St.

James, John, Fruiter, 13 Market St., res. Market St.

James, Robert, Printer, 3 Broad St., res. Cannon St.

James, William & Gitsinger, Steam Book & Job Printers, 3 Broad St.

James, William, Pilot, res. Marsh St.

Jander, Alexander, Planter, res. 6 Cannon St.

Jaridon, Thomas P., Clerk, res. cr. Chapel & Alexander Sts.

Jatho, G. W., Jeweller, 121 Meeting, res. 121 Meeting St.

Jeannerette, J. M., Commission Merchant, 94 East Bay St.

Jeannerette, John C., Bookkeeper at O'Neal & Crawford, res. Meeting St.

Jeffords, Arthur H., Clerk, 211 King St., res. 29 Friend St.

Jeffords, E. A., Bookkeeper, Accommodation Wharf, res. 4 Stoll's Alley

Jeffords, Edward, Clerk, 76 East Bay St., res. 29 Friend St.

Jeffords, H. L., Factor, South Atlantic Wharf, res. 9 Hales St.

Jeffords, James, Blacksmith, Marsh's Wharf, res. 138 East Bay St.

Jeffords, James, Shipsmith, res. 19 Wentworth St.

Jeffords, John H., Sail Maker, East Bay St., res. Franklin St.

Jeffords, Robert J., Clerk, 76 East Bay St., res. 29 Friend St.

Jeffords, Theodore A., Clerk, 14 Hayne St., res. 17 Hasell St.

Jeffords, William, Bookkeeper, Adger's Wharf, res. Radcliffe St.

Jeffords, William H., Clerk, 23 Hayne St., res. 17 Hasell St.

Jenkins, Cathrine, Mrs., res. 7 Lamboll St.

Jenkins, Christopher, Engineer, res. 98 Beaufain St.

Jenkins, Hugh, Junk Store, 2 Kerr's Wharf, res. Prince's Alley
Jenkins, John L., Printer, 117 East Bay St., res. Laurens St.
Jenkins, John, Timber Measurer, res. 98 Beaufain St.
Jenkins, William, Clerk, East Bay St., res. Price's Alley
Jenney, Robert, Saddlery, 344 King St., res. 344 King St.
Jennings, Abraham G., Clothing, 26 Hayne St., res. Charleston Hotel
Jennings, David, Saddlery, 157 Meeting St., res. 6 Montague St.
Jennings, Susan, Mrs., res. 8 Whim's Court
Jennings, Tomlinson & Co. Saddlery Warehouse, 157 Meeting St.
Jervey, J. C., Inspector, Custom House, res. 104 Tradd
Jervey, James P., Physician, 13 George St., res. 13 George St.
Jervey, Lewis, Bookkeeper, State Bank, res. cr. Montague & Lynch Sts.
Jervey, Lewis, Planter, res. Rutledge St.
Jervey, Theodore D., Factor, 18 Vanderhorst's Wharf, res. cr. Lynch & Montague Sts.
Jervey, Thomas D., Deputy Collector, Custom House, res. 15 Church St.
Jervey, W. C., Clerk 253 King St.
Jervey, William, Lawyer, 59 Meeting St., res. 22 George St.
Jessen, Frederick A., Grocer, 209 East Bay St., res. 209 East Bay St.
Jessen, Hans, Grocer, 139 East Bay St., res. Horlbeck Alley
Jessup, W. C., Saddlery, cr. Meeting & Hasell Sts., res. Augusta, Ga.
Jessup, Zadock R., Boots & Shoes, 142 King St., res. 142 King St.
Johannes, John, Tavern, cr. Elliot St. & Bedons Alley
Johnson, Adam, Shoemaker, res. Coming St.
Johnson, Ann, Colored, Seamstress, res. 19 Cumberland St.
Johnson, Ann, Miss, res. 149 Meeting St.
Johnson, Anna, Miss, res. 26 South Bay St.
Johnson, Augustus S., Clerk, 32 Broad St., res. Ashley St.
Johnson, Benjamin, Umbrellas, 263 King St., res. 263 King St.
Johnson, Charles H., Clerk, 157 Meeting St., res. Ashley St.
Johnson, Charles J., Colored, Tailor, 314 King St., res. 7 Coming St.
Johnson, Clarence, Flour Merchant, 10 Vendue Range, res. Charleston Hotel
Johnson, Henry L., Clerk, 149 King St., res. 122 King St.
Johnson, Hollis D., Boots & Shoes, 45 Hayne St., res. 122 King St.
Johnson, J. M. C., Teller, Bank of Charleston, res. 23 Pitt St.
Johnson, J., Mariner, res. 6 Elliott St.
Johnson, James, Butcher, Neck Market, res. Line St.
Johnson, James, Colored, Tailor, Queen St., res. 5 Friend St.

Johnson, James, State Assessor, res. 76 Wentworth St.
Johnson, John, Rigger, res. 50 Church St.
Johnson, John W., Blacksmith, res. America St.
Johnson, Joseph, Druggist, 11 Broad St., res. 107 King St.
Johnson, L., Grocer, cr. Magazine & Mazyck Sts.
Johnson, Mary, Mrs., Midwife, res. 14 Liberty St.
Johnson, Oscar E., Clerk, 279 King St., res. 15 John St.
Johnson, T. N., Cotton Broker, Boyce & Co. Wharf, res. 107 King St.
Johnson, Thomas A., Butcher, Neck Market, res. Line St.
Johnson, Timothy W., Inspector, Custom House, res. Ashley St.
Johnson, William, Wood Factor, 14 Marsh's Wharf, res. 76 Wentworth St.
Johnston, A. S., Dry Goods, 181 East Bay St., res. 193 Meeting St.
Johnston, Crews & Brawley, Dry Goods, 181 East Bay St.
Johnston, J., Liquor Merchant, 90 East Bay St., res. City Hotel
Johnston, Pinckney, Clerk, East Bay St., res. 14 New St.
Johnston, R. & J., Liquor Merchants, 90 East Bay St.
Johnston, R., Liquor Merchant, 90 East Bay St., res. 90 East Bay St.
Joiner, William, Carpenter, res. Williams' Row
Jones & Hanabergh, Clothing, 223 King St.
Jones & Lee, Architects, cr. Church & Broad Sts.
Jones, A. D., Clerk, 26 East Bay St., res. cr. Beaufain & Wilson Sts.
Jones, A. H., Commission Merchant, 60 East Bay St., res. 13 Pitt St.
Jones, Alexander, Carpenter, cr. Wilson & Beaufain Sts.
Jones, Allan, Drayman, res. 55 Anson St.
Jones, E., Miss, res. 1 Guignard St.
Jones, Edward C., Architect, cr. Broad & Church Sts., res. 17 Smith St.
Jones, Edward, Ship Carpenter, 13 George St., res. 13 George St.
Jones, J. Legare, Clerk, 251 King St., res. cr. Market & King Sts.
Jones, James C., Clerk, 251 King St., res. 17 Smith St.
Jones, James, Carpenter, res. 11 Rutledge St.
Jones, Jeremiah, Carpenter, res. 3 Henrietta St.
Jones, John H., Carpenter, res. Spring St.
Jones, L. M., Commission Merchant, 60 East Bay St., res. Planters Hotel
Jones, Marion, Carpenter, res. Lynch St.
Jones, O. C., Clothing, 223 King St., res. New York City
Jones, Paul, Carpenter, 120 East Bay St., res. Bee St.
Jones, Prince, Drayman, res. 14 Washington St.
Jones, Sarah, Colored, Washerwoman, 12 Washington St.
Jones, Sarah, res. 1 Guignard St.
Jones, Susan, res. 1 Guignard St.
Jones, William, Drayman, res. 5 Prince's Alley
Jones, William, Mariner, res. 72 King St.
Jordan, Edward, Sail Maker, Accommodation Wharf, res. 4 Stoll's Alley
Joseph, J. J., Mrs. res. 55 Wentworth St.

Jowitt, J. J., Police Officer, City Hall
Jowitt, Thaddeus C., Printer, 3 Broad St., res. 115 King St.
Jowitt, W. G., Wharfinger, Atlantic Wharf, res. 115 King St.
Joy, E. G., Mrs., res. cr. Gadsden & Wentworth Sts.
Joy, John P., Carpenter, South Carolina Railroad, res. Drake St.
Judge, P. & Co., Locksmiths, 34 Market St.
Judge, P., Locksmith, 34 Market St., res. 34 Market St.
June, Samuel, Tavern, 13 Elliott St.
Jungbluth, John, Germania Hotel, 31 Cumberland St.
Just, Margaret, Mrs., res. 34 Hasell St.
Justy, William, Tailor, 39 Broad St., res. cr. State & Queen Sts.
Kacy, William, Bricklayer, res. 6 Linguard St.
Kahao, Thomas, Harness Maker, Meeting St., res. Calhoun St.
Kain, Thomas, Clerk, South Carolina Railroad, res. Mary St.
Kairlain, Edward, Porter, 20 Broad St., res. 20 Broad St.
Kalb, Jacob H., res. Rutledge St.
Kanapaux, C. E., Attorney, Sheriff's Office, res. 131 King St.
Kanapaux, Charles, Clerk, res. 2 Gadsden St.
Kanapaux, J. A., Carpenter, res. 2 Gadsden St.
Kanapaux, J. Theodore, Clerk, 14 Hayne St., res. 2 Gadsden St.
Kanapaux, Oscar, Bricklayer, res. 2 Gadsden St.
Kanapaux, Victor Eugina, res. 2 Gadsden St.
Kane, John W., Clerk, Hayne St., res. 42 Society St.
Kaul, Lewis, Clothing, King St., Upper Ward
Kavanaugh, John, Tavern, 39 Queen St.
Keckeley, E. E., Conductor, South Carolina Railroad, res. Meeting St., near Mary St.
Keenan, John, Clerk, 43 Hayne St., res. East Bay St.
Keenan, William, Engraver, 250 King, res. 119 Queen St.
Keene, William, Mariner, res. 19 Meeting St.
Keine, John W., Clerk, 211 King St., res. cr. King & Wentworth Sts.
Keip, John P., Grocer, 62 Anson St., res. 62 Anson St.
Keith, P. T., Pastor, St. Michael's Church, res. 12 Lynch St.
Kellers, C., Coal Dealer, 51 Market St.
Kellers, Lewis, Laborer, 1 Bedons Alley
Kelly & Barritt, Auctioneers & Commission Merchants, 19 Vendue Range
Kelly & Brady, Dry Goods, 218 King St.
Kelly, Ann, res. 6 Linguard St.
Kelly, James, Cooper, 5 Wharf St., res. 5 Wharf St.
Kelly, John, Boat Builder, res. 8 Middle St.
Kelly, John G., Clerk, 207 King St., res. 3 Liberty St.
Kelly, Mary, Mrs., res. 20 Vernon St.
Kelly Michael, Clerk, South Carolina Railroad, res. St. Philip St.
Kelly, Owen, Clerk, Central Wharf, res. St. Philip St.
Kelly P., Watchman, South Carolina Railroad, res. Reid St.
Kelly, Teddy, Dry Goods, 212 King St., res. Victoria Hotel

Kelly, Thaddeus, Dry Goods, 218 King St., res. Victoria Hotel
Kelly, Thomas, Baker, res. Cannon St.
Kelly, Thomas, Bricklayer, res. 29 Montague St.
Kelly, William, Auctioneer, 19 Vendue Range, res. 44 St. Philip St.
Kelly, William, Plasterer, res. 44 St. Philip St.
Kemme, Daniel H., Tailor, 39 Broad St., res. 4 Court House Square
Kendrick, J. R., Pastor, Citadel Square Baptist Church
Kenifick & Skrine, Druggists, 277 King St.
Kenifick, John, Druggists, 277 King St.
Kennedy, A. J., Mrs., Proprietor, American Hotel, cr. King & George Sts.
Kennedy, Bridget, Mrs., Dry Goods, King St., Upper Ward
Kennedy, Edward, Laborer, res. 5 Cannon St.
Kennedy, G. D., Bookkeeper, 90 East Bay St., res. 90 East Bay St.
Kennedy, J. T., Tailor, 30 Broad St., res. 47 Coming St.
Kennedy, James, Drayman, res. 3 Linguard St.
Kennedy, James, Superintendent of Streets, res. 37 Calhoun St.
Kennedy, John D., State Contable, res. 36 Market St.
Kennedy, John, Waiter, Charleston Hotel, res. 40 State St.
Kennedy, Joseph D., Clerk, 243 King St., res. 260 King St.
Kennedy, M., Bar Keeper, 12 Linguard St., res. 12 Linguard St.
Kennedy, Michael, Laborer, res. America St.
Kennedy, Peter, Boots & Shoes, 79 Market St., res. 79 Market St.
Kennedy, William H., Clerk, 257 King St., res. Commercial House
Kernan, Patrick, Dry Goods, 70 State St., res. 70 State St.
Kernan, Patrick, Soda Water, 37 Market St., res. 70 State St.
Kerney, James, Carpenter, res. Queen St.
Kerr, Thomas, Clerk, 253 King St., res. cr. Market & East Bay Sts.
Kerr, Thomas J., Commission Merchant, 4 Kerr's Wharf, res. 1 Society St.
Kershaw, Ann, Mrs., res. 82 Wentworth St.
Kershaw, Charles, Cigar Store, 38 Anson St., res. 38 Anson St.
Kershaw, James C., Bookkeeper, 145 Meeting St.
Ketchum, Alexander, Bookkeeper, 45 Hayne St., res. 260 King St.
Ketchum, Joel, Dry Goods, 243 King St., res. Meeting St.
Ketchum, Taylor & Co., Dry Goods, 243 King St.
Keyley, Edward, Carpenter, 5 Pickney St., res. 5 Pickney St.
Keyley, John, Dry Goods, 5 Pinckney St., res. 5 Pinckney St.
Kiddell, Arthur, Clerk, 76 East Bay St., res. St. Philip St.
Kiddell, Benjamin, Bookkeeper, Accommodation Wharf, res. Coming St.

Kiddell, George, Clerk, 40 East Bay St., res. 1 Courthouse Square
Kilbride, Barney, Laborer, South Carolina Railroad, res. Woolf St.
Kilroy, Mary, Mrs., Boarding House, 30 Market St.
Kimball & Lange, Stoves & Tinware, King St.
Kimball, Elias W., Stoves, King St., res. 18 John St.
Kinchler, Thomas, Tavern, 67 East Bay St., res. 67 East Bay St.
King, Archibald, Dry Goods, 262 King St., res. 262 King St.
King, George, Boiler Maker, Hasell St., res. 8 Concord St.
King, Henry C., Lawyer, St. Michael's Alley, res. 68 Tradd St.
King, J. Gadsden, Dry Goods, 19 Hayne St., res. 14 George St.
King, John, Agent, South Carolina Railroad, res. 42 George St.
King, Latitia, Mrs., res. 26 Broad St.
King, Mitchell, Lawyer, res. 14 George St.
King, Robert E., Assistant Secretary, Insurance Co., 4 Broad St.
King, William A., Clerk, Central Wharf, res. St. Philip St.
King, William L., Clerk, 111 East Bay St., res. 26 Broad St.
Kingman, Eliab, Penny Post, res. 8 Guignard St.
Kingman, J. W., Clerk, 26 Hayne St., res. cr. Calhoun & Coming Sts.
Kingman, John, Bookkeeper, Mercury Office, res. cr. Calhoun & Coming Sts.
Kingman, Robert, Clerk, Planters & Mechanics Bank, res. 8 State St.
Kingman, Samuel, Bookkeeper, Planters & Mechanics Bank
Kinloch, George, Feed Merchant, North Atlantic Wharf, res. 223 East Bay St.
Kinloch, Henry, Machinist, res. 223 East Bay St.
Kinloch, John, Student, res. 223 East Bay St.
Kinloch, Mary, Mrs., res. 4 Wragg's Square
Kinloch, Robert A., Physician, 223 East Bay St., res. 223 East Bay St.
Kinloch, Robert, Millwright, res. Mill St.
Kinney, Patrick, Blacksmith, res. Cannon St.
Kinney, Thomas, Horse Shoer, 181 Meeting St., res. 181 Meeting St.
Kinney, Thomas, Laborer, res. 20 Vernon St.
Kinsey, G. F., Discount Clerk, People's Bank, res. 24 Pitt St.
Kinsley, Peter C., Shoemaker, res. Bogard St.
Kinsman, H. W. & Co., Upholsterers & Paper Hangers, 179 King St.
Kinsman, Henry W., Upholsterer, 179 King St., res. 179 King St.
Kinsman, Norman, Upholsterer, 179 King St., res. 179 King St.
Kinsman, Warren, Upholsterer, 179 King St., res. 86 Meeting St.
Kirk, Mary Ann, Mrs., Midwife, res. 8 Magazine St.

Kirk, Mary, Mrs., res. 4 Marsh St.
Kirk, Matthew, Clerk, res. 4 Marsh St.
Kirk, Stephen D., Collector, res. 8 Magazine St.
Kirkman, James W., Printer, 111 East Bay St., res. 26 Broad St.
Kirkpatrick, J. & J. D. Commission Merchants, North Atlantic Wharf
Kirkpatrick, John, Commission Merchant, North Atlantic Wharf, res. 47 East Bay St.
Kirkpatrick, John D., Commission Merchant, North Atlantic Wharf, res. 47 East Bay St.
Kirkpatrick, John, Pastor, Glebe Street Church, res. George St.
Kirkwood, W. D. H., Lawyer, 10 Broad St., res. 19 Laurens St.
Kirkwood, William, Shipwright, Dry Dock Wharf, res. 19 Laurens St.
Kitchen, William R., Druggist, 23 Hayne St., res. New York
Klenke, Henry, Grocer 40 Anson St., res. 40 Anson St.
Klenke, John, Grocer, 40 Anson St., res. 40 Anson St.
Klinck, & Wickenberg, Grocers, 42 Broad St., cr. of Church St.
Klinck, John, Grocer, 42 Broad St., res. 84 Church St.
Klinck, John, Jr., Clerk, 42 Broad St., res. 84 Church St.
Klinck, L. B., Clerk, 42 Broad St., res. 84 Church St.
Knauff, Henry, Engineer, res. Cedar court
Knauff, Thomas J., Carpenter, res. Cedar Court
Knee, Henry, Grocer, cr. Church St. & Stoll's Alley
Knight, Amos F., Superintendent, Neck Icehouse, res. Vanderhorst St.
Knight, Peter, Tavern, Line St., res. Line St.
Knighton, William, Boarding House, 72 Queen St.
Knobloch, John, Flour Merchant, 167 East Bay St.
Knobloch, William, Baker, 19 Calhoun St., res. 19 Calhoun St.
Knockman, Abraham, Junk Dealer, Bogard St.
Knowles, Elizabeth, Mrs., Millinery, 202 King St., res. 202 King St.
Knox, Catherine, Mrs., res. 16 Green St.
Knox, John, Dry Goods, 133 Meeting St.
Knox, John F., Shipwright, res. 8 Pritchard St.
Knox, Robert, Reporter, Evening News, res. 8 Pritchard St.
Knox, William P., Ship Carpenter, Dry Dock Wharf, res. 5 Middle St.
Kock, A., Clerk, 13 Hayne St., res. Pavilion Hotel
Koenig, John H., Grocer, 121 King St., res. 121 King St.
Koester, Theodore, Shoemaker, 100 Church St., res. 100 Church St.
Koldewey, Frederick, Jeweller, 202 King St., res. 202 King St.
Koopman, Jacob, Dry Goods, King St., Upper Ward
Koopman, M. & Co., Dry Goods, 334 King St.
Koopman, Morritz, Dry Goods, 334 King St., res. 334 King St.
Koopman, William, Dry Goods, 315 King St.
Krackes, F. D., Grocer, cr. Rutledge & Doughty Sts.
Krotes, Caspar, Butcher, res. St. Philip St.
Kruse, Jacob, Grocer, cr. St. Philip & Liberty Sts.

Kuck, A., Clerk, 80 East Bay St.
Kuck, Henry, Grocer, Mary St., res. Mary St.
Kugley, W. F. A., Carpenter, res. 36 Mazyck St.
Kulinski, John, Watchmaker, 98 Meeting St., res. 98 Meeting St.
Kurr, A., Boots & Shoes, 64 Market St., res. 64 Market St.
Kyall, William, Stevedore, res. 16 John St.
Labatat, Izadore, res. 45 St. Philip St.
Laborde, John P., Clerk, 143 East Bay St., res. cr. Glebe & George Sts.
Lacassagne, Edward, Fancy Goods, 148 King St., res. 148 King St.
Lachicotti, J. R., Clerk, Charleston Steam Sawmill, res. 1 Gadsden St.
Lacompte, Susan, Fruiterer, 28 Calhoun St., res. 28 Calhoun St.
Lacoste & Reed, Riggers, 77 East Bay St.
Lacoste, A. T. J., Rigger, 77 East Bay St., res. Mount Pleasant
Lacoste, A. W., Sailmaker, res. Elizabeth St.
Ladson, W. H., Commission Merchant, 18 Vanderhorst's Wharf, res. 4 Meeting St.
Lafar, David, Cooper, res. cr. Calhoun & Rutledge Sts.
Lafar, John G., res. Nassau St.
Lafar, M. L. L., Clerd & J. H. Schreiner's, res. 4 Coming St.
Lafar, William H., Bookkeeper, 235 King St., res. 4 Coming St.
Lafin, James, Mariner, res. 93 Church St.
Lafitte, Edward, Agent, Savannah Steamers, res. 15 Wentworth St.
Lafitte, John B., Commission Merchant, Fitzsimons' Wharf, res. 15 Wentworth St.
Laidler, William, Assistant Editor, Courier Office, res. Logan St.
Lalane, John A., Cigars & Tobacco, 46 East Bay St., res. 1 Queen St.
Lalane, P. B., Discount Clerk, Bank of Charleston, res. 118 King St.
Lamb, David, Physician, 191 Meeting St., res. 191 Meeting St.
Lamb, G. B., Clerk, 181 East Bay St., res. 191 Meeting St.
Lambert, Mary, Mrs., res. 27 Henrietta St.
Lambert, Walter, Carpets, 219 King St.
Lamont, D., Tailor, res. 12 Horlbeck Alley
Lamotte, Henry J., Printer, 68 Meeting St., res. 20 Middle St.
Lamotte, J. W., Printer, 115 East Bay St., res. 26 Coming St.
Lance, Francis., Col., Lawyer, res. 20 Montague St.
Lance, William S., Clerk, 181 East Bay St., res. 225 King St.
Landreth & Ring, Agricultural Warehouse, 297 King St.
Landreth, David, Agricultural Warehouse, 297 King St., res. Philadelphia
Lane, Edward H, Dry Goods, 41 Hayne St., res. Rutledge St.
Langdon, Edward D., Tailor, 111 Meeting St., res.

Coming St.
Lange, Henry, Miller, St. Philip St., res. Coming St.
Lange, John H., Tavern, 15 Vendue Range
Langley, J. T., Mrs., res. 35 Queen St.
Lanneau, Basil, Bookkeeper, 155 East Bay St., res. 7 Pitt St.
Lanneau, Benjamin, Teacher, res. 7 Pitt St.
Lanneau, Fleetwood, Grocer, 14 Hayne St., res. 43 Coming St.
Lanneau, George J., Machinist, Union Wharf, res. Anson St.
Lanneau, Mary, Mrs., res. 22 Anson St.
Lanneau, Smith & Whilden, Grocers, 14 Hayne St.
Lapiene, A. J., Bookbinder, 101 East Bay St., res. Radcliffe St.
Lark, Charlotte M., Mrs., Milliner, res. Anson St.
Larkin, John, Clerk, 151 East Bay St., res. 64 Anson St.
Latham, Abraham M., Fruit, 69 Market St., res. 69 Market St.
Lathrop, S. C., Mrs., Boarding House, 356 King St.
Latta, James H., Factor, East Bay St., res. 4 Meeting St.
Laurens, Edward R., res. 30 Society St.
Laurens, Henry, Lawyer, Broad St.
Laurens, Isaac, Carpenter, Queen St., res. 3 Middle St.
Laurens, John, Teller, Union Bank, res. Broad St.
Laurens, Joseph, Boarding House, 52 St. Philip St.
Laurey, H. Z., Clerk, 25 Vendue Range, res. 63 King St.
Laux, Martin, Boots & Shoes, 53 Broad St., res. 53 Broad St.
Laval, William J., Comptroller General, res. 47 Anson St.
Laval, William, res. 12 John St.
Lawrence, James H., Dentist, 217 King St., res. 47 Anson St.
Lawrence, Samuel P., Clerk, 147 Meeting St., res. King St.
Lawson, H., Grocer, cr. Magazine & Mazyck Sts.
Lawson, P. A., Clerk, 177 East Bay St.
Lawton, W. S. & Co. Factors & Commission Merchants, Southern Wharf
Lawton, W. S., Commission Merchant, South Atlantic Wharf, res. Mary St.
Lawton, William M. & Co., Factors & Commission Merchants, Southern Wharf
Lawton, William M., Commission Merchant, Southern Wharf, res. 17 Rutledge St.
Lawton, Winburn, Planter, James Island, res. 40 South Bay St.
Lay, George, res. Hampden Court
Lazarus, B. D., res. cr. Smith & Wentworth Sts.
Lazarus, G., Steam Boat Inspector, Custom House, res. Pitt St.
Lazarus, Joshua, President, Gas Company, res. cr. Laurens & Wall Sts.
Lazarus, Michael, Factor, res. 138 Queen St.
Lea, Charles A. L., Pilot, res. 1 Stoll's Alley
Lea, John, Pilot, res. 19 Church St.
Leader, Mary, Mrs., res. 126 Queen St.
Leard, Samuel, Pastor, Cumberland Church, res. 34 Archdale St.
Lebber, William, Planter, res. Rutledge St.

Lebby, John F., Finisher, Lebby's Iron Works, res. 43 Beaufain St.

Lebby, Robert, Physician, 25 Cumberland St., 43 Beaufain St.

Lebby, William, Iron Founder, Meeting St., res. Ashley St.

LeBlue, L. F., Architect, 122 East Bay St., res. 90 Queen St.

Leckie & Stewart, Umbrellas & Parasols, 106 King St.

Leckie, Clark, Umbrellas, 160 King St., res. 160 King St.

Leckie, David, Bookkeeper, 42 Broad St., res. 20 Beaufain St.

Lee, A. Markley, Secretary, Commercial Insurance Co., 4 Broad St., res. Judith St.

Lee, B. M., Assistant Cashier, State Bank, res. cr. Alexander & Charlotte Sts.

Lee, Edward S., Barber, 8 Market St., res. 8 Logan St.

Lee, Francis, Architect, cr. Broad & Church Sts., res. Elizabeth St.

Lee, Joseph T., Teacher, High School, res. 10 Middle St.

Lee, Patrick, Bookkeeper, 1 Hayne St., res. 1 Hayne St.

Lee, Sarah, Mrs., res. cr. Queen & Trapmann Sts.

Lee William, Carpenter, 8 Society St., res. 8 Society St.

Leffman, William, Baker, 8 Queen St., res. Calhoun St.

Legare & Colcock, Factors & Commission Merchants, North Commercial Wharf

Legare & Yates, Commission Merchants, 151 East Bay St.

Legare, J. J., Bookkeeper, 34 East Bay St., res. 43 Anson St.

Legare, James, Commission Merchant, 151 East Bay St., res. City Hotel

Legare, James, Factor, North Commercial Wharf, res. cr. Broad & Logan Sts.

Legare, James, Mrs., res. 4 Council St

Legare, John B., res. 19 Hasell St.

Legare, Louisa, Mrs., res. Reid St.

Legare, Samuel J., Planter, John's Island, res. 19 Hasell St.

Legare, Solomon L., Planter, John's Island, res. 103 Tradd St.

Legg, Maria, Mrs., Tailoress, res. 213 East Bay St.

LeHardy, Camille, Teacher of Languages, res. 2 Wall St.

Lehre, Thomas, res. Alexander St.

Leiding, Hermann, Fancy Goods, 141 Meeting St., res. Wentworth St.

Leitch, W. T., Bookkeeper, People's Bank, res. cr. Legare & Lamboll Sts.

Leitsch, G. M., Clerk, 133 Meeting St., res. 2 Wall St.

Leman, E. P., res. 5 Washington St.

Leman, Jeannette, Mrs., res. Bull St.

Leman, William W., Dry Goods, 211 King St., res. Paris, France

Lemmont, Margaret, Mrs., res. 2 Minority St.

Lenar, Joseph, Clerk, Pavilion Hotel, res. 37 Anson St.

Lengnick, Albert, Millinery Goods, 133 Meeting St., res. 133 Meeting St.

Lengnick, Alfred, Clerk, 133 Meeting St., res. 132 Meeting St.

Leonard, Edward, Porter, 45 Hayne St., res. 2 Clifford St.

Leonard, Peter, Drayman, res. 64 Anson St.

LePrince A., Bookkeeper, 189 East Bay St., res. 131 King St.

LeQuex, B. J., Clerk, 93 East Bay St., res. 356 King St.

Leseman, John D., Clerk, 203 East Bay St., res. 203 East Bay St.

Lesesne, Anna C., Mrs., res. 39 Society St.

Lesesne, Daniel, Commission Merchant, East Bay St., res. Wentworth St.

Lesesne, Henry D., Lawyer, St. Michael's Alley, res. Tradd St.

Leslie, James, Engineer, South Carolina Railroad, res. 93 Queen St.

Lester, A. H., Clerk, cr. Meeting & Hasell Sts., res. 4 Court House Square

Levin, Morritz, Clerk, Union Cotton Press, res. 1 Pickney St.

Levin, Nathaniel, Record Clerk, Custom House, res. Wentworth St.

Levitt, Edward, Junk Store, 32 Tradd St., res. 32 Tradd St.

Levy, A., Fruiterer, cr. Church St. & Lightwood's Alley

Levy, C. F., Auctioneer, 17 Vendue Range, res. cr. Blake & Drake Sts.

Levy, D. J. & G. J., Clothing & Gents Furnishing Goods, 288 King St.

Levy, David J., Clothing, 288 King St., res. New York City

Levy, E., Deputy Sheriff, res. 30 St. Philip St.

Levy, Elias, Gauger, res. Lightwood's Alley

Levy, George J., Clothing, 288 King St., res. Merchant's Hotel

Levy, M., Dry Goods, 72 Church St. res. 72 Church St.

Levy, Moses E., Police Officer, City Hall, res. 3 Tradd St.

Levy, Orlando, Second Lieutentant Guard, res. Columbus St.

Levy, Wagner & Co. Auctioneers & Commission Merchants, 17 Vendue Range

Lewey, C., Tailor, 39 Broad St.

Lewis, John, Butcher, res. St. Philip St.

Lewis, John, Cabinet Maker, 26 Tradd St., res. 26 Tradd St.

Lewis, John, Carpenter, res. cr. Montague & Rutledge Sts.

Lewis, John, Grocer, 47 King St., res. 47 King St.

Lewis, Phoebe, Colored, Seamstress, res. 13 Cumberland St.

Lewis, R., Carver, Queen St., near Friend St., res. 110 Meeting St.

Lewis, T., Mrs., res. 23 George St.

Lightburn, Eliza, Mrs., res. Morris St.

Ligman, Thomas, Factor, East Bay St., res. Vernon St.

Lillard, Jasper W., Dry Goods, 35 Hayne St., res. American Hotel

Lilles, John, Laborer, res. 28 Vernon St.

Lillienthal, C., Grocer, 18 State St., res. 18 State St.

Lillienthal, F., Grocer, 107 Tradd St., res. 107 Tradd St.

Lillienthal, Henry, Grocer, cr. Anson & Society Sts., res. Anson St.

Lindsay, George W., Factor, East Bay St., res. cr. Broad & Friend Sts.

Lindsay, Henry A., Clerk, 20 East Bay St., res. cr. Broad & Friend Sts.

Lindsay, J. W., Wharfinger, Accomation Wharf, res. cr. Broad & Friend Sts.

Lindsay, James L., Bookkeeper, 34 East Bay St., res. cr. Broad & Friend Sts.

Lindsay, John T., Bookkeeper, 141 East Bay St., res. Cannon St.

Lindsay, William, Lawyer, Broad St., res. cr. Broad & Friend Sts.

Lindstedt, Adolphus, Grocer, cr. Woolf & Meeting Sts.

Lindstedt, Charles, Grocer, cr. Woolf & Meeting Sts.

Lining, Charles, Notary, South Atlantic Wharf, res. Vanderhorst St.

Lining, E. B., Clerk, Bank of South Carolina, res. Drake St.

Link, Elizabeth, Mrs., Music Teacher, 158 King St.

Livingston, A., res. 1 St. Philip's St.

Livingston, Lewis, Merchant, 35 Market St.

Lloyd, Edward W., Clerk, 246 King St., res. cr. Bull & Lynch Sts.

Lloyd, F. C., Mrs., Private Boarding, Market St.

Lloyd, Stephen, Clerk, 211 King, res. Columbus St.

Lloyd, William, Carpenter, res. Bull St.

Lloyd, William, Exchange Broker, 7 Broad St., res. 59 King St.

Locke, B. C., Grocer, 57 East Bay St., res. 12 George St.

Locke, Edward H., Grocer, 66 East Bay St., res. 168 Meeting St.

Locke, Franklin, res. 12 George St.

Locke, George A., Grocer, 66 East Bay St., res. 3 George St.

Locke, George B. & Son, Grocers, 66 East Bay St.

Locke, George B., Grocer, 66 East Bay St., res. 12 George St.

Locke, George R., Outdoor Clerk, Southwest Railroad Bank, res. 12 George St.

Lockwood, Jacob A., Wheelwright, 108 Church St., res. 6 Atlantic St.

Lockwood, Paul L., Clerk, 39 Hayne St., res. cr. King & Vanderhorst Sts.

Lockwood, S. L., Physician, 73 Broad St., res. 73 Broad St.

Lockwood, Thomas P., Jr., Lawyer, 56 Broad St., res. St. Philip St.

Lockwood, Thomas P., Teacher, Orphan House, res. King St.

Logan, George W., Clerk, Farmers & Exchange Bank, East Bay St.

Logan, James C., Clerk, 223 King St., res. Rutledge St.

Londrick, George, Wood Factor, res. 39 King St.

Long, Augustus, Gas Fitter, 1 Minority St., res. 1 Minority St.

Long, F. H., Shoemaker, res. 42 Tradd St.

Long, John H., Ship Carpenter, res. Reid St.

Long, Joseph A., Carpenter, res. King St.

Long, Samuel, Mariner, res. 124 Queen St.

Long, T. H., Colored, Shoemaker, res. 42 Tradd St.

Loper, Francis, Tailor, 341 King St., res. Vanderhorst St.

Loper, H. G., Cashier, People's Bank, res. 15 Broad St.

Lopez, David, Carpenter, res. cr. Short & Franklin Sts.

Lopez, John, Carpenter, res. 24 Montague St.

Lopez, P., Mrs., res. 41 Coming St.

Lord, J. F. M., Bricklayer, res. Hampden Court

Lord, John, Barber, res. Vanderhorst St.

Lord, Richard, Tavern, King St., near Woolf St.

Lord, Robert, Carpenter, res. Vanderhorst St.

Lord, Samuel, Commission Merchant, Exchange St., res. 18 Liberty St.

Lord, Samuel, Jr., Lawyer, Church St., res. 18 Society St.

Loryea, A., Clothing, 66 Market St., res. 66 Market St.

Loryea, Isaac, Cigars & Tobacco, 66 State St., res. 66 State St.

Love & Wienges, Saddle & Harness Makers, 45 Broad St.

Love, Charles, Saddler, 45 Broad St., res. 46 Tradd St.

Love, William S., Clerk, 23 Hayne St., res. 270 King St.

Lovett, William, Tavern, 8 Bedons Alley, res. 8 Bedons Alley

Lowndes, Allen, Mrs., res. 1 Lamboll St.

Lowndes, C. B., Mrs., res. 7 King St.

Lowndes, Charles T., Planter, res. 37 East Bay St.

Lowndes, Thomas, Planter, Legare St.

Lowndes, William, Lawyer, res. 16 Church St.

Lowry, Henry, Clerk, Vendue Range, res. 63 King St.

Lowry, Thomas, Fireman, McLeish's Mill, res. 5 Wharf St.

Lowyal, Charles, Clerk, South CarolinaRailroad, res. Cannon St.

Lubken, Frederick, Grocer, 1 Tradd St., res. 1 Tradd St.

Lubs, C. F. & Co., Grocers, cr. Reid & Meeting Sts.

Lubs, Henry, Grocer, cr. Nassau & Woolf Sts.

Lucas, B., Proprietor, Steam Mill, foot of Calhoun St.

Lucas, Benjamin, Bricklayer, res. 6 Savage St.

Lucas, Dora, Mantuamaker, res. St. Philip St.

Lucas, J. Jonathan, Hardware, 273 King St., res. 260 King St.

Lucas, John, Bricklayer, res. Smith St.

Lucas, Robert, Planter, res. Rutledge St.

Lucas, Simon, Planter, res. Pitt St.

Lucas, T. B., Factor, North Commercial Wharf, res. Calhoun St.

Luceine, Daniel, Plasterer, res. Wentworth St.

Luceine, William, Teacher, res. 12 savage St.

Luhrs, John E., Grocer, cr. King & Tradd Sts.

Luhrs, Matthew, Grocer, cr. Marsh & Inspection Sts.

Lunsford, J. L., Cabinet Maker, 1 Liberty St., res. 1 Liberty St.

Lyall, Henry L., Printer, 119 East Bay St., res. 5 Minority St.

Lynch, C. C., Clerk at Robinson, Caldwell & Co., res. 66 Queen St.

Lynch, Francis C., Tailor, 91 Market St.

Lynch, James G., Printer, 119 East Bay St., res. 9 Inspection St.

Lynch, Thomas, res. cr. Broad & Mazyck Sts.

Lyons, Dennis, Porter, East Bay St., res. 10 Linguard St.

Lyons, J. R., Engineer, South Carolina Railroad, res.

Hampden Court

Lyons, James, Laborer, res. 12 Philadelphia St.

Lyons, Joseph J., Druggist, cr. Cannon & St. Philip Sts.

Lyons, Michael, Drayman, res. 3 Philadelphia St.

Lyons, Thomas, Clerk 182 King St., res. 12 Philadelphia St.

Lyons, Thomas, Laborer, res. 12 Philadelphia St.

Lyons, William E., Clerk, cr. Reid & Nassau Sts.

Lyons, William, Tailor, Radcliffe St.

Macaulay, Allen, 222 King St., res. 89 Church St.

Macaulay, John, Bookkeeper, 35 Hayne St., res. Planters Hotel

Macbeth, Charles, Lawyer, 41 Broad St., res. cr. Gibbes & Legare Sts.

Macbeth, Eliza, Mantuamaker, Radcliffe St.

Macbeth, James, Commission Merchant, 10 Vanderhorst's Wharf, res. 30 South Bay St.

Macdonnell, Alexander B., Clerk, 239 King St., res. American Hotel

Macken, Patrick, Porter, 141 Meeting St., res. 58 Wentworth St.

Mackenzie, John, Bookkeeper, 47 Broad St., res. St. Michael's Alley

Mackey, Albert G., Physician, Calhoun St., opposite East Bay St.

Mackey, John, Machinist, foot of Hasell St., res. 14 Vernon St.

Mackindon, George, Machinist, Hasell St., res. 14 Vernon St.

Macmillan, William B., Boots & Shoes, 69 King St., res. 120 King St.

Madden, Julia, Miss, res. 37 King St.

Magee, Martha, Mrs., res. St. Philip St.

Magrath, Edward, Lawyer, 29 Broad St., res. Bee St.

Magrath, James, Lawyer, 36 Broad St., res. St. Philip St.

Magrath, John, Factor & Commission Merchant, res. Bee St.

Maguire, Thomas, Machinist, res. Columbus St.

Magwood, Charles A., res. 9 Smith St.

Magwood, Henry, res. 9 Smith St.

Magwood, S. G., Planter, St. Andrew's Parish, res. Rutledge St.

Mahan, Peter, Porter, cr. Meeting & Hasell Sts.

Mahearn, M. A., Mrs., Dry Goods, 36 State St., res. 36 State St.

Mahoney, C., Clerk, 54 East Bay St., res. Tradd St.

Mahoney, Daniel, Wheelwright, McLeish's Foundry, res. Concord St.

Mahoney, James, Blacksmith, res. Washington St.

Mahoney, James, Books & Stationery, 258 King St., res. 258 King St.

Mahoney, James H., Slater, cr. Queen & Franklin Sts., res. 42 State St.

Mahoney, John, Blacksmith, Calhoun St., res. cr. Rutledge & Line Sts.

Mahoney, John, Hatter, 41 Broad St., res. 37 Montague St.

Mahoney, William, Boiler Maker, Hasell St., res. Concord St.

Main, Alexander R., res. 46 Anson St.

Main, Francis, Carpenter, res. cr. Morris & Coming Sts.

Maley, Mark, Porter, 219 King St., res. Franklin St.

Malloy, Patrick, Drayman, res. 40 Calhoun St.

Malone, Edward, Gas Fitter, 201 King St., res. Meeting St.

Malone, Michael, Laborer, res. St. Philip St.

Malone, Patrick, Laborer, res. St. Philip St.

Maloney, Michael, Dry Goods, 347 King St., res. McBride's Lane

Maloney, P., Drayman, 90 East Bay St., res. 90 East Bay St.

Maloney, Patrick J., Clerk, 347 King St., res. Burn's lane

Maloney, Thomas, Watchman, Bennett's Saw Mill, res. President St.

Managhan, John, Clerk, 21 Hayne St., res. Church St.

Manigault, A. M., Factor, 1 Vanderhort's Wharf, res. South Bay St.

Manigault, Charles, Planter, Cooper River, res. 6 Gibbes St.

Manigault, Heyward H., Planter, Colleton District, res. 12 Meeting St.

Manigault, William H., Planter, Colleton District, res. 12 Meeting St.

Manly, Thomas, Mariner, res. 9 Linguard St.

Mann, John, Mason, res. 23 Calhoun St.

Manson, Ellen, Mrs., res. 4 Marsh St.

Marcy, Patrick, Laborer, res. 4 Linguard St.

Mardley, John, Laborer, 12 Philadelphia St.

Marine, A., Mariner, res. 8 Anson St.

Marion, John, Confectioner, 254 King St., res. 254 King St.

Marjenhoff, E. H., Tavern, 153 East Bay St., res. 153 East Bay St.

Marsh, David, Ship Carpenter, res. 16 Hasell St.

Marsh, Elizabeth, Mrs., res. 138 East Bay St.

Marsh, G., Ship Carpenter, res. 16 Hasell St.

Marsh, James, Ship Carpenter, res. 16 Hasell St.

Marsh, John, res. Alexander St.

Marshall, Alexander, Pastor, St. John's Chapel, res. Amherst St.

Marshall, Andrew, Boots & Shoes, 29 Broad St., res. 120 King St.

Marshall, Edward, Dry Goods, 211 King St., res. Mills House

Marshall, John, Brick Factor, Gadsden's Wharf

Marshall, John T., Baker, 60 Tradd St., res. 60 Tradd St.

Marshall, M. C., Miss, res. cr. Broad & Friend Sts.

Marshall, Samuel R., Clerk, 54 East Bay St., res. Washington St.

Marshall, William, Baker, Queen St., res. Market St.

Marshall, William, Boots & Shoes, 43 Broad St., res. 89 Church St.

Martin, Anne, Mrs., res. 29 Coming St.

Martin, George, Drayman, res. Ann St.

Martin, Henry, Carpenter, res. Meeting St., near Ann St.

Martin, J. B., Tinsmith, King, res. Cannon St.

Martin, J. C., Clerk, 171 East Bay St., res. Pavilion Hotel

Martin, J. G., Bricklayer, res. Coming St.

Martin, J. J., Clerk, 19 Vendue Range, res. 19 Society St.

Martin, Jacob J., Commission Merchant 19 Vendue

Range, res. 19 Society St.

Martin, James, Clerk, 222 King St., res. Cannon St.

Martin, James, Factor, Boyce & Co. Wharf, res. 4 Green St.

Martin, John B., Agent, Neck Icehouse, res. St. Philip St.

Martin, John C., Banker, 58 East Bay St., res. 19 Society St.

Martin, John, Finisher, South Carolina Railroad, res. Cannon St.

Martin, John, Wheelwright, cr. King & John Sts., res. Bogard St.

Martin, S., Mrs., res. Charlotte St.

Martin, W. M. & J. C., Bankers & Exchange Brokers, 58 East Bay St.

Martin, William E., Lawyer, 10 Broad St., res. 5 Orange St.

Martin, William M., Banker, 58 East Bay St., res. 265 East Bay St.

Martly, Wade, Carpenter, Spring St., Upper Ward

Mashburn, Ezekiel H., Wharfinger, res. Calhoun St.

Mashburn, James H., Inspector, Custom House, res. 24 Calhoun St.

Mason, Daniel, Caulker, Dry Dock, res. Calhoun St.

Mason, George, Laborer, res. Woolf St.

Masterman, William, Jr., Clerk, 159 Meeting St., res. 173 Tradd St.

Masterman, William, Watchmaker, 249 King St., res. 73 Tradd St.

Matheson, John P., Bookkeeper, James Adger & Co., res. 37 St. Philip St.

Matheson, M. P., Bookkeeper, 13 Broad St.

Matte, Joseph, Fruitier, 110 King, res. 110 King St.

Matthews, Frazer, Planter, res. Rutledge St.

Matthews, Henry, Carpenter, Duncan St., res. Duncan St.

Matthews, Joseph, Colored, Carpenter, South Carolina Railroad, res. St. Philip St.

Matthews, M., Mrs., res. cr. Tradd & Logan Sts.

Matthews, Thomas D., Bookkeeper, Bank of Charleston, res. 43 Anson St.

Matthews, William E., Planter, John's Island, res. Washington St.

Matthieson & O'Hara, Clothing, 143 East Bay St.

Matthieson, C. F., res. 8 Church St.

Matthieson, Frederick C., Commission Merchant, res. 8 Church St.

Matthieson, John, Planter, res. 29 East Bay St.

Matthieson, Theodore, Bookkeeper, 177 East Bay St., res. 42 Church St.

Matthieson, William, Clothing 143 East Bay St., res. 19 Wentworth St.

Maule, C. S., Mrs., Milliner, 369 King St., res. 369 King St.

Maule, Phillip, Carpenter, res. St. Philip St.

Maxwell, T. B., Wood Factor, Dereef's Wharf

Maxy, Elizabeth, Mrs., Tailoress, res. Bogard St.

May, James W., Lawyer, Court House Square, res. 62 Queen St.

May, John, Cabinet Maker, 62 Queen St., res. 62 Queen St.

Mayes, M., Pastor, Jewish Synagogue, res. cr. Calhoun & Smith Sts.

Maynardie, Martha, Mrs., Tailoress, res. Bogard St.

Mazyck, Alexander H., Librarian, Charleston Library Society, res. 7 Smith's Lane

Mazyck, H. B., Clerk at Robinson, Caldwell & Co., res. Wentworth St.

Mazyck, Henry, Factor, East Bay St., res. 122 Meeting St.

Mazyck, N. B., Factor, South Atlantic Wharf, res. Alexander St.

Mazyck, Peter W., Painter, res. Concord St.

Mazyck, Son & Co., Factors & Commission Merchants, Commercial Wharf

Mazyck, W. St. Julien, Commercial Wharf, res. Charlotte St.

Mazyck, William, Factor, South Commercial Wharf, res. Charlotte St.

McAllitser, Charles, Dry Goods, 343 King St., res. 343 King St.

McAndrew, James, Grocer, 32 King St., res. 32 King St.

McBail, James, Mariner, res. 69 Church St.

McBirney, William, Dry Goods, 37 Hayne St., res. 29 George St.

McBride, Arthur, Bookkeeper, 40 Calhoun St., res. 40 Calhoun St.

McBride, M., Broker & Auctioneer, State St.

McBride, Patrick, Dry Goods, 347 King St., res. 347 King St.

McBride, Phillip A., Clerk, 347 King St., res. 347 King St.

McBride, Robert, Shoemaker, 69 King St., res. State St.

McCabe, James, Engineer, Hayne Street Cotton Press, res. 31 Anson St.

McCabe, John W., Bookkeeper, res. Calhoun St.

McCaffrey, James, Bar Room, 72 Market St., res. 14 Anson St.

McCaffrey, John, Clerk, King St., res. 41 Anson St.

McCall, Beckman, Clerk, 260 King St., res. 100 Tradd St.

McCall, J. W., Clerk, Charleston Hotel, res. 100 Tradd St.

McCall, John, Clerk, 259 King St., res. 100 Tradd St.

McCall, Joseph, res. 49 George St.

McCarroll, Henry, Showmaker, cr. King St. & Whim's Court

McCarroll, Terrence, Shoemaker, 43 Broad St., res. Queen St.

McCarroll, William, Mason, res. Calhoun St.

McCarter & Co., Book & Stationery, 116 Meeting St., cr. Pinckney St.

McCarter, J. Dawson, Books, 116 Meeting St., res. Charleston Hotel

McCarter, James J., Books, 116 Meeting St., res. 14 Hasell St.

McCarthy, D. L., Clothing, 193 East Bay St., res. 193 East Bay St.

McCarthy, Jeremiah B., Boots & Shoes, 142 East Bay St.

McCarthy, John, Clerk, 326 King St., res. 26 Ann St.

McCarthy, Timothy, Clerk, 257 King St., res. 3 Wilson St.

McCartney, John, res. 33 Calhoun St.

McCarty, Walter, Tavern, 80 Queen St., res. 80 Queen St.

McCaughran, T., Clerk, 10 Vendue Range

McClardy, Donald, Tavern, 9 Market St., res. 9 Market St.

McClure, J. B., House Agent, cr. State & Chalmers Sts., res. 16 Rutledge St.

McClure, Robert C., Deputy Flour Inspector, 14 Vendue Range

McCoa, W. L., Clerk at J. & J. B. Kirkpatrick's, res. 8 New St.

McCollum, Robert, Printer, 111 East Bay St., res. 1 Short St.

McConkey, J., Painter, 48 Broad St., res. 48 Broad St.

McCorkle, James, Clerk, 41 Hayne St., res. America St.

McCormick, A., Clerk, 5 Hayne St.

McCormick, Edward, Blacksmith, 28 Pinckney St., res. 9 Vernon St.

McCormick, H. L. P., Clerk, Georgetown Steamer Office, res. Planters Hotel

McCormick, Peter, res. 8 Pinckney St.

McCosker, Felix, Plumber, 31 Broad St.

McCoy, William, Clerk, 211 King St., res. King St.

McCready, Edward, Lawyer, Law Range, res. 20 Anson St.

McCready, William T., Clerk, Custom House, res. cr. Magazine & Wilson Sts.

McCreery & Hooke, Factors & Commission Merchants, Brown's Wharf

McCreery, B. B., Clerk, 135 Meeting St., res. 21 Cumberland St.

McCreery, Francis C. Commission Merchant, Brown's Wharf, res. 21 Cumberland St.

McCreery, Perry, res. 21 Cumberland St.

McCreery, Robert, Clerk, 135 Meeting St., res. 21 Cumberland St.

McCreery, Thomas A., Dry Goods, 135 Meeting St., res. Charleston Hotel

McCreery, Thomas, res. 21 Cumberland St.

McDaniel, Robert, Miller, Chisolm's Mill

McDermit, Mary, Mrs., Dry Goods, 60 Queen St., res. 60 Queen St.

McDermitt, Duncan, Engineer, res. 60 Queen St.

McDonald, A. A., Clerk, 211 King St.

McDonald, Allan, Clerk, 261 King St., res. Society St.

McDonald, Isaac, Pilot, res. Zig Zag Alley

McDonnough, James, Laborer, res. 5 Cannon St.

McDonnough, John, Laborer, res. 2 Archdale St.

McDonnough, John, Teacher, 5 Hasell St., res. 5 Hasell St.

McDonnough, William, Shoemaker, cr. King & Liberty Sts.

McDougal, David, Miller, Chisolm's Mill

McDowell, Andrew, Dry Goods, 32 East Bay St., res. 8 Meeting St.

McDowell, James E., Clerk, 205 King St., res. St. Philip St.

McDowell, R., Mrs., res. Wragg Square

McDowell, Robert H., Crockery, 205 King St., res.

Philip St.

McElleran, Ellen, Mrs., Milliner, 200 King St., res. 200 King St.

McElleran, William C., Blacksmith, 24 Wentworth St., res. 24 Wentworth St.

McElmore, Eliza, Mrs., res. Wragg Square

McElrath, H. McD., Clerk, 151 Meeting St., res. Pavilion Hotel

McElroy, James, Tavern, cr. King & Reid Sts.

McElroy, Robert, Superintendent of Drays, res. 15 Middle St.

McFelby, William, Planter, res. Meeting St., near Ann St.

McGahn, Thomas, Clerk, 151 Meeting St., res. Pavilion Hotel

McGee, C. S., Bookkeeper at W.R. Ryan's, res. St. Philip St.

McGee, John, Mariner, res. 22 Meeting St.

McGee, Mary, Mrs., res. 134 Queen St.

McGery, Catharine, Mrs., Dry Goods, 9 Tradd St., res. 9 Tradd St.

McGery, Francis, Shoemaker, 9 Tradd St., res. 9 Tradd St.

McGery, Patrick, Shoemaker, 9 Tradd St., res. 9 Tradd St.

McGilverey, William S., Builder, East Bay St., res. 10 Atlantic St.

McGilvery, A. C., Bookkeeper, 119 East Bay St., res. 10 Atlantic St.

McGinley, George, Bar Keeper, cr. Market & Meeting Sts.

McGinley, Samuel, Iron & Rags, 15 Price's Alley, res. 15 Price's Alley

McGinn, James, Lumber Factor, res. Rutledge St.

McGinney, James, Laborer, res. McBride's Lane

McGinniss, James, Proprietor, Ice House, res. McBride's Lane

McGinniss, John, Drayman, res. Charlotte St.

McGire, Mankin, State Constable, res. Spring St.

McGuire, Margaret, Mrs., Fruit, 65 King St., res. 65 King St.

McGuire, Robert, Confectionary, 2 King St., res. 2 King St.

McHugh, F. Q., Planter, Christ Church Parish, res. 58 Beaufain St.

McIntosh, John, Carpenter, res. President St.

McIntosh, L., Mrs., res. 96 Beaufain St.

McIntyre, Mary, Mrs., res. 122 Tradd St.

McKay, Donald L., President, Peoples Bank, res. 5 Church St.

McKean, James, Clerk, cr. Archdale & Princess Sts.

McKee, Abel, Ship Carpenter, res. 16 Pinckney St.

McKee, Francis, Miss, res. 8 Friend St.

McKeegan, John, Blacksmith, res. Calhoun St.

McKenzie, A. & R. B., Saddle & Harness Makers, cr. Church & Chalmers Sts.

McKenzie, Alexander, Boarding House, 27 Society St.

McKenzie, Archdale, Saddler, cr. Church & Chalmers Sts., res. Broad St.

McKenzie, B. F., Dry Goods, 171 East Bay St., res. Mills House

McKenzie, Cadow & Co., Dry Goods, 171 East Bay St.

McKenzie, David, Shoemaker, 120 King St., res. 53 King St.

McKenzie, Francis E., Dry Goods, 171 East Bay St., res. Queen St.

McKenzie, H. M., Dry Goods, 171 East Bay St., res. Charleston Hotel

McKenzie, James, Clerk, 165 Meeting St., res. 19 St. Philip St.

McKenzie, John, Cabinet Maker, 83 Church St., res. 83 Church St.

McKenzie, John, Clerk, res. St. Michael's Alley

McKenzie, John, Jr., Bookkeeper, cr. Broad & Church Sts., res. 83 Church St.

McKenzie, Richard B., Saddler, cr. Church & Chalmers Sts.

McKew, Mary, Mrs., res. 71 Beaufain St.

McKinlay, George, Colored, Tailor, 126 Meeting St., res. 126 Meeting St.

McKinlay, William, Colored, Tailor, 138 King St., res. 138 King St.

McKinney, Christopher, res. 69 Coming St.

McLarran, James, Engineer, res. Franklin St.

McLean, Samuel, Clerk, 19 Hayne St., res. Church St.

McLeish, Archibald, Machinist, 4 Cumberland St., res. Cumberland St.

McLeish, William, Dry Goods, 82 Church St., res. 82 Church St.

McLoy, Alexander, Dry Goods, 204 King St., res. 204 King St.

McLure, Thomas, Clerk, 21 Hayne St., res. Laurens St.

McMadden, Catharine, Mrs., res. cr. Elizabeth & Chapel Sts.

McMahan, N., Tavern, 5 Elliott St., res. 5 Elliott St.

McMann, Bridget, Mrs., res. 4 Linguard St.

McManus, S., Grocer, 20 South Bay St., res. 20 South Bay St.

McMaster, Martin, Dry Goods, 366 King St., res. 366 King St.

McMillan, James, Pressman, 111 East Bay St., res. cr. Amherst & America Sts.

McMillan, John, Boarding House, 25 Queen St.

McMillan, Thomas, Tailor, King St., near John St.

McNally, Patrick, Laborer, res. Drake St.

McNamara, Francis, res. 41 King St.

McNamee, J. V., Clerk, 135 Meeting St., res. King St.

McNanly, Patrick, Clerk, 222 King St., res. 8 Horlbeck Alley

McNeal, H., Mrs., res. 25 King St.

McNeal, Mary, Mrs., Grocer, 142 Tradd St., res. 142 Tradd St.

McNeal, Robert, Gardner, res. St. Philip St.

McNeal, Virginia, Mrs., res. Montague St., near Pitt St.

McNearney, Michael, Gun Cleaner, res. 114 Church St.

McNellage, John, res. 7 Hasell St.

McOwen, P., Bookkeeper at James Adger's & Co., res. 37 St. Philip St.

McOwen, S. L., Bookkeeper, 32 Broad St., res. 37 St. Philip St.

McPherson, Elizabeth, Mrs., res. 225 East Bay St.

McPherson, John, Conductor, South Carolina Railroad, res. Drake St.

McQue, Thomas, Laborer, res. 184 East Bay St.

McQue, William, Watchman, Bennett's Rice Mills

McQueen, Donald, Clerk, 251 King St., res. Duncan St.

McTrous, B. W., Clerk, 143 East Bay St., res. Spring St.

Meagher, George W., Gas Fitter, 109 Meeting St., res. 46 Queen St.

Meagher, John, Porter, 181 East Bay St., res. 174 East Bay St.

Meagher, Patrick, Dry Goods, 112 King St., res. 112 King St.

Meagher, William, Drayman, res. Calhoun St.

Means, R. T., Clerk at J. & J. D. Kirkpatrick's, res. 8 New St.

Mears, James J., Steward, Steamer Isabel, res. 84 Tradd St.

Mebus, Conrad, Show Maker, 36 Anson St., res. 36 Anson St.

Meetze, Felix, Drayman, res. Mary St.

Mehrtens, C. J., Grocer, 51 East Bay St., res. 51 East Bay St.

Mehrtens, J. C., Grocer, cr. Wentworth & Coming Sts.

Mehrtens, J., Mrs., Tavern, 89 East Bay St., res. 89 East Bay St.

Mehrtens, John, Grocer, cr. Meeting & John Sts.

Mehrtens, Louis, Grocer, Short St., res. Washington St.

Mehrtens, Rudolph, Liquors & Tobacco, 104 Meeting St.

Meissner, E., Grocer, cr. Archdale & Market Sts.

Meissner, H., Grocer, 124 Tradd St., res. 124 Tradd St.

Meitzler, Alfred, Cabinet Maker, res. 8 Whim's Court

Meitzler, Charles, Bootmaker, 28 Anson St., res. 28 Anson St.

Meitzler, Jacob, Bootmaker, 28 Anson St., res. 28 Anson St.

Meitzler, John, Bootmaker, 100 Meeting St., res. 100 Meeting St.

Meitzler, Phillip, Shoemaker, 21 Queen St., res. 100 Meeting St.

Melchers & Renken, Bakers, 97 King St.

Melchers, Alexander, Baker, 97 King St., res. 97 King St.

Melchers, Theodore, Clerk, 257 King St., res. 6 Queen St.

Meldraw, Jacob, Grocer, cr. Queen & Meeting Sts.

Melfi, Francis, Tavern, 37 Market St., res. 29 Market St.

Melfi, L. & Co., Tavern & Boarding House, 37 Market St.

Melfi, Leonard, Tavern, 37 Market St., res. 37 Market St.

Mellen, Emma, Miss, Milliner, 295 King St., res. 295 King St.

Mellichamp, W. S., Clerk, 253 King St.

Memminger & Jervy, Lawyers, 59 Meeting St.

Memminger, C. G., Lawyer, 59 Meeting St., res. cr. Smith & Wentworth Sts.

Mendell, Jacob, Fancy Goods, 165 King St., res. 165 King St.

Mendenhall, M. T., Mrs., res. 85 Broad St.

Menke, Anton, Tailor, cr. Church & Queen Sts.

Menke, C. F. Carpenter, res. William's Row

Menken, D., Grocer, 12 King St., res. 12 King St.
Menlove & Davidson, Commission Merchants, cr. East Bay St. & Adger's North Wharf
Mensing, John H., Tailor, 133 King St., res. 133 King St.
Mensing, John, Tavern, 87 Market St., res. 87 Market St.
Menzes, William, Bookkeeper, 215 King St., res. 260 King St.
Mercer, M. A., Mrs., res. 68 King St.
Meridith, Richard, Dry Goods, King St., Upper Ward
Merray, John, Engineer, South Carolina Railroad, res. St. Philip St.
Merrenn, Otto, Grocer, cr. Calhoun & Smith Sts.
Merrick, John, Blacksmith, res. 41 Archdale St.
Merrill, A., Mrs., res. Coming St.
Merritt, William B., Clerk, 29 Hayne St., res. 29 Pitt St.
Metcalf, William, Stevedore, res. 4 Elliott St.
Mey, F. C., Factor, Central Wharf, res. 8 Washington St.
Meyer, A. W., Grocer, 11 King St., res. South Bay St.
Meyer, B. H., Liquor Merchant, cr. State & Cumberland Sts.
Meyer, Claus, Grocer, cr. Calhoun & Alexander Sts.
Meyer, E. J., Clerk, 29 Vendue Range, res. Warren St.
Meyer, F., Grocer, cr. Meeting & Line Sts.
Meyer, George, Clerk, 171 East Bay St., res. Victoria Hotel
Meyer, George, Clerk, res. cr. Wentworth & Rutledge Sts.
Meyer, George, Grocer, cr. Columbus & Hanover Sts.
Meyer, Henry, Bookkeeper, 20 East Bay St., res. 20 East Bay St.
Meyer, Henry, Clerk, cr. King & Tradd Sts.
Meyer, J. D., Clerk, King St., res. 2 Coming St.
Meyer, J. S., Tavern, 117 Meeting St., res. 117 Meeting St.
Meyer, Johannah, Mrs., Boarding House, 146 King St.
Meyer, John D., Grocer, 320 King St., res. 320 King St.
Meyer, John, Grocer, 129 East Bay St., res. 129 East Bay St.
Meyer, L. C., Physician, 2 Coming St., res. 2 Coming St.
Meyer, Martin, Baker, 17 Tradd St., res. 17 Tradd St.
Meyer, Morris, Dry Goods, 108 East Bay St., res. Warren St.
Meyer, P. S., Clerk, East Bay St., res. cr. Meeting & Henrietta Sts.
Meyer, Phillip F., Clerk, 224 King St., Archdale St.
Meyer, Sarah, res. Wragg Square
Meyer, Washington, Boiler Maker, Hasell St., res. Concord St.
Meyerhoff, Benjamin, Grocer, Calhoun St.
Meynardie, Barney, Laborer, South Carolina Railroad, res. Line St.
Meynardie, C. D., Turner, res. Line St.
Meynardie, James, Carpenter, South Carolina Railroad, res. Line St.
Mich, W., Colored, Barber, 64 Queen St., res. 64 Queen St.
Michael, Charles, Fruiterer, Vanderhorst St., res. East Bay St.
Michael, Isabella, Colored, Seamstress, res. 8 Minority St.

Michael, John A., Architect, Civil Engineer & Surveyor, res. St. Philip St.
Michel, Adrian L., Jeweller, 256 King St., res. 116 Wentworth St.
Michel, Charles, Physician, res. St. Philip St.
Michel, Edward R., Jeweller, 256 King St., res. 34 Wentworth St.
Michel, Francis, Mrs., res. Coming St., Ward 6
Michel, R. F., Physician, 74 Queen St., res. Wragg's Square
Michel, William, Physician, 74 Queen St., res. 74 Queen St.
Mickelman, Henry, Carpenter, cr. Bogard & Coming Sts.
Middleton & Co. Factors & Commission Merchants, 20 Vanderhorst's Wharf
Middleton, Charles, Miller, Robb's Mill, res. Wharf St.
Middleton, Francis, Pilot, res. 6 Longitude lane
Middleton, Henry A., Planter, Georgetown, res. 44 South Bay St.
Middleton, James, Carpenter, res. 26 Coming St.
Middleton, John J., Planter, Waccamaw, res. 6 King St.
Middleton, N. R., Treasurer, Northeast Railroad, res. 44 South Bay St.
Middleton, O., Planter, Edisto Island, res. 3 New St.
Middleton, Thomas, Commission Merchant, 20 Vanderhorst's Wharf, res. 6 Meeting St.
Middleton, Thomas, Jr., Clerk, 20 Vanderhorst's Wharf, res. 6 Meeting St.
Middleton, William J., Bookkeeper at R. Mure's, res. 92 Church St.
Milan, E., Miss, res. 28 Archdale St.
Miler, Daniel, Dry Goods, 143 Meeting St., res. cr. Bull & Pitt Sts.
Miles, C. Richardson, Lawyer, Law Range, res. 175 Meeting St.
Miles, E. B., Clerk, 17 Hayne St., res. 175 Meeting St.
Miles, Edward K., Teacher, 53 Beaufain St., res. 53 Beaufain St.
Miles, F. T., Physician, 53 Beaufain St., res. 53 Beaufain St.
Miles, S. C., Clerk, Commercial Wharf, res. 99 East Bay St.
Miles, T. E. H., Clerk at Rico Dulin's, res. Charlotte St.
Miles, Thomas, Bookkeeper, East Bay St., res. Charlotte St.
Millar, Robert S., Baker, 58 Market St.
Miller & Son, Sailmakers, 116 East Bay St.
Miller, Archibald E., Printer, 3 State St., res. 43 Tradd St.
Miller, Francis C., Clerk, 223 King St., res. Vanderhorst St.
Miller, G., Clerk, 32 Broad St.
Miller, J. Claudius, Clerk, 240 King St., res. 65 Coming St.
Miller, J. D., Clerk, Commercial Wharf, res. cr. Wentworth & Pitt Sts.
Miller, J. H., Shoemaker, res. King St., near Line St.
Miller, James, Bookkeeper, res. Cannon St.
Miller, James, Tavern, Adger's South Wharf
Miller, John, Auctioneer, Fraser's Wharf, res. Mary St.

Miller, John D., Commission Merchant, 112 East Bay St.

Miller, John, Laborer, res. 22 Coming St.

Miller, John W., Carpenter, Vanderhorst St., 1 door from Pitt St.

Miller, L., Grocer, 62 Tradd St., res. 62 Tradd St.

Miller, L., Shoemaker, res. 37 Wentworth St.

Miller, Lewis, Grocer, 11 South Bay St., res. 11 South Bay St.

Miller, Mary, Mrs., res. 3 Vernon St.

Miller, Rudolph, Fruiterer, 63 Market St., res. 63 Market St.

Miller, Samuel D., Ropemaker, Vanderhorst St., 1 door from Pitt St.

Miller, Thomas A., Commission Merchant, 106 East Bay St., res. Warren St.

Miller, Thomas J., Clerk, 211 King St., res. Society St.

Miller, W. T., Clerk, 40 East Bay St., res. Planters Hotel

Miller, W. T., Sailmaker, 116 East Bay St., res. cr. Smith & Beaufain Sts.

Miller, William, Clerk, 153 Meeting St.

Miller, William, Teller, Bank of the State of South Carolina, res. Hudson St.

Miller, Zadock, Sailmaker, 116 East Bay St., res. 229 East Bay St.

Milligan, John J., Boiler Maker, res. Amherst St.

Milligan, Peter H., Porter, 211 King St., res. 130 King St.

Milliken, Adam T., Bookkeeper, 165 Meeting St.

Milliken, E. P., Dry Goods, 42 East Bay St., res. 162 Meeting St.

Milliken, Samuel B., Forcer, 155 East Bay St., res. cr. Society & East Bay Sts.

Milliken, Samuel, Grocer, 145 East Bay St.

Millings, Robert C., Coach Maker, 40 Wentworth St., res. 8 Horlbeck Alley

Mills, Beach & Co., Grain Merchants, 8 East Bay St.

Mills, John A., Clerk, South Carolina Railroad, res. 5 Cannon St.

Mills, Otis & Co., Proprietors, Atlantic Wharves

Mills, Otis, Grain Merchant, 8 East Bay St., res. 27 Meeting St.

Mills, S. S., res. 54 Market St.

Mills, Simon M., Clerk, 147 Meeting St., res. 27 Meeting St.

Milne, A., Planter, St. Andrew's Parish, res. cr. Rutledge & Bull Sts.

Milnor, George H., Bookkeeper, 41 East Bay St., res. 41 East Bay St.

Milnor, John G., Auctioneer & Commission Merchant, 19 Vendue Range, res. 1 East Bay St.

Milnor, Vincent, Clerk, 27 Broad St., res. 99 East Bay St.

Minniss, Robert, Plumber, 97 Meeting St., res. 97 Meeting St.

Minsing, Conrad, Clerk, cr. Calhoun & Washington Sts.

Miot, A., Bookkeeper at Caldwell, Blakeley & Co., res. 249 King St.

Miscally, David W., Bookkeeper, South Carolina Railroad, Office, res. 7 Marsh St.

Missroon, Henry, Agent, N.Y. Steamers, East Bay St.

Mitchell, A. R., Proprietor, Cotton Press, res. cr. Church & Water Sts.

Mitchell, A.R. & Co., Proprietors, Cotton Press, Longitude Lane

Mitchell, C. T. & Co., Factors & Commission Merchants, Boyce's North Wharf

Mitchell, Charles T., Commission Merchant, Boyce's Wharf, res. 15 Meeting St.

Mitchell, Edward, Clerk, 127 Meeting St., res. Calhoun & Coming Sts.

Mitchell, Edward J., Clerk, 9 Hayne St., res. cr. Coming & Calhoun Sts.

Mitchell, F. M., Bookkeeper, North Commercial Wharf, res. cr. Coming & Calhoun Sts.

Mitchell, Francis A., Boots & Shoes, 21 Hayne St., res. 98 Wentworth St.

Mitchell, G. H., Clerk, 118 Meeting St.

Mitchell, Horace W., Bookkeeper, 155 Meeting St., res. St. Philip St.

Mitchell, John S., Physician, 91 Meeting St., res. 269 East Bay St.

Mitchell, Mary Ann, Dressmaker, 4 Philadelphia St.

Mitchell, Nelson, Lawyer, St. Michael's Alley, res. 166 Meeting St.

Mitchell, Rebecca, Mrs., res. 2 Washington St.

Mitchell, Theodore C., Clerk at Ingraham & Webb's, res. Coming St.

Mitchell, William, Butcher, res. 24 Middle St.

Mitchell, William, Carpenter, res. Warren St.

Mitchell, William, Clerk, 118 Meeting St.

Mitchell, William E., Bookkeeper, 86 East Bay St., res. Reid St.

Moffett, Alexander, 35 Hayne St., res. 198 East Bay St.

Moffett, George H., Clerk, 54 East Bay St., res. Tradd St.

Moffett, James G., Clerk, 21 King St., res. Lagare St.

Moffett, John R., Grocer, 78 East Bay St., res. 4 Hasell St.

Moise, Abraham, Lawyer, Courthouse Square, res. 1 College St.

Moise, Benjamin F., Clerk, 29 Hayne St., res. 18 Beaufain St.

Moise, Charles H., Bookkeeper, 27 Hayne St., res. 1 College St.

Moise, Edwin W., Auctioneer & Commission Merchant, 32 Vendue Range, res. Glebe St.

Moise, Franklin, Clerk, 1 Hayne St., res. 18 Beaufain St.

Moise, Howard C., Clerk, 28 Vendue Range, res. 18 Beaufain St.

Moise, Isaac, Auctioneer, 119 East Bay St., res. 26½ Pitt St.

Moise, Jacob, Clerk, 1 Hayne St., res. 18 Beaufain St.

Moise, Jefferson, Clerk, 1 Hayne St., res. 18 Beaufain St.

Moise, Phillip A., Druggist, 221 King St., res. 18 Beaufain St.

Moise, Ward & Grierson, Druggists & Chemists, 221 King St.

Molloy, Ferdiand, Clerk, 211 King St., res. Charleston Hotel

Molony, John Grocer, cr. Church & Cumberland Sts.

Monefeldt, W. S., Dentist, 243 King St., res. 243 King St.

Monroe, George, Clerk, 211 King St., res. 10 Montague

St.

Monroe, John, Clerk, East Bay St., res. 10 Montague St.

Monroe, Robert, Judge, Court of Common Pleas, res. 10 Montague St.

Monroe, William, Clerk, Broad St., res. 10 Montague St.

Monsees, John, Grocer, cr. Calhoun & Coming Sts.

Montague, Charlotte, Mrs., res. 108 Wentworth St.

Montgomery, Andrew, Watchmaker, res. 27 George St.

Montgomery, Charles W., Clerk, 213 King St., res. 27 George St.

Montgomery, John W., Watchmaker, res. 27 George St.

Montgomery, William C., Clerk, 211 King St., res. 27 George St.

Mood, Edward, Turner & Pump Maker, res. Coming St.

Mood, James R., Physician, 302 King St., res. 302 King St.

Mood, John, Jeweller, 302 King St., res. 302 King St.

Mood, John M. W., Carpenter, South Carolina Railroad, res. Cannon St.

Moody, A. H., Tinsmith, 184 King St., res. 184 King St.

Moody, G. W., Bookkeeper, 18 East Bay St., res. 155 East Bay St.

Moody, Gordan, East Bay St., res. Cannon St.

Moore, Francis, Mrs., res. 32 Savage St.

Moore, Franklin, Patttern Maker, res. 3 Gadsden St.

Moore, George A., Printer, 3 Broad St., res. 5 Coming St.

Moore, George W., Pastor, Beaufort, res. 11 Wentworth St.

Moore, Henry, Student, res. 8 Liberty St.

Moore, James, Watchman, Cannonsborough Mills, res. Lucas St.

Moore, John, Tailor, East Bay St., res. Hasell St.

Moore, Robert D., Engineer, res. 3 Gadsden St.

Moran, Miles, Porter, 216 King St., res. Horlbeck Alley

Moran, Patrick, Porter, 216 King St., res. 210 King St.

Mordecai & Co., Commission Merchants, 110 East Bay St.

Mordecai, Benjamin, Broker, 5 State St., res. 49 Wentworth St.

Mordecai, J. R., Commission Merchant, 110 East Bay St., res. 43 Meeting St.

Mordecai, M. C., Commission Merchant, 110 East Bay St., res. 43 Meeting St.

Morehead, James, Grocer, cr. Archdale & Princess Sts.

Moreland, Andrew, res. 7 South Bay St.

Moreland, Edward M., Clerk, Adger's North Wharf, res. 7 South Bay St.

Morello, J. & J. B., Fruiterers, 129 King St.

Morello, James B., Fruiterer, 129 King St., res. 129 King St.

Morello, John B., Fruiterer, 129 King St., res. 129 King St.

Morgan, Benjamin, res. 16 Middle St.

Morgan, J. W., Clerk, 19 Hayne St., res. Merchants Hotel

Morgan, James R., Shoemaker, res. 70 Queen St.

Morgan, John B., Miller, Bennett's Rice Mills, res. 9 Middle St.

Morgan, John W., Tavern, cr. Calhoun & Meeting Sts.

Morn, Michael, Conductor, South Carolina Railroad, res.

Inspection St.

Moroso, Anthony, Fruiterer, 291 King St., res. 291 King St.

Morris, Albert A., Clerk, 243 King St., res. 249 King St.

Morris, Henry, Discount Clerk, Planters & Mechanics Bank, res. Planters Hotel

Morris, Mary R., Mrs., res. 200 East Bay St.

Morris, W. R., Clerk at Wyatt & Co., res. 104 Queen St.

Morrison, Samuel, Tavern, 48 East Bay St., res. 48 East Bay St.

Mortimer, Samuel H., Secretary, Charleston Insurance Company, res. Drake St.

Morton, Conrad, Shoemaker, 53 Broad St., res. 53 Broad St.

Morton, David, Clerk, 211 King St., res. Commercial House

Morton, Francis L., Bookkeeper, 243 King St., res. 297 King St.

Morton, W. R., Hardware, 133 Meeting St., res. 260 King St.

Moses, A. J., Clerk, Scruggs, Drake & Co., res. cr. Amherst & Hanover Sts.

Moses, Levy J., res. Chapel St.

Moses, Moses S., res. 6 Horlbeck Alley

Moses, Solomon, res. 47 Wentworth St.

Mosimann, William J., Printer, 111 East Bay St., res. Stoll's Alley

Mott, Emma, Miss, res. 8 Savage St.

Mott, William, Tavern, 3 Princess St., res. 3 Princess St.

Mottet & Huchet, Factors & Commission Merchants, Adger's North Wharf

Mottet, Edward, Factor, Adger's North Wharf, res. 323 King St.

Moultrie, Alexander, res. 34 Montague St.

Moultrie, James, Physician, 14 Montague St., res. 14 Montague St.

Moultrie, Roxana, Colored, Seamstress, res. 66 Calhoun St.

Moultrie, William, Colored, Barber, 106 Meeting St., res. 66 Calhoun St.

Mousseau, Adolphus, Carpenter, res. Mary St.

Mouzon, Charles, res. 4 St. Philip St.

Mouzon, Henry J., Daguerrean Artist, res. 38 St. Philip St.

Mouzon, John, Engineer, res. opposite Public Mall

Mouzon, Lewis H., General Agent, res. 38 St. Philip St.

Mowry, Elisha C., Lawyer, 20 Broad St., res. 126 Meeting St.

Mowry, L. D., Commission Merchant, 74 East Bay St., res. 8 Hasell St.

Mowry, S., Commission Merchant, 74 East Bay St., res. 175 Meeting St.

Mowry, S. L. & Co. Factors & Commission Merchants, 74 East Bay St.

Mowry, W. S., Commission Merchant, 74 East Bay St., res. 175 Meeting St.

Muckenfuss, H. W., Clerk, Market St., res. 86 Wentworth St.

Muckenfuss, Henry, res. 86 Wentworth St.

Mudge, E. W., Jr., Clerk, 232 King St., res. 228 King St.

Mueller, Gustave, Clerk, 54 Broad St.
Muetch, George, Clerk, 218 King St., res. Meeting St.
Muir, Eleanor, Mrs., res. 16 Cumberland St.
Muir, Jane, Mrs., Boarding House, 24 Broad St.
Mulkie, P., Bookkeeper, 30 Vendue Range, res. Queen St.
Mulkie, Thomas, Carpenter, res. 94 King St.
Mullan, John, Tavern, 3 Bedons Alley, res. 3 Bedons Alley
Muller, H., Clerk, 189 East Bay St., res. King St.
Muller, Lewis, Pastor, German Lutheran Church, res. 90 King St.
Muller, M., Grocer, cr. Columbus & Hanover Sts.
Mulligan, A. B., Clerk, 211 King St., res. 132 King St.
Mulligan, Peter, res. 132 King St.
Mullings, Timothy, Porter, 1 Hayne St., res. Church St.
Mullings, William, Pilot, res. 5 Atlantic St.
Murdens, -----, Misses, Female School, 34 Society St., res. 34 Society St.
Murdock, James, Clerk, 213 King St., res. cr. Society & Meeting Sts.
Murdock, Robert, 135 East Bay St., res. 56 Meeting St.
Mure, Robert, Commission Merchant, Boyce's Wharf, res. 68 Church St.
Murell, James H., Courier Office, 111 East Bay St., res. 8 Mazyck St.
Murphy, F., Clothing, 183 East Bay St., res. Merchants Hotel
Murphy, James, Drayman, res. Mary St.
Murphy, James, Produce Dealer, cr. State St. & Unity Alley
Murphy, John, Laborer, 14 Pinckney St.
Murphy, Laurence, Bar Keeper, 18 Pinckney St., res. 18 Pinckney St.
Murphy, Martin, Porter, 211 King St., res. Pitt St.
Murphy, Nicholas, Porter, King St., res. 40 State St.
Murphy, Thomas, Gardener, res. 24 Laurens St.
Murphy, Thomas, Laborer, res. 154 East Bay St.
Murphy, Thomas, Porter, 40 East Bay St.
Murray, B., Dry Goods, 99 King St., res. 99 King St.
Murray, George, Clerk, 26 East Bay St., res. cr. South Battery & Church Sts.
Murray, James, Collector, res. 3 Savage St.
Murray, James, Plasterer, res. Warren St.
Murray, Susan, Mrs., res. 72 Tradd St.
Murray, William C., Commission Merchant, 26 East Bay St., res. cr. South Battery & Church Sts.
Musgrave, James, Laborer, res. 3 Laurens St.
Mustard, David, Mrs., res. Calhoun St.
Myers, Christopher, Shoemaker, 53 State St., res. 53 State St.
Myers, D. H., Tavern, cr. Queen & State Sts.
Myers, G., Tailor, 34 Pinckney St., res. 34 Pinckney St.
Myers, Joseph, Boiler Maker, Hasell St., res. 9 Laurens St.
Myers, L. H., Clerk, City Treasurer's Office, res. Waverly House
Myhrmann, J., Draughtsman at Jones & Lee's, res. Church St.
Nachman, William, Dealer in Old Iron, res. Bogard St.

Nagle, John, Laborer, res. Alexander St.
Nail, Andrew F., Finisher, South Carolina Railroad, res. Hampden Court
Naser, John F., res. 16 Coming St.
Nathan, Hyman, Coach Trimmer, cr. Meeting & Wentworth Sts., res. 30 St. Philip St.
Nathan, Moses H., Carriage Maker, cr. Meeting & Wentworth Sts., res. 30 St. Philip St.
Nathan, S. N., Mrs., res. King St., Ward 5
Nayler & Smith, Dry Goods, 40 East Bay St.
Nayler, William, Dry Goods, 40 East Bay St.
Neal, Richard, Clerk, 228 King St., res. Queen St.
Neal, William M., Carpenter, 20 Queen St., res. 87 Tradd St.
Nebur, Andrew, Wheelwright, res. Morris St.
Nebur, Modestine, Mantuamaker, res. Morris St.
Nell, Clarence, Colored, Barber, King St., res. Coming St.
Nelson, Christian, Bootmaker, 28 Anson St., res. 28 Anson St.
Nelson, Hannah, Colored, Vegetable Woman, res. Ashley St.
Nelson, John E., Bookkeeper, 169 East Bay St., res. American Hotel
Nelson, Maria, Colored, Pastry Cook, res. Pitt St.
Nelson, Peter, Barber, 33 State St., res. 33 State St.
Nelson Samuel A., Clerk, 43 Hayne St., res. 101 Meeting St.
Nelson, William C., Clerk, 279 King St., res. King St.
Nelson, William, Tavern, 19 Berresford St., res. 19 Berresford St.
Nepley, Solomon, Laborer, res. 58 Queen St.
Nesbitt, Douglas, Commission Merchant, North Commercial Wharf
Neslon, Patsy, Seamstress, res. Morris St.
Neuffer & Hendrix, Commission Merchants, 148 East Bay St.
Neuffer, G. A., Commission Merchant, 148 East Bay St., res. Planters Hotel
Neufville, Benjamin S., res. 52 Anson St.
Neufville, C., Clerk, Accommodation Wharf, res. 52 Anson St.
Neuman, Phillip, Lumber Merchant, res. Montague St.
Neumeyer, Lewis, Cigars & Tobacco, 185 King St., res. 185 King St.
Neville, Thomas C., Printer, 111 East Bay St., res. 99 East Bay St.
Newbold, Martha, Mrs., Boarding, 34 Wentworth St.
Newell, John, Gas Fitter, 4 Montague St., res. 4 Montague St.
Newman, Nicholas, Ginger Pop Maker, King St., Upper Ward
Newton, Edward, Molder, State St., res. Cannon St.
Newton, Justice A., Clerk, Coming St., res. Coming St., Ward 6
Newton, William M., Shipwright, res. Coming St., Ward 6
Newton, William, Planter, St. George's Parish, res. Cannon St.
Nichols, Benjamin S., Saddlery, cr. Meeting & Hasell

Sts., res. Newark, N. J.

Nichols, Frederick, Teacher of Music, Mary St.

Nichols, George, Ship Blacksmith, opposite Marsh's Wharf, res. 5 Pritchard St.

Nickerson, George W., Printer, res. Calhoun St.

Nickerson, Thomas S., Proprietor, Mills House, cr. Queen & Meeting Sts.

Nihans, Frederick, Grocer, President St.

Nipson, Thomas S., Clerk, 228 King St., res. 124 Queen St.

Niselay, Mary, Mrs., res. 12 Atlantic St.

Nolam, John, Blacksmith, Calhoun St., res. 13 Anson St.

Nolam, John, Sr., Wheelwright, Calhoun St., res. 13 Anson St.

Nolkin, C., Tavern, Tivoli Garden, Meeting St.

Noomale, Thomas, Laborer, res. 3 Stoll's Alley

Nooman, John, Laborer, res. President St.

Norris, Joseph, Cooper, 49 Anson St., res. Calhoun St.

Norris, William, Cooper, Bennett's Mill, res. Heyward's Court

North, Edward, Physician, 79 Meeting St., res. 79 Meeting St.

Northrop & Allemong, Lawyers, 17 Broad St.

Northrop, C. B., Lawyer, 17 Broad St., res. 50 King St.

Northrop, Lucius B., res. Ashley St.

Norton, J., Bookkeeper, Bank of Charleston, res. 115 Queen St.

Norton, J. H., Clerk, 20 Vendue Range, res. 115 Queen St.

Norton, Rachel, Mrs., res. 214 King St.

Norton, William, Clerk, East Bay St., res. cr. Chapel & Alexander Sts.

Norton, William, Commission Agent, cr. Calhoun & Washington Sts.

Nowell, John L., Planter, Santee, cr. Reid & East Bay Sts.

Nowell, Richard, Fireman, South Carolina Railroad, res. William's Row

Nugent, Michael, Porter, 142 Meeting St., res. 5 Wall St.

Nuller, William, Laborer, res. Horlbeck Alley

Oakeley, Robert S., Druggist, 150 King St., res. 150 King St.

Oakeley, William C., Broker, 26 Broad St., res. 150 King St.

Oakes, Samuel, Shoemaker, 100 Queen St., res. 45 Beaufain St.

Oakes, Z. B., Broker & Auctioneer, 7 State St., res. 11 Coming St.

Oates & Brother, Books & Music, 234 & 236 King St.

Oates, George A., Books, 234 King St., res. Augusta, Georgia

Oates, Henry T., Books, 234 King St., res. 234 King St.

Oberhauser, John, Physician & Chemist, res. cr. Church & Linguard Sts.

Oelrich, J. C., Piano & Organ Builder, King St., near Calhoun St.

Ogeman, G. H., Grocer, 370 King St., res. 370 King St.

Ogeman, John, Grocer, 30 Calhoun St., res. 30 Calhoun St.

Ogier, Thomas, Physician, 35 East Bay St., res. 35 East

Bay St.

Ohlant, W. H., Clerk, King St., res. King St.

Oldenberg, E. H., Grocer, cr. Meeting & Pitt Sts.

Olney, George W., Commission Merchant, 14 Vendue Range, res. Coming St.

Olney, H. B., Clerk, 11 Vendue Range, res. Coming St.

Olrogge, P., Grocer, cr. King & Columbus Sts.

Olsen, C. M., Clerk, 47 Broad St., res. 102 Church St.

Oltjen, J. C., Grain Store, George St., res. George St.

Oppenheim & Brothers, Commission Merchants, 102 East Bay St.

Oppenheim, Henry, Commission Merchant, 102 East Bay St., res. cr. King & Hudson Sts.

Oppenheim, Joseph H., Commission Merchant, 102 East Bay St., res. 16 Warren St.

Oppenheim, Joseph H., Grocer, cr. King & Hudson Sts.

Oppenheim, Samuel, Commission Merchant, 102 East Bay St., res. cr. King & Hudson Sts.

Orbrecht, Nicholas, Grocer, 19 South Bay St., res. 19 South Bay St.

Orcutt & Hickey, Gilders & Frame Makers, 154 King St.

Orcutt, L., Frame Maker, 154 King St., res. 154 King St

Osborn, James, Daguerrean Artist, 233 King St., res. 233 King St.

Osborn, James, Mrs., Milliner, 233 King St., res. 233 King St.

Osborn, William, Ship Carpenter, Pritchard St., res. Pitt St.

Osgood, George, Engineer, res. 30 Tradd St.

Oshon, Lewis, Sail Maker, East Bay St., res. Concord St.

Oslee, Henry E., Clerk, res. 274 King St.

Ostead, E. H., Laborer, South Carolina Railroad, res. Coming St.

Ostendorf, J. M., Clothing, 95 East Bay St., res. 87 East Bay St.

Ostenholtz, D., Grocer & Rice Mills, cr. Ashley & Mill Sts.

Otgen, George, Porter, 61 East Bay St., res. 61 East Bay St.

Otman, H., Musician, res. 2 Archdale St.

Otten, Cordes, Grocer, cr. Tradd & Bedons Alley

Otten, E. B., Grocer, cr. Elizabeth & Henrietta Sts.

Otten, Heindrick, Grocer, cr. Tradd & Bedons Alley

Ottolengui, Abraham, Mrs., res. cr. Calhoun & Smith Sts.

Ottolengui, Israel, Auctioneer & Commission Merchant, 28 Vendue Range

Ottolengui, Jacob, Auctioneer, 22 Broad St., res. cr. Calhoun & Smith Sts.

Owens, Alexander, Butcher, res. Spring St.

Owens, James B., at Wardlaw, Walker & Burnside, res. 20 Beaufain St.

Owens, Stephen, Clerk, 193 East Bay St., res. 20 Beaufain St.

Oxlade, T. C., Jeweller, 61 Broad St., res. 16 Middle St.

O'Brien, Edward, Carpenter, res. Queen St.

O'Brien, J. W. & Co., Tinsmiths, King St. Upper Ward

O'Brien, J. W., Tinsmith, King St., res. Line St.

O'Brien, James, Laborer, res. Concord St.

O'Brien, John, Laborer, res. 14 Philadelphia St.

O'Brien, M., Shoemaker, King St., res. King St.

O'Brien, Maurice, Porter, 141 Meeting St., res. King St.
O'Brien, P., Telegraph Operator, 3 State St., res. City Hotel
O'Brien, Patrick, Carpenter, res. Queen St.
O'Brien, Peter, Clerk, 222 King St., res. 19 Horlbeck Alley
O'Brien, Thomas, Clerk, South Commercial Wharf, res. cr. Trapmann & Queen Sts.
O'Brien, William, Laborer, res. Calhoun St.
O'Commor, William, Watchmaker, res. 5 Savage St.
O'Connell, P., Laborer, res. 1 Archdale St.
O'Connor, B., Painter, res. Cedar Court
O'Connor, John, Laborer, res. 11 Anson St.
O'Day, John, Laborer, res. Calhoun St.
O'Day, Michael, Laborer, res. 9 Marsh St.
O'Dell, John, Laborer, res. Calhoun St.
O'Donnell, James, Laborer, res. Nassau St.
O'Door, Hariett, Mrs., res. 12 Stoll's Alley
O'Farrall, John, Clerk, 150 Meeting St., res. King St.
O'Gilvie, Mathew, Hardware, 21 Broad St., res. 5 Logan St.
O'Gorman, Peter, Wharfinger, Accommodation Wharf, res. 11 Church St.
O'Hanolon, Eliza, Mrs., Tailoress, Bogard St.
O'Hara, Martha, Mrs., res. Vanderhorst St.
O'Hara, Patrick, Drayman, res. Calhoun St.
O'Hara, William P., Clothing, 143 East Bay St., res. 60½ Wentworth St.
O'Hear, James, Factor, North Commercial Wharf, res. St. Philip St.
O'Hear, Roper & Stoney, Factors & Commission Merchants, North Commercial Wharf
O'Hear, Samuel, Wood Factor, Accommodation Wharf, res. Coming St.
O'Hearn, Patrick, Laborer, Calhoun St.
O'Kane, G., Clerk, 135 Meeting St., res. 56 Meeting St.
O'Keefe, Thomas, Laborer, res. 2 Bedons Alley
O'Kelly, Dennis, Stone Mason, res. St. Philip St.
O'Kelly, Patrick, Stone Mason, res. St. Philip St.
O'Leary, Daniel, Ship Carpenter, res. 59 Tradd St.
O'Mara, James, Laborer, res. 2 Philadelphia St.
O'Mara, John, Drayman, res. St. Philip St.
O'Mara, John, Variety Store, 90 Queen St., res. 88 Queen St.
O'Mara, Michael, Plasterer, res. St. Philip St.
O'Neill, A. E., Tavern, 20 Market St., res. 20 Market St.
O'Neill, Benjamin, Commission Merchant, 135 East Bay St., res. 56 Meeting St.
O'Neill, Cornelius, Printer, res. 2 Liberty St.
O'Neill, E. P., Bishop, St. Patrick's Church, res. King St.
O'Neill, Edmund, res. cr. Rutledge & Cannon Sts.
O'Neill, F., Bricklayer, res. Cromwell's Terrace
O'Neill, Hugh, Saddler, cr. Church & Chalmers Sts., res. 41 Queen St.
O'Neill, James, Carpenter, res. 20 Magazine St.
O'Neill, James, Shoemaker, 112 Church St., res. 112 Church St.
O'Neill, John F., Grocer, 145 East Bay St., res. cr. Queen & Trapmann Sts.
O'Neill, Mary, Mrs., Boarding House, King St., Upper Ward
O'Neill, Michael, Laborer, res. Pritchard St.
O'Neill, Patrick, Clerk, King St., res. 102 Church St.
O'Neill, Patrick, Laborer, res. Pritchard St.
O'Neill, Patrick, Planter, res. Cannon St.
O'Neill, Richard, Shoemaker, 174 East Bay St., res. 174 East Bay St.
O'Neill, Thomas, Clerk, 122 East Bay St., res. 20 Magazine St.
O'Neill, Thomas, Laborer, res. Pritchard St.
O'Neill, Thomas, Shoemaker, 112 Church St., res. 112 Church St.
O'Neill, William, Clerk, 25 Hayne St., res. 20 Magazine St.
O'Neill, William, Laborer, res. 5 Hard Alley
O'Neill, William T., Clerk, 182 King St., res. Queen St.
O'Reilly, James B., Printer, 119 East Bay St., res. 4 Mazyck St.
O'Reilly, William, Shoemaker, 184 Meeting St., res. 184 Meeting St.
O'Riggan, Margaret, Mrs., Dry Goods, 154 East Bay St., res. 154 East Bay St.
O'Rourke, Felix, Blacksmith, 28 Pinckney St., res. 9 Vernon St.
O'Rourke, John, Tavern, 40 Market St., res. 40 Market St.
O'Rourke, Patrick, Laborer, res. Concord St.
O'Sullivan, Martin, Drayman, res. 1 Linguard St.
O'Wen, James D., Mrs., Boarding House, 102 Church St.
O'Wen, Leslie D., Clerk, 13 Southern Wharf, res. 102 Church St.
O'Wen, Leslie, Dentist, 102 Church St., res. 102 Church St.
Padrow, Anthony, Cigar Maker, res. cr. Woolf & Nassau Sts.
Paine & Bickley, Commission Merchants, 70 East Bay St.
Paine, E. T., Commission Merchant, 70 East Bay St., res. Coming St., Ward 6
Paine, J. S., Planter, res. 19 Friend St.
Paine, R. P., Clerk, King St., res. 13 College St.
Paine, Robert, Surveyor, res. Blake St.
Paine, Thomas, U. S. Navy, res. Vanderhorst St., near Smith St.
Paine, W. R., Bookkeeper, Union Bank, res. 8 Green St.
Painter, N., Corn Physician, King St., Upper Wards
Palmer, Barnwell W., Clerk, 77 East Bay St., res. cr. Church St. & Longitude Lane
Palmer, John W., Police Officer, City Hall, res. 6 Hard Alley
Palmer, William, Rigger, 6 Guignard St., res. Cumberland St.
Panknin & Phin, Druggists, 123 Meeting St.
Panknin, C. H., Druggist, 123 Meeting St., res. 123 Meeting St.
Pansell, William, Shoemaker, 170 Meeting St., res. 188 Meeting St.
Panson, Elizabeth, Mrs., Seamstress, 149 King St.
Park, Adeline, res. 8 Calhoun St.
Park, F. A., res. Rutledge St.

Park, Manly, Mrs., Milliner, King St., Upper Ward

Parker, A. G., Mrs., Milliner, 242 King St., res. 242 King St.

Parker, Benjamin J., Clerk, 19 Hayne St., res. 6 George St.

Parker, Charles, Surveyor, res. 13 Church St.

Parker, Jane E., Mrs., res. 5 Horlbeck Alley

Parker, Mary, Colored, Mantuamaker, res. Coming St.

Parker, Robert, Brick Yard, Christ Church Parish, res. Charlotte St.

Parker, Rutledge, Surveyor, res. 1 Friend St.

Parker, Samuel D., Inspector, Custom House, res. 6 George St.

Parker, Thomas, Clerk, 211 King St., res. Tradd St.

Parry, James D., Clerk, 94 East Bay St., res. 26 Middle St.

Parsons, Charles M, Engineer, res. Coming St.

Parsons, John, Laborer, res. 20 Vernon St.

Parsons, M., Mrs., res. 21 Archdale St.

Partuza, Ferdinand, Rigger, 84 Anson St., res. 84 Anson St.

Paschke, Ernest, Watchmaker, 256 King St., res. 66 Broad St.

Passailaigue, Ann S., Mrs., res. cr. Charlotte & Elizabeth Sts.

Passailaigue, Lewis, Blacksmith, South Carolina Railroad, res. Spring St.

Patch, Alexander, Blacksmith, res. cr. Charlotte & Elizabeth St.

Patch, Nathaniel, Carpenter, res. 94½ Beaufain St.

Patrick, John B., Dentist, Society St., res. Society St.

Pattani, Joseph, Fruiterer, 19 & 23 Market St., res. 23 Market St.

Patter, William, res. 16 Laurens St.

Patterson & Stock, Commission Merchants, North Atlantic Wharf

Patterson, Francis, Wheelwright, res. cr. Woolf & Nassau Sts.

Patterson, James L., Commission Merchant, North Atlantic Wharf, res. Mansion House

Patterson, Simeon H., Agent & Collector, res. 8 Marsh St.

Patterson, W. P., Carpenter, res. 8 Liberty St.

Patterson, William, Bookkeeper at W. C. Duke & Sons, res. 21 Laurens St.

Patton, Edwin D., Watchmaker, 235 King St., res. 249 King St.

Patton, William A., Clerk, 37 Hayne St., res. American Hotel

Patty, James, Mariner, res. 1 Greenhill St.

Paul & Brown, Grocers, 47 Broad St., cr. Church St.

Paul, Dunbar, Grocer, 47 Broad St., res. 20 New St.

Paul, John, Clerk, 47 Broad St., res. 20 New St.

Paul, John H., Grocer, cr. State St. & Lodge Alley

Paul, William, Clerk, 47 Broad St., res. 20 New St.

Paxton, William Y. & Co., Proprietors of Evening News, 119 East Bay St.

Paxton, William Y., Proprietor of Evening News, res. cr. Smith & Montague Sts.

Peake, Henry T., General Superintendent, South Carolina Railroad, res. Spring St.

Pearce, Richard J., Furniture, 293 King St., res. 293 King St.

Pecher & Whitaker, Clothing, 352 King St.

Pecher, Henry A., Clothing, 352 King St., res. 352 King St.

Pegint, Lewis, res. 1 Hard Alley

Peixotte, Grace, Miss, res. 11 Berresford St.

Pelerin, M. A., Saddler, 294 King St., res. 294 King St.

Pelerin, Sophia, Mrs., 294 King St., res. 294 King St.

Pellessier, Olivia, Miss, res. 26 Laurens St.

Pelot, J. Alma, Accountant, 273 King St., res. cr. America & Amherst Sts.

Pelot, Stephen E., Accountant, 273 King St., res. 260 King St.

Pelot, W. L., Clerk, 40 East Bay St., res. 7 Water St.

Pelot, W. W., Clerk at Elm & Johnson's, res. Charlotte St.

Pelot, William L., Clerk, 19 Hayne St., res. 7 Water St.

Pelot, Wolford, Bookkeeper, 10 Vendue Range

Pelzer, A. P., Physician, 2 Beaufain St., res. 2 Beaufain St.

Pelzer, Francis J., Factor, North Adger's Wharf, res. Cannon St.

Pelzer, George S., Physician, King St., Upper Ward

Pelzer, Hannah, Mrs., res. President St.

Pendergrast, E., Dry Goods, 151 King St., res. 151 King St.

Pennall, Mary, Mrs., res. Calhoun St.

Penticost, Francis, Proprietor, Combs & Co. Southern Express, 127 Meeting St.

Pepper, Archibald, res. Meeting St., near Ann St.

Pepper, Lester M., Grocer, cr. Cannon & Coming Sts.

Pepper, R. H., Clerk, 127 Meeting St.

Peronneau, H. W., Lawyer, Broad St., res. 71 Church St.

Perriss, Mary, Colored, Washerwoman, res. 12 March St.

Perry, Archibald S. J., Dry Goods, 181 East Bay St., res. 293 East Bay St.

Perry, Edward P., Clerk, 33 Hayne St., res. 42 Beaufain St.

Perry, Joseph, Fruiterer, 53 Market St., res. 53 Market St.

Perry, S. B., Clerk, 43 Hayne St., res. 204½ King St.

Peterman & Mehrtens, Grocers, 1 Washington St.

Peterman, F., Grocer, cr. Meeting & Market Sts.

Peterman, Frederick, Grocer, cr. Church & Atlantic Sts.

Peterman, Henry, Grocer, 1 Washington St., res. 1 Washington St.

Peterman, Henry, Grocer, 71 Church St., res. 71 Church St.

Peters, George, Captain of the Dry Dock, res. 5 Pritchard St.

Peters, Henry T., Millinery, 317 King St., res. 317 King St.

Peterson, John L., Clerk, 226 King St., res. 212 King St.

Peterson, Mary Jane, Mrs., Boarding House, 212 King St.

Petigru & King, Lawyers, St. Michael's Alley

Petigru, Daniel, Assistant City Assessor, City Hall, res. 103 Broad St.

Petigru, J. J., Lawyer, St. Michael's Alley, res. 103

Broad St.

Petigru, James L., Lawyer, St. Michael's Alley, res. 103 Broad St.

Petit, Charles P., Painter, res. Woolf St.

Petit, Edmund W., Insurance Broker, 36 East Bay St., res. 19 Wentworth St.

Petit, F., Confectioner, 194 King St., res. 194 King St.

Petit, James M., Harness Maker, Meeting St., res. St. Philip St.

Petit, N. F., Tinsmith, 62 Market St., res. Cumberland St.

Petit, Victor, Music Teacher, 30 Pinckney St., res. 30 Pinckney St.

Pettigrew, William, Physician, 64 Broad St., res. 64 Broad St.

Peurifoy, Archibald M., Bookkeeper, Neck Ice House, Vanderhorst St.

Peurifoy, Archibald, Physician, Vanderhorst St.

Phelon, Julius R., Tailor, 21 Calhoun St., res. 21 Calhoun St.

Phelps, Francis L., Clerk, 31 Broad St., res. St. Philip St.

Philips, John, Lawyer, 84 Church St., res. 158 Meeting St.

Phillips, Edward, Clergyman, res. 44 Beaufain St.

Phillips, Eleazer, Carpenter, res. Spring St.

Phillips, John E., Teller, Bank of Charleston, res. Charlotte St.

Phillips, Otis, Grain Merchant, 116 East Bay St., res. 16 New St.

Phillips, Samuel M., Clerk, 253 King St., res. Chapel St.

Phillips, St. John, Physician, 44 Beaufain St., res. 44 Beaufain St.

Phin, A. C., Druggist, 123 Meeting St., res. King St.

Phynney & Co., Printers, 48 Broad St.

Phynney, C., Mrs., Dry Goods, 57 State St., res. 57 State St.

Phynney, Josiah, Printer, 48 Broad St., res. 48 Broad St.

Phynney, R. C., Mrs., Boarding House, 48 Broad St.

Picaulb, C., Mrs., Dry Goods, 57 State St., res. 57 State St.

Pickup, Mark, Peddler, res. 5 Cannon St.

Pierce, Jennings & Co., Clothing, 26 Hayne St.

Pierce, Matthew, Boots & Shoes, 326 King St.

Pierson, Benjamin E., Clerk, 211 King St., res. King St.

Pierson, Edward, Clothing, 26 Hayne St., res. Charleston Hotel

Pierson, J. S., Clothing, 26 Hayne St., res. Charleston Hotel

Pinckney, B. G., Commission Merchant, North Commercial Wharf, res. cr. Meeting & Wentworth Sts.

Pinckney, C. C., Cotton & Rice Broker, North Adger's Wharf

Pinckney, C. C., Pastor, Grace Church, res. 12 Coming St.

Pinckney, Charles, Clerk, Custom House, res. St. Philip St.

Pinckney, H. L., Tax Collector, res. 3 St. Philip St.

Pinckney, Hopson, 4th Lieutenant of the City Guard, Guard House

Pinckney, John, Tailor, Coming St., res. Coming St.

Pinckney, N. L., Planter, Barnwell District

Pinckney, R. Q., Jr., Commission Merchant, North Commercial Wharf, res. 34 Meeting St.

Pinckney, Robert, res. 34 Meeting St.

Pinckney, Roger, Planter, res. Pitt St.

Pinkerson, P., Clothing, 51 East Bay St., res. 51 East Bay St.

Plane, William A., Inspector, Custom House, res. 37 East Bay St.

Plenge, Charles, Tailor, 94 Meeting St., res. 94 Meeting St.

Plessman, G. W., Tavern, cr. King & Cannon Sts.

Plien, H., Grocer, cr. Beaufain & Pitt Sts.

Plumet, Anthony, Tailor, 209 East Bay St., res. Amherst St.

Poincett, Paul, Barber, 199 East Bay St., res. 199 East Bay St.

Poincignon, Emile, Tinsmith, 11 Queen St., res. 11 Queen St.

Police, Francis, res. 78 Church St.

Pollock, Theodore, Clerk, 208 King St., res. Merchants Hotel

Pope, J. R. W., Lawyer, Court House Square

Pope. Joseph J., Lawyer, 51 Broad St., res. 42 Bull St.

Poppen, Dederick, Grocer, Calhoun St.

Poppenheine, John, res. 10 John St.

Porcher, C. J., Clerk, 77 Broad St., res. cr. Church & Tradd Sts.

Porcher, Catherine, Mrs., res. Pitt St., near Calhoun St.

Porcher, Charles, Lawyer, Broad St., res. cr. Church & Tradd Sts.

Porcher, F. J., Broker, 34 East Bay St., res. 7 Water St.

Porcher, F. P., Physician, Mansion House, res. Mansion House

Porcher, F. T., Physician, cr. Church & Cumberland Sts.

Porcher, Frederick, Teacher, Charleston College, res. 32 South Bay St.

Porcher, Isaac, Mrs., res. 88 Broad St.

Porcher, John, Mrs., res. 202 East Bay St.

Porcher, P. J., Broker & Auctioneer, 25 Broad St., res. 28 South Bay St.

Porcher, Peter, Jr., Clerk, Meeting St., res. 53 Church St.

Porcher, Peter, Physician, 53 Church St., res. 53 Church St.

Porcher, S. T. Reuben, Physician, 57 Broad St., res. 57 Broad St.

Porter, A. T., Pastor, Church of Holy Communion, res. Rutledge St.

Porter, Noman M., Grocer, 222 King St., res. 13 College St.

Porter, R., Clerk, Charleston Hotel, res. 75 Wentworth St.

Porter, William, Clerk, 222 King St., res. 13 College St.

Porter, William D., Lawyer, 32 Broad St., res. 1 Pitt St.

Posser, M. H., Clerk, 210 King St., res. 29 Society St.

Posser, William H., Coachmaker, 142 Meeting St., res. 35 Society St.

Potter, J. V., Carpenter, res. 11 Franklin St.

Potter, John, Coachmaker, 142 Meeting St., res. Society St.

Potter, L. T., Proprietor, Steam Mill, Office, 147 East

Bay St., res. Charleston Hotel
Potter, Mary, Mrs., res. Judith St.
Potter, Nelson, Druggist, 17 Hayne St., res. Charleston Hotel
Powers, John, res. 101 King St.
Powers, Mary, Mrs., res. 31 State St.
Powers, Michael, Drayman, res. 76 Tradd St.
Powers, Patrick, Laborer, res. 25 Calhoun St.
Poyas, A., Mrs., res. 122 Queen St.
Poyas, John, Planter, res. 2 Wragg Square
Pratt, C. D., Dry Goods, 19 Hayne St., res. Charleston Hotel
Pratt, George, Engineer, South Carolina Railroad, res. 120 Wentworth St.
Pratt, W. F., Druggist, 153 Meeting St., res. Newbury, South Carolina
Pregnall, Henry, Carpenter, res. Henrietta St.
Presley, Benjamin C., Lawyer, cr. Church & Broad Sts., res. 44 Tradd St.
Pressler, P., Shoemaker, 59 Market St., res. 59 Market St.
Preston, James, Liquors, 100 East Bay St., res. 66 Queen St.
Preston, John, Grocer, 97 Church St., res. 97 Church St.
Prevost, Joseph, Proprietor, Accommodation Wharf, res. Hasell St.
Price, Alfred, Hardware, 14 Hayne St., res. 59 Meeting St.
Price, James, Bookkeeper, 169 East Bay St., res. Calhoun St.
Prince, Charles, Mrs., res. 108 King St.
Prince, George, Botanic Druggist, 330 King St., res. 330 King St.
Prince, Hamilton, Clerk, King St., res. Ashley St.
Prince, James H., Clerk, 10 Vendue Range, res. Ashley St.
Prince, S. H., Bookkeeper, 159 Meeting St., res. King St.
Prince, Samuel, Printer, 3 Broad St., res. King St.
Prince., A., Clerk, South Carolina Railroad, res. Woolf St.
Pringle, E., Clerk, 288 King St., res. 120 Wentworth St.
Pringle, James R., Factor, 7 North Adger's Wharf, res. 9 Legare St.
Pringle, John, Clerk, King St., res. 120 Wentworth St.
Pringle, Mott A., Factor, 12 Vanderhorst's Wharf, res. 58 Broad St.
Pringle, R. A., Boots & Shoes, 177 East Bay St., res. 20 Society St.
Pringle, William Allston, Lawyer, cr. Broad & Church Sts.
Pringle, William B., res. 9 King St.
Prioleau, C. F., Commission Merchant, Central Wharf, res. 4 Gibbes St.
Prioleau, C. K., Factor, Central Wharf, res. 4 Gibbes St.
Prioleau, Francis C., Clerk, Planters & Mechanics Bank, res. 1 Legare St.
Prioleau, H., Bookkeeper, Commercial Wharf, res. 1 Legare St.
Prioleau, J. Ford, Physician, cr. Society & Meeting St.
Prioleau, T. B., Physician, res. cr. Wentworth & Glebe Sts.

Prioleau, W. H., Clerk, 1 Hayne St., res. 69 Wentworth St.
Prior, Bernard R., Clerk, 21 Hayne St., res. 43 George St.
Prior, Dennis, Clerk, 131 Meeting St., res. 131 Meeting St.
Prior, Eugene, Clerk, 21 Hayne St., res. 43 George St.
Prior, John, Clerk, 37 Hayne St., res. 43 George St.
Pritchard, Columbus C., Physician, 150 East Bay St., res. 150 East Bay St.
Pritchard, George W., Clerk, 277 King St., res. Society St.
Pritchard, Paul, Ship Carpenter, res. 1 Horlbeck Alley
Pritchard, William, Clerk, cr. Hasell & Meeting Sts., res. Pinckney St.
Proctor, H. G., Clerk at James E. Adger's, res. 25 Wentworth St.
Proctor, William, Bookkeeper, 141 East Bay St., res. 25 Wentworth St.
Prothro, H. W., Mrs., res. 7 Liberty St.
Prothro, Nelson B., Steam Planing Mill, east end of Calhoun St.
Proughton, Charles Marion, res. 3 Zig Zag Alley
Puckhaber, F., Baker, King St., res. Mary St.
Pulliam, R. W., Dry Goods, 131 Meeting St., res. New York
Pulverman, V., Clothing, King St., Upper Ward
Purcell, Jacob, Turner, 188 Meeting St., res. 188 Meeting St.
Purfear, Joseph, Tavern, cr. Calhoun & East Bay Sts.
Purse, Robert S., res. Coming St., Upper Ward
Putnam, Charles B., Clerk, 253 King St., res. Wentworth St.
Pyatt, John, Planter, Georgetown, res. cr. Meeting & Charlotte Sts.
Pyatt, Joseph, Planter, Georgetown, res. cr. Meeting & Charlotte Sts.
Pyors, John, Planter, res. 2 Wragg Square
Quackenbush, Thomas L., Grocer, cr. Church & Cumberland Sts.
Quaile, James, Clerk, 135 East Bay St.
Quash, E. H., Bookkeeper, Bank of Charleston. res. Green St.
Quash, F. B., Jr., Bookkeeper, Bank of Charleston, res. cr. Rutledge & Spring Sts.
Quash, Francis D., Inspector, Custom House, res. cr. Rutledge & Spring Sts.
Quash, Joseph, Colored, Barber, King St., res. 40 Pitt St.
Quigley, Charles, Boots & Shoes, 76 Church St., res. 76 Church St.
Quigley, William A., Clerk, 173 East Bay St., res. St. Philip St.
Quinlan, John, Shoemaker, 74 Meeting St., res. 25 King St.
Quinn, Daniel, Wheelwright, 28 Pinckney St., res. 9 Vernon St.
Quinn, Elizabeth, Fruit & Confectionary, King St., Upper Ward
Quinn, James, Wheelwright, 4 Cumberland St.
Quinn, Michael, Tavern, 5 Bedons Alley, res. 5 Bedons

Alley

Rabb, Jacob, Pump Maker, Market Wharf, res. 32 Pinckney St.

Rabe, J., Mrs., Millinery, King St., Upper Ward

Rabe, Robert, Livery Stable, George St., res. 43 Calhoun St.

Rabear, Charles, Grocery, 4 Tradd St., res. 4 Tradd St.

Radcliffe, George S., Clerk at Adams & Frost

Radinger, Peter, Tailor, 183 King St., res. 183 King St.

Rahall, John, Tavern, King St. Upper Wards, res. King St.

Raine, James, Clerk, 234 King St., res. Chapel St.

Ralyae, Charles, Seaman, res. 8 Anson St.

Rames, C., Baker, 83 East Bay St., res. 83 East Bay St.

Ramsay, David, Lawyer, 62 Broad St.

Ramsay, John, Seaman, res. 15 Water St.

Randall, Daniel J., Engineer, res. Meeting St.

Rankin, George F., Clerk, 27 Hayne St., res. Charleston Hotel

Rankin, John, Barkeeper, res. Columbus St.

Rankin, Pulliam & Co., Dry Goods, 131 Meeting St.

Rankin, W. D., Dry Goods, 131 Meeting St.

Ranser, James, Conductor, South Carolina Railroad, res. Hampden Court

Rantin, Richard, Turner, res. 24 Washington St.

Raoul, Alfred, Physician, 41 Broad St., res. Wentworth St.

Rapp, James, Engineer, South Carolina Railroad, res. America St.

Ravenel & Co., Factors & Commission Merchants, 16 East Bay St.

Ravenel & Huger, Dry Goods, 12 & 14 East Bay St.

Ravenel, A. T., Factor, 16 East Bay St., res. 2 East Battery St.

Ravenel, Alfred, Clerk, East Bay St., res. Logan St.

Ravenel, Daniel, President, Planters & Mechanics Banks, res. 23 East Battery St.

Ravenel, Eliza, Mrs., res. 58 Broad St.

Ravenel, F. G., Factor, 16 East Bay St., res. 2 East Battery St.

Ravenel, Henry, President, Union Bank, res. 114 Tradd St.

Ravenel, J. & S. P., Factors & Commission Merchants, 22 East Bay St.

Ravenel, James, Factor, 22 East Bay St., res. Water St.

Ravenel, S. P., Factor, 22 East Bay St., res. Water St.

Ravenel, S. T., Physician, res. cr. South Bay & East Battery Sts.

Ravenel, William, Commission Merchant, 16 East Bay St., res. 11 East Bay St.

Raymond, Henry H., Lawyer, 21 Broad St., res. cr. Pitt & Montague Sts.

Read, J. R., Laces, etc., 237 King St., res. 249 King St.

Read, W. W. & J. R., Laces & Embroideries, 237 King St.

Read William W., Laces, etc., 237 King St., res. Lowell, Mass.

Rebb, Lewis, Carpenter, res. 25 Bull St.

Redfern, Ann S., Miss, res. Cannon St.

Redmond, Edward, Rigger, res. 5 Pinckney St.

Reed, Andrew, Wood Factor, Bennett's Wharf, res. Rutledge St.

Reed, Isaac, Carpenter, res. Coming St.

Reed, J. P., Dry Goods, King St., Ward 6

Reed, William, Rigger, 79 East Bay St., res. Church St.

Reeder & DeSaussure, Factors & Commission Merchants, Adger's North Wharf

Reeder, Oswell, Factor, Adger's North Wharf, res. King St., Ward 8

Reeder, W. B., Clerk, Adger's North Wharf, res. 86 Wentworth St.

Reedy, Frederick, Blacksmith, 24 Wentworth St., res. 24 Wentworth St.

Reeves, Matthew M. S., Professor of Music, res. Warren St.

Reeves, Solomon L., Carpenter, 184 Meeting St., res. Reid St.

Reeves, William, Laborer, res. Washington St.

Reid, Andrew, Factor, Bennett's Wharf, res. Charlotte St.

Reid, B. F., Clerk, 19 Hayne St., res. Victoria Hotel

Reid, Benjamin, Planter, Georgetown, res. Rutledge St.

Reid, George B., Cashier, Bank of South Carolina, res. 18 New St.

Reid, George, Bookkeeper, 38 East Bay St., res. 3 Logan St.

Reid, Harleston, Planter, Pee Dee, res. Charlotte St.

Reid, James, Drayman, res. Charlotte St.

Reid, John, Planter, Georgetown, res. Rutledge St.

Reid, R., Clerk, King St., res. 74 Wentworth St.

Reid, William, Rigger, res. 7 Atlantic St.

Reilly, Mitchell, Carriage Maker, 40 Wentworth St., res. 8 Horlbeck Alley

Reilly, T., Factor, 2 Southern Wharf, res. Mansion House

Reils, Benjamin, Grocer, cr. Rutledge & Montague St.

Reinhardt, Henry D., Surgical Instruments, 117 King St.

Remily, Amanda, Mrs., Tailoress, Bogard St.

Renken, John G., Baker, 97 King St., res. 97 King St.

Renneker, John H., Grocer, cr. King & Queen Sts., res. cr. Queen & Smith Sts.

Rennett, William, Dry Goods, 44 Anson St., res. 44 Anson St.

Renter, John, Shoemaker, 205 East Bay St., res. 205 East Bay St.

Reynolds & Co., Carriage Makers, 89 Meeting St.

Reynolds, George N., Jr., Carriages, 89 Meeting St., res. cr. John & Meeting Sts.

Reynolds, J. W., Bricklayers, res. Calhoun St.

Reynolds, R. F., Carriages, 89 Meeting St., res. cr. Lamboll & Legare Sts.

Rhett & Robinson, Factors & Commission Merchants, Atlantic Wharf

Rhett, B. S., Factor, Atlantic Wharf, cr. Meeting & Wentworth Sts.

Rhett, B. S., Jr., Clerk at Rhett & Robinson, res. Rutledge St.

Rhett, Barnwell, Lawyer, 20 Broad St., res. Vanderhorst St.

Rhett, J. W., Factor, Atlantic Wharf, res. Rutledge St.

Rhett, Roland, Teller, Planters & Mechanics Bank, res. America St.

Rhett, William, Lawyer, 62 Broad St.
Rhodes, James, Shoemaker, 53 Broad St., res. Church St.
Rhodes, Sarah, Mrs., res. St. Philip St.
Ricahrd, Mary A., Mrs., Fruit, King St., Upper Ward
Rice, David B., res. Merchants Hotel
Rice, William, Judge, City Hall, res. 9 Lamboll St.
Rich, John, Wheelwright, res. Bogard St.
Richards, Charles, Grocer, cr. Queen & Smith Sts.
Richards, F., Merchant Tailor, 35 Broad St., res. 2 Bull St.
Richards, George R., Shipsmith, 130 East Bay St., res. 251 East Bay St.
Richardson & Brother, Locksmith & Bell Hangers, 89 Meeting St.
Richardson, C. B., Bell Hanger, 89 Meeting St., res. 12 Tradd St.
Richardson C. Y., Bell Hanger & Locksmith, 89 Meeting St.
Richardson, F. E., Lawyer, 49 Broad St.
Richardson, J. K., Mariner, res. 105 Meeting St.
Richland, W., Shoemaker, res. 9 Queen St.
Richon, Lewis, Sailmaker, South Atlantic Wharf, res. Concord St.
Rickborn, Harmon, Shoemaker, res. 9 Queen St.
Ricker, Hacker & Co., Car Builders, King St., Upper Ward
Ricker, Robert, Machinist, King St., res. Cannon St.
Riddell, Isaac S., Deputy Sheriff, City Hall, res. Trapmann St.
Ridgaway, J. L., Furnishing Store, under the Mills House
Riecke, George A., Clothing, East Bay St., res. East Bay St.
Riggs, John S., Harness Maker, 185 Meeting St., res. St. Philip St.
Riggs, John S., Jr., Broker & Auctioneer, 4 State St.
Riggs, Richard, Carpenter, res. Line St.
Riggs, W. C., Harness Maker, 185 Meeting St., res. St. Philip St.
Righton, J. M., Import Inspector, Custom House, res. 8 Bull St.
Rihall, James, Carpenter, res. Amherst St.
Riker, J., Car Builder, King St., Upper Ward, res. Cannon St.
Riker, Robert, Car Builder, Upper Wards, res. Cannon St.
Riley, Alexander, Molder, res. Concord St.
Riley, Francis W., Clerk, 257 King St., res. 257 King St.
Riley, Hugh, Gardener, res. 14 Pinckney St.
Riley, James, Laborer, res. Radcliffe St.
Riley, James, Laborer, res. Line St.
Riley, Michael, Bootmaker, res. 11 Anson St.
Riley, William, Blacksmith, res. Calhoun St.
Riley, William, Carpenter, res. Elliott St.
Riley, William, Carpenter, res. Radcliffe St.
Rincker, C. F., Physician, 104 King St., res. 104 King St.
Ring, Conrad, Agent, 297 King St., res. 30 Savage St.
Ring, David A., Merchant, King St., res. 30 Savage St.
Ripley, Samuel S., res. 7 Calhoun St.
Rippe, W., Grocer, 102 Tradd St., res. 102 Tradd St.
Risley, H. W., Druggist, 43 Hayne St., res. New York

Ritter, John, Tailor, 99 East Bay St., res. Franklin House
Ritty, George, Carpenter, res. 69 Anson St.
Rivers, Edward, Lawyer, 49 Broad St., res. Wragg's Square
Rivers, John E., Lawyer, 49 Broad St., res. Wragg's Square
Rivers, William J., Teacher, res. 22 Coming St.
Rivers, Winfield M., Teacher, res. 19 Smith St.
Roach, Edward, Bricklayer, res. 20 Mazyck St.
Roach, Edward, Drayman, res. McBride's Lane
Roach, Edward, Wharfinger, Atlantic Wharf, res. 11 Society St.
Roach, J. B., Clerk, 143 East Bay St., res. 20 Montague St.
Roach, W. F., Clerk at Holmes & Stoney's, res. 20 Wentworth St.
Roach, William, Bookkeeper at H. Missroon's, res. 11 Society St.
Roach, William, Clerk at H. Missroon's, res. 23 Society St.
Robb, James, res. 11 Archdale St.
Robb, William, Clerk, 264 King St., res. Percy St.
Robb, William, Rice Mills, Gadsden's Wharf, res. 2 Rutledge St.
Roberts, Albert, Printer, 3 Broad St., res. 26 Church St.
Roberts, Isaac, Mattress Maker, res. President St.
Roberts, James F., Outdoor Clerk, Peoples Bank, res. 122 Wentworth St.
Roberts, James S., Teller, Bank of South Carolina, res. 18 John St.
Roberts, Samuel T., Blacksmith, res. 44 Coming St.
Roberts, Stephen, Bookkeeper, 21 Broad St., res 8 Vernon St.
Roberts, W., Sailor, res. 7 Linguard St.
Roberts, William, Jr., Clerk, 265 King St. res. American Hotel
Robertson & Blacklock, Factors & Commission Merchants, 18 East Bay St.
Robertson, Alexander, Factor, 18 East Bay St., res. East Battery St.
Robertson, Ann, Mrs., res. Vanderhorst St.
Robertson, Charles, Clerk at Robert Mure's, res. 37 Church St.
Robertson, Francis M., Physician, Pinckney St., res. Pinckney St.
Robertson, I. R., Clerk, 143 Meeting St., res. Maiden Lane
Robertson, James L., Dry Goods, 281 King St., res. 249 King St.
Robertson, Lewis F., Teller, Bank of South Carolina, res. 43 East Bay St.
Robertson, Stephen A., Coach Maker, 142 Meeting St., res. Henrietta St.
Robins, A., Fruiterer, 9 & 70 Market St., res. 70 Market St.
Robins, Franklin, Clerk, 211 King St., res. 22 Wentworth St.
Robinson & Thompson, Dry Goods, 281 King St.
Robinson, C., Mrs., res. 15 State St.
Robinson, Caldwell & Co., Commission Merchants,

North Atlantic Wharf
Robinson, Charles, Merchant, East Bay St., res. 37 Church St.
Robinson, E. D., Clerk at J. E., Adger's, res. 155 East Bay St.
Robinson, George, Factor, Fraser's Wharf, res. cr. Meeting & South Bay Sts.
Robinson, J. R., Commission Merchant, North Atlantic Wharf, res. Judith St.
Robinson, James L., Dry Goods, 281 King St., res. 249 King St.
Robinson, John, Clerk, 169 East Bay St., res. Judith St.
Robinson, John W., res. Nassau St.
Robinson, Joseph, Proprietor, Cotton Press, Anson St., res. Washington St.
Robinson, S. A., Outdoor Clerk, Bank of Charleston
Robinson, S. J., Mrs., Teacher, res. 7 John St.
Robinson, S. T., Jr., Clerk, North Atlantic Wharf, res. Judith St.
Robinson, W. J., Clerk, South Carolina Railroad, res. Radcliffe St.
Robinston, S. T., Commission Merchant, North Atlantic Wharf, res. Judith St.
Robson, James R., Factor, Atlantic Wharf, res. 36 Wentworth St.
Robson, Sarah, Mrs., res. 36 Wentworth St.
Rodrigues, A. B., Dentist, 101 Meeting St., res. 101 Meeting St.
Rodster, Abraham, Tailor, Broad St., res. Calhoun St.
Roempke, J., Mrs., res. 85 Tradd St.
Roessler, Frederick, Gunsmith, res. 20 St. Philip St.
Rogers, E. H. & Co., Factors & Commission Merchants, Adger's Wharf
Rogers, E. H., Factor, Adger's Wharf, res. King St., Ward 8
Rogers, E., Mrs., res. 6 Orange St.
Rogers, John F., Clerk, 31 King St., res. American Hotel
Rogers, John, Laborer, South Carolina Railroad, res. Line St.
Rogers, Lewis, Wheelwright, res. Warren St.
Rogers, S. W., Grocer, King St., Ward 8
Rogers, Thomas L., Clerk, Adger's Wharf, res. 43 Archdale St.
Rogers, Washington, Grocer, King St., res. St. Philip St.
Rogers, William, Bookkeeper, 11 East Bay St., res. 41 Tradd St.
Rohlfing, H., Shoemaker, res. 86 Meeting St.
Roland, Martin, Laborer, res. Hanover St.
Rollin, William, Wood Factor, McLeish's Wharf
Roman, P. B., Molder, res. cr. Beaufain & Coming St.
Romanier, James, Laborer, res. Vernon St.
Ronan, William, Druggist, King St., Ward 6
Roper, Benjamin D., Lawyer, St. Michael's Alley, res. 11 Meeting St.
Roper, R. W., Mrs., res. 30 Soceity St.
Roper, Richard, Factor, North Commercial Wharf, res. 27 Legare St.
Rose, A. G., President, Bank of Charleston, res. 9 Rutledge St.
Rose, E. H., Mrs., res. Ann St.

Rose, S. A., Mrs., res. 12 Stolls Alley
Rosis, Joseph, Cigars & Tobacco, 51 State St., res. 51 State St.
Ross, Ann, Mrs., res. 275 East Bay St.
Ross, James, Port Warden, 17 Exchange St., res. Legare St.
Ross, John, Millwright, res. Hampden Court
Ross, M., Coach Maker, cr. Wentworth & Meeting Sts.
Ross, Mary, Mrs., res. cr. George & Glebe Sts.
Rotereau, Jane, Mrs., res. 4 Stolls Alley
Rouhoe, James, Mariner, res. 7 Elliott St.
Roulain, Abraham, Coach Maker, 102 Meeting St., res. 5 Glebe St.
Roumeir, Frederick, Mariner, res. 5 Bedons Alley
Roumillat, A., Confectioners, 247 King St., res. 247 King St.
Roumillat, A. J. A., Clerk, 3 Broad St., res. Hanover St.
Roumner, H., Laborer, res. 14 Linguard St.
Rourk, Patrick, Laborer, res. 50 State St.
Rouse, William M., Jeweller, 70 Meeting St., res. 70 Meeting St.
Row, Franklin, Bookkeeper, East Bay St., res. 6 Water St.
Rowand, Robert, res. 14 Savage St.
Rowe, G. W., Printer, 29 Pinckney St., res. Amherst St.
Roweson, J., Carpenter, res. Coming St.
Royals, Bartholomew, res. 48 Wentworth St.
Roye, M., Tinsmith, 7 Queen St., res. 7 Queen St.
Ruddick, Theodore, Teacher of Music, res. 23 Pinckney St.
Ruff, O. C., Druggist, 153 Meeting St., res. American Hotel
Rung, John, Grocer, cr. Cannon & Smith Sts.
Runken, John S., Proprietor, French Coffee House, East Bay St.
Rush, Frederick, Blacksmith, 142 Meeting St., res. 35 Society St.
Rusk, John, Ship Carpenter, res. 7 Calhoun St.
Russell, Albert, Carpenter, res. 4 Atlantic St.
Russell, Charles B., Carpenter, res. America St.
Russell, John, Books & Stationery, 251 King St., res. 17 Smith St.
Russell, John, Carpenter, res. 19 State St.
Russell, M. F., Mrs., Boarding House, 86 Broad St.
Russell, T. M., Druggist, Broad St., res. Tradd St.
Russell, Thomas, Watchmaker, 238 King St., res. 27 Broad St.
Russell, William M., Engraver, cr. Hasell & King Sts., res. Tradd St.
Ruth, James, Drayman, res. 10 Savage St.
Rutjes, Adolphus J., Confectioner, 174 King St., res. 174 King St.
Rutledge, Benjamin H., Lawyer, 48 Broad St., res. Mansion House
Rutledge, Edward, Clerk, 16 East Bay St., res. 101 Tradd St.
Rutledge, H. B., Mrs., res. 101 Tradd St.
Rutledge Hugh, Physician, 25 Lynch St., res. 25 Lynch St.
Rutledge, James R., Bookkeeper, Southwest Railroad

Bank, res. Smith St.
Rutledge, John, Planter, res. Smith St.
Rutledge, William, Laborer, res. 14 Pinckney St.
Ryan, Henry, Printer, Standard Office, 117 East Bay St.
Ryan, John E., Carpenter, res. 7 Friend St.
Ryan, John S., Broker & Auctioneer, 22 Broad St., res. 19 King St.
Ryan, Matthew, Carpenter, South Carolina Railroad, res. President St.
Ryan, Michael, Laborer, res. 5 Pinckney St.
Ryan, Michael, Laborer, res. 9 Marsh St.
Ryan, O. M., res. 11 Archdale St.
Ryan, Patrick, Guardman, res. 63 Tradd St.
Ryan, Thomas & Son, Brokers & Commission Agents, res. 12 State St.
Ryan, Thomas, Broker & Auctioneer, 12 State St., res. 11 Archdale St.
Ryan, Thomas C., Clerk, 141 Meeting St., res. 42 Church St.
Ryan, Thomas E., Bookkeeper, 85 Meeting St., res. 11 Archdale St.
Ryan, W. K., Factor & Commission Merchant, Boyce & Co. Wharf, res. 64 King St.
Ryan, William B., Broker, 12 State St., res. 29 Archdale St.
Ryan, William, Laborer, res. 4 Linguard St.
Ryan, William, Printer, 117 East Bay St., res. 32 Tradd St.
Sachtelben, Augustus, Teacher, res. Tradd St.
Sage, William M., China & Glass Ware, 145 Meeting St., res. American Hotel
Sahlman, Herman, Grocer, 2 Middle St., res. Laurens St.
Salas, F., Clerk, Hall & Co., res. cr. King & Wentworth Sts.
Salas, R., Commission Merchant, Central Wharf, res. Planters Hotel
Salcedo, Augustus, Cigar & Tobacco Dealer, Meeting St., opposite South Carolina Institute Hall
Salinas, A. J., Broker & Auctioneer, 1 State St., res. cr. King & Wentworth Sts.
Salter, Thomas R., Mrs., res. Mary St., near Meeting St.
Saltus, F. W., Clerk, John Fraser & Co., res. 25 Mazyck St.
Saltus, Philip, Drayman, res. Duncan St.
Salver, William, Shoemaker, 11 Anson St., res. 11 Anson St.
Salvo, F., Madame, Dry Goods, King St., near Spring St.
Salvo, Francis, Cabinet Maker, South Carolina Railroad, res. Vanderhorst St.
Salvo, James, Boots & Shoes, 74 King St., res. 74 King St.
Salvo, James, Clerk, 110 East Bay St., res. 88 King St.
Salvo, P. A., Tailor, King St., near Spring St.
Salvo, William M., South Carolina Railroad Office
Sampleton, John, res. cr. John & Meeting Sts.
Sampson, Joseph, Bookkeeper at Capers & Hayward, res. 98 Tradd St.
Sampson, Samuel, Deputy Sheriff, City Hall, res. 7 Wentworth St.
Samuel, Moses, Tailor, 340 King St., res. 340 King St.

Sanders, Augustus, Carpenter, res. 32 Wentworth St.
Sanders, F. A., Factor, Accommodation Wharf, res. Charleston Hotel
Sanders, John, Bricklayer, res. Washington St.
Sanders, Joseph A., Bricklayer, res. Pitt St.
Sanders, Joseph T., Bricklayer, res. 9 Bull St.
Sanders, Mark, Mariner, res. cr. Rutledge & Queen Sts.
Sanders, Samuel, Barber, Church St., res. Church St.
Sanders, Thomas, Factor, East Bay St., res. Washington St.
Sanders, Thomas M., Bricklayer, res. Calhoun St., Ward 6
Sanders, William, Carpenter, res. Cannon St.
Sargent, Mary A., Mrs., res. Morris St.
Sass, J. K., Cashier, Bank of Charleston, res. 34 Society St.
Savage, George, Clerk, 211 King St., res. 34 Savage St.
Savage, Sarah, Mrs., res. cr. Broad & Savage Sts.
Scanlan, B., Mrs., res. 24 Queen St.
Scanlan, Charles, Shipsmith, 9 Pritchard St., res. 13 John St.
Scanlan, E., Blacksmith, Marsh St., res. America St.
Scanlan, M., Porter, King St., res. 19 Princess St.
Scanlan, Patrick, Watchman, Union Wharf, res. 58 Wentworth St.
Scanlan, Thomas, Laborer, res. 14 Pinckney St.
Schachte, John, Tavern, cr. King & Vanderhorst Sts.
Schackelford, Edward, Engineer, res. 9 College St.
Schake, D. H., Grocer, cr. King & Line Sts.
Schalken, Henry, Grocer, 9 Pinckney St., res. 9 Pinckney St.
Scheer, Bernard, Jeweller, 328 King St., res. Broad St.
Schirmer, Jacob F., Cooper, North Commercial Wharf, res. King St.
Schiver, M. C., Mrs., res. 44 Queen St.
Schmeitzer, Charles G., Butcher, res. Ashley St.
Schmeitzer, Otto, Jeweller, 333 King St., res. Broad St.
Schmidt, J. M., Clerk, Southern Wharf, res. King St.
Schmidt, John, Grocer, cr. Marsh & Inspection Sts.
Schnaars, D., Clerk, 67 Tradd St., res. 67 Tradd St.
Schnibbe, C., Tavern, 9 Elliott St., res. 9 Elliott St.
Schnibbe, H., Tavern, 3 Elliott St., res. 3 Elliott St.
Schnierle, John, Planter, res. 21 Pitt St.
Schoen, Johanna, Mrs., Milliner, 147 King St., res. 147 King St.
Schouboe, Frederick M., Police Officer, City Hall, res. 41 Society St.
Schreiber, Gottlett, Butcher, res. St. Philip St.
Schreiner, J. F., res. 124 King St.
Schriner, John H., Bacon, Pork, etc., South Atlantic Wharf, res. 237 East Bay St.
Schroder, C., Grocer, cr. Beaufain & Coming Sts.
Schroder, H., Grocer, 85 Queen St., res. 85 Queen St.
Schroder, H. W., Carpenter, res. 12 Mazyck St.
Schroder, H. W., St. Michael's Alley, res. 24 George St.
Schroder, John C. & Co., Grocers, cr. America & Reid Sts.
Schroder, Thomas E., Fruiterer, 62 Meeting St., res. 62 Meeting St.
Schroder, William H., Clerk, Work House, res. Work

House
Schuld, C., Grocer, 143 Queen St., res. 143 Queen St.
Schultz, Charles, Clerk, 198 King St., res. Church St.
Schultz, Herman, Lumber Factor, 100 Beaufain St., res. 100 Beaufain St.
Schwing, Sophia, Mrs., Saleswoman, res. 33 St. Philip St.
Scott, Benjamin F., Factor, 15 Vanderhorst's Wharf, res. 18 Coming St.
Scott, Catherine, Mantuamaker, res. 54 Anson St.
Scott, Deveaux & Heyward, Factors & Commission Merchants, 15 Vanderhorst's Wharf
Scott, John D., Clothing, 199 King St., res. New York City
Scott, M. B., Mrs., res. 44 Society St.
Scott, Margaret, Mrs., res. 7 Pinckney St.
Scott, Mary, Mantuamaker, res. 14 Marsh St.
Scott, Sarah Ann, Seamstress, res. 68 Anson St.
Scott, Thomas L., Carpenter, res. 68 Anson St.
Scriven, R. E., Commission Merchant, 62 East Bay St., res. 33 Meeting St.
Scrivener, John J., Engineer, res. Hanover St.
Scruggs, Drake & Co., Commission Merchants, North Atlantic Wharf
Scruggs, J. W., Commission Merchant, North Atlantic Wharf, res. Charleston Hotel
Seabrook, Arthur, res. Meeting St., near John St.
Seabrook, Edward, Physician, 13 Bull St., res. 13 Bull St.
Seabrook, Ephraim, res. Pitt St., near Calhoun St.
Sebring, Edward, President, State Bank, res. Calhoun St.
Seedorf, John, Grocer, cr. State & Queen Sts.
Seigling, Henry, Agent, 227 King St., res. 227 King St.
Seignous, Charles, Coal Yard, East Bay St., res. 336 King St.
Seignous, Francis P., Coal Yard, East Bay St., res. Calhoun St.
Seigwald, John, Carpenter, res. Coming St.
Seiler, John, Bar Room, cr. King & Queen Sts.
Seimcke, J. E., Grocer, cr. Columbus & Meeting Sts.
Seixas, David C., Factor, Atlantic Wharf, res. 204 East Bay St.
Sergeant, George, Boots & Shoes, 89 Market St., res. 89 Market St.
Service, Susan, Mrs., res. 11 Friend St.
Seuder, John, Laborer, res. 74 Anson St.
Sexton, Ellen, Mrs., Dry Goods, 30 Anson St., res. 30 Anson St.
Sexton, J. M., Carpenter, res. Coming St.
Seyle, Charles C., Collector, 211 King St., res. 12 Bull St.
Seyle, J. H., Architect, 57 Broad St., res. cr. Bull & Smith Sts.
Seyle, P. W., Tavern, King St., Upper Ward
Seyle, Robert E., Clerk, 211 King St., res. 12 Bull St.
Seymour, Julia Ann, Mrs., Boarding House, 49 East Bay St.
Seymour, R. W., Lawyer, 58 Meeting St., res. 7 Franklin St.
Seymour, William, Tavern, Pond Point, res. 101 Queen St.

Shackelford, Frederick R., Factor, 1 Southern Wharf, res. 67 Tradd St.
Shackelford, James M., Commission Merchant, Exchange St., res. 43 Church St.
Shackelford, William G., Clerk, 33 Hayne St., res. 43 Market St.
Shackey, Robert, Mariner, res. 4 Elliott St.
Shaffer, Charles G., Printer, res. Rutledge St.
Shaffer, F. J., Lawyer, 20 Broad St., res. cr. Pitt & Calhoun Sts.
Shaffer, Frederick, Planter, res. cr. Pitt & Calhoun Sts.
Shane, Patrick, Coachman, res. 51 Meeting St.
Shankling, Augustus, Pastor, res. Broad St.
Shannon, Charles, Bookkeeper, Boyce's Wharf, res. St. Philip St.
Shannon, Michael, Watchman, U. S. Arsenal, res. President St.
Shannon, Patrick, Laborer, U. S. Arsenal, res. President St.
Shaw, Abisha, Wharf Builder, res. St. Philip St.
Shaw, James, House Furnishing Goods, 178 King St., res. 178 King St.
Shaw, John, Clerk, 218 King St., res. 91 Market St.
Shay, M., Laborer, res. America St.
Shea, Barton, Clerk, 36 East Bay St., res. 51 East Bay St.
Shecut, F. A., Bookkeeper at John Fraser & Co., res. 27 Pitt St.
Shecut, L. A., Bookkeeper, Central Wharf, res. 27 Pitt St.
Sheppard & McCreery, Dry Goods, 135 Meeting St.
Sheppard, John, Saddler, res. 34 Coming St.
Sheppard, Joseph, Dry Goods, 135 Meeting St., res. George St.
Sheppard, Thomas C., Wharfinger, Boyce's Wharf, res. 6 Charlotte St.
Sheppard, William A., Clerk, 219 King St., res. King St.
Sheppard, William, Clerk, 120 Meeting St., res. Rutledge St.
Sheppard, William H., Blacksmith, 40 Wentworth St., res. 41 Coming St.
Sherman, E., Saddler, cr. Meeting & Hasell Sts., res. Newark, N. J.
Shiffer, H. W., Indian Rubber Goods, 270 King St., res. Mills House
Shingler Brothers, Exchange Brokers, 9 Broad St.
Shingler, Pinckney, Broker, 9 Broad St., res. 105 Wentworth St.
Shingler, Thomas, Broker, 9 Broad St., res. 105 Wentworth St.
Shirrar, J. E., Clerk at E. H. Rodgers & Co., res. 8 Rutledge St.
Shirrar, John E., Grocer, East Bay St., res. 8 Rutledge St.
Shirrar, M., Clerk, W. C. Duke & Sons, 8 Rutledge St.
Shoen, David, Boot & Shoemaker, 36 Anson St., res. 36 Anson St.
Shokes, George, Engineer, res. 53 Coming St.
Shokes, George, Molder, res. Hanover St.
Shokes, Henry, Pump & Block Maker, res. Public Mall
Shokes, John, Engineer, South Carolina Railroad, res. Hampden Court

Shubrick, Edmund, res. 120 Tradd St.

Siddon, Lawrence L., Jeweller, 231 King St., res. 231 King St.

Sider, William J., Clerk, 257 King St., res. 318 King St.

Siegling, John, Jr., Lawyer, Court House Square, res. 227 King St.

Siegling, John, Music Store, 227 King St., res. 227 King St.

Sielaff, Charles W., Printer, res. 31 Coming St.

Sifly, Henry, res. 18 Friend St.

Sigwald, C. B., Boots & Shoes, King St., Upper Ward

Sigwald, Henry, Engineer, res. Hampden Court

Silcox, Daniel H., Furniture, 224 King St., res. Archdale St.

Silcox, James, Clerk, 211 King St., res. Montague St.

Silliman, Henry R., Clerk, 211 King St., res. Montague St.

Silvery, Joseph, Ship Carpenter, res. Alexander St.

Simes, George, Carpenter, res. Spring St.

Simms, Edward T., Clerk, cr. Hayne & Meeting Sts., res. 249 King St.

Simms, W. Gilmore, res. Smith St.

Simonds, A., Druggist, 153 Meeting St., res. Charleston Hotel

Simonds, James, Tailor, res. 6 Minority St.

Simonds, Ruff & Co., Druggists, 153 Meeting St.

Simons Brothers, Commission Merchants & Grocers, 169 East Bay St.

Simons, Caroline, Dressmaker, res. Morris St.

Simons, Harris, Factor, Adger's South Wharf, res. Lynch St.

Simons, Henry, Factor, Adger's Wharf, res. Lynch St.

Simons, Hume, Teacher, res. Warren St.

Simons, Isabella, Seamstress, res. Morris St.

Simons, John A., Clerk at Hall & Co., res. 270 King St.

Simons, John C., Paints, Oils, Etc, 226 King St., res. 11 Bull St.

Simons, John H., Factor, 20 Vanderhorst's Wharf, res. cr. Wentworth & Lynch Sts.

Simons, Joseph, Laborer, res. Line St.

Simons, Maria, Mrs., res. Wragg Square

Simons, Mordecai, Carpenter, res. Spring St.

Simons, N. L., Commission Merchant, 169 East Bay St., res. 26 Montague St.

Simons, R. W., Printer, 119 East Bay St., res. 4 Spring St.

Simons, Sedgwick, Commission Merchant, 169 East Bay St., res. 26 Montague St.

Simons, Thomas G. & Sons, Factors, 20 Vanderhorst's Wharf

Simons, Thomas G., Factor, 20 Vanderhorst's Wharf, res. 30 Bull St.

Simons, Thomas G., Jr., Factor, 20 Vanderhorst's Wharf, res. Smith St.

Simons, Thomas Y., Jr., Lawyer, Court House Square, res. 9 Savage St.

Simons, Thomas Y., Physician, 49 Tradd St., res. 49 Tradd St.

Simons, William, Drayman, res. Mary St.

Simons, William, Lawyer, 77 Broad St., res. 26 Montague St.

Simonton, Charles H., Lawyer, 44 Broad St., res. cr. John & Meeting Sts.

Simonton, J. R., Assistant Clerk, Bank of Charleston, res. 267 East Bay St.

Simpson, Catharine, Miss, res. 59 Wentworth St.

Sinclair, William, Planter, St. John's Parish, res. 24 South Bay St.

Singleton, Daniel, Speculator, res. cr. Hanover & Line Sts.

Singleton, James W., Clerk, 135 Meeting St.

Sires, Francis, Carpenter, res. Spring St.

Sires, Peter J., Bookkeeper, 145 East Bay St., res. Spring St.

Skahn, Pierce, Fruit, cr. King & John Sts.

Skehan, Michael, Clerk, 224 King St., res. Clifford St.

Skrine, Thomas C., Physician, 21 Hasell St., res. Church St.

Skrine, William A., Druggist, 277 King St., res. 226 King St.

Slager, Abraham, Clothing, cr. King & Line Sts.

Slater, Margaret, Mrs., res. 21 Society St.

Slaver, Catharine, Mrs., res. 37 State St.

Slawson, H., Collector, res. 8 Archdale St.

Sledge, Charles H., Coach Trimmer, res. cr. Beaufain & Coming Sts.

Sloman, Ann, Miss, Teacher of Music, res. 28 Meeting St.

Sloman, Eliza, Miss, Teacher of Music, res. 28 Meeting St

Sloman, John, res. 28 Meeting St.

Sloughton, John M., Tailor, Queen St., near King St.

Slyer, Claus, Carpenter, res. Archdale St.

Slyer, Henry, Carpenter, 6 Pritchard St., res. Line St.

Small, Jacob, Baker, 193 King St., res. 193 King St.

Small, John, Clerk, 137 Meeting St.

Small, John S., Clerk, 33 Hayne St., res. Liberty St.

Small, Robert, Collector, res. 16 Libery St.

Small, W. C., Clerk, 143 Meeting St., res. cr. Calhoun & Coming Sts.

Smith & Whilden, Books & Stationery, 229 King St.

Smith, A., Bootmaker, res. 34 South Bay St.

Smith, A. C., Cashier, Union Bank, res. 125 East Bay St.

Smith, A. P., Soda Water, 97 Meeting St., res. 97 Meeting St.

Smith, A. Sydney, Bookkeeper, Accommodation Wharf, res. Montague St.

Smith, Alexander, Dry Goods, 131 Meeting St., res. 20 Wentworth St.

Smith, Andrew, Butcher, res. Alexander St., Upper Ward

Smith, Angus, Rigger, res. 6 Whim's Court

Smith, Benjamin F., Paints, Oils, etc., cr. Washington & Calhoun Sts.

Smith, E. Benson, Clerk, 139 Meeting St.

Smith, E. D., Dry Goods, 131 Meeting St., res. 20 Wentworth St.

Smith, Edward, Clerk, Boyce & Co. Wharf, res. 8 Atlantic St.

Smith, Elifelet, Coach Trimmer, cr. Meeting & Wentworth Sts.

Smith, Eliza L., Mrs., res. 10 Wentworth St.
Smith, Elizabeth, Mrs., res. 15 Montague St.
Smith, Ensly M., Clerk, 139 Meeting St.
Smith, H. L., Clerk, 1 Hayne St.
Smith Henry A., Clerk, 216 King St.
Smith, Henry J., Painter, 181 Meeting St., res. 181 Meeting St.
Smith, Henry M., Pastor, Flynn's Church, res. Limehouse St.
Smith, Horace, Jr., Clerk, 1 Hayne St., res. Horlbeck Alley
Smith, J. A., Miss, res. 69 Broad St.
Smith, J. J. G., Dry Goods, 122 Meeting St., res. Charleston Hotel
Smith, J. L., Assistant Bookkeeper, 19 Hayne St., res. Chapel St.
Smith, James, Blacksmith, East Bay St., res. 41 Anson St.
Smith, James, Clerk of Weights & Measures, Market St., res. 32 Society St.
Smith, James E., Jr., Clerk at H. Missroon's, res. Horlbeck Alley
Smith, James E., Teller, Union Bank, res. 125 East Bay St.
Smith, John L., Millinery, 132 King St., res. 132 King St.
Smith, John, Porter, 147 Meeting St., res. King St.
Smith, Joseph, Painter, res. St. Philip St.
Smith, Joseph, res. Henrietta St.
Smith, Julius A., Clerk, 35 Hayne St., res. Horlbeck Alley
Smith, Julius C., Books & Stationery, 229 King St., res. 10 Wentworth St.
Smith, Middleton, Mrs., res. 34 South Bay St.
Smith, N. C., Grocer, 165 Hayne St., res. Charleston Hotel
Smith, O., Clerk, Hayne St., res. 45 Wentworth St.
Smith, P. A., Teacher, 54 Wentworth St., res. 54 Wentworth St.
Smith, P. B., Factor, East Bay St., res. Broad St.
Smith, P., Bookkeeper at P. T. Villepigue's, res. Broad St.
Smith, Pringle, Planter, Savannah River, res. 18 Meeting St.
Smith, Rebecca, Mrs., Teacher, res. 11 Price's Alley
Smith, Richard F., res. cr. Calhoun & Washington Sts.
Smith, Richard, Messenger of Council, res. Meeting St.
Smith, Robert, Mrs., Planter, Ashepoo, res. 18 Meeting St.
Smith, S. C., Clerk, 54 Broad St.
Smith, T. Ogier, Dry Goods, 41 Hayne St., res. 45 Wentworth St.
Smith, Theodore A., res. 10 Wentworth St.
Smith, Thomas B., Clerk, 122 Meeting St., res. 10 Beaufain St.
Smith, Thomas, Clerk, 17 Vendue Range, res. 28 Lightwood Alley
Smith, Thomas, Molder, res. cr. Beaufain & Coming Sts.
Smith, Thomas P., Dry Goods, 40 East Bay St., res. 82 Beaufain St.
Smith, Thomas, Plumber, 31 Broad St.
Smith, Thomas, Tavern, 12 Elliott St., res. 12 Elliott St.

Smith, W. B. & Co, Commission Merchants, 60 East Bay St.
Smith, W. B., Commission Merchants, 60 East Bay St.
Smith, William C., Clerk, 14 Hayne St., res. Charlotte St.
Smith, William, Engineer, res. Bogard St.
Smith, William H., res. Atlantic St.
Smith, William H., Wheelwright, res. cr. Washington & Calhoun Sts.
Smith, William J., Coastwise Inspector, Custom House, res. Rutledge St.
Smith, William K., Clerk, 257 King St., res. 11 Laurens St.
Smith, William R., Planter, Ashley River, res. 22 King St.
Smith, William, Rigger, res. 4 Laurens St.
Smith, William Rogers, Bookkeeper, 41 Hayne St., res. Wentworth St.
Smith, William, Turpentine, etc., East Bay St., res. Alexander St.
Smith, William W., Shipwright, res. Rutledge St.
Smith, William Walton, Clerk, Commercial Wharf, res. Anson St.
Smyser, Henry, Jr., Ship Joiner, 6 Pritchard St., res. 156 East Bay St.
Smyser, Henry, Ship Joiner, 6 Pritchard St., res. 156 East Bay St.
Smyth, E., Clerk, 145 East Bay St., res. State St.
Smyth, George, Porter at James E. Adger's
Snavely, John, res. 21 Pitt St.
Snow, J. J., Clerk, 11 Hayne St., res. 96 Meeting St.
Snowden, William D., Clerk, Vendue Range, res. Montague St.
Snowden, William E., Factor, 6 Southern Wharf, res. 257 East Bay St.
Snowden, William T., Cotton Factor, 6 Southern Wharf, res. 257 East Bay St.
Soheke, George H., Clerk, Post Office, res. 49 Broad St.
Solle, Arthur, Clerk, East Bay St., res. cr. Bull & Pitt Sts.
Solle, H. J., Shipping Clerk at Gibbs & Battersby, res. Bull St.
Solle, Henry, Factor, East Bay St., res. cr. Bull & Pitt Sts.
Somger, Henry, Porter, 165 Meeting St., res. Bedons Alley
Sommers, E., Dry Goods, 33½ King St., res. 334 King St.
Spady, S. G., Clerk, King St., res. Mazyck St.
Sparks, Howell, Coach Blacksmith, Hasell St., res. Henrietta St.
Sparnick, Henry, Export Inspector, Custom House, res. Calhoun St.
Spear, James E., Jeweller, 235 King St., res. 235 King St.
Spear, Thomas S., Clerk, 235 King St., res. 235 King St.
Spear, W. W., Pastor, Grace Church, res. 260 King St.
Spearing, Mary, Nurse, res. Warren St.
Speght, F., Boot & Shoemaker, 59 Wentworth St.
Speissegger, T. C., Grocer, 17 Pinckney St., res. 17 Pinckney St.
Speissegger, T. W., Druggist, Columbus St., res. Columbus St.
Spelman, A., Grocer, cr. Market & Church St.

Spencer, Allen, Mrs., Boarding House, 277 King St.
Spencer, George W., Clerk, 250 King St., res. cr. Marsh & Laurens St.
Spencer, Seth, Broker & Auctioneer, 6 State St.
Spinck, Eady, Clerk, cr. Meeting & Society Sts.
Spinwell, A., Basket Maker, King St., Upper Wards
Sprague, E. N., Clerk, 2 Hayne St., res. Smith St.
Sprague, J. W., Grain Merchant, 2, 4, 6 & 8 Hayne St.
Spratt, L. W. & Co., Proprietors of Southern Standard, 115 East Bay St.
Spratt, Leonidas W., Lawyer & Editor, 115 East Bay St., res. 230 King St.
Sprigg, R., Livery Stables, King St., near Spring St.
Springer, Isaac, Pastor, res. 275 King St.
Springs, Richard, Dry Goods, 1 Hayne St., res. Charleston Hotel
St. Amand, Alexander, Clerk, 3 Hayne St., res. Cannon St.
St. Amand, M. W. J., Wines & Liquors, 179 East Bay St.
St. Amand, Mary, Mrs., res. Hasell St.
Stacey, M. P., Proprietor, Mercantile Agency, 54 Broad St., res. Charleston Hotel
Stackly, John, Dry Goods, King St., near Line St.
Staff, H. M., Tailor, 32 Broad St., res. Pavilion Hotel
Stafford, Elizabeth, Mrs., res. Ashley St.
Stafford, John F., Tinner, 5 State St., res. Rutledge St.
Stair, R. C., Clerk, 17 East Bay St, res. cr. King & Duncan St.
Stalham, Thomas B., Clerk, 211 King St., res. Beaufain St.
Stall, George, Clerk, 161 Meeting St., res. 9 Queen St.
Stanton, Frederick, Grocer, cr. Meeting & Society Sts.
Stanton, Valentine, Printer, 119 East Bay St., res. 26 Middle St.
Starr, Edwin P., res. 7 King St.
Steadman, Susan, Mrs., res. America St.
Steadman, Thomas, Mrs., res. cr. Coming & Cannon Sts.
Steadman, William B., Bookkeeper, 31 Hayne St., res. Drake St.
Steadman, William R., Clerk, res. Cannon St.
Steele, E. C., Physician, cr. Beaufain & Smith Sts.
Steele, James, Fruiterer, 18 Hasell St., res cr. Mary & Elizabeth Sts.
Steele, John N., Clerk, 231 King St., res. 31 Coming St.
Steele, Robert, Tailor, Duncan St., res. Duncan St.
Steele, W. N., Clerk, 225 King St., res. 31 Coming St.
Steele, Walter, Hats & Caps, 231 King St., res. Vanderhorst St.
Steen, John B., Mariner, res. 9 Stolls Alley
Steffens, G. W., Grocer, cr. King & Radcliffe Sts.
Steinberry, C., Grocer, 59 East Bay St., res. 59 East Bay St.
Steinman, Joshua, Wheelwright, Church St., res. Calhoun St.
Steinmeyer, John F., Carpenter, res. Calhoun St.
Steinmeyer, John F., Jr., Carpenter, res. Calhoun St.
Steinmeyer, John H., Jr., Bookkeeper, 100 Beaufain St.
Steinmeyer, John H., Steam Sawmill, 100 Beaufain St.
Stellass, H., Grocer, 47 Church St., res. 47 Church St.
Stellings, E. H., Grocer, 29 King St., res. 29 King St.

Stellys, T., Grocer, 53 Market St., res. 53 Market St.
Stemmenger, C., Grocer, cr. Church & Chalmers Sts.
Stemmerman, C., Clerk, 18 Bull St., res. 18 Bull St.
Stemmerman, H., Grocer, 18 Bull St., res. 18 Bull St.
Stenders, H., Dry Goods, King St., Ward 6
Stenhouse, Allen & Co., Commission Merchants, 7 Hayne St.
Stenhouse, E., Clerk, 1 Hayne St., res. 3 Laurens
Stenhouse, Thomas, Commission Merchant, 7 Hayne St., res. 3 Laurens St.
Stent, Caroline, Mrs., res. 21 King St.
Stenton, John, Drayman, res. 16 Mazyck St.
Stevens & Betts, Hardware Merchants, 80 East Bay St.
Stevens, C. H., Cashier, Planters & Mechanics Bank, East Bay St.
Stevens, Ebenezer, Agent, South Carolina Railroad, res. Laurens St.
Stevens, George, Hardware, 80 East Bay St., res. 49 Tradd St.
Stevens, Joel, Hardware, 80 East Bay St., res. 49 Tradd St.
Stevens, John, Tobacconist, King St., above Vanderhorst St.
Stevens, Joseph, Clerk, 189 King St., res. 33 St. Philip St.
Stevens, Sarah, Mrs., res. 31 Coming St.
Stevenson, W., Druggist, 23 Hayne St., res. Mills House
Stewart, Balfour H., Umbrellas, 160 King St., res. 160 King St.
Stewart, James, Factor, North Atlantic Wharf, res. 5 Meeting St.
Stewart, Jane, Mrs., res. 5 Greenhill St.
Stewart, Joseph, Tavern, 5 Market St., res. 5 Market St.
Stewart, Robert, Carpenter, res. St. Philip St.
Stewart, Samuel, Carpenter, res. 13 Henrietta St.
Stewart, W. J. H., Printer, 111 East Bay St., res. 22 Middle St.
Stewart, William, Mariner, res. Concord St.
Stewart, William, res. cr. King St. & Price's Alley
Stillman, Alfred R., Clerk, 211 King St., res. Beaufain St.
Stincken, M., Grocer, cr. Broad & Savage Sts.
Stinston, Thomas, Clerk, King St., res. 9½ Queen St.
Stites, Henry, Clerk, cr. Columbus & Meeting Sts.
Stock, John Y., Factor, North Atlantic Wharf, res. 11 Montague St.
Stock, N. Bowen, Clerk, North Atlantic Wharf, res. 11 Montague St.
Stocker, James M., Wharfinger, Palmetto Wharf, res. 200 East Bay St.
Stocker, John D., Clerk, 131 Meeting St., res. 200 East Bay St.
Stocker, Samuel H., Clerk, 135 Meeting St., res. 200 East Bay St.
Stocking, D. S., Grain Merchant, 8 East Bay St., res. cr. Meeting & Chalmer's Sts.
Stockman, A. L., Mrs., Dry Goods, King St., Ward 6
Stoddard, E. B. & Co., Boots & Shoes, 165 Meeting St.
Stoddard, Ezekiel B., Boots & Shoes, 165 Meeting St., res. Charleston Hotel
Stoddard, G. B., Stevedore, res. 7 Atlantic St.

Stoddard, Hartford, Boots & Shoes, 45 Hayne St., res. Charleston Hotel

Stoddard, John D., Clerk, 45 Hayne St., res. Charleston Hotel

Stoddard, Johnson & Co., Boots & Shoes, 45 Hayne St.

Stoddard, S. Bates, Clerk, 45 Hayne St., res. Charleston Hotel

Stogner, James, Factor & Commission Merchant, North Adger's Wharf

Stokes, E. R., Bookbinder, 104 Church St., res. 104 Church St.

Stolls, Elizabeth, Mrs., res. 12 Stolls Alley

Stone, Margaret, Miss, res. Mill St.

Stone, Peter C., Bookkeeper, 142 Meeting St., res. Victoria House

Stone, Richard G., China & Glassware, 149 Meeting St.

Stoney & Wiltberger, Druggists & Apothecaries, 245 King St.

Stoney, Christopher F., Physician & Druggist, 245 King St., res. 26 Hasell St.

Stoney, Elizabeth, Mrs., res. 26 Hasell St.

Stoney, John T., Physician, 269 East Bay St., res. 269 East Bay St.

Stoney, S. B., Cotton Factor, North Atlantic Wharf, res. 269 East Bay St.

Stoney, S. S., Factor, Accommodation Wharf, res. 269 East Bay St.

Stoney, Theodore, Factor, South Commercial Wharf, res. 36 Meeting St.

Stoppell, Gottfrey, Bootmaker, 126 Meeting St., res. 126 Meeting St.

Stoppleheim, Laurence C., Lumber Merchant, Rutledge St.

Storry, R. G., Clerk, 155 Meeting St.

Stowell, William, Machinist, res. Hanover St.

Stoy, John W., Commission Merchant, 234 King St., res. Mount Pleasant

Strain, William, Bookbinder, 59 Broad St., res. 4 Magazine St.

Stratford, T. G., Carpenter, 118 Wentworth St., near Lynch St.

Stratton, William, Baker, St. Philip St.

Strauss, Benhart, Dry Goods, 114 King St., res. 114 King St.

Strauss, George, Dry Goods, 114 King St., res. 114 King St.

Street & Brothers, Commission Merchants, 64 East Bay St.

Street, Gustavus, Commission Merchant, 64 East Bay St., res. 6 Society St.

Street, Henry, Commission Merchant, 64 East Bay St., res. 2 Atlantic St.

Street, Samuel A., Commission Merchant, 64 East Bay St., res. 6 Society St.

Stroble, B. M., Ship Grocer, 147 East Bay St., res. 6 Society St.

Stroble, Hayne, Superintendent, South Carolina Railroad, res. Rutledge St.

Stroggin, Edward B., Engineer, res. 3 Smith St.

Strohecker, Henry F., Hardware, 151 Meeting St., res. cr. Bull & Pitt Sts.

Strohecker, John P., Hardware, 273 King St., res. John St.

Strong, George, Carpenter, res. America St.

Stuart, Alexander A., Porter at Webb & Sages, res. 69 King St.

Stuart, Harper & Co., Commission Merchants, North Atlantic Wharf

Stuart, James P., Commission Merchant, North Atlantic Wharf, res. 5 Meeting St.

Stuart, William, Drayman, res. St. Philip St.

Sturges, James T., Bookkeeper, 21 Hayne St., res. 26 King St.

Sturges, Morgan R., Clerk, 21 Hayne St., res. 11 Hasell St.

Styles & Douglass, Painters, King St.

Styles, C. W., Painter, King St., res. Spring St.

Suares B., Clerk, 179 East Bay St., res. East Bay St.

Suares, Benjamin C., Tailor, 13 Middle St., res. 13 Middle St.

Suares, J. E., Furniture, 284 King St., res. 32 St. Philip St.

Subat, Frederick, Carpenter, res. St. Philip St.

Sullivan, H. W., Commission Merchant, North Atlantic Wharf, res. Church St.

Sullivan, James, Laborer, res. 14 Philadelphia St.

Sullivan, John S., Carpenter, res. 74 Tradd St.

Sullivan, L. A., Printer, 117 East Bay St., res. 13 Middle St.

Sullivan, Mary T., Mrs., res. 72 Anson St.

Sullivan, S. O., Mrs., res. cr. Coming & Green Sts.

Sullivan, Thomas, Laborer, res. cr. Coming & Green Sts.

Sulters, Thomas, Mariner, res. 2 Friend St.

Susdorff & Leiding, Fancy Goods, 141 Meeting St.

Susdorff, Gustavus, Fancy Goods, 141 Meeting St.

Sutton, Ambrose, Commission Merchant, 14 Central Wharf, res. Mansion House

Swasey, Alexander, Mariner, res. 22 Savage St.

Sweegan, Edward F., Commission Merchant, Central Wharf, res. Market St.

Sweeney, James, Ship Carpenter, res. 109 Church St.

Sweeney, John, Laborer, res. 14 Pinckney St.

Sweetman, W., Clerk, cr. King & Broad Sts.

Swift, John H., Civil Engineer, South Carolina Railroad, res. 6 State St.

Swinton, Thomas, Mariner, res. Meeting St., near John St.

Swinton, William H., Lumber Merchant, res. 28 Montague St.

Sylvester, Angewith, Laborer, res. 1 Hard Alley

Symes, J. T., Clerk, cr. Market & King Sts., res. 67 Beaufain St.

Symes, Theophilus P., Clerk, 211 King St., res. 67 Beaufain St.

Symmers, George, Clerk, 257 King St., res. 270 King St.

Symms, John H., Bricklayer, res. Hanover St.

Symms, Thomas B., Bricklayer, res. Hanover St.

Symons, John, Rigger, 6 Guignard St., res. 6 Guignard St.

Taber, William R., Jr., Lawyer, Mercury Office, res. Coming St.

Taber, William R., Teller, Bank of the State of South Carolina, res. Coming St.

Taft, A. R., Commission Merchant, 141 East Bay St., res. 29 Laurens St.

Taft, Davis, Boots & Shoes, 141 Meeting St., res. American Hotel

Tagliorani & Guerorsch, Fruit, 75 Market St.

Tagliorani, Nicholas, Fruit, 75 Market St., res. 75 Market St.

Talmadge, John A., Dauguerean Artist, 273 King St.

Tamplet, Charles D., Clerk, 39 Hayne St., res. Pavilion Hotel

Tannlunson, Aaron, Upholsterer, 170 King St., res. Pavilion Hotel

Tarvel, B. V., Carpenter, res. America St., near King St.

Tarvel, L. D., Carpenter, res. American St., near King St.

Tarvel, Richard A., News Reporter, res. 8 Pritchard St.

Tarvo, Augustus, res. 200 East Bay St.

Tate, Emma, Miss, res. 18 Princess St.

Taylor, Henry P., res. Smith St.

Taylor, Isaac, Colored, Tailor, 41 Society St., res. 30 Society St.

Taylor, J. D., res. 43 East Bay St.

Taylor, J. M., Military Goods, 225 King St.

Taylor, James H., Commission Merchant & Insurance Agent, 127 East Bay St., res. 7 Rutledge St.

Taylor, James, Laborer, res. Columbus St.

Taylor, John, Boots & Shoes, 241 King St., res. 241 King St.

Taylor, Joseph, Conductor, South Carolina Railroad, res. 43 St. Philip St.

Taylor, Mary, Mrs., res. 117 Queen St.

Taylor, Robert, Bookkeeper, 40 East Bay St., res. 37 Church St.

Taylor, Thomas B., Dry Goods, 243 King St., res. 297 King St.

Taylor, Thomas, Planter, res. cr. Calhoun & East Bay Sts.

Taylor, William M., Factor, 13 Southern Wharf, res. 58 Meeting St.

Tea, John, res. cr. Woolf & America Sts

Teague, Isaac N., Bookkeeper, 257 King St., res. King St., Ward 7

Tenket, Isabella, Mrs., res. 7 Minority St.

Tennant, Charles, Brick Mason, 112 Wentworth St.

Tennant, Gilbert H., Hardware, 35 Hayne St.

Tennant, William, Planter, res. Calhoun St.

Tenpenny, James, Laborer, res. 124 Church St.

Teppe, Frederick, Clerk, 257 King St., res. St. Philip St.

Teppe, William, Constable, res. St. Philip St., Ward 6

Teppe, William, Jr., Clerk, Broad St., res. St. Philip St.

Terry, Joseph, Tailor, Anson St., res. Anson St.

Thackman, F. Portelle, Clerk, 21 Broad St., res. Spring St.

Thames, Alfred, Clerk, 248 King St., res. St. Philip St.

Thames, John A., Clerk, 248 King St., res. St. Philip St.

Thames, John E., Clerk, 248 King St., res. St. Phlip St.

Tharin, Edward C., Inspector, 14 Vendue Range, res. America St.

Tharin, Joseph, Tailor, Calhoun St., res. Spring St.

Tharin, Marion, Finisher, res. America St., Ward 7

Tharin, Robert S., Teacher, 273 King St., res. America St.

Thauss, William, Gas Fitter, Church St., res. 345 King St.

Thauss, William, Mrs., Millinery, 345 King St., res. 345 King St.

Thayer, Dewing & Co., Fancy Goods, 149 Meeting St.

Thayer, Ebenezer, Teacher, Free School, res. 20 Mazyck St.

Thayer, Emory, Fancy Goods, 149 Meeting St.

Thayer, Robert, Mariner, res. 33 St. Philip St.

Thayer, T. Heyward, Exchange Broker, State St.

Thayer, William, Teller, State Bank, res. Anson St.

Thee, John H., Porter, 81 East Bay St., res. America St.

Theirs, Simeon, Clerk, res. 82 Beaufain St.

Thierman & Pringle, Factors & Commission Merchants, 12 Vanderhorst's Wharf

Thierman, H., Factor & Commission Merchant, 12 Vanderhorst's Wharf

Thomas, Alfred, Pressman, 111 East Bay St., res. 9 Cumberland St.

Thomas, C. C., Blacksmith, 5 Chalmers St., res. 3 Inspection St.

Thomas, Christopher, Coachmaker, 9 Inspection St.

Thomas, Henry, Tavern, 11 Elliott St., res. 11 Elliott St.

Thomas, Stephen, Bookkeeper, 26 Hayne St., res. 6 Pinckney St.

Thomas, Stephen, Clerk, 250 King St., res. 9 Wentworth St.

Thomas, Stephen, Jr., Clerk, King St., res. 6 Pinckney St.

Thomas, William, Bookkeeper, 256 King St., res. 256 King St.

Thomas, William, Stonecutter, res. 11 Horlbeck Alley

Thomlinson, Robert, Saddlery, 157 Meeting St., res. New York

Thompson, Alexander, Rigger, 6 Guignard St., res. 8 Elliott St.

Thompson, D., Carpenter, res. 83 Queen St.

Thompson, Frederick, Furniture, 126 King St., res. 126 King St. .

Thompson, George, Bricklayer, res. 10 Glebe St.

Thompson, Isabel, Mrs., res. 1 New St.

Thompson, James A., Bookkeeper, 32 Vendue Range, res. 78 Meeting St.

Thompson, James C., Printer, Mercury Office, res. 31 Coming St.

Thompson, John M., Dry Goods, 281 King St., res. Merchants Hotel

Thompson, John, Seed Store, 264 King St., res. Percy St.

Thompson, Ninian, res. 2 Charlotte St.

Thompson, Paul S., Factor & Commission Merchant, 5 Adger's North Wharf

Thompson, Robert H., Bookkeeper, 141 Meeting St.

Thompson, Sarah, Mrs., res. 8 Princess St.

Thompson, Thomas, Laborer, res. 11 Horlbeck Alley

Thompson, William B., Tavern, 41 Wentworth St., res. 41 Wentworth St.

Thompson, William, res. 10 Glebe St.

Thompson, William, Tavern, 7 Elliott St., res. 7 Elliott St.
Thrower, Catherine, Mrs., res. 27 Beaufain St.
Thurston, E. M., Clerk, 18 East Bay St., res. 107 Meeting St.
Tiedeman & Carsten, Grain Merchants, cr. Radcliffe & Coming St.
Tiedeman, Harmon, Carpenter, res. Warren St.
Tiedeman, Otto, Grocer, cr. Calhoun & Washington St.
Tiencken, John, Grocer, cr. Amherst & America Sts.
Tilghman, J. H., Clerk, 215 King St.
Timbroecks, Emily, res. 12 Cumberland St.
Timmons, A. G., Cotton Shipper, res. 4 Smith's Lane
Timmons, George, res. 4 Smith's Lane
Tinsley, Samuel, Seaman, res. Reid St.
Tobias & Sons, Brokers & Auctioneers, cr. East Bay St. & Vendue Range
Tobias, A., Auctioneer, Vendue Range, res. 96 Wentworth St.
Tobias, Augustus L., President, South Carolina Insurance Co., res. Ashley St.
Tobias, C. H., Clerk, 141 Meeting St., res. Magazine St.
Tobias, J. L., Auctioneer, Vendue Range, res. 96 Wentworth St.
Tobias, S. J., Commission Merchant, Vendue Range, res. Montague St.
Tobias, T. J., Stock Broker, 86 East Bay St., res. 22 Wentworth St.
Tobias, V. J., Lawyer, 30 Broad St., res. Magazine St.
Tobin, John, Clerk, 29 Hayne St., res. State St.
Tobin, Richard, Farmer, res. Amherst St.
Tobin, S. A., Clerk, 179 East Bay St., res. Merchants Hotel
Togno, -----, Madame, Teacher, res. 47 Tradd St.
Tohanning, F., Clerk, 13 Hayne St., res. 13 Hayne St.
Tohey & Coates, Tavern, 11 Elliott St.
Tohey, Patrick, Tavern, 11 Elliott St., res. 11 Elliott St.
Tolk, Charles, Grocer, 100 Calhoun St.
Tolla, John, Laborer, res. Mary St.
Tomey, William, Wheelwright, 4 Cumberland St., res. 12 Water St.
Tomlinson, Lawrence, Clerk, 165 Meeting St.
Toomer, E. P., Clerk, 19 Hayne St., res. 21 Bull St.
Toomer, H., Mrs., res. Judith St.
Toomer, H. V., Physician, Chapel St., res. Elizabeth St.
Toomer, Lawrence, Planter, res. Ashley St.
Torlay, John B., Coach Trimmer, 40 Wentworth St., res. 17 Beaufain St.
Torlay, Joseph, Painter, res. Cannon St.
Torre, A. Della, Steam Sawmill, Washington St., res. Aiken's Row
Torre, R. Della, Steam Sawmill, Washington St., res. Wragg Square
Tourin, Joseph, Clerk, Vendue Range, res. Meeting St.
Tous, John, Grocer, Beaufain St., res. Beaufain St.
Trace, William, Carpenter, res. Spring St.
Tracey, Maurice, Printer, 117 East Bay St., res. City Hotel
Trapier, Paul, Pastor, Calvary Church, res. 37 Meeting St.

Trapier, William, Planter, Georgetown, res. cr. Meeting & Charlotte Sts.
Trapman, W. H., Commission Merchant, 20 East Bay St., res. 100 Broad St.
Trapmann, Louis, Commission Merchant, 20 East Bay St., res. 100 Broad St.
Trenholm, Charles L., Commission Merchant, res. 18 Smith St.
Trenholm, George A., Factor, Central Wharf, res. Rutledge St.
Trescott, George, Clerk, East Bay St., res. 19 Archdale St.
Trescott, George E., Medical Student, res. 4 Anson St.
Trescott, Henry, Cashier, State Bank, res. 4 Anson St.
Triest, John, Laborer, res. 10 Bedons Alley
Triest, Joseph, Clothing, 386 King St., res. 42 Church St.
Triest, Joseph, Druggist, 368 King St., res. 42 Calhoun St.
Triest, Maer, Bookkeeper, 216 King St.
Troche, Caroline, Mrs., res. 34 Queen St.
Trott, E. M., Mrs., res. 71 King St.
Trott, W. G., Druggist, cr. King & Broad Sts.
Trou, A. W., Mrs., Milliner, 187 King St., res. 187 King St.
Trouche, J., Clerk, North Commercial Wharf, res. 34 Queen St.
Troudman, Joseph, res. 55 Church St.
Troussel, John J., Taxidermist, res. Spring St.
Trout, Thomas & Co., Commission Merchants, 112 East Bay St.
Trout, Thomas B., Commission Merchant, Union Wharf, res. 94 Wentworth St.
Trout, Thomas, Commission Merchant, 112 East Bay St., res. 94 Wentworth St.
Trout, William, Clerk, 112 East Bay St., res. 94 Wentworth St.
Trumbo, Columbus C., Brick Mason, res. 55 Tradd St.
Tully, Thomas, Laborer, Custom Hosue, res. 3 Henrietta St.
Tully, Thomas R., Pastry Cook, res. 40 Queen St.
Tunnelly, William, Dry Goods, 106 King St., res. 106 King St.
Tunno, Matthew, Clerk, North Commercial Wharf, res. cr. East Bay & Amherst Sts.
Tunno, William, Factor, North Commercial Wharf, res. East Bay St.
Tupper, C. A., Clerk, 186 King St., res. 180 King St.
Tupper, F., Bookkeeper at T. Tupper & Sons, res. 52 Tradd St.
Tupper, G., Clerk at T. Tupper & Sons, res. 52 Broad St.
Tupper, James, Lawyer & Master in Equity, 52 Broad St.
Tupper, Samuel Y., President, Fireman's Insurance Company, res. 60 Church St.
Tupper, T. & Son, Commission Merchants, Brown's Wharf
Tupper, Tristam, Commission Merchant, Brown's Wharf, res. 52 Tradd St.
Tupper, Tristam, Jr., Commission Merchant, Brown's Wharf, res. 52 Tradd St.
Turnbull, Andrew, Planter, res. 14 Meeting St.

Turnbull, Ann, Mrs., Tailoress, 5 Marsh St.
Turnbull, J., res. 22 Water St.
Turnbull, R. J., Mrs., res. 1 Logan St.
Turnbull, William W., Bookkeeper, 146 Meeting St.
Turner, Margaret, Mrs., cr. Blake & Anson Sts.
Turner, Richard, Ship Carpenter, res. Woolf St.
Tweed, Ellen, Mrs., Teacher, res. Charlotte St.
Twohill, Daniel, Dry Goods, 19 Anson St., res. 19 Anson St.
Twohill, John, Boiler Maker, Hasell St., res. Hasell St.
Tylee, N., Jr., Clerk, South Carolina Railorad, res. 34 Chalmers St.
Tylee, N., Ship Chandler, 123 East Bay St., res. 34 Chalmers St.
Ufferhardt & Campsen, Dry Goods, 140 King St.
Ufferhardt, William, Dry Goods, 140 King St., res. 140 King St.
Ufferholoh, Charles, Carpenter, Coming St., res. Coming St.
Ulmo, P. H., Ship Carpenter, res. Amherst St.
Unfal, Charles, Tailor, 39 Broad St.
Utes, John, Printer, 119 East Bay St., res. 115 King St.
Valentine, H., Wharfinger, Brown's Wharf, res. 148 Meeting St.
Valentine, J. D., Clerk at Gibbes & Battersby's, res. 148 Meeting St.
Valentine, Samuel, res. 148 Meeting St.
Van Dohlen, Albert, Grocer, State St., res. 88 Anson St.
Vanderclipp, Frederick, Farmer, res. Bogard St.
Vanderhorst, Elias, Planter, Ashepoo, res. cr. Chapel & Alexander Sts.
Vanderhorst, Martha, Colored, Pasty Cook, 117 King St.
Vanderpool, Lyman, Blacksmith, 40 Wentworth St.
Vanika, Henry, Carpenter, res. King St.
Vanness, Joel S., Bookkeeper, 40 Wentworth St., res. 51 Tradd St.
Vannoy, J. A., Clerk, 149 Meeting St., res. Charleston Hotel
VanWinkle, John, Hardware, 308 King St., res. 63 Coming St.
Vardell, Susan, Mrs., res. Vanderhorst St.
Varner, Henry, res. 28 Mazyck St.
Venning, David B., Clerk, East Bay St., res. 16 Society St.
Venning, Henry, Lumber Merchant, Gadsden's Wharf, res. Society St.
Venning, Jonah M., Wood Factor, Gadsden's Wharf, res. 15 Beaufain St.
Vente, E., Physician, 15 Beaufain St., res. 15 Beaufain St.
Vermillion, John, Clerk at H. F. Baker & Co., res. Washington St.
Vernon, Henry, Carpenter, res. cr. Cannon & Ashley Sts.
Vernon, William H., Bookkeeper, 37 East Bay St., res. 99 East Bay St.
Veronee & Brother, Stoves & Tinware, 63 State St.
Veronee, G. H., Tinner, 63 State St., res. 29 Cumberland St.
Veronee, Samuel, Bookkeeper, South Carolina Railroad, res. Line St.

Veronee, William, Tinner, 63 State St., res. 29 Cumberland St.
Verree, Eliza, Miss, Dressmaker, 77 King St.
Vicar, William, Grocer, cr. America & Reid Sts.
Vidall, Lewis, res. 23 Middle St.
Videll, Lewis, Jr., Clothing, 303 King St., res. American Hotel
Vierfelder, Sarah J., Mrs., Boarding House, 312 King St.
Vierhon, Albert, Watchmaker, 256 King St., res. 66 Broad St.
Villipigue, Paul T., Factor, Accommodation Wharf, res. 6 College St.
Vincent, Hugh E., Ship Chandler, 75 East Bay St., res. 75 East Bay St.
Vincent, J. Wilder, Clerk, 69 East Bay St., res. 69 East Bay St.
Vincent, James C., Clerk, 155 East Bay St., res. Commercial House
Vincent, W. J., Clerk, 69 East Bay St., res. 69 East Bay St.
Vitt Cusky, Henry, Engineer, South Carolina Railroad, res. St. Philip St.
Vitt Cusky, John, Fireman, South Carolina Railroad, res. St. Philip St.
Volger, Bernard, Cigars & Tobacco, 345 King St., res. 345 King St.
Vollars, John H., Clerk, cr. King & Queen St.
Von Dohlen, A., Grocer, 46 State St., res. 88 Anson St.
Von Haiten, C., Grocer, 24 Archdale St., res. 24 Archdale St.
Von Hollen, John, Grocer, cr. Hudson & Market Sts.
Von Santen & Baruc, Fancy Goods, 208 King St.
Von Santen, Bernard S., Fancy Goods, 208 King St., res. 9 Wentworth St.
Von Sprecken, Frederick, Tavern, 67 Market St., res. 67 Market St.
Voss, Frederick, Liquor Dealer, Warren St., res. Warren St.
Wagner, A. R., Auctioneer, 17 Vendue Range, res. Pavilion Hotel
Wagner, Frederick, Grocer, 237 East Bay St., res. 237 East Bay St.
Wagner, George, Mrs., res. Coming St.
Wagner, Samuel J., Storekeeper, Custom House, res. 114 Queen St.
Wagner, Theodore D., Commission Merchant, Central Wharf, res. Rutledge St.
Wagner, Thomas M., Secretary, Blue Ridge Railroad Co., Adger's Wharf
Wagner, W. H., Commission Merchant, cr. East Bay St. & Vendue Range, res. Coming St.
Walburn, C., Clerk, 55 East Bay St., res. 55 East Bay St.
Walch, John, Carpenter, 67 Anson St., res. 67 Anson St.
Waldron, A. W., Clothing, 27 Hayne St., res. Mills House
Waldron, G. Z. & Co., Cothing, 27 Hayne St.
Waldron, G. Z., Clothing, 27 Hayne St., res. Mils House
Waldron, Tunis A., Clothing, 27 Hayne St., res. New York
Walker & Evans, Stationers & Bookbinders, 101 East

Bay St., near Broad St.

Walker & Wagner, Commission Merchants, cr. East Bay St. & Vendue Range

Walker, Benjamin, Planter, res. Mary St.

Walker, Betsy, Colored, Pastry Cook, 53 King St., res. 53 King St.

Walker, David A., Stone Cutter, 4 Anson St., res. 4 Anson St.

Walker, Edward J., Bookkeeper, 42 Broad St., res. 23 Wentworth St.

Walker, G., Commission Merchant, North Commercial Wharf, res. 10 Pitt St.

Walker, George, Grocer, cr. East Bay St. & Vendue Range, res. 10 Pitt St.

Walker, George, Ship Carpenter, res. Alexander St.

Walker, H. C., Carpenter, res. 18 Magazine St.

Walker, H. Pinckney, Lawyer & Clerk, City Court

Walker, Hencke, Clerk, Churubusco Mills, res. Calhoun St.

Walker, J., Blacksmith, Church St., res. 4 Clifford St.

Walker, J. C., Stationer, 101 East Bay St., res. 155 East Bay St.

Walker, James & Co., Commission Merchants, 171 East Bay St.

Walker, James, Commission Merchant, 17½ East Bay St., res. 155 East Bay St.

Walker, John F., Commission Merchant, North Atlantic Wharf, res. Rutledge St.

Walker, Joseph F., Clerk at Wardlaw, Walker & Burnside

Walker, Joseph, Paper Warehouse, 82 East Bay St., res. 9 Wentworth St.

Walker, Legare J., Clerk, 211 King St., res. 10 Pitt St.

Walker, Maria, res. 54 Anson St.

Walker, Martha, Colored, Pastry Cook, res. Radcliffe St.

Walker, R. T., Factor, Boyce's Wharf, res. 250 East Bay St.

Walker, Richard, Factor, res. Washington St.

Walker, W. H., Cotton Press, 69 Church St., res. 23 Friend St.

Walker, William S., Stone Cutter, 4 Anson St., res. 4 Anson St.

Walker, Williman & Co., Paper Warehouse, 82 East Bay St.

Wall, William, Bootmaker, 126 Meeting St., res. 126 Meeting St.

Wallace, C., Pastor, St. Stephen's Chapel, res. 191 East Bay St.

Wallace, David, Dry Goods, 149 King St., res. 149 King St.

Wallace, George M., Finisher, Lebby's Iron Works, res. Calhoun St.

Wallace, Thomas, Dry Goods, 364 King St., res. 364 King St.

Wallanstein, George, Poulterer, Market St., res. Spring St.

Wallis, Earnest, Bootmaker, Calhoun St., res. Calhoun St.

Walpole, Horace, Teller, Bank of the State, res. 18 New St.

Walsh, Patrick, Porter, 35 Hayne St., res. 38 Market St.

Walsh, Thomas, Porter, 35 Hayne St., res. 38 Market St.

Walter, George, Clerk, 107 East Bay St., res. cr. Woolf & Meeting Sts.

Walter, W. D., Factor, Vanderhorst's Wharf, res. Rutledge St.

Walter, William F., Clerk, 39 Broad St., res. Ashley St.

Walter, William, Factor, Vanderhorst's Wharf, res. Rutledge St.

Walter, Wilmot, Factor, Vanderhorst's Wharf, res. Rutledge St.

Walton, Harriet, Colored, Mantuamaker, res. Coming St.

Walton, John M., Boots & Shoes, 139 Meeting St., res. 79 Wentworth St.

Wanger, John A., Notary, res. 59 Wentworth St.

Wanless, John, Coach Maker, Hasell St., res. King St.

Ward, Ellen, Mrs., res. cr. Mazyck & West Sts.

Ward, Harriet, Mrs., res. 24 Smith St.

Ward, John F., Clerk, 24 Hayne St., res. 24 Hayne St.

Ward, John G., 1st Lieutenant of Guard, res. 53 Wentworth St.

Ward, John J., Druggist, 221 King St., res. Carolina Hotel

Ward, -----, Misses, res. 19 George St.

Ward, Peter, Fisherman, res. Inspection St.

Ward, William M., Clerk, 52 Broad St.

Wardlaw, J. W., Factor, North Atlantic Wharf, res. Hasell St.

Wardlaw, W. A., Factor, North Atlantic Wharf, res. Hasell St.

Wardlaw, Walker & Burnside, Factors, North Atlantic Wharf

Waring, H. S., Physician, 109 King St., res. 9 King St.

Waring, Thomas, Auditor, South Carolina Railroad, res. 109 King St.

Waring, Thomas R., Cashier, Bank of the State, res. Cannon St.

Warley, Felix, Clerk at Holmes & Stoney

Warren, Benjamin W., Clerk, 29 Hayne St.

Warren, Wallace, Student, res. 8 Liberty St.

Washington, William, Mrs., Planter, res. 255 East Bay St.

Wass, John, Mariner, res. Coming St.

Waston, Lydia, Colored, Seamstress, res. 2 Inspection St.

Waterbury, John C., Notary, 24 Cumberland St., res. 24 Coming St.

Waterman, C., Grocer, 63 Market St., res. 63 Market St.

Waterman, John, Grocer, cr. Mary & Meeting Sts.

Waters, Ashael B., Druggist, 17 Calhoun St., res. 17 Calhoun St.

Waters, Robert, Plasterer, res. Gadsden St.

Watkins, Alfred M., Clerk, 33 Hayne St.

Watkins, Rebecca, Colored, Mantuamaker, res. Radcliffe St.

Watson, Henry C., Bricklayer, res. Rutledge St.

Watson, John, Engineer, South Carolina Railroad, res. Duncan St.

Watson, Thomas F., Coach Maker, Hasell St., res. Church St.

Watson, Thomas, Mariner, res. 59 Tradd St.

Watts, Sarah, Mrs., Milliner, 196 King St., res. 196 King St.

Wayne, Daniel G., Carpenter, St. Philip St., res. St. Philip St.

Wear, John, Shoemaker, res. St. Michael's Alley

Wearing, John, Laborer, Custom House, res. 9 Horlbeck Alley

Weatherspoon & Porcher, Cotton & Rice Brokers, 34 East Bay St.

Weatherspoon, R., Broker, 34 East Bay St., res. 3 Friend St.

Webb & Sage, China & Glass Ware, 145 Meeting St.

Webb, Charles, Clerk, 253 King St.

Webb, Daniel, Bricklayer, res. Cannon St.

Webb, Daniel, Mrs., res. Rutledge St.

Webb, James, Blacksmith, South Carolina Railroad, res. Cannon St.

Webb, Ladson, Carpenter, res. Cannon St.

Webb, Michael, Shipping Master, 85 East Bay St., res. 8 Water St.

Webb, Thomas L., Factor, South Commercial Wharf, res. Cannon St.

Webb, Walter, res. 40 King St.

Webb, Warren R., Clerk, 185 East Bay St., res. Commercial House

Webb, William H., Commission Merchant, East Bay St., res. 8 Water St.

Webb, William H., Merchant, Exchange St., res. Savage St.

Webb, William L., China & Glassware, 145 Meeting St., res. Cannon St.

Webb, William R., Boat Builder, Port Warden's Office

Weber, A. A., Bar Room, 51 Broad St., res. 51 Broad St.

Weber, John H., Shoemaker, 119 King St., res. 119 King St.

Weber, Peter, Tavern, 33 Queen St., res. 33 Queen St.

Weeling, Edward, Carpenter, res. Meeting St., near Reid St.

Wehman, Frederick, Grocer, 135 King St., res. 135 King St.

Wehren, John, Physician, res. Henrietta St.

Weinholtz, Frederick, Grocer, Hasell St., res. Hasell St.

Welch & Harris, Bookbinders, 59 Broad St.

Welch, John, Carpenter, 67 Anson St., res. 67 Anson St.

Welch, John, Carpenter, res. east end of Chapel St.

Welch, Maximan, Crockery Store, res. Hampden Court

Welch, Michael, Laborer, res. Woolf St.

Welch, Peter, Planter, res. 48 Bull St.

Welch, R. M., Gents Furnishing Store, cr. Meeting & Market Sts.

Welch, S. B., Bookbinder, 59 Broad St., res. Calhoun St.

Welch, Sarah, Mrs., res. cr. Blake & Drake Sts.

Welch, W. H., Bookbinder, 59 Broad St., res. Morris St.

Wells, Daniel, Mariner, res. 24 Marsh St.

Wells, H. D., Clerk, cr. Market & King Sts., res. Hasell St.

Wells, Robert, Carpenter, Warren St., res. Warren St.

Wells, Samuel, Clerk, 246 King St., res. cr. Liberty & King Sts.

Wells, William P., Clerk, 211 King St., res. cr. Liberty & King Sts.

Welser, Edward, Tavern, 31 Elliott St., res. 31 Elliott St.

Welsh, John J., Carpenter, 21 State St., res. 67 Anson St.

Welsman, J. T., Commission Merchant, Central Wharf, res. 2 Church St.

Welsman, James, Commission Merchant, 5 Vanderhorst's Wharf, res. 2 Church St.

Wendtorn, Augustus, Piano Tuner, 237 King St., res. 37 Calhoun St.

Werner, C., Iron Foundry, cr. Cumberland & State Sts., res. 43 State St.

Werner, D., Grocer, cr. Legare & Tradd Sts., res. cr. Legare & Tradd Sts.

West & Welch, Carpenters, 21 State St.

West, A. R., Carpenter, 21 State St., res. Meeting St.

West, C. H. & Son, Ship Chandlers, 77 East Bay St.

West, Charles H., Jr., Auctioneer, 26 Vendue Range, res. 9 Wentworth St.

West, Charles H., Ship Chandler, 77 East Bay St., res. 3 Church St.

West, E. A., Ship Chandler, 77 East Bay St., res. 3 Church St.

West, Preston, Livery Stable, 56 Queen St., res. 97 Queen St.

Westcoat, George W., Physician, King St., above Hudson St.

Westendorff, Charles S., Clerk, Mercury Office, res. 8 Guignard St.

Westendorff, James, Bookkeeper, 165 Meeting St.

Westlotorn, Josiah, Broker, 139 Meeting St.

Weston, Anthony, Colored, Machinist, res. Henrietta St.

Weston, Anthony, Millwright, res. Calhoun St.

Weston, C. F., Mariner, res. 6 Savage St.

Weston, F., Colored, Millwright, res. Henrietta St.

Weston, Francis, Planter, Pee Dee, res. Columbus St.

Weston, Jacob, Colored, Tailor, 100 Queen St., res. 48 Coming St.

Weston, Lydia, Colored, Seamstress, res. 2 Inspection St.

Weston, S. & J., Colored, Tailors, 100 Queen St.

Weston, S., Colored, Tailor, 100 Queen St., res. 48 Coming St.

Weyhe & Wuhrman, Liquor Dealers, 104 East Bay St.

Weyhe, J. L., Liquors, 104 East Bay St.

Weymann, Charles F., Cigars & Tobacco, King St., Upper Ward

Whaley & Rutledge, Lawyers, 48 Broad St.

Whaley, Benjamin J., Lawyer, 48 Broad St., res. 9 George St.

Whaley, Thomas, Clerk at John Fraser & Co., res. cr. Queen & Church St.

Whaley, Thomas, Planter, res. St. Philip St.

Whaley, William, Lawyer, 48 Broad St., res. cr. Rutledge & Bull Sts.

Wharton, Edward, Carpenter, res. Woolf St.

Wharton, George C., Bricklayer, res. America St.

Wharton, John, Clerk, 6 Vendue Range, res. King St.

Wharton, Thomas, Carpenter, res. Woolf St.

Wheeler, Eliza, Mrs., res. 183 Meeting St.

Wheeler, Stephen H., Saddlery, 157 Meeting St., res. New York

173

Whilden, B. F., Grocer, 16 Hayne St., res. Glebe St.
Whilden, Joseph, Books & Stationery, 229 King St., res. 16 Magazine St.
Whilden, Robert, Engineer, res. Beaufain St.
Whilden, William G., Jeweller, 250 King St., res. Rutledge St.
Whilden, William H., Clerk, 257 King St., res. Hasell St.
Whippy, Cornelius F., Clerk, 211 King St., res. Commercial House
White, Abbey, Colored, Washerwoman, res. 221 East Bay St.
White, Alonzo J., Broker & Auctioneer, 27 Broad St., res. cr. Laurens & East Bay St.
White, E. B., Civil Engineer & Architect, 122 East Bay St.
White, Fanny, Colored, Fruit, res. Calhoun St.
White, George, Clerk, 308 King St., res. 297 King St.
White, Granville, Hats & Caps, 25 Hayne St., res. New York
White, J. A., Physician, 21 Legare St., res. 21 Legare St.
White, Jacob, Boots & Shoes, King St., Upper Ward
White, James, res. 13 Rutledge St.
White, Joseph, Bar Room, 356 King St., res. 356 King St.
White, Levina, Colored, Washerwoman, res. 221 East Bay St.
White, O. G., Clerk, Custom House, res. 21 Legare St.
White, Patrick, Blacksmith, 28 Pinckney St., res. 9 Vernon St.
White, Robert D., Stone Cutter, 119 Meeting St., res. 119 Meeting St.
White, Robert, Furniture, 342 King St., res. 342 King St.
White, Thomas, Planter, Christ Church Parish, res. Alexander St.
White, W. T., Stone Cutter, 119 Meeting St., res. 119 Meeting St.
White, W. W., Wood Factor, Southern Wharf, res. 43 East Bay St.
White, William, Mariner, Sailors Home, 8 Market St.
Whitehead, Marion, Mrs., res. 7 Minority St.
Whitemore, C., Soap & Candle Factory, Radcliffe St.
Whiting, E. M., Turner, res. Calhoun St., Ward 5
Whiting, William, Porter, 149 Meeting St., res. King St.
Whitney, Alonzo G., Collector, Accommodation Wharf, res. Cumberland St.
Whitney, Cornelius G., Broker & Auctioneer, 3 State St., res. 5 Franklin St.
Whitney, Cornelius, Wood Factor, res. Cannon St.
Whitney, F. H., Soap & Candle Factory, cr. Reid & Nassau Sts.
Whitney, Octavius L., Wood Factor, Woolf St., res Morris St.
Whitney, Theodore A., Broker, res. 5 Franklin St.
Whitschen, N., Grocer, cr. Cannon & St. Philip Sts.
Whittaker, Charles F., Clothing, 352 King St., res. 352 King St.
Wickenberg, E. A., Clerk, 42 Broad St., res. Church St.
Wickenberg, F. R., Grocer, 42 Broad St., res. Church St.
Wickman, Henry, Grocer, cr. Bogard & Coming Sts.
Wiebens, Henry, Grocer, cr. Calhoun & Marsh Sts.

Wienges, Conrad, Commission Merchant, Exchange St., res. 26 Savage St.
Wienges, Conrad M., Saddler, 45 Broad St., res. Thomas St.
Wienges, E. J., Engineer, South Carolina Railroad, res. Columbus St.
Wienges, G. W., Clerk, 116 Meeting St., res. 11 John St.
Wienges, Henry, Clerk, cr. Market & Meeting Sts., res. 59 Beaufain St.
Wienges, John, Laborer, res. Hampden Court
Wienholtz, F., Grocer, 63 East Bay St., res. 63 East Bay St.
Wightman, John, Jr., Pastor, Bethel Church, Coming St., near Green St.
Wightman, John, res. Coming St., near Green St.
Wightman, William, res. 20 George St.
Wilbur, B. B. M., Wood Factor, foot of Hasell St., res. Coming St.
Wilbur, Henry, Grocer, cr. State & Cumberland Sts.
Wilbur, N. G., Porter, 101 East Bay St., res. St. Michael's Alley
Wilbur, T. A., Bookkeeper, 21 Vendue Range, res. 16 Liberty St.
Wilbur, W. W., Clerk, South Carolina Railroad, res. Coming St.
Wilbur, William W., Auctioneer & Commission Merchant, cr. Church & State Sts.
Wilcox, Daniel, Grocer, 1 Hayne St., res. Augusta, Ga.
Wild, Vincent, Boiler Maker, res. Columbus St.
Wiley, Banks & Co., Dry Goods, 41 Hayne St.
Wiley, James, Grocer, King St., res. 4 Atlantic St.
Wiley, Mary, Mrs., res. 4 Atlantic St.
Wiley, Samuel, Grocer, 365 King St., res. 365 King St.
Wiley, W. J., Clerk, 361 King St., res. 16 Green St.
Wiley, William, Clothing, 361 King St., res. 16 Green St.
Wilkenham, William, res. 4 Magazine St.
Wilkie, A. C., Mrs., Boarding House, 80 Society St.
Wilkie, George W., Inspector, Custom House, res. 8 Liberty St.
Wilkie, James, res. 8 Liberty St.
Wilkie, Joseph B., Clerk, 179 East Bay St., res. 8 Liberty St.
Wilkie, Octavius, Paper Merchant, 82 East Bay St.
Wilkinning, John H., Grocer, 57 Market St., res. 57 Market St.
Wilkins, Berkley, Factor, Atlantic Wharf, res. 271 East Bay St.
Wilkins, -----, Mrs., res. 11 Lamboll St.
Wilkins, William, Clerk, 80 East Bay St., res. Planters Hotel
Wilkinson, James, Planter, St. Andrew's Parish, res. 13 Meeting St.
Williams, Butler & Co., Commission Merchants, 165 East Bay St.
Williams, Catharine, Mrs., res. 19 Beaufain St.
Williams, Charles, Clerk, 260 King St., res. 270 King St.
Williams, E. C., Clerk, 1 Hayne St., res. King St.
Williams, George P., res. 19 Beaufain St.
Williams, George W. & Co., Grocery Merchants, 1 Hayne St.

Williams, George W., Grocer, 1 Hayne St., res. 20 George St.

Williams, H., Clerk, East Bay St., res. 27 Friend St.

Williams, Henry, Colored, Barber, 28 Tradd St., res. 28 Tradd St.

Williams, Henry, Drayman, res. Meeting St.

Williams, Henry H., Hats & Caps, 159 Meeting St., res. 3 Liberty St.

Williams, Hugh, Hats & Caps, King St., Upper Ward

Williams, James, Clerk, 171 East Bay St.

Williams, James W., Clerk at J. Walker's, res. 113 Queen St.

Williams, John, Commission Merchant, 165 East Bay St., res. Baltimore

Williams, Paris, Colored, Barber, 44 Society St., res. 41 Society St.

Williams, Samuel K., Printer, 3 Broad St., res. King St.

Williams, Waddy S., Clerk, 253 King St., res. 330 King St.

Williams, Winthrop B., Commission Merchant, Central Wharf

Williamson, John, Broker, res. Coming St.

Willie, Henry, Carpenter, res. St. Philip St.

Williman, Albert, Physician, 70 Church St., res. 70 Church St.

Williman, C., Paper Warehouse, 82 East Bay St., res. 70 Tradd St.

Williman, Jacob, Lawyer, St. Michael's Alley, res. 43 East Bay St.

Willington, A. S. & Co., Proprietors of the Charles Courier

Willington, A. S., Editor, Courier, 111 East Bay St., res. 10 New St.

Willington, H., Engineer, res. 26 Mazyck St.

Willington, P., Old Iron & Rags, 14 Mazyck St.

Willis, Benjamin G., Clerk, 261 King St., res. Merchants Hotel

Willis, Henry & Son, Exchange Brokers, 59 Broad St.

Willis, Henry, Exchange Broker, 50 Broad St., res. Line St.

Willis, Henry, Jr., Broker, 50 Broad St., res. Mills House

Willis, John G., Boots & Shoes, 182 King St., res. 182 King St.

Willy, J. H., Forwarding & Commission Merchant, 6 Vendue Range, res. Charleston Hotel

Wilmans & Price, Hardware, 24 Hayne St.

Wilmans, A. F., Hardware, 24 Hayne St., res. 6 Hasell St.

Wilson, A. B., Planter, St. George's Island, res. St. Philip St.

Wilson, Abraham, Planter, Turkey Hill, res. 136 King St.

Wilson, Angus, Teacher, 87 Wentworth St., res. 87 Wentworth St.

Wilson, Bachman, Clerk, Post Office, 12 Water St.

Wilson, Eliza, Mrs., Mantuamaker, 46 Society St.

Wilson, Hugh, Factor, North Atlantic Wharf, res. New Orleans

Wilson, Hugh, Planter, res. 6 Smith St.

Wilson, J. H., Factor, 14 Vanderhorst's Wharf, res. 6 Smith St.

Wilson, James, Clerk, 186 King St., res. Anson St.

Wilson, James M., Boots & Shoes, 43 Hayne St., res. 6 New St.

Wilson, John, Cabinet Maker, King St., Ward 6

Wilson, John, Clerk, East Bay St. 136 King St.

Wilson, John, Dry Goods, King St., Ward 6

Wilson, Joseph, Teacher, 87 Wentworth St., res. 87 Wentworth St.

Wilson, Julian A., res. 6 Smith St.

Wilson, M., Clerk, res. 136 King St.

Wilson, Maria C., Mrs., res. cr. Coming & George Sts.

Wilson, Moultrie R., Clerk, 243 King St., res. Calhoun St.

Wilson, Radcliffe W., Planter, res. 6 Smith St.

Wilson, Samuel, Physician, 10 New St., res. 10 New St.

Wilson, W. A., Watchmaker, 95 King St., res. 275 East Bay St.

Wilson, W. M., Porter, Bank of Charleston, res. State St.

Wilson, William, Watchmaker, East Bay St., res. 295 East Bay St.

Wiltberger, John R., Druggist, 245 King St., res. Pinckney St.

Winberg, J. W., Fancy Goods, 276 King St., res. 276 King St.

Winberg, Julia, Mrs., Fancy Goods, 238 King St., res. 238 King St.

Winey, John, Engineer, res. 26 Mazyck St.

Wing, Robert, Bell Hanger & Locksmith, 130 King St., res. 238 King St.

Winkle, Francis J., Clerk, 52 Broad St., res. Water St.

Winkler, E. T., Pastor, First Baptist Church, res. 48 Church St.

Winneman, Philip, Druggist, 29 Hayne St.

Winnigham, Robert, Machinist, res. Hanover St.

Winslow, Edward, res. 18 Coming St.

Winthrop & Sons, Factors & Commission Merchants, 6 Adger's Wharf

Winthrop, Francis, Factor, 6 Adger's Wharf, res. 99 Tradd St.

Winthrop, H., Physician, 95 Tradd St., res. 30 Society St.

Winthrop, John, Stevedore, res. 6 Mazysk St.

Winthrop, Joseph A., Factor, 6 Adger's Wharf, res. 99 Tradd St.

Winthrop, Joseph, Physician, 95 Tradd St., res. 30 Society St.

Wise, Alfred, Painter, 113 King St., res. 113 King St.

Wish, Mary, Mrs., res 16 Cumberland St.

Withers, Caroline, Mrs., res. South Bay St.

Witing, Elizabeth, Mrs., res. 5 Atlantic St.

Witschen, Claus, Grocer, 53 Calhoun St., res. 53 Calhoun St.

Witschen, F., Grocer, 3 South Bay, res. 3 South Bay

Witschen, Henry, Baker, 115 Church St., res. 115 Church St.

Witsell, John, Collection Clerk, Bank of the State of South Carolina, res. 18 New St.

Witsell, T. L., Clerk at Fackler, Colcock & Co.

Witsell, Walter H., Bricklayer, res. Pitt St.

Witt, Andrew, Barber, 159 King St., res. 159 King St.

Witt, Henry, Engineer, South Carolina Railroad, res. Spring St.

Witt, Mary, Mrs., Mantuamaker, res. Spring St.

Witte & Goodwin, Liquor Merchants, 114 East Bay St.

Witte, Charles O., Liquors, 114 East Bay St.

Wittemore, Ceaphs, Soap Chandler, res. Radcliffe St.

Wittin, O., Printer, 119 East Bay St., res. Commercial House

Wittis, W., Bookkeeper, 177 East Bay St., res. 17 Market St.

Wohlers, John C., Grocer, 30 Coming St., res. 30 Coming St.

Wood, George W. E., Boots & Shoes, 21 Hayne St., res. Charleston Hotel

Wood, Lucius S., Bookkeeper, cr. Meeting & Hayne St.

Wood, Mary, Mrs., Confectionery, Anson St., res. Anson St.

Woodman, Henry, Fisherman, res. Spring St.

Woodruff, J. S., Clerk, 2 Hayne St., res. Smith St.

Woodruff, Josephus, Clerk, Mercury Office, res. 7 Broad St.

Woodruffe, T., Bookbiner, res. 5 Coming St.

Woodside, John, Tavern, 191 East Bay St., res. 191 East Bay St.

Woodward, Peter, Miller, Bennett's Mills, res. 8 Washington St.

Woodward, W. T. J. O., Adam's Express Agent, res. 27 Wentworth St.

Woody, Thomas, Finisher, res. Meeting St., near Reid St.

Woolfe, Isaac, res. 1 Pinckney St.

Woolfe, William, Tavern, 27 Market St., res. 17 Market St.

Wragg, Mary, Mrs., res. 72 Broad St.

Wragg, T. L., Commission Merchant, Adger's Wharf, res. 72 Broad St.

Wragg, W. T., Physician, 66 Wentworth St., res. 66 Wentworth St.

Wrede, John W., Clothing, 99 East Bay St.

Wreden, Benjamin, Grocer, cr. Coming & Cannon Sts.

Wright, C. F., Dry Goods, King St., res. King St.

Wright, Fritz, Gas Fitter, Church St., res. St. Philip St.

Wriglesworth, William, Bookkeeper, 1 Hayne St.

Wuhrman, J. H., Liquors, 104 East Bay St, cr. Wentworth & Anson Sts.

Wuhrman, Justice, Architect, cr. Broad & Church Sts.

Wyatt & Co., Commission Merchants, Adger's Wharf

Wyatt, S., Commission Merchant, Adger's Wharf, res. Waverly House

Wyley, A. C., Clerk, 37 Hayne St., res. Charleston Hotel

Wynne, J. B., Factor, South Atlantic Wharf, res. American Hotel

Yates, E. L., Clerk, 6 Vendue Range, res. City Hotel

Yates, J. Legare, Commission Merchant, 151 East Bay St., res. City Hotel

Yates, Jeremiah D., State Sheriff, Court House, res. 7 Church St.

Yates, Joseph A., Bookkeeper, 96 East Bay St., res. 4 Logan St.

Yates, W. B., Pastor, Mariners Church, res. 12 Church St.

Yates, William J., Boots & Shoes, 354 King St., res. 354 King St.

Yeadon, Macbeth & Ford, Lawyers, 41 Broad St.

Yeadon, Richard, Lawyer, 41 Broad St., res. 56 Wentworth St.

Yeadon, Samuel A., Carpenter, res. America St.

Yglesias, Y., Draper & Tailor, 92 Meeting St., res. 92 Meeting St.

Young Catherine, Mrs., res. Calhoun St.

Young, Charles D., Bookkeeper at Melrose & Davidson, res. State St.

Young, Henry, Pianoforte Maker, 201 King St., res. 201 King St.

Young, John, Clerk, cr. Meeting & Market Sts., res. 8 Clifford St.

Young, Phillip R., Civil Engineer, 69 East Bay St., res. 69 East Bay St.

Young, William, Bricklayer, res. 94 Beaufain St.

Young, William, Clerk, cr. Church & Broad Sts., res. 9 Horlbeck Alley

Young William, Clerk, cr. Meeting & Market Sts., res. 8 Clifford St.

Zealy, Joseph, Discount Clerk, Union Bank, res. Hasell St.

Zehe, J. H., Grocer, cr. King & Warren Sts.

Zeigler, Michael W., Coachmaker, 181 Meeting St., res 181 Meeting St.

Zengenbien, William, Grocer, Calhoun St., res. Calhoun St.

Zerbst, Henry, Grocer, cr. Pitt & Duncan Sts., res. cr. Pitt & Duncan Sts.

Zeresatskie, John, Grocer, cr. Coming & Line Sts.

Zunderburg, Frederick W., Grocer, east end of Hasell St.

CPSIA information can be obtained at www.ICGtesting.com
Printed in the USA
244153LV00004B/57/P